D1131663

Morphology of Vascular Plants

THE MACMILLAN BIOLOGY SERIES
General Editors: Norman H. Giles and John G. Torrey

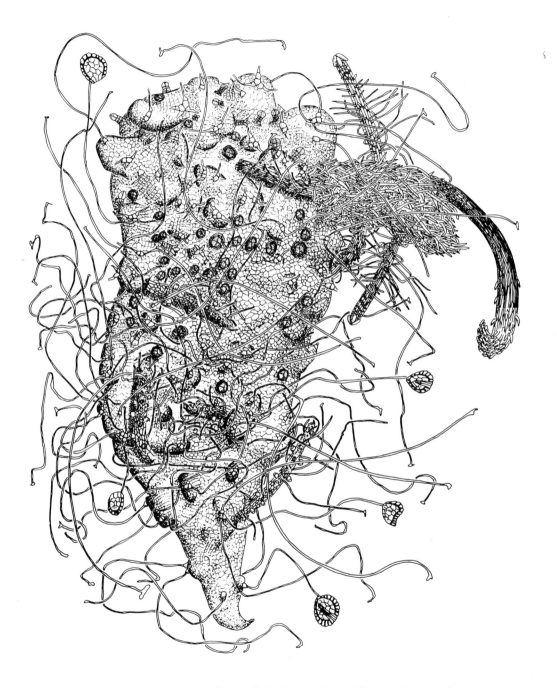

Old tuberous gametophyte of *Actinostachys obligostachys* bearing a young sporophyte, primary gametophytic axes, and sporangia at the tips of gametophytic rhizoids.

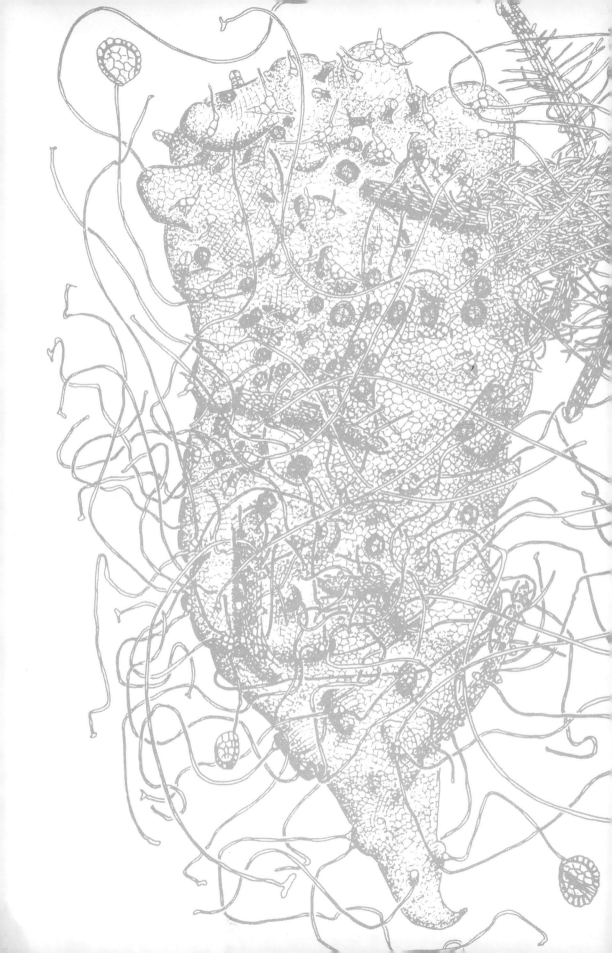

Morphology of Vascular Plants

David W. Bierhorst

University of Massachusetts

The Macmillan Company, New York

Collier-Macmillan Limited, London

The jacket illustration is a transverse section of the stele of a young root of Smilax *spp. (greenbriar) showing the heavily lignified walls of the peripheral endodermal cells. Polarized light. X 350. It is from* Plant Structure and Development: A Pictorial and Physiological Approach *by T. P. O'Brien and Margaret E. McCully (New York: Macmillan, 1969).*

The Macmillan Company
866 Third Avenue, New York, New York 10022

Collier-Macmillan Canada, Ltd., Toronto, Ontario

Library of Congress catalog card number: 70–112853

First Printing

Preface

This book has been written to satisfy what is considered to be a particular need. After teaching vascular plant morphology at the university level for the past seventeen years and finding no recent book written in sufficient detail and depth to serve as both a text and a reference, I found it necessary to attempt one.

As a textbook, it is written primarily for a particular kind of university course. On entering such a course the student should have some background knowledge of morphology and life cycles such as has been traditionally presented in a second semester of a general botany sequence or presented under another name, such as "Survey of the Plant Kingdom." A course in plant structure beyond the general botany level would be advantageous in order to save time and effort in the presentation of routine histological terminology and recognition.

A text in plant morphology should be reasonably comprehensive in the taxa covered. Degree of emphasis on various taxa should be unrelated to material availability (that is, the volume should not be regionally or geographically oriented). Such orientation in the past has given false impressions as to which genera are "typical" of various plant groups. For example, the Psilotaceae have been thought of primarily in terms of the tetraploid race of *Psilotum nudum*, the conifers in terms of the genus *Pinus*, the liverworts in terms of *Marchantia*, and the ferns in terms of aspidiads.

In the view held here, the text should emphasize the fundamental (generalized) as well as the specialized features of the taxa covered. It should also emphasize the taxa that illustrate special morphological lessons of general significance. In this text, in addition, special consideration is given certain plant groups whose exceptionally abbreviated treatments elsewhere have led to what are considered distorted viewpoints.

How much factual material should be presented? Many of us in recent years have said that the student should be encouraged to do more original thinking, that his individual reasoning power should be stimulated, and that he should be given the opportunity to digest material presented to him and to logically appraise it. Yet, too many morphologists have been guilty of not presenting enough factual material to allow students to have opinions of their own. Plant morphology cannot be taught at a reasonable level without the introduction of maximum amounts of detailed, descriptive evidence. It is hoped that there is sufficient detail presented in the following chapters to allow for a reasonable appraisal of the accompanying interpretations.

D. W. B.

Contents

ix

1

Introduction

To define morphology as the study of form is accurate and complete but is grossly misleading to all but the morphologist. The subject involves form at all levels of organization from submicroscopic through organismic and at times colonial. A reasonable understanding of the form of an organ necessitates a complete knowledge of its gross and minute structure and a knowledge of its range of variation, that is, the minimal and maximal developmental potential in a particular species as well as in many others.

The range of developmental potential of an organ in a species (or higher taxon) includes its total morphological expression as influenced by a variety of minor and major genetic and environmental changes. The morphologist studies organ expression in the field and under controlled laboratory conditions.

The study of form involves not only its present state but also its history of development. Both ontogeny and phylogeny are integral aspects of the subject. To understand form, a knowledge of evolution, past and present, is prerequisite.

One organ or organ component cannot be considered out of context of the entire organism of which it is a part. It is known that organs mutually influence each other's development and that a given primordium up to a certain point in ontogeny may have two or more possible subsequent developmental pathways. Under certain conditions the specific pathway to be followed may be controlled and determined in the laboratory. For example, in certain ferns an organ primordium may have both leaf and stem potential. Under natural conditions the developmental pathway is determined by geometrical interrelationships and physiological interactions among groups of primordia. These interrelationships may be altered surgically to cause somewhat predictable changes in subsequent developmental pathways.

Form and function are inseparable entities. Physiology and morphology completely intergrade. This is particularly evident when causal factors during the ontogeny of form are considered. It must be kept in mind that often it is the physiology of the organ as it is superimposed on the physiology of the organism and how this effects its reproductive potential that is of selective value in the evolutionary process. Morphology is inseparable and indistinct not only from physiology but also from genetics, ecology, paleophytology, and the study of evolution.

Systematics, which has evolved from classical taxonomy, has a special relationship to morphology. The work of the modern systematist and the modern morphologist is very similar; it differs only in emphasis. The differences are to a large extent historical rather than those of present-day practice. A gradual convergence of the two disciplines has been occurring for several decades; the systematist has broadened his outlook and the morphologist has come more and more to use classification to demonstrate his accomplishments.

The establishment of homologies represents one major step in the understanding of form. The term "homology" has various shades of meaning. In the purest sense two structures or physiological mechanisms are homologous if they were arrived at by the same genetic or phylogenetic pathway. We can say that a leaf of *Quercus alba* is homologous (homogenous) to a leaf of *Q. rubra* since it is certain that the common ancestor of these two oaks had already evolved this organ and that leaves did not evolve independently in each after their divergence. Similar organs of different phylogenetic origins are analogous but homologous. Flattened photosynthetic appendages borne on terete aerial axes may represent various morphological entities. The "leaf" of a *Lycopodium* is the analog of the very similar appearing "leaf" of some species of conifers, but it is presumably not the homolog. In many angiosperms (e.g., *Asparagus*) the organs that are presumed to be the homologs of oak leaves are extremely diminutive and the flattened photosynthetic organs are, in the morphological sense, entire lateral shoots.

The interpretation of homologies may be based on a variety of types of evidence. Similarities in gross mature form give a suggestion of homology. Similarities in early stages of development strengthen the suggestion. Similar vascular supplies to two different organs are indicative of homology. The existence of intermediate forms, if properly interpreted, strengthens the conclusion. Two organs appearing in the same positions of similar life cycles are generally homologous (e.g., the organs of vascular plants in which meiosis occurs).

The establishment of homology between two dissimilar organs of two distantly related species generally involves subtle argument and complex interpretation. Many examples of this are presented in subsequent chapters.

Interpretation of relationships among taxa, and classification itself, necessitate some relative emphasis and de-emphasis of evidence. This introduces a degree of subjectivity to the subject matter, but despite considerable controversy there is also considerable agreement. Emphasis is placed on those features considered to be phylogenetically conservative as opposed to more plastic ones, which are relatively de-emphasized. A feature greatly modified by a single gene mutation without resultant lethality is certainly a plastic one, as opposed to one that is constant in many species and presumed to be relatively fixed by a larger segment of the genome. Among the more conservative features of vascular plants (and other plants) are the details of meiosis, mitoses, photosynthesis, and respiration. Among more plastic features are distribution of epidermal hairs, leaf shape, and stomatal frequency. A single feature may be conservative in one family and plastic in another. For example, among angiosperms leaf form and venation are less conservative in the family Moraceae than in the family Melastomaceae.

There is abundant evidence to suggest that early stages in development are more conservative than later ones. Leaves of closely related species that appear quite different in shape at maturity are often nearly identical in primordial stages. The more closely related species, the later in ontogeny morphological divergence occurs. New mutations appearing in a species are less apt to be lethal or have a very negative

TABLE 1–1. Geologic time table. Data from Kulp (1961); Devonian date modified by H. P. Banks (personal communication); Precambrian from Eicher (1968).

Era	Period	Epoch	Time to Beginning, in Years × 10^6
Cenozoic	Quaternary	Pleistocene	1
	Tertiary	Pliocene	13
		Miocene	25
		Oligocene	36
		Eocene	58
		Paleocene	63
Mesozoic	Cretaceous		135
	Jurassic		181
	Triassic		230
Paleozoic	Permian		280
	Carboniferous		
	Pennsylvanian		310
	Mississippian		345
	Devonian		395
	Silurian		425
	Ordovician		500
	Cambrian		600
Precambrian			4,550–4,800

selective advantage if they are expressed in later stages of ontogeny. These facts have been expressed in a variety of ways in the past and form the basis for at least partial acceptance of the overstated "biogenetic law" of Haeckel.

Some knowledge of geologic time is indispensable in the study of morphology. This should be integrated with some understanding of genetic change, rates of evolution, generation time, climatic and physiographic changes, and modes and conditions of fossilization. At this point the student of morphology is strongly advised to commit the geologic time table (Table 1–1) to memory.

Critical consideration of the possible origins of angiosperms, for example, would necessarily be based on the broadest of frames of reference. The time of origin of flowering plants is not known, but most estimates fall between Carboniferous and Lower Cretaceous times. One can ask for each estimate: Did the angiosperms have time to evolve their characteristic morphology, diversity, and floristic dominance between those times and mid-Cretaceous time? One can consider the paucity of early angiosperm fossils and attempt to explain it in terms of climate and conditions for fossilization. This may well lead to a consideration of habitats of extant, presumed primitive flowering plants, their geography and degree of isolation, and even continental drift. All of this is in addition to purely comparative morphological considerations.

A knowledge of the various kinds of fossils is necessary to evaluate the specific kind of information derivable from each. A fossil in general may be defined as any concrete evidence of the existence of a prehistoric organism. Fossilization occurs under a variety of conditions and fossils occur in a variety of forms, such as—

Imprints

Examples of imprints are footprints or leaf impressions made on a soft substratum that is transformed later into a harder substance (e.g., on soft clay that becomes shale).

Casts and Molds

An organic object trapped within sediments later decomposes, leaving a space in its place.

When the space becomes filled with another sediment, the space is called a mold, and its filling, which has the form of the organic object, is called a cast.

Products of Activity of Organisms

These may be in the form of manufactured artifacts, such as pottery or secreted limy deposits of algae, or in a variety of other forms.

Petrifactions

These are minerally replaced or impregnated organic parts. They often exhibit cellular detail and sometimes even a degree of subcellular structure. For petrifaction to occur, the organic part must be protected in some way from rapid decay while mineralization proceeds. In the past this has been accomplished by exclusion of air (as in water-saturated sediments), by low pH in combination with inhibiting effects of accumulated byproducts of microorganisms (as in a putrid swamp), or by the specific physical and chemical conditions existing under a layer of volcanic dust. The most common petrifying minerals are calcium carbonate, magnesium carbonate, iron pyrites, various silicates, and iron hydroxide.

Actual Remains

Plant fossils in the form of actual remains are mostly of relatively young age and have been prevented from completely decomposing by low temperatures or by air exclusion. Exceptions to this are plant cuticle, cutinized wall, or spore walls containing sporopollinin—all materials that are outstandingly resistant to natural decomposition.

Chemical Remains

Chemical materials may frequently be extracted from a rock in which organic matter has been incorporated. These may be highly modified or in a nearly natural state. Examples are amino acids and hydrocarbons.

The terms "carbonization" and "compression" are self-explanatory in terms of fossil types. Compression is not necessarily categorically different from casts, petrifactions, actual remains, or carbonizations.

On Vascular Plant Classification

All systems of classification of organisms are at best grossly unnatural. The fundamental nature of classification is contrary to our knowledge of the process of evolution. A system based upon the concepts of Linné, no matter how modified by later developed evolutionary concepts, is basically one of categorization, or pigeonholing, of taxa of various levels. A morphological (or physiological, etc.) hiatus is assumed to exist between any two categories in the system (e.g., two species differ at least by a "specific" difference, two genera by one of "generic magnitude," two orders by an "ordinal difference" that is greater than that which distinguishes species, families, etc.). There has been controversy over what constitutes a taxonomic difference of a particular magnitude, but the amazing degree of agreement has allowed systems to survive and be useful.

The unnaturalness inherent in all "pigeonhole" systems is based on the fact that the individual steps in evolution are almost entirely at the subspecific level (i.e., they arise from the accumulation of small genetic differences and by various new recombinations of these). Only as exceptions are major changes involved at a single step. We may expect, therefore, as has happened many times in the past, to bridge gaps or to break down categorical differences as new organisms are discovered (especially fossil forms) and as new information is uncovered about presently known ones. Although new information occasionally brings out parallel evolutionary lines and necessitates taxonomic splitting, more often the reverse is true. It is anticipated that during the next few centuries a spectral system to include extinct and extant organisms will replace the pigeonhole system, while for extant forms the pigeonhole system will remain more or less intact because of its practical value to mankind.

The system of classification used in the present text is unnatural, as are all others. It points out that we have some knowledge of the plants concerned, but it also points out that we are much more ignorant than informed. Classes, orders, and so on, are recognized only because of complete ignorance concerning, or lack of recognition of, intermediate forms that we must assume to have existed in times past. The system, which is not greatly different from previously published ones, is presented for its usefulness at the present time only. It is to be used as a frame of reference and hopefully as a source of stimulation for future research.

The taxon "subdivision" is omitted, for very special reasons. It has become a casualty of what appears to be a fad among recent authors of shifting classes, with resultant diminution of the usefulness of the category. More significant, however, are new bits of information that either bridge gaps or point in that direction. The dropping of subdivisions may be considered as a first small step away from a pigeonhole system toward a spectral system.

Division Tracheophyta
  Class Rhyniopsida
    Order Rhyniales
  Class Zosterophyllopsida
    Order Zosterophyllales
  Class Lycopodiopsida (Lycopsida)
    Order Asteroxylales
           Lycopodiales
           Protolepidodendrales
           Selaginellales
           Lepidodendrales
           Isoetales
  Class Cladoxylopsida
    Order Cladoxylales

ARTHOPHYTA

Class Equisetopsida (Sphenopsida)
  Order Hyeniales
         Pseudoborniales
         Sphenophyllales
         Equisetales
Class Coenopteridopsida
  Order Coenopteridales
Class Filicopsida
  Order Noeggerathiales
         Filicales
         Marsileales
         Salvinales
Class Ophioglossopsida
  Order Ophioglossales
Class Marattiopsida
  Order Marattiales
Class Aneurophytopsida
  Order Aneurophytales
         Archeopteridales
         Protopityales
Class Cycadopsida
  Order Pteridospermales
         Cycadales
         Cycadeoidales
         Caytoniales
Class Coniferopsida
  Order Cordaitales
         Coniferales
         Taxales
         Ginkgoales
Class Gnetopsida
  Order Ephedrales
         Gnetales
         Welwitschiales
Class Angiospermopsida
  Subclass Dicotyledonidae
           Monocotyledonidae

2

Lycopodiaceae

The family Lycopodiaceae, as recognized here, consists of the genera *Lycopodium* and *Phylloglossum*. The approximately 400 species of *Lycopodium*, with all their variation in form and habit, have tempted various authors to classify the species into two (*Urostachys* and *Lycopodium*) or into several genera, corresponding to sections in a more conservative system of classification. There are, however, no differences of generic rank (much less familial as some have contended) among the sections of the genus such as might appear if one would compare extreme species. The less conservative approach to this genus is an expression of "taxonomic convenience," a concept that cannot be allowed in modern systematics. *Lycopodites* is used to designate certain fossil forms particularly similar to the extant *Lycopodium*. *Phylloglossum* includes one specialized, reduced, and very distinct species.

For the most part *Lycopodium* plants are rather small, with some shoots up to a few feet long, as in *L. phlegmaria* and *L. densum*, and a little longer in the running or climbing forms. In habit the range includes upright, terrestrial, sparsely branched (*L. annotinum*, Fig. 2–1, *A*) or much-branched forms (*L. obscurum*, Fig. 2–1, *C*); some of these have creeping above-surface (*L. densum*) or below-surface (*L. obscurum*, Fig. 2–1, *C*) rhizomes. The most attractive esthetically are the pendulous epiphytes (Fig. 2–1, *B*, *E*). Many of the muck dwellers, such as *L. carolinianum* and *L. drumondii* (Fig. 2–1, *D*), have rather short surface stems and upright reproductive branches. A few forms are quite viny (e.g., *L. volubile*).

Branching throughout the genus *Lycopodium* is fundamentally dichotomous (i.e., within an apical meristem, a single center of meristematic activity becomes two). Overtopping in the form of dominance of one of two

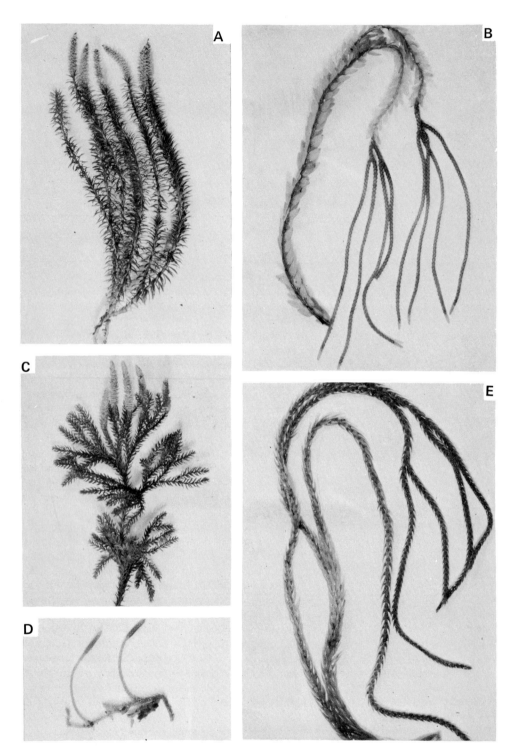

FIGURE 2–1. Habit of *Lycopodium* species. *A. L. annotinum*, a terrestrial, upright species with a sessile strobilus. *B. L. phlegmarioides*, a pendulous epiphyte with branched, tasseloid strobili. *C. L. obscurum*, a terrestrial, upright species with sessile strobili. *D. L. drumondii*, a species of wet, exposed habitats with creeping stems and upright strobilar branches. *E. L. carinatum*, a pendulous epiphyte with long strobili; the strobili of this species are less obvious than in other species, owing to greater similarity between sterile and fertile leaves.

centers of equal size or of the initiation of two unequal centers is common, and, in its extreme expression, pseudomonopodial branching results, as in *L. densum* or *L. obscurum* (Fig. 2–1, *C*). The most unequal branching occurs in the formation of specialized vegetative reproductive branches called "bulbils" or "gemmae" in species such as *L. lucidulum* or *L. selago* (Fig. 2–5, *E*). In these cases it is even difficult to describe the branching as truly apical.

The leaves of *Lycopodium* are always simple and single-veined. They range from minute scales, as in *L. densum*, to broad and quite leafy in species of the section *Phlegmaria* (Fig. 2–1, *B*). Most are entire, but few are serrate (*L. serratum*, Fig. 2–4, *G*).

Some leaf dimorphism occurs in flattened species, especially in the section Complanata (see Wilce, 1965). Some species exhibit decurrent leaf bases (e.g., *L. complanatum*). Leaf arrangement seems fundamentally helical in the genus, but opposite and whorled leaf forms occur (e.g., species of the section *Phlegmaria*).

All *Lycopodium* stems possess a central tissue mass of procambial origin (i.e., a protostele). While arrangement of xylem, phloem, and stelar parenchyma within the stele varies with species, it varies much more with stem diameter within individual species (see the illustrations in Wardlaw, 1924). The smallest stems of possibly all species show a stellate mass of xylem in cross section (Fig. 2–2, *C*) separated from the phloem between the extended arms by a layer or two of stelar parenchyma. In larger stems, the cross-sectional configuration of xylem and phloem becomes increasingly complex, and the details of this complexity characterize many species. Stems of intermediate sizes frequently show a stellate xylem mass with one or more separate xylem strands (Fig. 2–2, *A*) with phloem between the groups and, as always in the genus, separated from the xylem by a layer of stelar parenchyma. In many species further elaboration involves an increasing number of xylem strands and their becoming platelike (Fig. 2–2, *E*). In others, bands of xylem seem to ramify and anastomose (Fig. 2–2, *D*, *F*), with an extreme in *L. cernuum*, where bands are hardly recognizable and it appears that the xylem and phloem are nearly uniformly intermixed (Fig. 2–2, *B*).

The maturation of xylem in the stem is almost uniformly exarch (Fig. 2–2, *A* to *F*), with protoxylem situated at the outer edge of each xylem arm, band, or patch. Only rarely in large stems is weak mesarchy observed (Sinnott, 1909).

The xylem configuration changes progressively along a portion of the stem as the bands or arms branch and anastomose. A three-dimensional reconstruction of a stele may be reminiscent of abstract art (see Hill, 1914).

The cortex in *Lycopodium* stems varies with stem diameter and position. Larger, aboveground stems generally show distinct tissue zonation with chlorenchyma in the hypodermal position, sclerenchyma surrounding the stele (Fig. 2–2, *D*, right edge), and parenchyma between. In smaller stems the sclerenchyma is reduced or absent, and often the entire cortex is composed of loosely packed chlorenchyma cells similar to and continuous with leaf mesophyll. The cortex of subterranean stems is often completely sclerenchymatous.

The leaf traces branch off protoxylem points of the stem stele (Fig. 2–2, *A*, *F*) and at their points of attachment retain the exarch pattern of maturation of the cauline xylem. As they traverse the cortex, centrifugal primary xylem is added and mesarchy results (Fig. 2–3, *B*).

All tracheary elements in *Lycopodium* are tracheids; perforate elements have never been observed. The first elements to mature have secondary cell walls in the form of rings that are longitudinally interconnected by thin strands of additional wall material (Bierhorst, 1960). There are usually one or two such interconnecting strands, but they do not suggest portions of helices as do similar interconnecting strands in other taxa (Fig. 27–8, *A*, *B*). In later-matured elements, the interconnections grade into sheets of wall material and the element becomes quite reticulate in appearance (Fig. 27–8, *B*). The succession of later-maturing elements shows progressively more rounded openings in the reticulum with progressively greater border development (Fig. 27–8, *C*). The first clearly pitted elements to mature have circular bordered pits (Fig. 27–8, *D*) and these are followed by elements with scalariformly bordered pits (Fig. 27–8, *E*). In some species all the pitted elements have circular bordered

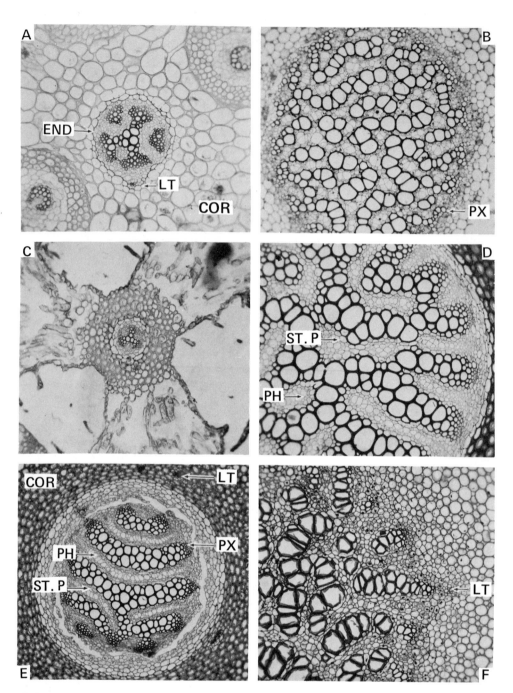

FIGURE 2–2. Stem anatomy in *Lycopodium*. *A. L. serratum*. Cross section of the central core of the stem showing the stem stele and two roots in the cortex. *B. L. cernuum*. Cross section of the stem stele. *C. L. densum*. Cross section of the central part of the stem. *D. L. densum*. Part of the stele of a larger stem than the one in *C*. *E. L. flabelliforme*. Stem stele and inner cortex. *F. L. phlegmarioides*. Portion of the stem stele. END = endodermis; LT = leaf trace; COR = cortex; PX = protoxylem; ST.P = stelar parenchyma; PH = phloem.

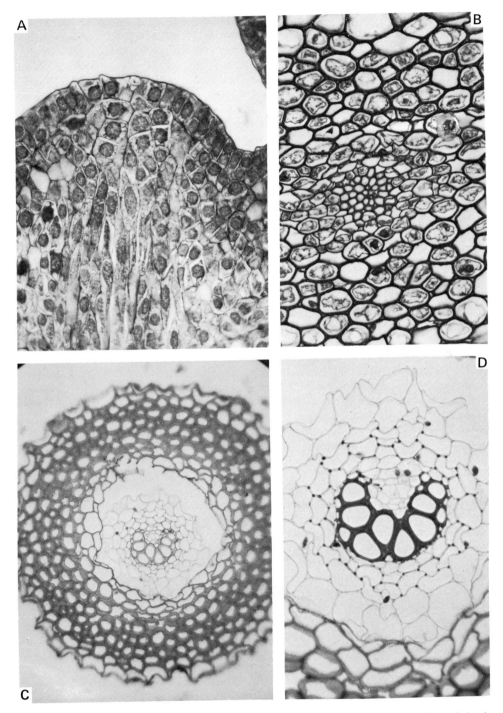

FIGURE 2–3. *A*. Stem apex of *Lycopodium samoanum* in median longitudinal section. *B*. Leaf trace of *L. phlegmarioides* as it appears in cross section in the stem cortex. *C*. Root of *L. phyllanthum* in cross section. *D*. Portion of *C* enlarged.

pits (e.g., *L. selago*, *L. lucidulum*, and *L. serratum*). It seems significant that the species in this category are all in the selago group, a section generally interpreted as primitive in terms of the phyllotaxy, the undifferentiated strobilus, and the close similarity between vegetative leaves and sporophylls shown by the component species.

The appearance of circular bordered pits before scalariformly bordered ones in the ontogenetic sequence is of some significance in interpreting tracheary element specialization. The order of appearance of pit types in *Lycopodium* is similar to that in the cycads and in the Ophioglossaceae but the reverse of that seen in flowering plants. In flowering plants the interpretation is that circular bordered pits have arisen phylogenetically from scalariformly bordered ones by a "breaking-up" process. This conclusion is supported by a wealth of evidence, including the order of appearance of pit types. This conclusion is, however, dubiously applied to taxa other than angiosperms, in which, for the most part, it seems that the difference between circular bordered pits and scalariformly bordered ones is of size only and not of phylogenetic level of specialization.

The phloem elements of *Lycopodium* are sieve cells with relatively inconspicuous sieve areas on their lateral walls and sloping tips (see Lamoureux, 1961).

The stem apex of *Lycopodium* exhibits a pattern of growth in which there are two or three initial cells involved (Dwyer, 1967). "Initial cell" is used here in the most restricted sense—to apply to a cell of a meristem at least one derivative of which remains in the meristem (i.e., it is a perpetuating cell of the meristem). It is possible to examine median longitudinal sections of shoot tips (Fig. 2–3, *A*) and point out the initial zone at the crest of the dome, but only in a carefully prepared set of cross-sectional camera lucida drawings can one extrapolate cell lineages back to initials.

The cauline procambium differentiates in the center of the axis only a few cells from the apical initials (Fig. 2–3, *A*) and is clearly distal to the first recognizable appendicular primordium.

The roots of *Lycopodium* show features peculiar to themselves and also suggest in some ways those of *Selaginella* and *Isoëtes*. Externally the roots of *Lycopodium* exhibit distinct and usually equal dichotomous branching, a calyptra of ordinary appearance over the apical meristem, and, proximal to the apex, a long zone where unicellular, hairy extensions are borne in profusion. At levels where tissue maturation has been completed, the cortex is often completely sclerenchymatous (Fig. 2–3, *C*). In large roots (not produced by all species) the stele often shows the same kind of vascular complexity as in the stem (e.g., *L. clavatum*) with the xylem mass dissected in the form of plates. The smaller roots of these species and all roots of others show a stele with a crescent-shaped xylem mass with phloem located in the concavity (Fig. 2–3, *C*, *D*). Some of these roots are diarch, but usually they are not (Pixley, 1964). There is a protoxylem pole situated at each end of the U-shaped cross section and often one or more poles located elsewhere on the periphery of the xylem mass. Sometimes there seems to be almost an entire layer of protoxylem elements along the convex side of the mass. The protoxylem at the two expected loci begins maturation first; only later are elements matured on the convex side of the xylem. The roots of *Lycopodium* are thus unique in having protoxylem poles of different ages and in having a lack of conformity between the number of protoxylem poles and the shape of the xylem mass.

Roots originate from other roots within the pericyclic region or from stems in the comparable position. In many species they arise on portions of stems well above ground level, then grow vertically through the stem cortex (Fig. 2–2, *A*) before emerging below. In the figure note that the two root steles in the cortex are oriented with the open ends of their xylem cross sections toward the outside of the stem. This relationship seems to be constant and suggests comparison with *Selaginella*, *Lepidodendron*, and *Isoëtes*.

The sporangium originates on the adaxial (upper) side of a leaf (called a sporophyll when sporangium-bearing) very near its axil (Fig. 2–6, *A*, *F*). This position may be held, or the sporangium may shift during ontogeny and become situated at maturity on the stem just above the sporophyll axil or well out on the

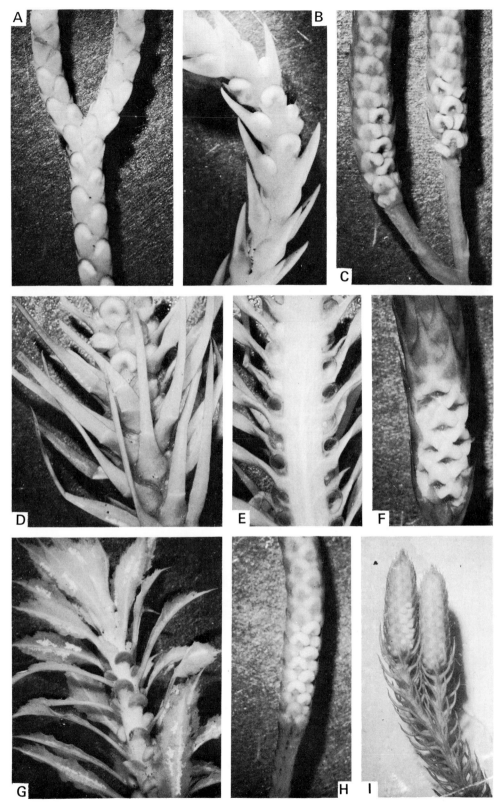

FIGURE 2–4. Fertile axes of *Lycopodium* showing sporangia and sporophylls. *A. L. phlegmari-oides*. *B. L. carinatum*. *C. L. flabelliforme*. *D. E. L. samoanum*. The specimen in *E* is split longitudinally. *F. L. carolinianum*. *G. L. serratum*. *H. L. densum*. *I. L. cernum*. Several sporophylls have been removed from *B* to *D*, *F* to *I*.

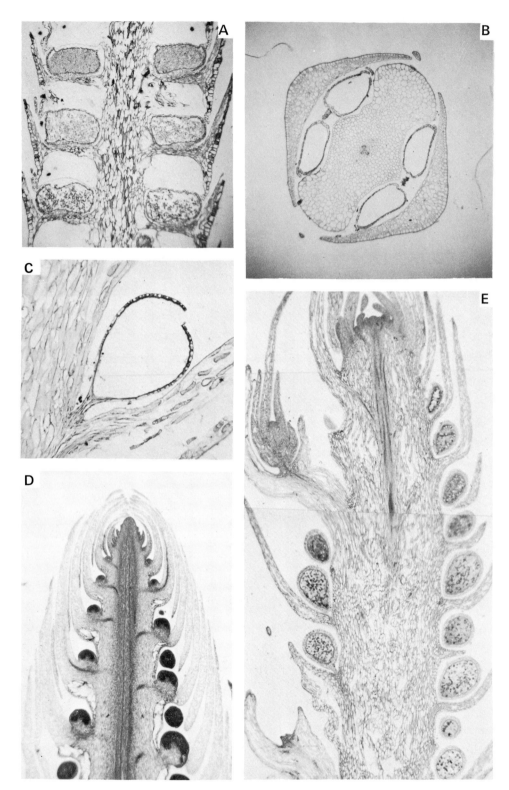

FIGURE 2–5. *A.* Longitudinal section of part of the strobilus of *Lycopodium cernuum.* *B.* Cross section of the strobilus of *L. phyllanthum.* *C.* Empty sporangium of *L. selago* from a longitudinal section of the fertile stem. The line of dehiscence is shown in cross section. *D.* Longitudinal section of a still-growing strobilus of *L. obscurum.* *E.* Longitudinal section of the fertile stem tip of *L. selago.* The stem apex is at the top of the figure. On the upper left a bulbil is shown, and on the lower left a stalk remaining after bulbil abscission is shown.

sporophyll surface, depending on the species (Fig. 2–5, *A*, *D*).

The sporangia attain a length of 2 mm or slightly longer and are characteristically reniform at maturity. They are oriented in such a way that the full length and curvature are observed in surface view of the stem (Fig. 2–4, *A* to *I*) or in tangential section. The shape may be ascertained from the cross section in Fig. 2–5, *B*, where one can see the two ends of each of two sporangia on either side of a sporangial stalk.

The orientation of the line of dehiscence is constant in the genus and is transverse to the sporophyll (Fig. 2–4, *D*; note the two slightly gaping sporangia). The line is seen in cross-sectional view in a radial section of the stem and may be directly opposite the stalk (Fig. 2–5, *C*) or in various other positions, depending upon the species.

The distinctiveness of the stalk (and its presence or absence) varies with the species, but when it is present it is always several cells thick.

The sporophylls are always grouped along a zone of the stem. The zone may be terminal on a determinate stem or somewhere along the axis on an indeterminate one. In either case, sporophylls and vegetative leaves may be similar or morphologically divergent from each other.

When the sporophylls are terminally grouped and appear quite different from vegetative leaves, they, together with the stem that bears them, constitute a strobilus (Fig. 2–1, *A* to *D*; Fig. 2–4, *C*, *H*, *I*). Owing to the fine gradation between strobilate and nonstrobilate species, the application of the term as in some other taxa becomes somewhat subjective. Species with the least suggestion of a strobilus (i.e., little or no difference between vegetative leaves and sporophylls and no terminalization) fall in the section containing *L. selago*, *L. lucidulum*, *L. serratum*, and their allies (see Nessel, 1939) and are considered by most morphologists to exhibit the most primitive morphology in the genus. The most distinct strobili occur in the species related to *L. complanatum* and *L. clavatum*. In the section that includes *L. inundatum*, *L. carolinianum*, *L. drumondii*, and their relatives, the strobilus is reasonably distinct and terminal on an upright branch. However, in

L. drumondii the strobilar apex resumes growth at a later date; it produces more stem with reduced leaves, such as those which occur below the strobilus, and another strobilus. This is often repeated several times. Strobili of several distinctly strobilate species under special growth conditions frequently produce a vegetative extension of the strobilus (e.g., *L. obscurum* and *L. flabelliforme*). Strobili in the pendulous epiphytic forms (e.g., the sections Carinata and Phlegmaria) are often (and sometimes constantly) highly branched tassels (Fig. 2–1, *B*, *E*).

Sporangia are initiated on very young sporophylls, and in a longitudinal section of a growing strobilus an entire developmental series can often be seen (Fig. 2–5, *D*). First, a group of two to five surface cells on the adaxial side of the sporophyll adjacent to its axil divides periclinally (i.e., by new walls formed parallel to the surface; Fig. 2–6, *A*). In some species the first divisions are slightly oblique and some are delayed slightly in time. In Fig. 2–6, *F*, for example, two cells just to the left of the arrow have divided and the one to the right of the pointer is in late prophase. The initial set of periclinal divisions establishes the sporogenous tissue (inner cells). The outer cells eventually will give rise to the wall of the sporangium, part or all of the stalk (depending on the species), and part of the tapetum.

Following the two-layered stage, the inner cells form an expanding, mitotically active tissue mass causing an upward bulging, while anticlinal divisions (i.e., division walls perpendicular to the surface) in the surface layer keep pace with changing surface area (Fig. 2–6, *B*, *C*, *G*). Soon periclinal divisions take place in the surface-layer cells and then in their derivatives until the sporogenous mass is ultimately covered by up to five cell layers (Fig. 2–6, *D*, *E*, *H*, *I*). The layer adjacent to the sporogenous mass stains deeply, indicative of high protein content, and acts as the initial tapetal layer, decomposing completely at about the time meiosis commences. The tapetal layer completely surrounds the sporogenous mass, and only the distal portion, not that located proximally, is traceable to the original sporangial initials.

Differential growth of the sporangium

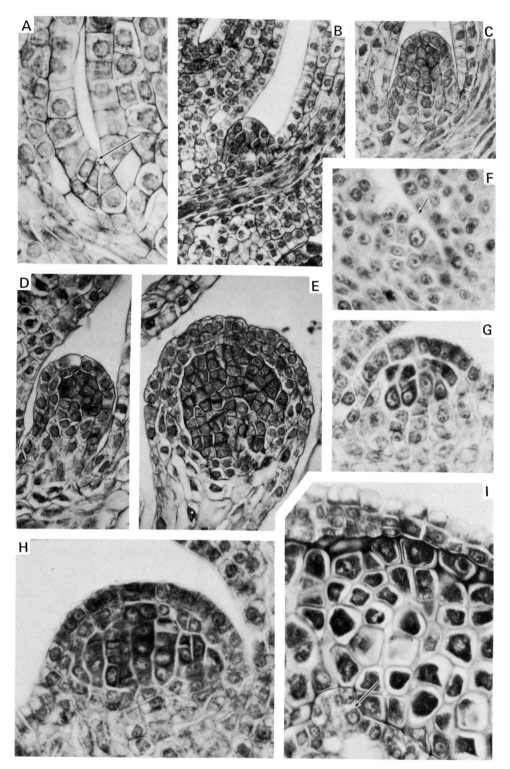

FIGURE 2–6. Sporangium development in *Lycopodium*. *A* to *E. L. samoanum*. *F* to *I. L. obscurùm*.

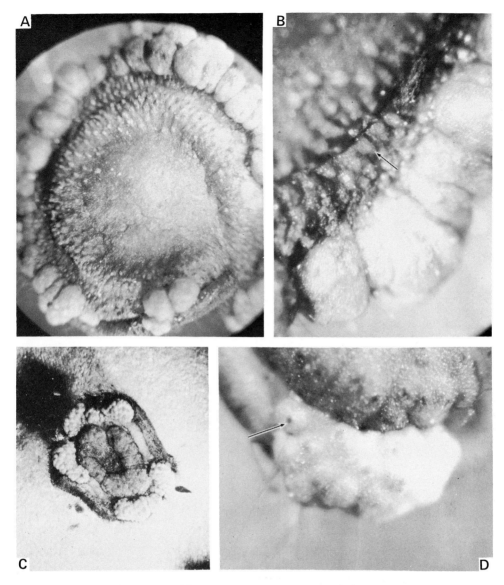

FIGURE 2–7. Gametophytes of *Lycopodium obscurum* from the upper surface.

proper is primarily responsible for the final assumption of the reniform shape, but very active growth in area occurs in layers immediately proximal to the sporogenous mass (arrow in Fig. 2–6, *I*). The tissue below is, therefore, also actively growing into the sporangium.

As the sporangium matures, the cells of the outer wall layer begin to elongate anticlinally (Fig. 2–6, *I*), and eventually all surface cells develop thickened inner and radial walls (Fig. 2–5, *C*). This is later followed by complete, or nearly complete, breakdown of all inner wall layers. Thus the mature sporangium has a wall of one cell layer.

The immature spores come to be more or less free in a fluid mass, thought to be derived by breakdown of tapetum and aborted sporocytes. This, however, is a dubious assumption since the volume of the fluid is too great to be

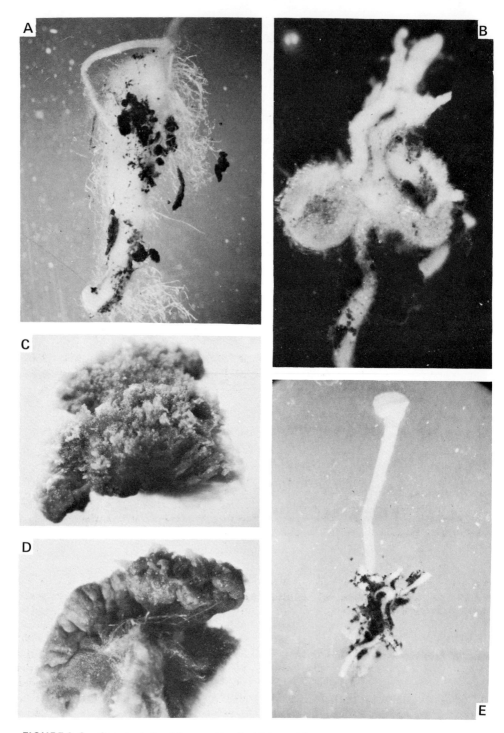

FIGURE 2–8. Gametophyte of *Lycopodium lucidulum* with a young sporophyte attached (shown in part at the top). *B.* Gametophyte of *L. phlegmarioides*. The cup-shaped structure on the left held the foot of a young sporophyte before it was dislodged. *C, D.* Upper and lower views of the gametophyte of *L. cernuum*. *E.* Gametophyte and young sporophyte of *L. phlegmarioides*.

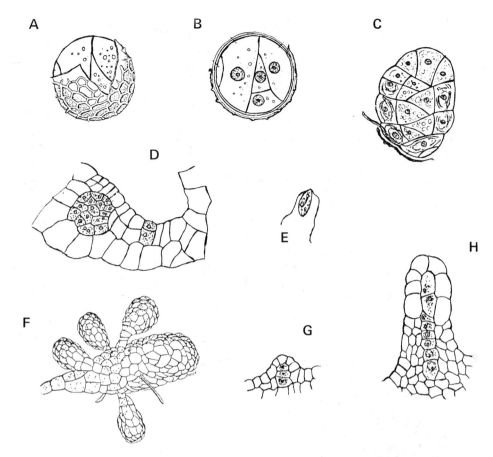

FIGURE 2–9. *A, B.* Surface and sectional views of a young gametophyte of *Lycopodium anno-tinum* which is still mostly within the spore wall. *C.* Young gametophyte of *L. clavatum.* The spore wall is shown opened out on the lower left. *D.* Two stages in the development of the antheridium of *L. clavatum.* *E.* Sperm of *L. clavatum.* *F.* Vegetative reproductive bodies on the gametophyte of *L. phlegmaria.* *G, H.* Two stages in the development of the archegonium of *L. clavatum.* *A* to *E, G, H,* after Bruchmann (1910); *F,* after Treub (1884).

accounted for in this manner. The fluid matrix seems to deposit some of the outer spore coat; other functions have not been demonstrated.

Sporangial dehiscence takes place along a line where surface cells failed to elongate anticlinally. All cells of the surface, by the nature of the distribution of their wall thickenings, shrink on drying, which reduces the exposed surface area and opens the spore-producing body.

In many species the sporophylls fold backward, exposing the sporangia as they mature. This is accomplished by the shrinkage of a large mucilage cavity which occurs on the abaxial side of the sporophyll and extends into the stem cortex (Fig. 2–5, *D*).

The spores at maturity retain the triradiate marks that reflect the manner in which the four fit together in the intact tetrad. *Lycopodium* spores are produced in large quantities and may be collected easily. The high surface area exposed has made them useful as the reducing agent in gunpowder and as coating for pills.

Gametophytes are known in approximately 10 per cent of *Lycopodium* species. Those found in nature seem to fall into two types:

(1) those which are green, surface living, and derived from spores that germinate soon after falling onto a suitable substratum (examples are *L. inundatum*, *L. carolinianum*, and *L. cernuum*) and (2) those which are subterranean, nongreen, and derived from spores whose germination is delayed for some time. The latter characteristic has been assumed but not demonstrated for a number of species. All the subterranean types are mycorrhizal, with the endophytic fungus, a phycomycete, often restricted to definite tissue zones. Examples of the second type are *L. obscurum*, *L. complanatum*, *L. flabelliforme*, *L. lucidulum*, *L. phlegmaria*, *L. phlegmarioides*, and *L. selago*.

All young *Lycopodium* gametophytes are three-dimensional masses of cells, generally with an organized apical meristem (Fig. 2–9, *C*). From this stage on, the various species diverge conspicuously. In the surface-living, green types, the apex is lost quite early and the mass grows in bulk indiscriminately, producing a basal pad and a series of short upright lobes (Fig. 2–8, *C*, *D*). In some subterranean types, the apex retains its organization and a branching axial body is produced. This is the Phlegmaria type (Fig. 2–8, *B*, *E*). In other subterranean types the axial growth *and* organization are maintained for a variable time and are only sometimes lost as the apex loses its organization and fans out slightly. This is the selago or lucidulum type (Fig. 2–8, *A*). In still other subterranean types the apex is lost quite early in the "teardrop" stage (Fig. 2–10, *A*), and a marginal meristem is established which causes the gametophyte to become disc-shaped (Fig. 2–7, *A*, *C*; Fig. 2–10, *C*). This is the obscurum type. The margin of the disc may become highly convoluted and grow laterally or upright, as in *L. clavatum*, or the gametophyte may grow uniformly upward and become cone-shaped, as in *L. complanatum*.

Spores of some species that normally produce subterranean gametophytes may be made to germinate readily on the surface of a nutrient medium containing only mineral nutrients and sucrose. This is done by scarifying the spores or treating them with acid (Freeberg and Wetmore, 1957). The gametophytes produced appear as indiscriminately growing masses of callus tissue with upright lobes and a little green color, but they bear quite normal gametangia. They resemble the *L. cernuum* type of gametophyte in many respects.

As the spore of subterranean species germinates in nature, the first division is very asymmetrical, resulting in a very small cell and a large cell. Divisions in the larger cell and its derivatives result in the early formation of an apical meristem (Fig. 2–9, *A* to *C*). The smaller cell (left side of Fig. 2–9, *B*), which does not develop further, seems to be the equivalent of the "prothallial cell" in the microgametophyte of *Selaginella*, which has been interpreted as being the last remnant of a vegetative body. The fact that in *Lycopodium* a rather massive body is formed from the other cell greatly dilutes the interpretation applied to *Selaginella*. The term "prothallial cell" is an example of one of the many terms with which plant morphology is saddled that fall in the category of "loaded terminology." It is unfortunate that many such terms are used in a descriptive sense.

The "irregular" types of subterranean *Lycopodium* gametophytes (i.e., the convoluted discs) actually grow in a uniform manner and exhibit a quite fixed and uniform morphology. In *L. obscurum*, the apical meristem persists until the young gametophyte is about 0.5 mm long, at which time the distal cells enlarge laterally and a uniform, continuous, circular, marginal meristem is initiated. The meristem is pushed early into a groove by growth upward from below (arrow in Fig. 2–10, *B*, which is one edge of Fig. 2–10, *C*). As this occurs, the entire plant body is increasing in thickness, owing to the activity of a peripheral thickening meristem over the entire lower surface (the orientation within the soil is usually quite fixed). The marginal meristem adds tissue in two directions at the surface and also to the inside of the body. The tissue added on the surface toward the center of the disc is either in distinct ridges or relatively flat. Within the ridges (Fig. 2–7, *A*, *C*, *D*; Fig. 2–10, *B*, *C*) large numbers of antheridia are formed. On the flat areas of the disc archegonia are initiated, often in large numbers (Fig. 2–7, *A*, *B*), and also a few antheridia (Fig. 2–10, *C*). Rhizoids are produced from the lower surface only.

In the larger gametophytes of *L. obscurum* and similar species, such as *L. clavatum*, the

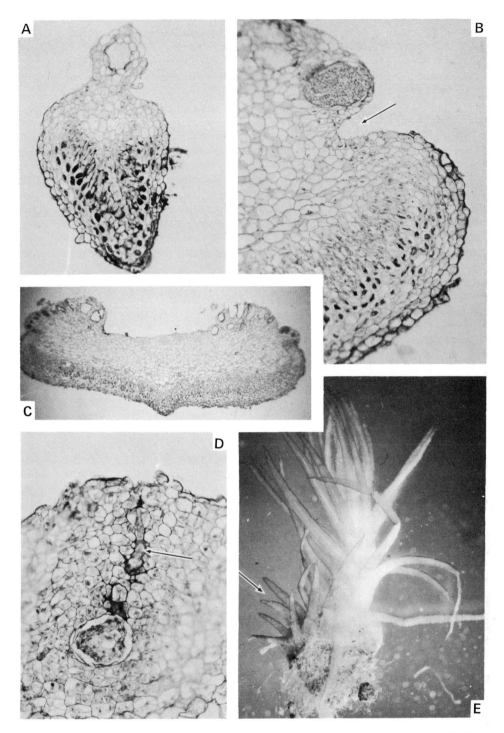

FIGURE 2–10. *A*. Relatively young gametophyte of *Lycopodium obscurum* in longitudinal section. *B*. Margin of an older gametophyte of *L. obscurum* in longitudinal section. The arrow indicates the marginal meristem. *C*. Median longitudinal section of an older gametophyte of *L. obscurum*. *D*. Young embryo of *L. obscurum* within the gametophyte. The arrow indicates the suspensor. *E*. Gametophyte and young sporophyte of *L. cernuum*. The gametophyte is obscured by its mass of rhizoids. The arrow indicates "prophylls."

marginal meristem becomes discontinuous as the result of localized injuries or unknown factors that cause localized cessation of growth. Such plants often superficially resemble walnut cotyledons.

The subterranean types of *Lycopodium* gametophyte have been collected only a relatively few times and are considered by some to be rare. In many parts of their range, they may be found in large numbers after a season of uniform precipitation and no substratum drying. They are found just beneath the surface to a depth of nearly 10 cm in highly organic soil, decomposed wood, or old sawdust. Gametophytes of the *phlegmaria* type are readily found in the accumulation of peaty material around the roots of epiphytes in rainforests. The surface-living, green types are easily grown in the laboratory or readily found on wet clay banks near the mature sporophytes.

Vegetative reproduction occurs in gametophytes of most species of *Lycopodium* either by fragmentation, surface budding, or bulbil formation at the tips of specialized uniseriate outgrowths (Fig. 2–9, *F*). There probably is no dissemination of propagules, however.

The antheridia of *Lycopodium* are relatively large, with a high sperm output (Fig. 2–10, *B*). They are essentially sunken but bulge somewhat at the surface (Fig. 2–7, *C, D*). They originate from single surface cells that first divide periclinally (Fig. 2–9, *D*) to establish the jacket mother cell (outer cell) and the primary spermatogenous cell (inner cell). A series of synchronous divisions in the spermatogenous tissue ultimately produces the spermatids, which mature into biflagellate sperm (Fig. 2–9, *E*).

In the mother cell of two spermatids, a centriole appears, then divides into two. Each centriole assumes a polar position, and after division each spermatid contains a centriole. During spermatogenesis, the one centriole of the spermatid divides to form two structures similar to itself which will be the basal bodies of the flagella. The two bodies together make up the blepharoplast (there are minor inconsistencies in the application of this term in the literature). In taxa in which multiflagellate sperm are produced, the blepharoplast is a string of granules. The presence of a centriole with an associated astral apparatus is a general feature of all plants that produce motile sperm.

The antheridial jacket is formed principally as the result of anticlinal divisions in the initial and its derivatives. Occasional periclinal divisions occur, so that here and there the jacket is two cells thick (Fig. 2–9, *D*).

The one operculum per antheridium is formed by the decomposition of a single cell (dark spot at the arrow in Fig. 2–7, *D*).

The superficial archegonial initial, as in other vascular plants, divides periclinally to establish the neck mother cell (outer cell) and axial-row mother cell (inner cell). The neck mother cell then divides anticlinally; each of its two daughter cells also divides anticlinally but at right angles to the division that produced them. The mother cells of the four vertical rows of neck cells are thus established. The neck then grows in length (Fig. 2–9, *G*) and the axial row along with it. The archegonium of the large, fleshy, subterranean gametophytes comes to be relatively massive (Fig. 2–9, *H*; Fig. 2–11, *A*) with the axial cell row being composed of an egg at the proximal end, then its sister cell, the ventral canal cell, and a long file of neck canal cells distally. The basal part of the neck becomes thicker as later divisions occur, with some of its cells derived from cells adjacent to the original archegonial initial. The mature archegonia, as seen externally, appear as fat fingers projecting from the surface (one of a number is pointed out in Fig. 2–7, *B*, and many may be seen in Fig. 2–7, *A* just inside the antheridiate outgrowths and surrounding the central flattish dome).

The embryogeny of *Lycopodium* is not known with the degree of certainty implied in many general accounts. None of the information on embryogeny has been documented with photographs. For the most part the descriptions are based on a limited and insufficient quantity of material, and there have been no confirmative studies. As compared to most vascular plants, the embryogeny of *Lycopodium* is quite difficult to study because the significant events are chronologically widely separated and many occur when the embryos are quite large. In addition, there are some suggestions that there is considerable variation within individual species in embryological events.

The embryo of *Lycopodium clavatum* is certainly the best known of all the species.

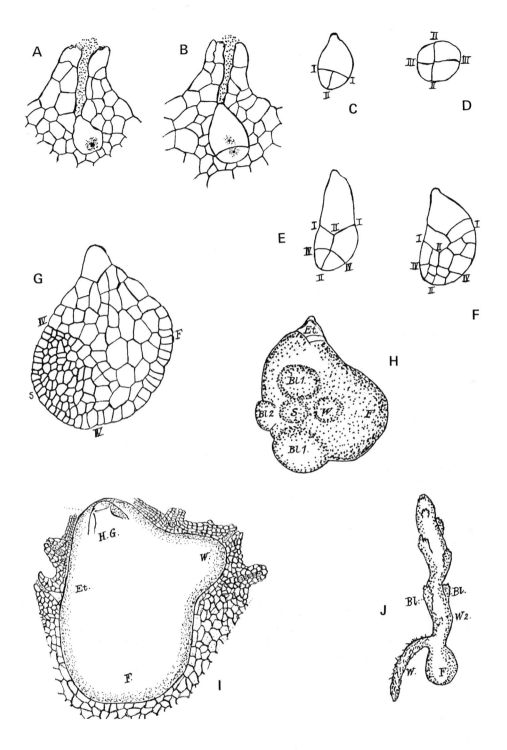

FIGURE 2–11. Embryo of *Lycopodium clavatum*, after Bruchmann (1898). S = stem; F = foot; Et = suspensor; W = root; Bl = leaf

The most meticulous and accurate of researchers, H. Bruchmann, based his detailed account on a considerable amount of material and we are all indebted to him for his many contributions to *Lycopodium* life histories.

During the embryogeny of *Lycopodium*, the zygote divides transverse to the long axis of the archegonium (Fig. 2–11, *B*, division I–I in *C*); of the two cells thus produced, the outer one is the suspensor and it has not been reported to divide further. In *L. obscurum* it elongates appreciably (Fig. 2–10, *D*) but possibly inconsistently. In other species described its elongation is slight (Fig. 2–11, *C*, *E* to *H*) and it does not seem to push the proembryo deeper into the gametophytic tissue.

The inner cell (proembryo cell) of the two-cell stage divides at right angles to the first division (division wall II in Fig. 2–11, *C*). The third division (actually a pair of divisions) is at right angles to the second such that it is parallel to the plane of the paper in Fig. 2–11, *C* and shown (III-III) in a cross section of the five-celled embryo in Fig. 2–11, *D*. The fourth division (actually four divisions) is parallel to I-I. Thus the embryo in Fig. 2–11, *E* is composed of nine cells: one suspensor cell and eight proembryo cells.

The four cells of the proembryo adjacent to the suspensor cell form the foot. In those species of *Lycopodium* with subterranean gametophytes, the four foot cells enlarge, divide, and redivide to form an asymmetrically growing tissue mass pushing the other four cells and their derivatives to a more lateral position (Fig. 2–11, *E* to *I*). The foot thus becomes a bulbous mass of tissue, the most prominent part of the embryo, bulging out from the rest of the embryo in a position nearly at right angles to its starting position (Fig. 2–11, *G* to *J*).

The cup-shaped mass extending to the left of the photograph in Fig. 2–8, *B* is gametophytic tissue that grew with and enclosed the foot of the embryo before the latter physically separated from it on removal from the soil. The foot of some other species (e.g., *L. obscurum*) is more completely enclosed in gametophytic tissue.

Of the other four cells of the eight-celled proembryo in the subterranean species, two eventually give rise to leaf and two to stem

apex. The first root, considered by some workers not to be part of the embryo, is of somewhat later origin (W in Fig. 2–11, *H* to *J*), appearing near the stem apex. The first several leaves are very diminutive and avascular.

In the subterranean types, the gametophyte may remain alive and attached to young sporophytes for several years and even continue to grow and produce one or more additional embryos. One gametophyte of *L. obscurum* collected by A. J. Eames bore nine young sporophytes.

In species of *Lycopodium* with surface-living green gametophytes the stages up to the nine-celled stage are similar to those of the subterranean species. The foot has a similar origin and develops asymmetrically but becomes a relatively small part of the embryo. The four cells that in subterranean types form leaf and stem here form instead a bulbous tissue mass that has been called a "protocorm." This is a parenchymatous mass bearing rhizoids over its lower surface (Fig. 2–10, *E*) and a number of avascular, leaflike structures ("prophylls") of indefinite arrangement on its upper surface (arrow in Fig. 2–10, *E*). A stem apex is said to arise among the "prophylls" and give rise to the first leafy shoot (the major upright axis in Fig. 2–10, *E*). The first root arises from the base of the first recognizable stem. These events are in need of further study, verification, and more complete photographic documentation.

Phylloglossum

Phylloglossum is a highly reduced and specialized genus known only from a relatively few sites in New Zealand and Australia. It is adapted to wet growing conditions and survival through underground tubers over very dry seasons.

The entire plant body is only 4 to 7 cm high, including the strobilus and its stalk (Fig. 2–12, *A*). The basal part of the sporophyte is a tuberous body from which arises a short axis (stem) bearing a cluster of quill-like leaves. A very few adventitious roots extend from the stem (one is shown on the left in Fig. 2–12, *A*). When the plant is fertile, the stem is elongated upward as a naked stalk terminated

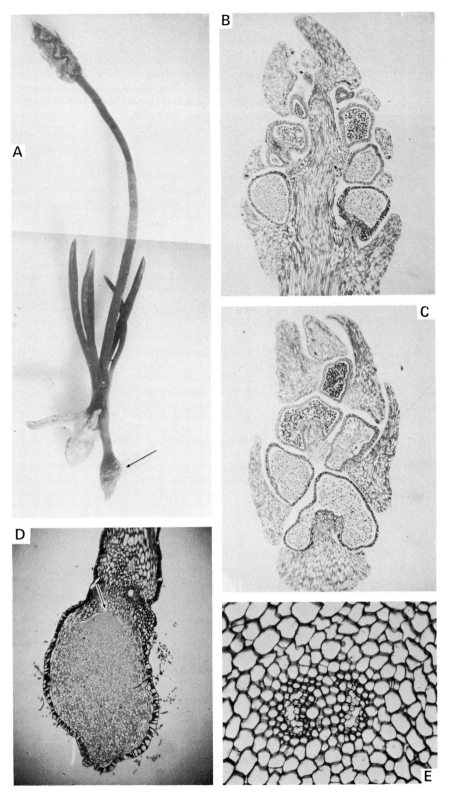

FIGURE 2–12. *Phylloglossum drumondii.* *A.* Habit. *B, C.* Strobilus in longitudinal section. *D.* Longitudinal section of a new tuber. *E.* Two mesarch vascular strands of the stele of the strobilar stalk.

25

by a small strobilus. Leafless branches of the stem grow downward or outward and at the tip of each (arrow in Fig. 2–12, *A*) a new tuber is formed that is capable of living through dry periods and then producing a complete new plant.

The tuber (Fig. 2–12, *D*) contains an internal mass of food-packed parenchyma and is covered with a protective cell layer. The apex of the tuber is situated some distance from the distal end and pointed back toward the parental plant (arrow in Fig. 2–12, *D*).

At the base of the stem a hollow, amphiphloic, closed cylinder of vascular tissue is present. This breaks up into several bundles at higher levels and there is generally a reduction in bundle number as the strobilar stalk is approached. Figure 2–12, *E* shows a two-bundle stele near the base of the strobilar stalk. The xylem is mesarch throughout the plant axis and in the leaf trace. At certain levels of the stem, leaf gaps have been designated.

The strobilar structure is quite lycopodioid in all its known details. Each sporophyll bears a typical reniform sporangium on or near its axil (Fig. 2–12, *B* near-radial section, *C*, tangential section). Sporangial histology and spore structure are as in *Lycopodium*.

The gametophyte of *Phylloglossum* is poorly known (Holloway, 1935) and no satisfactory illustrations are available. It is in part green and aerial, more or less cylindrical, less than 6 mm long, and bears a slightly flaring crown. A fungus is present within its tissue. Its gametangia are lycopodioid.

The embryogeny of *Phylloglossum* is essentially unknown; only relatively old embryos have been described (A. P. W. Thomas, 1901). The embryo axis bears at one end a prominent foot embedded in the gametophyte and at the other end an apex that extends usually laterally from the gametophyte. The first leaf, which grows upward, and the first tuber, which extends downward, develops from the apex. There is no embryonic root; the first root, which does not develop until the second season, forms on the first tuber.

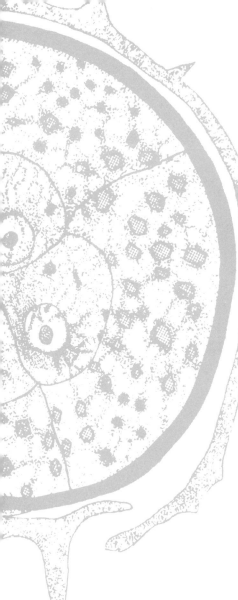

3

Selaginellaceae

The family Selaginellaceae includes *Selaginella* and several very closely related fossil forms which are known from Lower Carboniferous and more recent strata. *Selaginella* is probably one of the oldest of all extant genera of vascular plants, second only to *Lycopodium*. Despite its great antiquity, which might lead one to expect specialization and relative genetic stagnation, there are approximately 700 extant species and much evidence of recent speciation. Evolutionists such as Dobzhansky have very logically and with considerable supporting evidence led us to believe that the longer a taxon exists, the more closely in harmony it becomes with its environment and the more fixed its morphology and the more rigid its genetic makeup becomes. In this regard *Selaginella* and *Lycopodium* are truly enigmas. The only apparent explanation is that relatively recent genetic changes have occurred in the genus which have greatly modified the ability of other genes to mutate.

The species of *Selaginella* are distributed from the tropics to subarctic latitudes. Most inhabit relatively damp places, but some (e.g., *S. rupestris* and its relatives) are found on exposed rocks and hillsides. Many are nearly flat creepers (e.g., *S. apoda* and *S. kraussiana*; Fig. 3–1, *A*); some produce tufts of upright mosslike branches (e.g., *S. rupestris*; Fig. 3–1, *B*); still others are viny; and some are upright plants to several feet tall (e.g., *S. viridangula*; Fig. 3–1, *D*).

Some species of *Selaginella* show uniformly developed leaves, radially organized shoots, and simple cauline steles (e.g., *S. rupestris*). Other species are more dorsiventral (e.g., *S. kraussiana*; Fig. 3–1, *E*, *F*) with differential development of certain rows of leaves on the stem and dorsiventrally organized vascular tissue within.

The leaves of *Selaginella* are small, with a single vein that remains unbranched throughout its length. The

FIGURE 3–1. *A. Selaginella kraussiana. B. S. rupestris. C. S. selaginoides. D. S. viridangula. E, F.* Upper and lower views of a portion of *A.*

leaf trace at its departure from a cauline bundle is seen to arise by a nearly radial division of a vertical protoxylem strand.

In or near the axil of each vegetative leaf and sporophyll there is a tonguelike structure called a ligule (LIG in Fig. 3–2, *A*, *C*). The ligule is a fixed feature not only of members of the Selaginellales but also of the Isoëtales and Lepidodendrales. The ligule has a well-defined and embedded foot with a distinctive outer cell layer. The entire ligule is composed of cells with dense contents that stain heavily with stains ordinarily thought to be proteophilic. It develops precociously and matures long before its associated leaf. It has long been suggested that the ligule is in some way associated with water conservation, holding water and preventing shoot desiccation. Another possibility, in the absence of real evidence, is that it is concerned with the upward movement of inorganic solutes as they may be passed on from leaf primordium to leaf primordium within the orthostichies. This idea is based upon work on *Cucurbita* by F. C. Steward, who demonstrated such an acropetal movement among leaf primordia. The ligules in *Selaginella* may compensate for the smaller and less effective leaf primordia in facilitating such movement.

Stem apices of some *Selaginella* species have a single apical cell; others are apparently of the lycopodioid type with two or more initial cells.

Stems are dichotomously branched and anatomically variable among species and within certain species according to stem diameter. Larger stems tend to be tough with a zone of hypodermal sclerenchyma (Fig. 3–2, *B*, *E*). A relatively simple protostele with exarch primary xylem is found in *S. rupestris* and its close allies. Some dorsiventral species are distelic (Fig. 3–2, *C*) with the plane of the two steles parallel to the substratum and with the insertion of the two rows of major leaves lateral to them. In each of the two steles the protoxylem is exarch and laterally situated.

Larger stems of species with dimorphic leaves show steles with vascular plates often in conjunction with small terete meristeles. The hand section of *S. vogelii* appearing in Fig. 3–2, *B* shows one plate meristele and one small stele at the arrow. The hand section of *S. viridangula* in Fig. 3–2, *E* shows three plates and two cavities from which the cross sections of the terete meristeles have fallen out.

The plate meristeles within the genus vary from flat in cross section through curved and U-shaped to closed O's. According to one interpretation (Majumdar, 1942) this series represents the probable phylogenetic pathway to the *Selaginella* type of siphonostele represented by the closed, hollow types.

In larger cauline bundles of *Selaginella* both mesarchy and exarchy occur, depending on the level within the stem and the particular pole of maturation observed. Figure 3–2, *F* shows a mesarch pole, and Fig. 3–2, *G* shows two exarch poles.

A conspicuous feature of *Selaginella* stems is the suspension of each stele in a cavity by trabeculate endodermal cells (Fig. 3–2, *C*, *D*; Fig. 3–4, *E*). The casparian strip is of an ordinary type and often results in a conspicuous localized constriction (Fig. 3–2, *D* at arrow).

Roots of *Selaginella* are dichotomously branched axes arising from both vertical and horizontal stems in some species and only from the latter in others. In some species, at least, their origin is superficial rather than endogenous and often in specific locations relative to stem dichotomies. In many creeping, dorsiventral forms the roots arise only at or just proximal to a stem dichotomy and on the lower side (Fig. 3–1, *E*, *F*), in others they arise in this position as well as elsewhere on the stem (Fig. 3–3, *A*, *B*), and in others no fixed relationship exists. In many species adventitious shoots arise adjacent to the points of root attachment (Fig. 3–3, *A*, where RH is a root that has been cut off, SH is the adventitious shoot, and PUL is a pulvinus at the base of the slightly overtopped branch of the dichotomy).

Exposed *Selaginella* roots are generally very smooth and cutinized externally. Root hairs and a more delicate epidermis are produced as the calyptrate apices penetrate the substratum.

The bilateral distribution of vascular tissues, seen in the roots of the Isoëtales, Lepidodendrales, and in all but the larger roots of the Lycopodiales, appears also in all *Selaginella* roots. The roots are monarch to tetrarch with

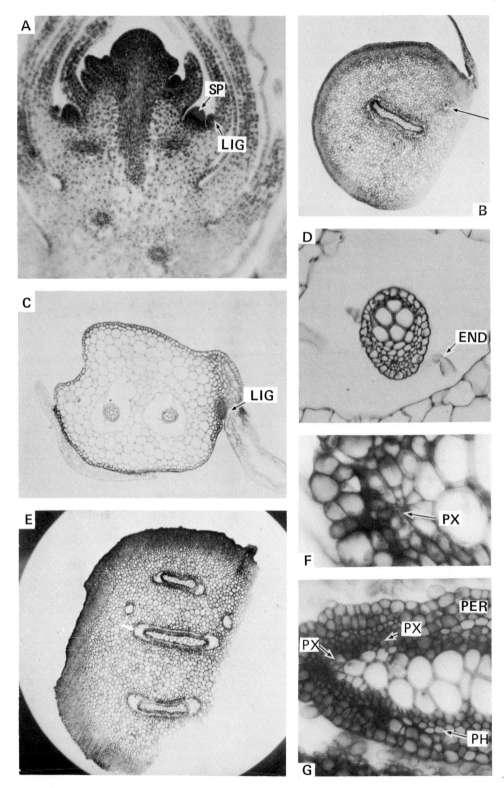

FIGURE 3–2. *A.* Tip of a young strobilus of *Selaginella selaginoides* in longitudinal section. *B.* Cross section of the stem of *S. vogelii.* *C.* Cross section of the stem of *S. kraussiana.* *D.* Portion of *C* enlarged. *E.* Cross section of the stem of *S. viridangula.* *F.* Edge of the cauline bundle enlarged from *E.* *G.* Edge of the cauline bundle enlarged from *B.*

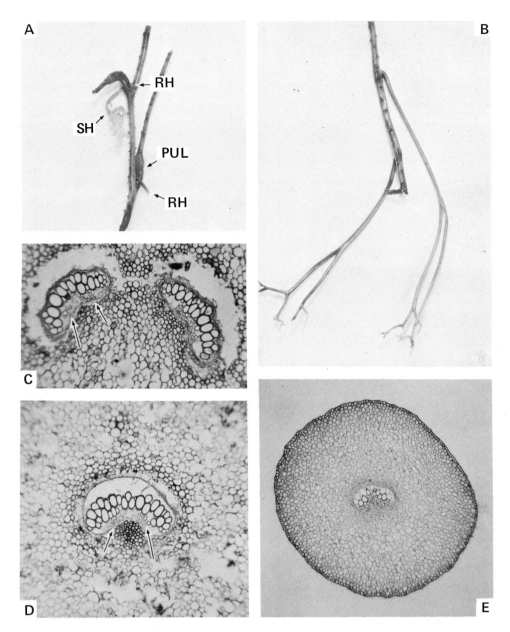

FIGURE 3–3. *A.* Portion of the upright shoot system of *Selaginella viridangula*. Two major dichotomies are shown, but differential development has occurred at each. Each apparent lateral shoot shows a conspicuous pulvinus (PUL). Almost at the axil of each dichotomy a root (RH, stub shown) has arisen, and lateral to its insertion a new shoot (SH) has appeared. *B.* Stem and two attached root systems of *S. viridangula*. These are not associated with dichotomies of the stem as are those in *A.* *C.* Cross section of a root proximal to the first dichotomy in *S. viridangula*. *D.* As *C*, but between the first and second dichotomies. *E.* As *C*, but between the second and third dichotomies.

FIGURE 3–4. *A*. Strobilus of *Selaginella selaginoides* after spore discharge. *B*. Strobilus of *S. kraussiana*. *C*. Strobili of *S. pulcherrima*. *D*. Strobili of *S. rupestris*. *E*. Longitudinal section of the strobilar axis of *S. selaginoides*.

protoxylem poles on the same side of the stele as the phloem (Fig. 3–3, C to E). In addition, as in each of the three orders mentioned above, the xylem is in a particular and constant position relative to the parental stem.

In terms of our general concepts of stem and root, the *Selaginella* root, specifically that part of the dichotomously branching truss near its point of attachment to a stem, is somewhat stemlike, because it is calyptra-less during part of its existence, is exogenous in origin, and is capable of developing as a typical leafy stem under certain conditions. This led earlier botanists to introduce the name "rhizophore" for this organ and to initiate a perennial argument as to whether it is stem or root. The term and the arguments are now certainly of historical interest only. They were rooted in a monophyletic concept of the root that is now known to be far from true. In addition, it was once thought that the "true roots" of *Selaginella* arose endogenously from the tip of the "rhizophore" rather than by apical division (see Webster and Steeves, 1964). A number of well-defined roots of various taxa are now known that show the same "stemlike" features as do those of *Selaginella*.

Primary xylem elements of *Selaginella* show rather generalized structure with annular elements maturing first and scalariformly pitted ones last. One peculiar feature that as far as is known is restricted to *Selaginella* is the occasional reversal of the direction of coiling of helical bands within individual cells (Zamora, 1958). In some species mataxylem elements are perforate with predominantly simple plates.

The sporangia of *Selaginella* are borne singly on the upper surface near the axils of sporophylls which are grouped in terminal strobili. The strobili are often inconspicuous not only by their size but also as a consequence of similarity between sporophyll and vegetative leaf. (Figure 3–4, B shows one of a number of strobili present on Fig. 3–1, A; several are present in Fig. 3–1, B, three of which are enlarged in Fig. 3–4, D; arrow in Fig. 3–1, D.) Figure 3–4, A, which is part of Fig. 3–1, C enlarged, shows a portion of the strobilus of *S. selaginoides*, a species in which strobilar

axial elongation occurs in conjunction with sporangial dehiscence.

Sporangia are completely dimorphic. The microsporangia produce many microspores, while megasporangia produce from one to four or rarely 12 or more megaspores. Subsequently in the life cycle, the microspores develop into male gametophytes, while megaspores (same as macrospores) develop into female gametophytes. The two kinds of sporangia occur in various, often specific, patterns within the strobili (Horner and Arnott, 1963). In *S. kraussiana* (Fig. 3–4, B), for example, a single megasporangium occurs at the base of the strobilus, with microsporangia in the axils of all the distal sporophylls. In a number of species the megasporangia are grouped in a basal zone, and in others they occur in one or more vertical rows within the strobilus. A series of nonfunctional sporangia occur basally in *S. selaginoides* strobili.

It should be noted particularly that while both kinds of sporangia always occur on the same plant, there are no sporangia producing two types of spores, much less two types from a single tetrad. The two types of sporangia are initially alike but diverge from each other morphologically at a relatively early stage in ontogeny, before meiosis occurs. This allows us to conclude that the expression of maleness or femaleness is not genetically determined but that the specific environment in which each sporangium develops determines the particular developmental pathway it will follow. This is true of all heterothallic vascular plants, with the possible exceptions of *Equisetum* and a few filicalean ferns. In these, which are homosporous, only a partial sexual differentiation of gametophytes is suggested. This should be contrasted to bryophyte heterothallism, which is associated with morphological homospory and in which a one-to-one segregation for gametophytic sex occurs at meiosis.

The sporangia of *Selaginella* are distinctly stalked (Fig. 3–5, A, B, D). Each has a line of dehiscence across its distal end oriented transversely to the axis of the sporophyll. Structural modifications of surface cells at the line of dehiscence and on its flanks are as in *Lycopodium*. The microsporangia are slightly longer,

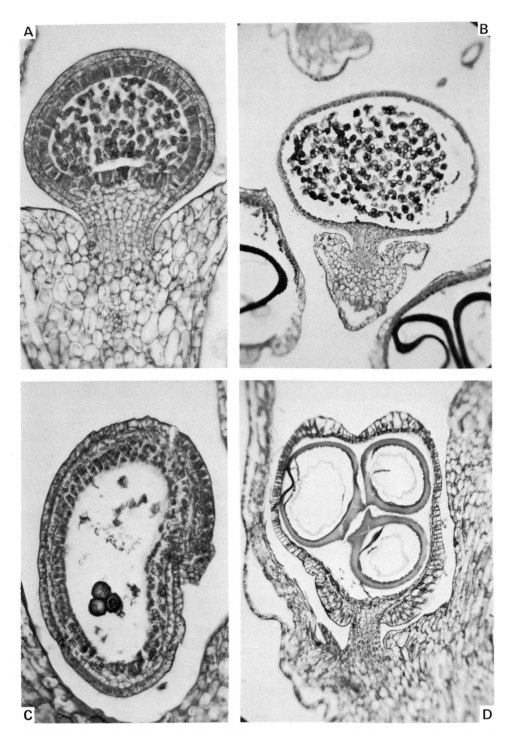

FIGURE 3–5. *Selaginella selaginoides.* *A.* Immature microsporangium in a tangential section of the strobilus such that the microsporangium is in median longitudinal section and the sporophyll in cross section. *B.* As *A,* but older. *C.* Section through a young megasporangium. A young spore tetrad and several disintegrated spore mother cells are shown. *D.* Nearly mature megasporangium on its sporophyll in a radial longitudinal section of the strobilus.

in a direction transverse to the sporophyll, but not to the extent that the isosporangia are in *Lycopodium*, and they lack the extended lateral lobes that make the latter reniform. The megasporangia assume a shape dictated by the enlarging megaspores within (Fig. 3–4, *B*, *C*; Fig. 3–5, *D*).

Sporangial ontogeny in *Selaginella* is as in *Lycopodium*. It begins with a small patch of surface initials that divide periclinally. The outer cells produce the several wall layers and the tapetum and the inner ones the sporogenous mass. The tapetal layer is characteristically more conspicuous than in *Lycopodium* (Fig. 3–5, *A*). All wall layers except the outer one decompose before dehiscence (Fig. 3–5, *B*, *D*).

In the development of the megasporangium, although generally only one megasporocyte is functional, up to a dozen or more are recognizable. In the young megasporangium shown in Fig. 3–5, *C*, three of the four spores of a young tetrad are visible and also the remnants of about 10 nonfunctional sporocytes. In some species spore abortion is common after meiosis and during various stages of spore development. It is common in *S. rupestris* to see one, two, or three large megaspores in a tetrad, the remainder being abortive. The geographical races of this species show differences in this regard, as Tryon has shown.

The microgametophytes, or male gametophytes, of *Selaginella* are entirely endosporic (contained within the spore wall) and are in a multicellular stage when shed from the sporangium. The microspore (Fig. 3–6, *A*) first divides very unequally to produce a larger cell (the "antheridial initial") and a very much smaller cell, which may be called a "prothallial cell" (in the interpretative but not in the descriptive sense; Fig. 3–6, *B*). The antheridial cell then divides (Fig. 3–6, *C*, *D*) to produce a group of four cells, all of which intersect along a very short polar furrow in the center of the spore. Each of these cells then cuts off one primary spermatogenous cell toward the inside and a jacket cell to the outside (Fig. 3–6, *E*; Fig. 3–7, *A*). Successive mitoses establish the total number of spermatids while the jacket layer and the sister cell of the antheridial initial decompose (Fig. 3–6, *F* to *H*; Fig. 3–7, *B*, *C*). The sperm are prob-

ably the smallest of those of any vascular plant, and the biflagellate bodies are similar in form to those of *Lycopodium*.

The megagametophytes of *Selaginella* also begin their development within the megasporangia and are shed at varying stages in their development. Under certain conditions in certain species they may be retained until maturity of the megagametophyte and even after embryo development has started within. This has been widely mentioned in connection with seed phylogeny, since a seed is fundamentally an embryo within a gametophyte retained by a sporangium and enclosed by other modified organs of the sporophyte. In *Selaginella* there is only the variable retention of female gametophytes without any modification of enclosing parts.

The nucleus of the megaspore divides and its derivatives divide karyokinetically without any associated cytokineses. The free nuclei come to be unequally distributed, with many clustered beneath the triradiate ridge of the spore and fewer round the periphery elsewhere, all within the spore wall. Wall formation begins in the apical region, establishing a lens-shaped, apical pad of small cells. Large cells are blocked out elsewhere in the gametophyte as wall formation proceeds from the periphery inward. The apical pad comes to be separated by a plane of thick walls along its base except at certain loci (Fig. 3–7, *D*, *E*; Fig. 3–8, *B*). Archegonia develop at the surface of the pad, as do rhizoid tufts (Fig. 3–7, *D*, *E*; Fig. 3–8, *A*, *B*). In some species the pad protrudes from the now-split-open triradiate ridge, so the gametophyte is not completely endosporic. In other species the maximum development of the pad and of the cellularization of the inner mass of the gametophyte is dependent on the stage at which fertilization occurs, the events being inhibited or stopped by a developing embryo.

The archegonial necks are two cells long and four cells in cross section (Fig. 3–8, *A*, *B*). The four terminal cells only extend beyond the surface and appear as asymmetric nipples (Fig. 3–7, arrow in *E*; Fig. 3–8, *B*). There are in the axial row an egg, a ventral canal cell, and one neck canal cell, all related by cell lineages, as are those of other archegoniate vascular plants. The mother cell of the egg

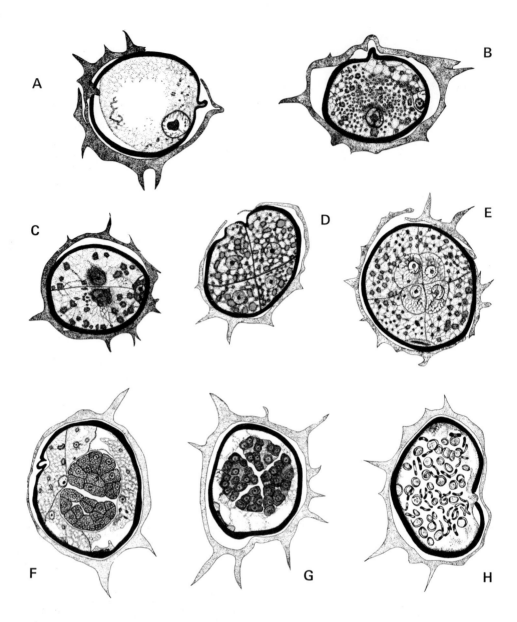

FIGURE 3–6. Development of the microgametophyte in *Selaginella kraussiana*, after Slagg (1932).

and the ventral canal cell is the sister cell of the neck canal cell, and the mother cell of these three (axial row mother cell) is the sister cell of the primary neck cell (neck mother cell).

Although the gametophytes of *Selaginella* appear to rely entirely on food reserves traceable to the parental sporophyte, their complete development is dependent on light.

Beneath matted sporophytes one often finds hundreds of megagametophytes and many thousands of microgametophytes submature and arrested in development. If the older sporophyte cover is removed, gametophyte growth continues and in a few weeks many young sporophytes appear.

Following fertilization, the zygote divides

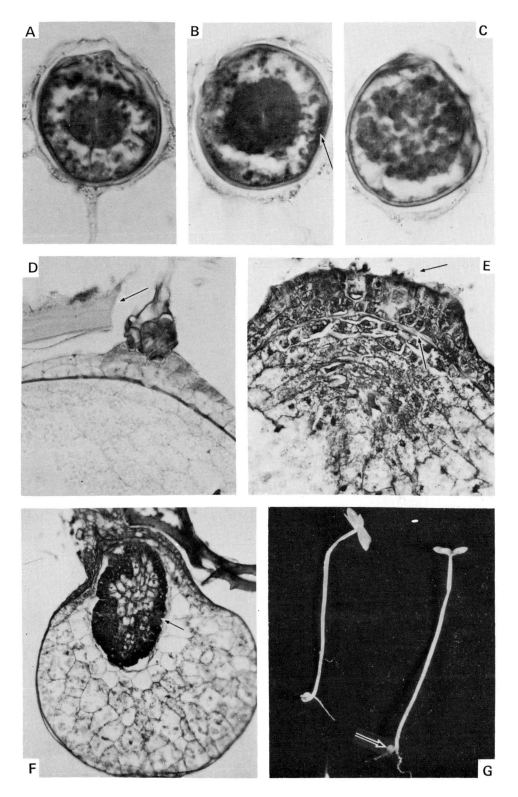

FIGURE 3–7. *Selaginella kraussiana. A* to *C*. Successively older stages in the development of the microgametophyte. *D*. Portion of the apex of a megagametophyte. The arrow indicates a portion of the spore wall. One rhizoid tuft is shown. *E*. Median longitudinal section through the apical pad of the megagametophyte. Portions of several archegonia are visible. *F*. Foot of an embryo within the megagametophyte. *G*. Young sporophytes with their parental megagametophytes still attached.

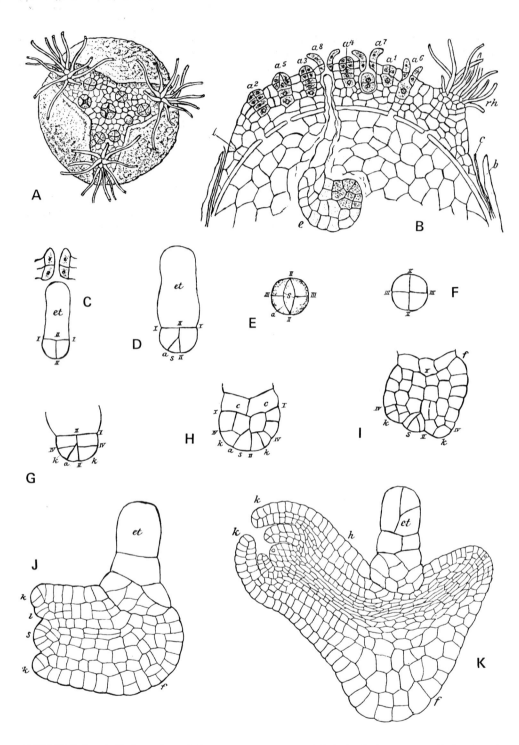

FIGURE 3–8. *A.* Surface view of the megagametophyte of *Selaginella kraussiana.* *B.* Section of the upper portion of a megagametophyte of *S. poulteri* showing the apical pad, archegonia, a rhizoid tuft, and an embryo that has been pushed below the pad by suspensor elongation. *C* to *K.* Development of the embryo in *S. martensii.* All after Bruchmann (1909, 1912). et = suspensor; s = stem; l = ligule; k = leaf.

transversely, establishing the primary suspensor cell (et in Fig. 3–8, C) and primary embryonic cell. The latter divides longitudinally (division wall II-II in Fig. 3–8, C to H) and one of its derivatives divides obliquely (wall a) to establish the apical cell of the stem (s). As development proceeds, the suspensor increases in cell number and elongates, pushing the embryo deeper into the gametophyte (Fig. 3–8, B). The entire embryo apex goes through a turn of almost 180 degrees as a result of differential growth, so that eventually it emerges through the gametophytic pad. The foot at first develops on one side (Fig. 3–8,

f in I, J) but comes eventually to lie opposite the suspensor. The root, last to form, develops on the side away from the stem apex. The first leaf appears relatively early (k in Fig. 3–8, I to K), but along with the root it may be interpreted as not being a primary organ of the embryo. During later embryogeny the foot enlarges (Fig. 3–7, F), and in the young sporeling stage (Fig. 3–7, G; the arrow points out the spore wall) it essentially completely fills the spore cavity.

The embryogeny of very few species of *Selaginella* is known, and detailed studies of the others are highly desirable.

4

Zosterophyllophytes and Fossil Lycopods

The lycopods have had a long history. Their phylogeny is well known and is an interesting and informative story, presenting many morphological lessons not readily learnable from other taxa. The lycopods at one time dominated the terrestrial flora, holding a position difficult to imagine when one considers only the relatively insignificant extant genera, *Lycopodium*, *Selaginella*, *Phylloglosum*, *Isoëtes*, and *Stylites*.

The most feasible interpretation presently available is that the lycopods represent a monophyletic line of zosterophyllaceous derivation. The family, Zosterophyllaceae, placed alone in its own order and class (Table 4–1), is recognized (following Banks, 1968a; Banks and Davis, 1969) in terms of five genera of Lower and Middle Devonian occurrence: *Bucheria* (Fig. 4–1, *B*), *Zosterophyllum* (Fig. 4–1, *A*), *Gosslingia* (Fig. 4–1, *D*), *Crenaticaulis*, and *Psilophyton ornatum* (Fig. 4–1, *C*). The latter is of different ordinal affinity than *Psilophyton princeps* (Banks, 1968b) and thus requires a new generic name. The Zosterophyllaceae are characterized by small herbaceous plants with laterally inserted sporangia grouped along an axis in regions devoid of other appendages. In *Zosterophyllum* and *Bucheria* the fertile regions were terminal and spikelike (Fig. 4–1, *A*, *B*). *Zosterophyllum* may have had ribbon-form branches (this may be an artifact in the compressions) suggestive of a submerged aquatic, and it is possible that the entire family was aquatic. Branching in the family was dichotomous. Although the creeping rhizome system of *Zosterophyllum* showed a high frequency of H-type branching, this is interpreted as dichotomous, in which a pair of branches at a point of ramification diverged from each other at 180 degrees

TABLE 4–1. Classification of lycopods and zosterophyllophytes.

Class	Order	Family	Genera Mentioned in Text
Zosterophyllopsida	Zosterophyllales	Zosterophyllaceae	*Zosterophyllum* *Bucheria* *Psilophyton (in part)* *Gosslingia* *Crenaticaulis*
Lycopodiopsida	Asteroxylales	Asteroxylaceae Kaulangiophytaceae	*Asteroxylon* *Kaulangiophyton*
	Lycopodiales	Drepanophycaceae	*Baragwanathia* *Drepanophycus*
		Lycopodiaceae	*Lycopodites* *Lycopodium* *Phylloglossum*
	Protolepidodendrales	Eleutherophyllaceae	
		Protolepidodendraceae	*Protolepidodendron* *Lepidodendropsis*
		Colpodexylaceae Sublepidodendraceae	*Colpodexylon*
		Leptophloeaceae	*Leptophloem*
		Archaeosigillariaceae	*Archaeosigillaria* *Thursophyton*
	Selaginellales	Paurodendraceae	*Paurodendron*
		Selaginellaceae	*Selaginella* *Selaginellites*
	Lepidodendrales	Lepidosigillariaceae	*Lepidosigillaria*
		Lepidodendraceae	*Lepidodendron* *Lepidophloios*
		Bothrodendraceae Cyclostigmataceae Sigillariaceae	*Bothrodendron* *Cyclostigma* *Sigillaria*
	Isoetales	Pleuromeiaceae Nathorstianaceae	*Pleuromeia* *Nathorstiana*
		Isoetaceae	*Isoëtes* *Stylites*

instead of the more usual acute angle. *Crenaticaulis*, whose name is derived from the toothed margin of its stem, bore scars at or very near the axils of stem dichotomies. Banks and Davis (1969) suggest that these were scars of organs similar to the root trusses (they use the term rhizophore) of *Selaginella*. The sporangia were slightly flattened with their faces parallel to the axis on which they were borne and also parallel to the apical line of dehiscence. They were thus essentially of the lycopodioid form (Fig. 4–1, *C*). The family was homosporous. The stem as described for *Zosterophyllum* (Banks, 1968a) and *Crenaticaulis* (Banks and Davis, 1969) possesses a small terete-to-elliptical xylem strand with protoxylem in the exarch position.

The Asteroxylaceae, represented by *Asteroxylon*, seem morphologically to bridge the gap between the Zosterophyllaceae and those lyco-

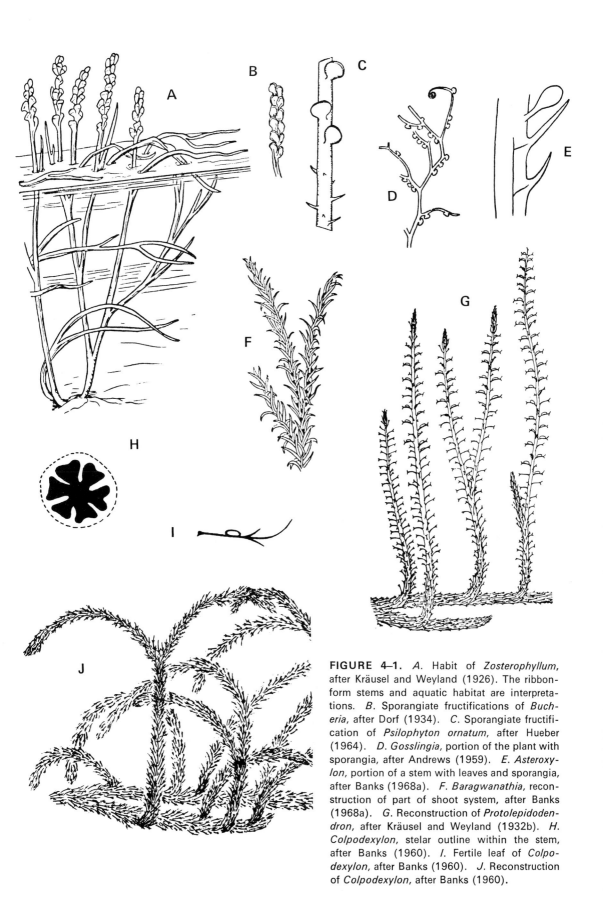

FIGURE 4–1. *A.* Habit of *Zosterophyllum*, after Kräusel and Weyland (1926). The ribbon-form stems and aquatic habitat are interpretations. *B.* Sporangiate fructifications of *Bucheria*, after Dorf (1934). *C.* Sporangiate fructification of *Psilophyton ornatum*, after Hueber (1964). *D. Gosslingia*, portion of the plant with sporangia, after Andrews (1959). *E. Asteroxylon*, portion of a stem with leaves and sporangia, after Banks (1968a). *F. Baragwanathia*, reconstruction of part of shoot system, after Banks (1968a). *G.* Reconstruction of *Protolepidodendron*, after Kräusel and Weyland (1932b). *H. Colpodexylon*, stelar outline within the stem, after Banks (1960). *I.* Fertile leaf of *Colpodexylon*, after Banks (1960). *J.* Reconstruction of *Colpodexylon*, after Banks (1960).

pods with *Lycopodium*-type morphology. *Asteroxylon*, found in rocks of Lower Devonian age, had the gross appearance of a *Lycopodium*. It had a creeping underground axial system and an aboveground, vertical, nearly pseudo-monopodial stem system. The underground axes were leafless and some seemed to grow downward. The aerial stems were clothed with a close spiral series of leaves. A small leaf trace extended through the stem cortex to the base of each leaf but not into it. The xylem strand of larger stems was solid and deeply lobed in cross-sectional outline, with one to several protoxylem poles in the mesarch position near the end of each xylem arm. The sporangia were lateral, cauline, and *not* definitely associated with appendages that might be called sporophylls. *Asteroxylon* was homosporous.

The leafless, more vertically oriented subterranean axes of *Asteroxylon* have been called rootlike stems. Anatomical differences among the aerial stems, horizontal subterranean stems, and down-growing subterranean stems, other than those related to leaf traces and photosynthetic tissue, are very slight. The entire plant body seems to be the product of apical branching of fundamentally a single axis. Therefore, one cannot refer to roots and stems. It should be recalled that, in *Lycopodium*, the larger roots differ anatomically from stems in ways related only to leaf presence and absence. They are, however, not of apical origin but arise endogenously from horizontal stems, and the attachment of their steles to those of the parental stems clearly reflects this. Even so, there seems to be a very close analogy in "root–stem" differences between the two genera which cannot be ignored. The rootlike stem of *Asteroxylon* seems well on the phylogenetic pathway toward becoming a root of the *Lycopodium* type, which is anatomically poorly differentiated from the stem. Therefore, one can interpret the root in this phyletic line as having been derived by the introduction of a progressive dimorphism within the subterranean system of axes.

The family Kaulangiophytaceae, represented by *Kaulangiophyton* (Gensel et al., 1969) of probable Lower Devonian occurrence, suggests affinity with *Asteroxylon* and *Psilophyton princeps*. *Kaulangiophyton* was a plant up to several decimeters in height with horizontal and upright axes ranging from 5 to 9 mm in diameter and exhibiting wide (to H-type) dichotomies. The axes bore stout spines about 2 mm long. Upright axes included fertile zones in which were located stalks 2 to 4 mm long each bearing a terminal sporangium 6 to 8 mm long and 4 to 5 mm in diameter.

The morphological series (and suggested phylogenetic one) represented by the Zosterophyllaceae, Asteroxylaceae, and Lycopodiaceae shows plants of essentially the same gross form, habit, sporangial form, sporangial insertion, and stem anatomy. All have peripheral or nearly peripheral protoxylem, differences that represent variations of what must be considered a phylogenetically unconservative character, as evidenced by the range existing among the extant species of *Lycopodium* and *Selaginella*. Among the three families there seems to be a series from naked to leafy stems. *Psilophyton ornatum* in the Zosterophyllaceae shows what may be described as enations. *Asteroxylon* shows what seem to be the same structures but in a more fixed phyllotactic order and with weakly developed vascular traces. At this point the term "leaf" may be introduced. The leaf of *Lycopodium* differs further only in the better development of the leaf trace. The three families also show a series from sporangia completely disassociated with leaves or leaflike structures to sporangia borne in leaf axils or on a sporophyll.

The Drepanophycaceae, represented by the herbaceous forms *Drepanophycus* and *Baragwanathia* of Lower to Upper Devonian rocks, is particularly lycopodioid, so much so in fact, that one could question its familial integrity. *Baragwanathia* (Fig. 4–1, *F*) had stems up to 6.5 cm in diameter which bore leaves up to 2 cm long arranged spirally to pseudowhorled. In its stem was a protostele with exarch primary xylem in which annular elements have been described. The sporangia were reniform and "probably cauline above the leaf" (Grierson and Hueber, 1963). The stems of *Drepanophycus* are reported to be up to 4 cm in diameter, bearing leaves up to 2 cm long arranged irregularly to spirally to nearly whorled. The sporangia were of various shapes and situated on the adaxial side of sporophylls.

The Protolepidodendrales were a diverse

group of lycopods, probably all herbaceous. The order is well represented in Lower Devonian rocks and is found well into Mississippian rocks. It may have been the first group of vascular land plants to experience "radiation" in the sense used by modern evolutionists.

Heterospory has never been demonstrated in the Protolepidodendrales, although some have presumed that it did exist, since the feature is so well developed in several families of the Lepidodendrales, an order presumed to be directly descended from the Protolepidodendrales. To date, heterospory has been demonstrated to occur in only five Devonian genera: the lepidodendrid, *Cyclostigma*; three aneurophytes, *Enigmophyton*, *Barinophyton*, and *Archeopteris* (Mortimer and Chaloner, 1967, Chaloner, 1968); and in the probable pteridosperm *Archaeosperma* (Pettitt and Beck, 1967). Studies of free spores isolated from Devonian rocks, however, indicate that heterospory was more common than the meager list of five would indicate (Chaloner, 1967)· The total numbers of free spore genera known from the Silurian and the various stages of the Devonian are shown in Chaloner's histogram (Fig. 4–11). Spore distinctions are somewhat arbitrary. The numbers of genera that contain species with a mean size exceeding 200 μ are shown shaded, as megaspores ("mega-"), in contradiction to miospores (microspores and isospores) with a smaller mean size ("mio-")· The rate of appearance of new genera is surprisingly low, which Chaloner suggests may be explained by supposing that some of the simpler spore genera are equivalent to several genera of parental plants. Inferences readily drawn from the histogram are (1) that spore-producing land plants, probably initiating in Silurian times, experienced a relatively late diversification, beginning possibly near the end of Lower Devonian times (Siegenian, "Si.") and (2) that homospory preceded heterospory. The spore evidence is closely correlated with macrofossil evidence, as the "first appearances" of a number of genera in the Lower Devonian (Table 4–2) indicate. Using Chaloner's artificial limit of 200 μ, there are 16 known free megaspore genera from the Devonian, which are likely aneurophytes in part and lycopods in part.

The Protolepidodendrales were relatively small herbaceous plants with creeping stems and upright dichotomously branched ones (Fig. 4–1, *G, J*). Their roots, if they existed, are not described. Their stems were small (up to 9 mm in diameter in *Protolepidodendron* and up to 2.5 cm in *Colpodexylon*) and covered with leaves (to 1.5 cm long in *Protolepidodendron* and 2 to 3 cm long in *Colpodexylon*) arranged in spirals or pseudowhorls. The stems contained central, lobed xylem masses (Fig. 4–1, *H*) in which the pattern of maturation was either exarch or mesarch. The leaves were forked in *Protolepidodendron* and three-pronged in *Colpodexylon*; most other genera had simple leaves.

The stems of various genera of the order have been reported to have produced raised leaf cushions on the stem like those which occurred in the Lepididendrales. These, however, have been interpreted by Grierson and Banks (1963) as decortication patterns (i.e., impression patterns left by stems after the surface has rotted away). Several genera did, however, produce decurrent leaf ridges, and these, in association with their tissue modification responsible for the decortication patterns, may be considered precursory to the elaborate surface cushions of the Lepidodendrales.

The sporangia of most protolepidodendrids have never been described, but those which have been were on the adaxial side of a sporophyll and slightly elongate parallel to its axis (Fig. 4–1, *G, I*). The sporophylls were not organized into a clearly definable strobilus but were more as they are in *Lycopodium selago*.

All protolepidodendrids were eligulate, unless, as is not done here, one recognizes the order as including the Lepidosigillariaceae.

The Lepidodendrales are by far the best known of the fossil lycopod taxa. They were also the most specialized and diverse. They reached their peak in phylogenetic development during Carboniferous times, when they were dominant elements in many floras. Material in the form of casts and impressions is very common and accessible, being readily found in the dumps around most coal mines in Carboniferous strata. Structurally preserved material is abundant in calcareous concretions associated with certain coal beds, especially in Great Britain and the central United States.

TABLE 4-2. Earliest definitely known occurrence of certain vascular plant taxa.

Period		Time to beginning, in years (× 10⁶)	Rhyniales	Zosterophyllales	Lycopodiopsida	Cladoxylales	Aneurophytopsida	Equisetopsida	Coenopteridales	Seed Plants
Pennsylvanian		310						*Equisetales*		*Coniferales* *Cordaitales*
Mississippian		345			*Selaginellites* *Paurodendron*		*Siderella* *Protopitys*	*Calamites* *Sphenophyllum*	*Botryopteris* *Metaclepsydropsis* et al.	*Pteridospermales*
Devonian	Upper	365			*Cyclostigma* *Stigmaria* *Lycopodites* *Bothrodendron* *Lepidodendron* *Lepidosigillaria* *Colpodexylon*		*Ginkgophyton* *Callixylon–* *Archeopteris* *Tetraxylopteris* *Rhacophyton*	*Eviostachya* *Pseudobornia* *Asterocalamites*	*Clepsydropsis*	
	Middle	390	*Rhynia* *Horneophyton*		*Lepidodendropsis* *Leptophloem*	*Cladoxylon* *Calamophyton* *Schizopodium* *Zenocladia*	*Aneurophyton* *Sphenoxylon* *Protopteridium*		*Asteropteris* *Reimannia* *Arachnoxylon* *Iridopteris*	
	Lower	395	*Eogaspesiea* *Hicklingia* *Trimerophyton* *Dawsonites* *Psilophyton* *princeps*	*Crenaticaulis* *Bucheria* *Gosslingia* *Psilophyton* *ornatum* *Zosterophyllum* *Kaulangiophyton* *Baragwanathia*	*Asteroxylon* *Archeosigillaria* *Thursophyton* *Drepanophycus* *Protolepidodendron*	*Pseudosporochnus* *Protohyenia*		*Hyenia* *Broggeria* *Sphondylophyton*		
Silurian	Upper	?	*Taeniocrada* *Cooksonia*							
	Middle	415								

46

The lepidodendrids were trees, with some species attaining a height of more than 30 m and a diameter of possibly 2 m. Some species were highly dichotomously branched at the base of the crown (Fig. 4–2, *A*); others were unbranched or branched to a lesser degree (Fig. 4–2, *B*).

The basal and subterranean portions of the lepidodendrids, known under the organ generic names of *Stigmaria* and *Stigmariopsis*, were dichotomously branched and bore either spirally arranged appendages, known as stigmarian appendages or stigmarian rootlets, or the circular scars which they left behind. After the first pair of dichotomies in *Stigmariopsis*, branching resulted in the production of two rows of branches on the lower surface of each of the four major axes. These in turn dichotomized and bore stigmarian rootlets. On the main axes longitudinal ridges suggestive of those on the basal parts of sigillarian trunks were present.

The leaves were spirally arranged, simple, and nearly linear. In width they mostly ranged from a few millimeters to slightly over 1.5 cm. Some representative leaf lengths (data from Hirmer, 1927) were *Lepidophloios* sp., 4 to 5 cm; *L.* sp., about 10 cm; *Sigillaria* spp., mostly long, some up to 1 m; *Bothrodendron* sp., 1 cm; *Ulodendron* sp., 20 to 25 cm; *U.* sp., 1.5 to 3 cm; *Lepidodendron* sp., about 2.5 cm; *L.* sp., about 1.5 cm; and *L.* sp., about 2 cm. Some species are known to have borne much smaller leaves on the smaller ultimate branches (e.g., *Lepidodendron obovatum* is reported to have had leaves 4 to 5 cm long on smaller twigs and leaves 60 to 80 cm on larger stems). The smaller ones have been interpreted as immature leaves, but it is probable that both reported length ranges are for mature leaves (Eggert, 1961). It is also likely that *L. obovatum* was not at all exceptional in exhibiting this extreme range, as evidenced by leaf-scar observations.

The paleobotanist encounters problems of nomenclature rarely of concern to one working with extant plants. This is because fossil plants are commonly found as fragments and not as entire plants. When it is found that two or more fragments previously described under different generic names in reality belong to the same plant, the problem becomes how to name the whole plant. Within the lepidodendrids, for example, there are generic names (same as organ genera) for free spores, stems with leaf scars, stems with various decortication patterns, vegetative leaves, sporophylls, strobili, and underground axes. The rule is that the oldest validly published name that applies to any part of the plant becomes the name of the entire plant, but this has not been universally applied. This is especially true in the lepididendrids, where the custom has been to apply the form generic name of the stem with leaf cushions to the natural genus. The organ generic names are still retained for convenience, especially when the part under consideration cannot be assigned to a particular species of the natural genus. Among the extant plants the same problem has recently appeared in studies of marine algae, where it has been found that two or more species are in reality different phases in the life cycle of one species. Here the rule of name antiquity has been applied, and the additional names have been retained to indicate "stages" in the life cycle.

Lepidodendrid stems show characteristic patterns of leaf scars and leaf cushions suggestive of reptilian bodies (lepido, scale; dendro, tree). In *Lepidodendron* the cushions are somewhat vertically elongate and tapering at the base (Fig. 4–2, *F*). In *Sigillaria* they are hexagonal and appear in vertical rows (Fig. 4–2, *B*), much like *Archeosigillaria* (Fig. 4–2, *H*). In *Lepidophloios* the cushions are laterally tapering and appear similar to those illustrated for *Pleuromeia* (Fig. 4–9, *B*). The cushions represented expanded decurrent leaf bases from which, on the lowermost branches of the trees, the leaves abscised, leaving small scars upon the cushions (Fig. 4–2, *I*). Immediately above the leaf scar there was a ligule scar within a pit (LP in Fig. 4–2, *G*). Within the leaf scar three smaller scars are seen. The central one is the leaf-trace scar (LT). On either side of the bundle scar and on the cushion below the leaf scar there are a total of four parichonos scars (P), which represent localized areas of loose, presumably aerating, tissue which were continuous as strands into the stem. The strands extending from the lower two scars were confluent with those from the two on the leaf scar within the stem tissues. A tangential

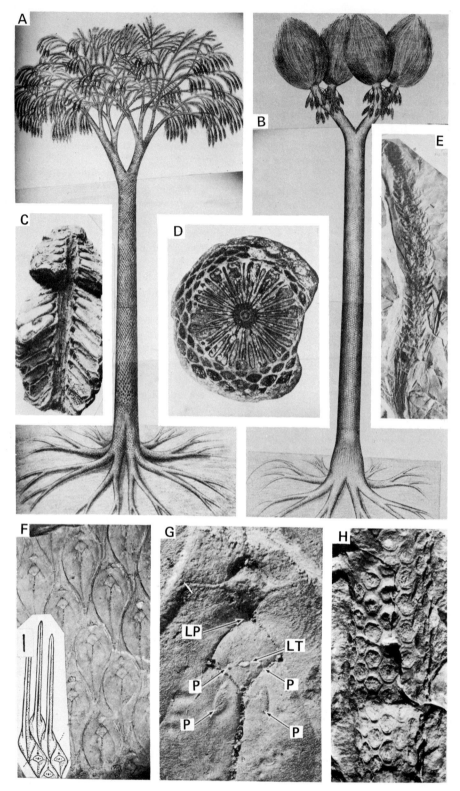

FIGURE 4–2. *A.* Reconstruction of *Lepidodendron*, from Hirmer (1927). *B.* Reconstruction of *Sigillaria*, from Hirmer (1927). *C. Lepidostrobus*, after Zeiller (1911). *D.* Transverse section of *Lepidostrobus*, after Zeiller (1911). *E. Sigillariostrobus*, after Renier (1910). *F, G, I* (from Walton, 1940). *Lepidodendron*. Several leaf cushions with leaf scars are shown in *F* and one of these is enlarged in *G*. *I* shows the manner in which the leaves were attached. *H.* Stem surface of *Archeosigillaria*, after Banks (1960). LP = ligule pit; LT = leaf trace; P = parichnos scars.

section through a part of the stem surface is shown in Fig. 4–4, C, where L indicates the ligule and LT a leaf trace. Below the leaf trace appear cross sections of a pair of parichnos.

Lepidodendrid stems, although massive, possessed a relatively small amount of vascular tissue. The great bulk of the axial tissue was composed of "secondary cortex," or periderm. In *Lepidophloios* the meristem responsible for the periderm has been described (Smith, 1964) as originating from a zone three cells wide rather than from a single cell layer. Tissue derived from the meristem matured mostly toward the inside; thus it is comparable to the phelloderm of dicots in origin. In the cross section in Fig. 4–3, A, a small stele is shown in the center (S) (enlarged in B). Surrounding the stele is a cavity that formed in whole or in part by decay of tissue previous to petrifaction, and around it is the cortex and periderm (LC = leaf cushion). Approximately three fifths of the outer zone is periderm.

A section of a single leaf cushion is shown enlarged in Fig. 4–4, A, in which PE is periderm and PG is primary ground tissue. Note that the primary ground tissue is composed of relatively tightly packed, isodiametric cells. Thus, although this leaf cushion is a number of times larger than small cushions found on the small stems of the same plant, its primary tissues did not expand laterally following its maturation. What this seems to mean is that large stems initially produced large leaf cushions and that the primary tissues were growing at the same time as most of the secondary cortex was produced.

The entire stem, although massive, was probably quite succulent, and one could perhaps have chopped through a 1-m-thick trunk with a machete.

Add this information to the fact that, despite the great abundance of lepidodendrid material, no young plants have ever been found and one wonders about the growth habit of the plants, as many botanists have. Was the plant short-lived (one or a few seasons) or perennial? If severe thunderstorms occurred during Carboniferous times, and it is assumed that they did, it is particularly doubtful that arboreal lycopods could have remained vertical for any long period. There is little (except in *Bothrodendron*) to indicate that the plants pro-duced a series of reproductive structures at different times; they very possibly went through a single reproductive phase. If they were in reality giant, near-herbaceous annuals, as this author suspects, their closest growth-habit analogs are to be found among the large monocots, as Eggert (1961) suggests. Within the palms we find trees of primary tissue composition which reach their maximum diameters while they are still at ground level by building up their crowns before extending their axial length. They are, however, slow-growing perenials, and their lateral expansion occurs immediately below the shoot tip. A much closer analogy, it seems, if found between lepidodendrid shoots and agavaceous aerial axes (e.g., the common century plants or the large succulent shoots of certain species of *Phytolacca*). In both of these flowering plants the aerial shoots attain tree proportions, as they grow in length and in width in a short time. *Phytolacca* also produces a considerable amount of soft secondary tissue as its primary tissues expand laterally.

The xylem of stem steles of lepidodendrids varied from solid with a complete series of intermediates to hollow with a well-defined parenchymatous core. It can be said with reasonable certainty that a kind of siphono-stele evolved within the order more than once by progressively fewer tracheids and more parenchyma cells maturing in the stelar core. The entire series is represented in the genus *Lepidodendron*: *L. pettycurense*, solid primary xylem core; *L. vasculare*, intermediate stelar type with mixed pith (Fig. 4–3, A, B); *L. veltheimii*, well-defined pith, as also in *Lepidophloios* and *Sigillaria*. The primary xylary cores were nearly rounded on their outer peripheries, with a number of small protoxylem poles in which maturation was exarch (PX in Fig. 4–3, B to D). Lemoigne (1966) described the phloem as being composed of smaller, presumed parenchyma, cells and larger, presumed sieve, cells. In general the secondary xylem (SX in Fig. 4–3, B to D) produced in aerial stems of lepididendrids was quite restricted in quantity in terms of stem diameter. The entire vascular cylinder rarely exceeded 10 cm in diameter and did not show indications of growth rings. Secondary xylem began immediately outside of protoxylem (a

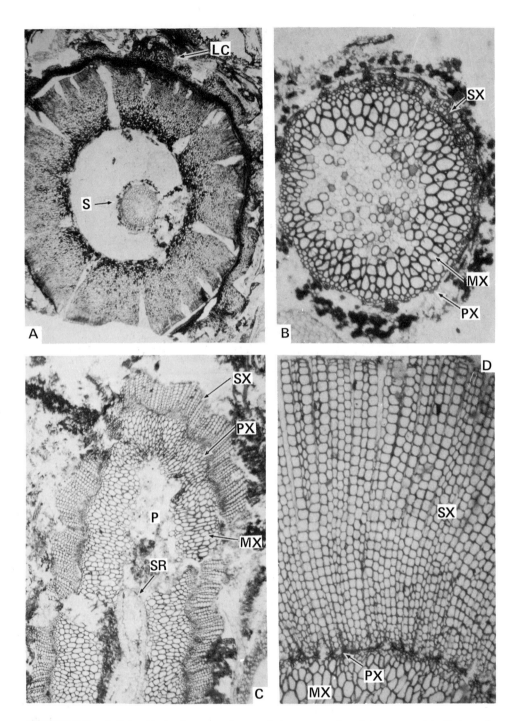

FIGURE 4–3. *A, B. Lepidodendron vasculare*, a whole cross section of the stem and, in *B*, the stele only enlarged. *C. Sigillaria elegans*, stele, and pith region in cross section. *D. Lepidodendron* sp., cross section of part of the stele. LC = leaf cushion; S = stele; SX = secondary xylem; MX = metaxylem; PX = protoxylem; SR = stigmarian rootlet.

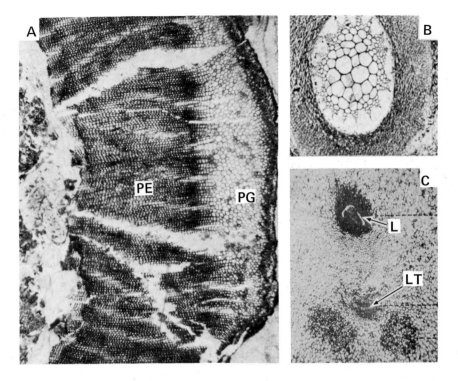

FIGURE 4–4. *A. Sigillaria scutellata*, outer tissues of the stem in cross section. *B. Paurodendron*, central part of the stem, after Fry (1954). *C.* Tangential section of the stem of *Lepidodendron*, after Ogura (1938), by permission of Gebrüder Borntraeger, Berlin. PE = periderm; PG = primary ground tissue; L = ligule; LT = leaf trace.

small arc of SX appears in *B*). It consisted of radial rows of elongate tracheids and less numerous rays. Although the rays were mostly one cell thick and many cells high, occasionally they were two or more cells thick in the central part. The tracheids were scalariform in appearance with vertical strands of second-order secondary wall material ("Williamson's striations") between the more prominent transverse bars of first-order secondary wall (Fig. 27–13, *C, D*). In certain lepidodendrids, protoepidodendrids, and in *Asteroxylon* (Fig. 27–13, *B*) the second-order secondary wall material was more reticulate in appearance, outlining a number of pitlike openings between the major bars of the first-order system.

The "genus" *Stigmaria*, which constitutes the underground major axes of the lepidodendrids, is known in the external morphological sense as one artificial species, *S. ficoides* (*S. verrucosa*), which belonged to many species

and several genera in the more natural sense. *Stigmaria ficoides* has been found attached to stems of *Lepidodendron*, *Lepidophloios*, and *Sigillaria*. All casts and other specimens with the characteristic external morphological features are generally assigned to this species in its less restricted sense. Various species of *Stigmaria* have been described on the basis of internal structure, including *S. ficoides* in its more restricted sense. Such nomenclatural problems are not at all unique to the lepidodendrids. When one considers impression material of fernlike foliage, one might be dealing with three or more natural classes within a single genus.

Stigmaria consisted of four major axes, each one occasionally up to $\frac{1}{2}$ m in diameter (Fig. 4–2, *A, B*; Fig. 4–5, *A*). One can guess that there was one dichotomy and then a pair of dichotomies in the ontogeny of the system. The four axes either spread out at the point

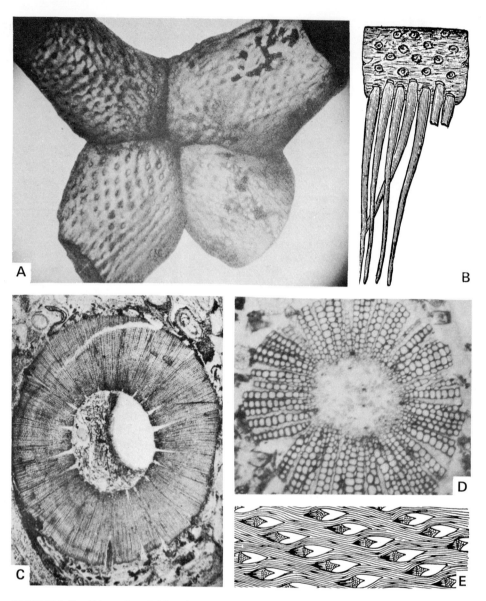

FIGURE 4–5. *Stigmaria.* *A.* View from below its attachment to the aerial stem, after Williamson (1887). *B.* Portion with rootlets attached, after Potonié (1902). *C.* Xylem cylinder of the stigmarian axis, after Ogura (1938), by permission of Gebrüder Borntraeger, Berlin. *D.* Stele of a young axis. *E.* Tangential section through the wood showing traces to the rootlets, from Hirmer (1927).

of branching (Fig. 4–2, *B*) or first grew downward (Fig. 4–2, *A*). They were also associated with degrees of buttress formation. By extrapolation from knowledge of buttress formation in living genera such as *Taxodium* and *Nyssa*, it has been assumed that variations in lepido-dendrids were associated with varying depths of the water in which the plants grew. The major axes tapered down and branched dichotomously (Fig. 4–2, *A*, *B*) and bore stigmarian rootlets or their scars in a spiral order over their entire surface.

FIGURE 4–6. Stele of a stigmarian rootlet, after F. E. Weiss (1902). PX = protoxylem; TR = transfusion elements.

The internal structure of the major axes of *Stigmaria ficoides* (in its restricted sense) was quite different from that of the aerial axes to which it was attached. At its periphery was an epidermis, a thin hypodermal zone, then a thick, apparently resistant outer cortex, and a middle cortex of thin-walled cells. Between the outer and middle cortical zones, a phellogen formed, producing radially aligned, fiberlike cells toward the outside. Abutting the middle cortex was the presumed phloem and then a continuous cylinder of xylem around a central well-defined pith or pith cavity. Radial alignment of the tracheids was continuous from the internally situated protoxylem (i.e., maturation was endarch; Fig. 4–5, *C, D*). The xylem was conspicuously dissected by broad rays through which extended the simple traces to the rootlets (Fig. 4–5, *E*).

Some anatomical species of *Stigmaria* differ from *S. ficoides* in being devoid of a pith and in having a central core of centripetally matured primary xylem. Other species have a pith surrounded by a layer of centripetally matured primary xylem.

The stigmarian rootlets or appendages were slender, delicate structures, mostly 20 to 40 cm long (Fig. 4–5, *B*). A cross section of one shows a thin cylinder of tissue (epidermis and outer cortex) surrounding a larger central cavity. The slender monarch vascular bundle is suspended near the center (probably falsely excentric in many specimens) of the cavity by a ridge of tissue (Fig. 4–6) that also surrounds the bundle and represents the only persisting inner cortex. The rest of the inner cortex probably began to break up at a very early stage in ontogeny, as it did not keep pace with the growth of the rest of the rootlet (i.e., the cavity is interpreted as schizolysigenous). On the side of the bundle toward the cavity was the phloem (represented by a space adjacent to the xylem in Fig. 4–6). On the other side was the protoxylem and a few transfusion tracheids. The xylem was always on the same side of the root with respect to the axis upon which

it was borne (note the constant orientation of the traces through the xylem of the stigmarian axis in Fig. 4–5, *E*), but it is not certain from any publication or specimen available to the author whether it was adaxial or abaxial. To determine this accurately one would need a petrified stigmarian axis with definite knowledge as to which end was distal and which was proximal.

Stigmarian rootlets did break their way out through the outer few layers of the stigmarian axis and, therefore, seem to have been in part endogenous. The mere application of the term, however, may be misleading. Roots of certain ferns (e.g., *Ceratopheris*) originate from the outermost layer of the cortex immediately below the epidermis. The epidermis keeps pace for a period by dividing anticlinally; then the root breaks out. Some additional growth of the epidermis, as occurs over the endogenous root of *Stromatopteris*, and an early determination of the entire lateral organ might lead to various interpretations and application of terminology. In effect, this is what happens in the ontogeny of a dicot leaf, where the initial bulge forms as a result of subepidermal cell divisions and the surface layer continues to grow and keep pace until the entire organ ceases to grow.

In sections of coal balls containing a variety of petrified plant materials there is a high degree of physical association between stigmarian rootlets and other organs. For example, in Fig. 4–3, *A* and *C*, cross sections of the rootlets are shown (SR) that apparently grew down into these stems after they had fallen onto the ground or into the muck. The close association is suggestive of saprophytism on the part of the lepidodendrids. This is of significance if, in reality, they did produce a massive plant body in a very short time, since their dependence on photosynthate would be less of a limiting factor.

The sporangia of lepididendrids were on the adaxial surface of sporophylls grouped in definite strobili, which are known under the form generic names *Lepidostrobus* (Fig. 4–2, *C*, *D*; Fig. 4–7, *A*), *Sigillariostrobus* (Fig. 4–2, *E*), *Bothrostrobus*, *Mazocarpon*, and *Lepidocarpon*. It is possible that all species were heterosporous. Some cones bore both micro- and megasporophylls, others entirely one or the other. Some species are known only as megasporangiate or microsporangiate strobili.

The sporangia were massive and in most species somewhat elongate in the direction of the sporophyll axis (Fig. 4–2, *C*). The ligule was inserted on the sporophyll distal to the sporangium and, therefore, some distance from the strobilar axis. The large number of microspores produced is indicated in Fig. 4–7, *B*, which shows a longitudinal section of little more than half of a microsporangium. The sporangium wall was multilayered, the outer layer being composed of anticlinally elongate cells (Fig. 4–7, *B*). The inner wall, which was composed of thin-walled cells slightly elongate in the periclinal plane, contained from 2 or 3 up to 15 cell layers, depending on the species. In *Mazocarpon* and in one specimen of *Lepidostrobus* described (Reed, 1941), the tissue at the base of the sporangium adjacent to the sporogenous cavity (that which is derived from cells beneath the sporangial initials in extant lycopods) had grown up to form a rather distinctive columellar ridge, quite analogous to what occurs in some living species of *Lycopodium*.

The megasporangia are similar in structure to the microsporangia. The number of megaspores per sporangium varied with the species, and a number-reduction series is interpreted. The spore number is reported to be 8 to 16 in *Lepidostrobus veltheimianus*, 4 in *L. foliaceus* and *Bothrostrobus*, and a single developed spore with three undeveloped ones in *Lepidostrobus braidwoodensis* and *L. monospora*.

Both megaspores and microspores bore trilete markings, as *Triletes*, the form generic name for megaspores indicates.

The female gametophytes are common as free bodies in well-preserved material. They were particularly *Selaginella*-like with a pad of tissue protruding through the spore wall opening at the triradiate ridge (Fig. 4–8, *B*). They bore a number of rather short-necked archegonia of a not-unusual structure. Male gametophytes remain undescribed.

The form generic name *Lepidocarpon* is applied to the most advanced lepidodendrid megasporangiate fructification. In this form, a flap of the sporophyll grew up on either side to completely envelop the megasporangium (Fig. 4–7, *C*). The flaps were not continuous with the margins of the distal upturned portion of the sporophyll beyond the sporangium but overlapped it in part. Balbach (1962) described some early ontogenetic stages in *Lepidocarpon* in which the flaps appeared quite early and grew contemporaneously with the developing sporangium. From this she concluded that they were not new organs but simply outgrowths of the lateral margins of the pedicel. Similar flaps also occurred, but were much less developed, at the margins of megasporangia and microsporangia in *Lepidostrobus*, some species of which probably were borne on the same plant as *Lepidocarpon*. The most distinctive feature of *Lepidocarpon*, and certainly that of greatest theoretical significance, is the presence of a single functional megaspore that developed into a mature gametophyte without being shed from the strobilus. Figure 4–8, *A* shows a vertical section through a part of the structure; in this a female gametophyte with archegonia (y, and enlarged in inset) is surrounded by a sporangium wall that in turn is enclosed by the sporophyll flaps (i, "integument"). The slit exposing the megagametophyte has been referred to as the "micropyle." Embryos have not been seen. Some have referred to *Lepidocarpon* as a seed; others refer to it as seedlike. There is no controversy as to the nature or interpretation of the structure, merely as to the desirable breadth of application of the term "seed."

Another genus, *Miadesmia* of Lower Carboniferous age (Fig. 4–7, *D*), is similar to *Lepidocarpon* in some ways but shows a sporangium enveloped in much-branched

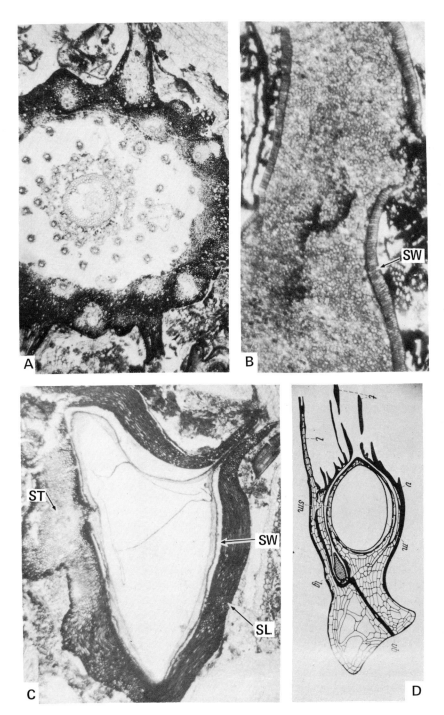

FIGURE 4–7. *A, B. Lepidostrobus.* Strobilar axis in cross section and, in *B*, a portion of one microsporangium. *C.* Cross section of a sporophyll of *Lepidocarpon. D. Miades-mia* in longitudinal section, from D. H. Scott (1920–1923). ST = sporophyll trace; SW = megasporangial wall; SL = lateral outgrowths of the sporophyll enveloping megasporangium.

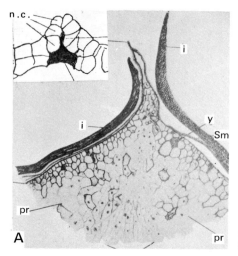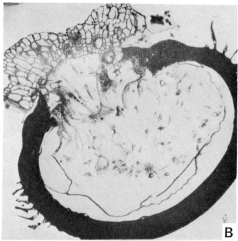

FIGURE 4–8. *A.* Cross section of the upper edge of the fertile part of a sporophyll of *Lepidocarpon*, showing the megagametophyte within the megasporangial wall, all enveloped by the lateral outgrowth of the sporophyll, after D. H. Scott (1901). Inset, after Gordon (1910), shows an archegonium. *B.* Longitudinal section of a gametophyte of *Bothrodendron* (*Bothrostrobus*), after McLean (1912).

sporophyll flaps. Its sporangium is attached by a narrow region and is bent outward along the sporophyll. It is not at all certain that *Miadesmia* was borne on an arborescent lycopod.

The cone genus *Lycostachys*, described by Pant and Walton (1961) from Lower Carboniferous rocks, is worthy of note in that it is eligulate and yet shows many structural features suggestive of *Lepidostrobus*. The xylem elements of the cone show second-order secondary wall material in a reticulate organization between the scalariform bars, similar to that found through the leipdodendrids and in some protolepididendrids. The cone was associated with a stem described by Beck (1958) as *Levicaulis*, which shows similar tracheary structure. If *Lycostachys* is of close lepidodendrid affinity, the conservativeness of the ligule is to be questioned and the possibility of the derivation of eligulate forms from ligulate forms is real.

The stem genus *Paurodendron* (Fig. 4–4, *B*) has been known for some years from Carboniferous rocks (Fry, 1954) and is thought to be an herbaceous lycopod. The genus was ligulate and had in its stem a core of xylem that was slightly stellate and exarch, suggesting certain lepidodendrids and also certain extant *Selaginella* spp., such as *S. rupestris* or *S. selaginoides*. Metaxylem elements showed second-order secondary cell walls highly suggestive of arboreal lycopods. Phillips and Leisman (1966) described the base of the *Paurodendron* stem (the "rhizomorph") as swollen and bearing a number of endogenous roots. Schlanker and Leisman (1969) reported finding the stem of *Paurodendron* attached to a cone previously described as *Selaginellites crassicinctus* Hoskins and Abbott and renamed the plant *Selaginella fraiponti* (Leclercq) Schlanker and Leisman. They indicated their belief that the plant was closely related to the extant taxon *Selaginella selaginoides*.

The cone genus *Spencerites*, known from several species (see Leisman and Stidd, 1967), is eligulate and shows a peculiarly wide range of variation in sporangial attachment from species to species; its sporophylls are fleshy and peltate. Save for size, the cone may have resembled that of the cycad, *Zamia*, in gross appearance. This genus, and others not mentioned, point to the great diversity that evolved among the lycopods and how difficult it is to present anything but a very tentative classification above the familial level or to recognize clear-cut phyletic lines.

There are six Mesozoic lycopods particularly

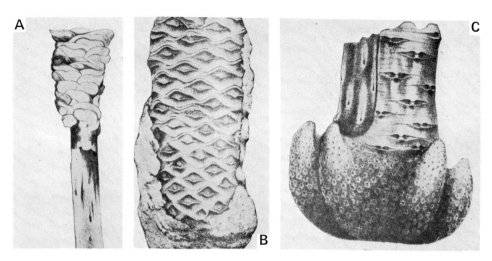

FIGURE 4–9. *Pleuromeia,* after H. Potonié (1904). *A.* Base of the strobilus. *B.* Central part of the trunk. *C.* Lower part of the trunk with rhizomorph and root scars.

worthy of note, as they seem to be part of a reduction series beginning with the arborescent lepidodendrids and culminating with the reduced aquatics in the Isoëtaceae (see Chapter 5). These are the cones *Lycostrobus* of late Triassic beds and *Cylostrobus* of Lower Triassic beds, the compression axis "*Caulop-teris*" sp. in the same beds as *Cylostrobus*, the compression and cast whole plant genera *Pleuromeia* and *Pleuromeiopsis* of Lower Triassic, and the compression whole plant genus (minus sporophylls) *Nathorstiana* of Cretaceous rocks. *Paurodendron* may also belong here.

Pleuromeia had an unbranched, erect trunk slightly over 1 m high. At the base of the plant were four or more stubby upturned lobes that bore the scars of many spirally arranged root-lets (Fig. 4–9, *C*). At the apex of the plant was a single large cone (15 to 20 cm) bearing spirally arranged, short, concave sporophylls (Fig. 4–9, *A*). The plant was heterosporous and it may have been ligulate. Below the sessile strobilus was a crown of long tapering leaves that fell and left scars (Fig. 4–9, *B*) similar in shape to those of *Lepidophloios* or *Isoëtes* (see Chapter 5). If one were to take one of the unbranched lepidodendrids and shorten its aerial axis and its stigmarian axes, a model very close to *Pleuromeia* would be obtained. Since Potonié's description (1904), *Pleuromeia* has generally been placed in its own order,

but Neuburg (in Reymanowne, 1962) believes it to be lepidodendralian. The genus *Pleuro-meiopsis*, although poorly known, seems intermediate between more typical lepidodendrids and *Pleuromeia*. Only certain external features are known, and its spores have not been described. Sixtel's (1962) reconstruction (in Boureau, 1967) shows a plant 3 m tall and about 25 cm in diameter. Its leaf scars are similar to those of *Pleuromiea* and *Lepido-phloios*, and it apparently bore parichnos scars. Its basal portion was extended laterally, as in *Stigmaria*, and not upturned, as in *Pleuromeia*. The crown of *Pleuromeiopsis* appears similar to that of *Pleuromeia* but was forked once. What appear to be differences between these last-mentioned genera may well be no more than reflections of our ignorance of the range in variation in each.

Nathorstiana was a smaller plant perhaps 20 cm in height. It bore a crown of elongate leaves with broad attachments (Fig. 4–10), and around its base were several longitudinal ridges, to which its rootlets were attached. From what is known of this genus it could be placed in its own order, in the Pleuromeiales, or in the Isoëtales. It has all but attained the habit of the latter. The major difference between it and *Pleuromeia* is that it had completely lost the axial nature of the rootlet-bearing organs.

"*Caulopteris* sp." was described as the stem

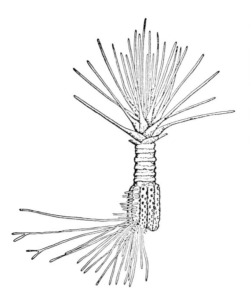

FIGURE 4–10. Reconstruction of *Nathorstiana*, after Mägdefrau (1932).

of a fern by Burges (1935). Helby and Martin (1965) redescribed the same specimens by reversing the plant and calling the apex what Burges had called the base. They presented a convincing case that the plant had a gross morphology similar to that of *Pleuromeia*. They thought that "*Caulopteris* sp." may have been the vegetative portion of the plant bearing the strobilus, *Cylostrobus*. The latter was a

compact structure of tightly associated sporophylls that had a relatively inextensive development of tissue distal to the elongate sporangia. It was also heterosporous and possibly ligulate.

Lycostrobus scottii (which is a cone differing from *Cylostrobus* in details not pertinent here), *Cylosporous, Pleuromeia, Isoëtes,* and *Stylites* quite significantly are the only known genera of vascular plants in which the megaspores are trilete and the microspores are monolete.

A full appreciation of the interpretation of the Isoetaceae in terms of the arborescent lycopods cannot be obtained until after the material in Chapter 5 is considered.

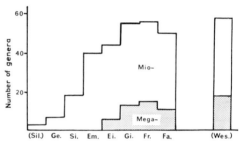

FIGURE 4–11. Histogram showing numbers of spore genera from the Upper Devonian and from each of the stages of the Devonian, after Chaloner (1967). See the text for details.

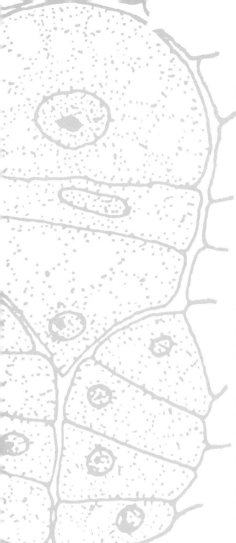

5

Isoetaceae

Isoetaceae, a family of lycopods, includes the extant genus *Stylites* (if generically recognized) and the genus *Isoëtes*, which is both living and known from rocks as old as Triassic.

Isoëtes, from the Greek "leek," which it superficially resembles, includes approximately 40 species that inhabit wet or completely inundated areas from the tropics to near-subarctic latitudes. Externally the plant appears to have a bulbous stock from which a tuft of roots descend at the base and a tuft of quill-like leaves arise on the upper surface (Fig. 5–1, *B*, *D*). The resemblance to a leek stops here, as *Isoëtes* has a uniquely complex, bi- or trilaterally symmetrical internal anatomy and leaves and roots with lycopod features, all superimposed with histological features generally considered characteristic of aquatic plants in general.

If the leaves of *Isoëtes* are pulled away from its "corm," a tight spiral of leaf attachments may be seen, with individual scars similar in shape to those of *Lepidophloios* of the Lepidodendrales. The spiral originates at the sunken, medianly situated apex (Fig. 5–1, *E*; Fig. 5–2, *A*, *B*). If the roots are pulled away (Fig. 5–1, *C*, *G*), the bilobed (or occasionally trilobed) nature of the corm is seen, with root scars in definite rows radiating across each lobe from the central groove (Fig. 5–1, *G*; Fig. 5–3, *B*). Within each root row, younger roots are found nearest the groove and progressively older ones away from it. Most roots are unbranched, but a few are branched dichotomously (arrow in Fig. 5–1, *D*).

The leaves of *Isoëtes* have a somewhat expanded base and an attenuated distal portion. All leaves bear sporangia and may be considered sporophylls, although sporangial abortion is the rule on young plants and on the last several leaves produced on older plants in a

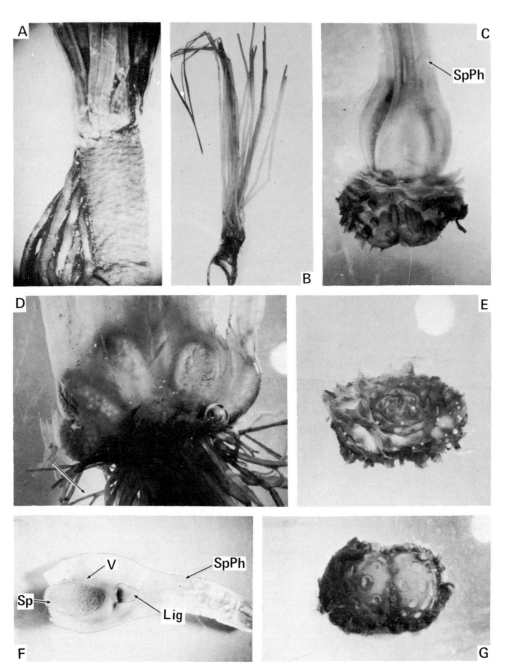

FIGURE 5–1. *A.* Stem of *Stylites* with a crown of leaves and a group of roots on the left, from Rauh and Falk (1959). *B* to *G. Isoëtes muricata.* *B.* Entire plant. *C.* Lower portion of *B* with roots removed. *D.* Basal portion of *B* enlarged. Arrow indicates a forked root. *E.* Basal portion of *B* as viewed from above with leaves removed. *F.* Single sporophyll as viewed from the adaxial side. *G.* Basal portion of *B* as viewed from below, with the roots removed. SpPh = sporophyll; Sp = sporangium; Lig = ligule; V = velum.

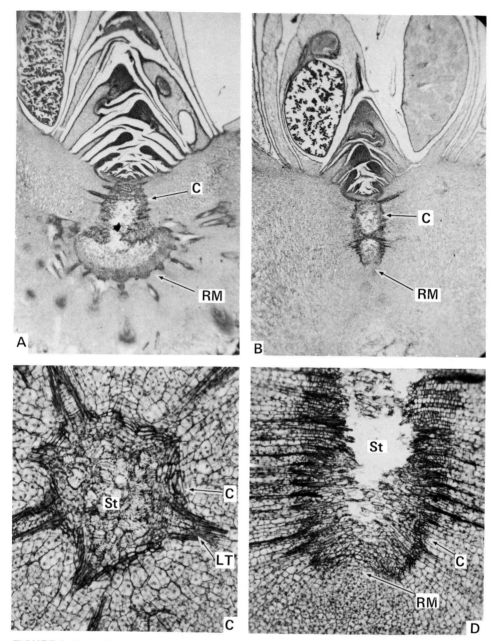

FIGURE 5–2. *Isoëtes muricata.* *A, B.* Longitudinal sections of the plant axis in planes at right angles to each other. *C.* Cross section of the vertical portion of the stele of the axis. *D.* Lower portion of the stele in *B* enlarged. C = cambium; RM = root-producing meristem; St = stele; LT = leaf trace.

given growing season. The sporangium, which is generally at or near the base on the adaxial side of the leaf (Fig. 5–1, *F*), is partly sunken in leaf tissue. The sunkenness is accentuated by the growth of a flap of leaf tissue, the velum (V in Fig. 5–1, *F*), around and over the distal portion (more or less according to species) of its margin. A ligule is present on each leaf just distal to the velum (Lig in Fig. 5–1, *F*; Fig. 5–3, *D*). In structure it is similar to the ligule seen in *Selaginella*, but it is quite flat, with a more sunken base.

The genus *Stylites*, first discovered in 1957 and now known from two species of the high Andes of Peru, was first thought to represent a very distinct genus more comparable to the Mesozoic *Nathorstiana*. Recent work by Kubitzki and Borchert (1964) on *Isoëtes triquetra*, however, indicates that *Stylites* merely represents a divergent type of *Isoëtes* at one end of its morphological range.

Stylites superficially appears quite different from *Isoëtes*. Whereas in the latter the axis is condensed within the basal corm and is rarely dichotomously branched at the crown, *Stylites* possesses an obvious vertical axis up to several inches in length (Fig. 5–1, *A*; Fig. 5–4, *A* to *D*) and frequently is dichotomously branched. In *Stylites* the root groove is extended up each side of the axis (Fig. 5–4, *E*), and above a dichotomy only one lateral groove is seen on each branch (Fig. 5–1, *A*; Fig. 5–4, *A* to *E*, *G*). In *Isoëtes*, on the other hand, although the basal root groove is generally nearly flat and curved up only slightly on each side, its vertical extension is certainly recognizable, especially in *Isoëtes triquetra*, a Colombian species presumed to be the close relative of *Stylites*.

The sporangium of *Stylites* is inserted some distance from the base of the sporophyll, but this feature is also found in *Isoëtes triquetra*.

A large part of the volume of the leaf of *Isoëtes* and *Stylites* is occupied by four longitudinally oriented lacunae that surround the single unbranched vein and are subdivided by a series of transversely oriented diaphragms. The vein itself is composed of protoxylem and some phloem elements. Areas of transfusion tissue occur on the adaxial side of the vein above the insertion of the ligule and near its base within the velum (TrT in Fig. 5–3, *D*).

Each root of *Isoëtes* and *Stylites* possesses a single monarch vascular bundle located on that side of a central lacuna which is toward the groove where new roots originate (Fig. 5–4, *E*, *G*). Within the vascular bundle, the xylem is on the side away from the lacuna and the phloem toward it. A small amount of transfusion tissue may be present. The similar-

ity between isoetaceous roots and stigmarian rootlets of the Lepidodendrales is truly striking in a number of details (see Fig. 4–6).

The growing point from which the leaves arise in *Isoëtes* and *Stylites* is a rather slight dome in the center of a depression (Fig. 5–2, *A*, *B*; Fig. 5–4, *C*). Initial cells of the apex are variously described in the literature, but probably the most complete and accurate description is presented by Paolillo (1963), who has also reviewed the earlier reports. There seem to be several apical initials at the crest of the dome with tissue derivation comparable to that in the smaller stem apices of *Lycopodium*. Paolillo did report several apices of young plants in which there was a single cell that "dominated the apical group."

Within the corm of *Isoëtes* there is an anchor-shaped stele (Fig. 5–2, *A*, in which the broad side of the anchor shows and Fig. 5–2, *B*, cut at right angles to *A*). To the vertical part of the stele are attached the spirally arranged leaf traces (Fig. 5–2, *A* and shown in cross section in Fig. 5–2, *C* and Fig. 5–3, *A*). To the basal, usually bilobed, portion of the stele are attached the roots, the steles of which are seen in Fig. 5–2, *A* and in cross section in Fig. 5–3, *B*, *C*. Since two lobes of the stele are oriented at right angles to the lobes of the entire corm seen externally in Fig. 5–1, *G*, the section in Fig. 5–2, *A* is cut along the externally seen basal groove and the one in Fig. 5–2, *B* at right angles to the groove and through each external lobe.

Running lengthwise along the base of the anchor-shaped stele is the linear root-producing meristem, which is seen in cross section in Fig. 5–2, *B* (RM), enlarged in *D*, and in its full length in *A*. A section transverse to the corm at the level of the root-producing meristem (Fig. 5–3, *B* and enlarged in *C*) shows the regularity in sites of origin of new roots and a progression of older and older roots at distances increasingly removed from the meristem.

To visualize *Stylites* one needs only to contract the lobes of the stelar anchor and extend the root-producing meristem vertically.

Over the entire surface of the stele of *Isoëtes* and *Stylites* is a perennially active cambium (C in Fig. 5–2, *A* to *D*; Fig. 5–4, *F*) that is interrupted only just below the apical

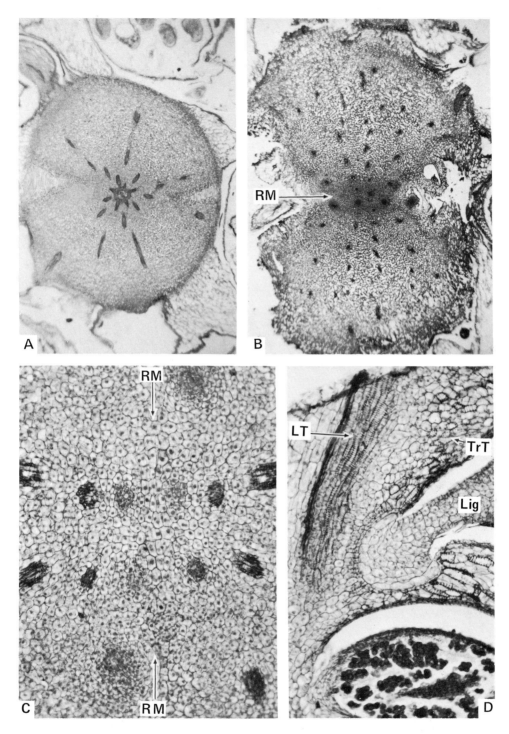

FIGURE 5–3. *Isoëtes muricata.* *A.* Cross section of the axis showing the vertical part of the stele and leaf traces. *B.* Cross section of the axis at the level of the root-producing meristem (RM), showing rows of roots. *C.* Enlargement of a portion of *B.* The root-producing meristem is oriented at right angles to its orientation in *B.* *D.* Longitudinal section through a portion of a sporophyll. LT = leaf trace; TrT = transfusion tissue; Lig = ligule.

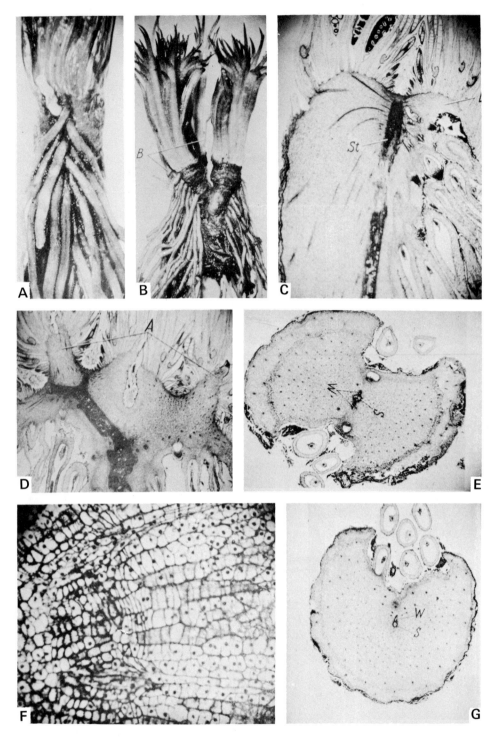

FIGURE 5–4. *Stylites.* *A.* Plant axis from the side, showing rows of roots. *B.* Bifurcated plant. *C.* Longitudinal section of the plant axis. *D.* Longitudinal section of a branched axis. *E.* Cross section of a plant axis with root-producing meristem on two sides *F.* Cross section of axis at cambial zone. *G.* Cross section of a plant axis with root-producing meristem on one side. W = root; S = stele. All from Rauh and Falk (1959).

meristem and at the root-producing meristem. The latter has been interpreted by Paolillo to be a part of the cambium; this may be so in a purely descriptive sense for *Isoëtes* in its present state of extreme reduction. From a comparative point of view it is probably something different.

The cambium originates very early in the life of the young sporophyte. Once it has become fully established, it produces the mass of secondary parenchyma to the outside ("secondary cortex"), which constitutes the major bulk of the entire body and eventually sloughs off the outside as flakes of dead tissue. Secondary cortex production results in the stretching of the leaf traces and in a considerable shift in their orientation.

Toward the inside the cambium produces secondary xylem, secondary phloem, or layers of parenchyma, depending on the species and the age of the plant. Certain patterns of cellular differentiation within the stele led Rauh and Falk (1959) to suggest that there may be multiple cambia; Paolillo, however, attributes these patterns to layers of late-maturing primary xylem elements.

Isoetaceous sporangia are larger than those of most other extant non-seed-bearing plants, in general measuring 3 to 7 mm in length and having a very high spore output. Megasporangia are reported to produce 50 to 300 megaspores each. A figure of this order of magnitude is suggested by the number of megaspores visible through the walls of the bulging megasporangia in Fig. 5–1, *D*. The spore output of microsporangia is reported to range from 150,000 to 1,000,000, but estimates made in the preparation of this text from three species native to northeastern United States ranged from 130,000 to 250,000.

Within a given growing season, a mature *Isoëtes* plant will generally produce megasporangia first, then microsporangia, then several aborted sporangia. The sporophylls and their sporangia from the previous season will have mostly rotted and fallen away by this time, so that toward the end of its growing season a plant will appear as the one in Fig. 5–1, *D*, with megasporangia on the outside.

Isoetaceous sporangia are traversed by terete or ribbonform strands called trabeculae (Tr in Fig. 5–5, *D*; portions shown in *B*).

Their function is obscure. They do not subdivide the sporangial cavity, as it is continuous around them. They are too delicate to afford any mechanical resistance to crushing. They do extend the tapetal layer, which covers them and lines the inner surface of the sporangial wall, and this may be a clue to their possible significance.

Each sporangium develops from a group of initials aligned transversely on the sporophyll. The first set of periclinal divisions sets off the wall (outer cells) and the sporogenous tissue (inner cells). The wall comes to be several cells thick and the inner cell layer matures into a part of the tapetum. The trabeculae and their covering of tapetum have a common ontogenetic origin with the sporogenous tissue. An early stage in the differentiation of the functional sporogenous tissue from the trabeculae is shown in Fig. 5–5, *A* (LT, leaf trace; V, velum). Much of the tapetum in the region of attachment of the sporangium is derived from cells that were below the original sporangial initials. Meiosis is much less synchronous in the sporangia of *Isoëtes* than in vascular plants with smaller sporangia. It is common to find in the same sporangium all stages from late prophase I to young spore tetrads.

There is no specialized dehiscence mechanism in *Isoëtes*; the sporangial walls merely decompose, releasing the spores. Some species are reported to release spores in a gelatinous mass that floats to the surface of water or thick muck.

The megaspores are trilete in marking, from 250 to 900 μ in diameter, and often bear conspicuous spiculate projections. The microspores are monolete in marking and are 20 to 45 μ in length. When megaspores are collected free in nature they are usually seen to have several hundred microspores attached and entangled among the spore-wall projections.

If environmental conditions are proper, spores of *Isoëtes* may germinate immediately on shedding to produce gametophytes. Such conditions are often not met until the following growing season. At any time during the winter in temperate climates gametophytes may be cultured merely by taking mud from the immediate vicinity of the mature sporophytes,

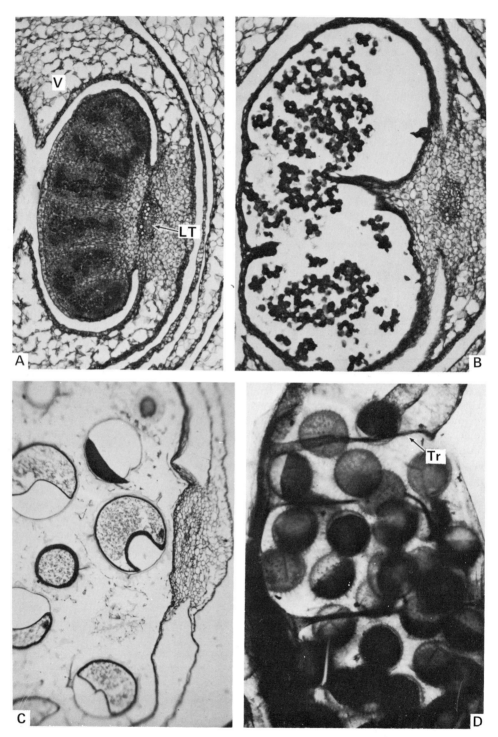

FIGURE 5–5. *Isoëtes muricata.* *A, B.* Younger and older microsporangia in cross section. *C.* Portion of a megasporangium in cross section. *D.* Cleared megasporangium. V = velum; LT = leaf trace; Tr = trabecula.

transporting it to the laboratory, and keeping it wet. Mature gametophytes may be thus obtained in about 2 weeks and visible young sporophytes 1 week or so later.

The microgametophyte, or male gametophyte, is endosporic and composed of a total of nine cells. The spore first divides to produce a small, apparently functionless cell, which has been interpreted as a prothallial cell (A in Fig. 5–6, *A, B*), and a larger cell, the antheridial initial. The latter, by a series of divisions (Fig. 5–6, *A* to *C*), cuts off four jacket cells that surround the primary spermatogenous cell (in *C*). From this spermatids are mitotically produced, each of which develops into a ribbon-form, multiflagellate sperm with a pronounced terminal vesicle. Internal cell walls eventually disappear and the sperm are released by way of an irregular break in the spore coat.

As in *Selaginella*, the megagametophyte of *Isoëtes* begins its development with a series of free nuclear divisions. Similarity is also found in the assumption of a peripheral position of the free nuclei (30 to 50 in *Isoëtes*), by cell formation beginning at the apical end of the gametophyte and by the formation of small cells below the apex and larger central and basal cells. There is no apical pad separated by a diaphragm as in *Selaginella*. The apex of the gametophyte of *Isoëtes* is nonbulging,

exposed only slightly by megaspore wall opening, and is devoid of rhizoids. Several archegonia may mature on the exposed surface; they stand out conveniently for observation because of the brown color of their terminal neck cells against the white background of adjacent cells.

The archegonium is derived from a conspicuous initial (Fig. 5–6, *F*), which divides periclinally to produce the neck mother cell (outer) and the axial row mother cell (inner). By the usual sequence of divisions (Fig. 5–6, *G* to *J*), an egg, a ventral canal cell and one neck cell in the axial row, and a neck of four vertical rows each about four cells long are produced (Fig. 5–8, *B*). The entire archegonium is surrounded by a jacket derived from cells adjacent to the archegonial initial.

The first division of the zygote is nearly transverse to the archegonial axis and the second pair of divisions at right angles to the first (Fig. 5–7, *A*). Within the limits of accuracy by which organ boundaries may be specified, the foot is derived from the two distal cells, the first embryonic leaf from one of the two inner cells, and the root in part from the other inner cell and in part from one of the distal cells. In Fig. 5–7, *H* the root projects upward, the leaf to the right, and the foot is the slight bulge to the lower left. The line of cell walls

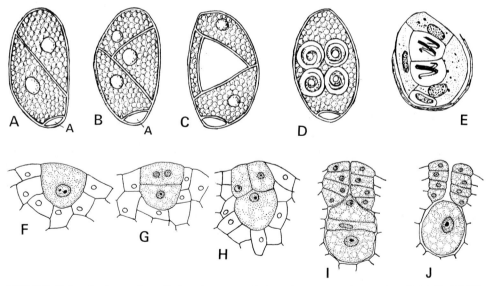

FIGURE 5–6. *Isoëtes. A* to *E*. Development of the microgametophyte, after Belajeff (1898). *F* to *J*. Development of the archegonium, after La Motte (1933).

Isoetaceae **67**

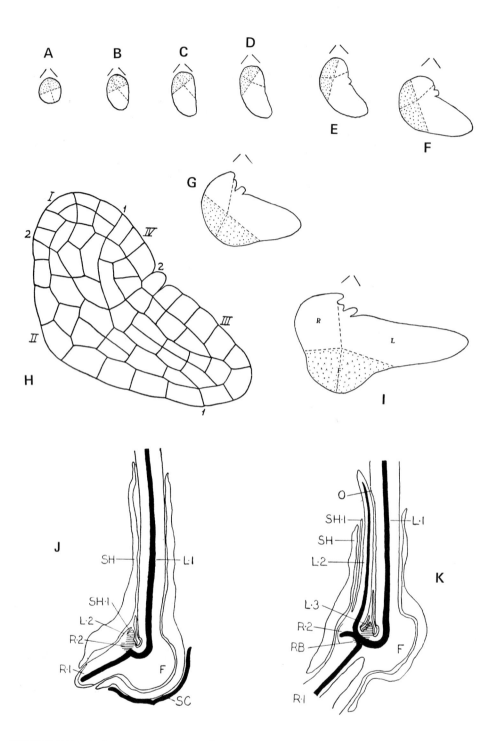

FIGURE 5–7. *Isoëtes.* *A* to *I*. Embryo development. *J, K.* Older sporelings. *A* to *G*, *I*, after La Motte (1933); *H*, after La Motte (1937); *J, K.* after Baldwin (1933). R = root; L = leaf; F = foot; SH = leaf sheath; SC = spore coat; RB = root-producing meristem.

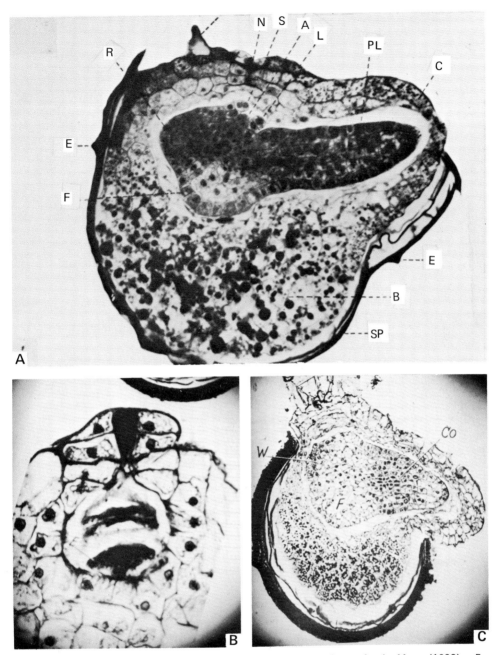

FIGURE 5–8. *A.* Megagametophyte of *Isoëtes* containing an embryo, after La Motte (1933). *B.* Archegonium of *Stylites*, after Rauh and Falk (1959). *C.* As *A*, but of *Stylites*, after Rauh and Falk (1959). R = root; F = foot; L = leaf.

along 1-1 indicates the extrapolated position of the first division of the zygote, and those along the line 2-2 that of the second pair of divisions. The bulging cell on the right at the figure "2" represents the first ligule. Differential growth during embryogeny results in the foot assuming an inner position and the leaf and root an outer position (Fig. 5–7, *A* to *K*).

The embryos shown in Fig. 5–8, *A* (*Isoëtes*) and *C* (*Stylites*) are similar to the one in Fig. 5–7, *I* and at a stage just before the first leaf emerges. The stem, as a recognizable entity, is not present until the second plastochron in the growth of the young sporophyte. At this stage the stem apex is seen adjacent to the first leaf.

In the young sporeling, the vascular tissue supplying the first leaf (L-1 in Fig. 5–7, *J*) is continuous with that of the first root (R-1). The second leaf (L-2 in *J* and *K*) and the second root (R-2) are supplied by tracheids that differentiate across the plant axis. The root-producing meristem is established at this stage (RB in *K*). Radial seriation of cells indicative of cambial establishment is detectable around the central core when the plant has "several" leaves, according to Paolillo.

Isoëtes seems to represent a highly reduced and specialized form. A multitude of features clearly establish it as a lycopod. Its present state of reduction has led some researchers to describe the entire plant as a single strobilus bearing roots on its bottom and telescoped with other vegetative parts that may still be present.

The most plausible phylogenetic interpretation of the isoetaceous plant body is that it represents a highly reduced derivative of a sigillarian in the Lepidodendrales, with intermediate forms represented by *Pleuromeia* and *Nathorstiana*. Insofar as these two mesozoic genera are known, they are both similar, part for part, to *Isoëtes*, with a greater development of an upright axis and a more distinct rhizomorph (basal portion to which roots were attached). Internal structure of these two genera remains unknown, and one can only speculate as to the presence or absence or secondary tissues on the outside of what has been preserved as impressions. Evidence for lepidodendralean ancestry of the Isoetaceae is found in the form of the leaf scars, leaves, presence of ligules, ligule pits, massive elongate sporangia, very close correspondence in root structure, heterospory, reduced gametophytes, and definite root arrangement (spiral in *Stigmaria* and *Pleuromeia*, rowed in *Isoëtes*, *Stylites*, and *Nathorstiana*).

The stigmarian appendages, although rootlike in superficial features, are much more leaflike in their morphology and anatomy. Their spiral arrangement and form suggest that they probably originated apically on an axis, although the growing point of the stigmarian axis has not been described nor have any early stages in the development of the stigmarian appendages (the so-called "roots"). If they were of apical origin one might expect some indication of this in *Isoëtes*. There is, however, no vestige of apical growth at the bottom end of the *Isoëtes* plant axis, but the meristems seem so highly condensed that the root-producing meristem is not clearly distinguishable from the vascular cambium.

6

Rhyniales

It was common until recently to give the order Rhyniales familial status in the order Psilophytales. The latter, along with the extant order Psilotales, was included by many authors in the subdivision Psilopsida or Psilophytina. Recently acquired knowledge has forced a reconsideration of the order Psilotales, and its sole family, the Psilotaceae, has been transferred to a position near the extant ferns (see Chapter 12). The order Psilophytales in its broadest sense similarly has not withstood the test of new information. The families Zosterophyllaceae, Protopteridaceae, and Pseudosporochnaceae, once included here, were transferred elsewhere as they become better known (see Chapters 4, 9, and 10). The "genus" *Psilophyton* has been redefined and it appears that it will be very difficult to retain the name. The original collections of Dawson (1859) included under the name "*Philophyton princeps*" three different taxa, no one of which was designed as a type (Hueber and Banks, 1967). The rhizomes attributed to the original "plant" have been identified as *Taeniocrada*. The spiny axes, described by Dawson in 1871 as "*Psilophyton princeps* var. *ornatum*" have recently been shown to bear lateral sporangia of the general lycopod type and have been transferred to the Zosterophyllales (see Chapter 4). The naked axes bearing lateral sporangial trusses and ultimately terminal sporangia, thought by Dawson to be a part of his "plant" but not found in organic connection, were given the name *Dawsonites* by Halle in 1916. Hueber and Banks (1967) presented an emended diagnosis of *Psilophyton princeps*, restricting it to Dawsonites. Banks (1968a) used only the name *Dawsonites*, as is done in this text, but he informs the present author that he prepared the 1968 manuscript before Hueber and Banks wrote the 1967 article.

The Rhyniales include relatively simple plants of Silurian and Devonian age. They present no morphological features that would allow us to specify organs such as roots or leaves. The sporophytic body was merely a branched axial (stem) system with vertical aerial parts and horizontal surface or sub-surface parts (Fig. 6–1, *I*; Fig. 6–2, *A*). Branching was equally or unequally dichotomous to monopodial (pseudomonopodial?) (Fig. 6–1, *A* to *C*, *E*, *F*, *H* to *J*; Fig. 6–2, *A*, *B*). Sporangia were borne terminally on ultimate axial entities.

The genera included in the group as listed by Banks (1968a) with the addition of *Nothia* (Lyon, 1964) follow. His classification is contrasted to the views taken by the present author. The family Rhyniaceae may have been much more diverse than present fragmentary knowledge indicates, and it is expected that it will undergo frequent taxonomic revisions in years to come. The two systems presented below merely reflect different views as to the extent of the morphological hiatus that must exist between any pair of taxa of a given rank.

dichotomy, *D*; Fig. 6–4, *D*) with centrally located protoxylem. Maturation was therefore centrarch. The cortex, where known, is composed of relatively simple parenchyma (Fig. 6–2, *B*, *D*) with indication of subepidermal chlorenchyma. The stomatal apparatus was of an ordinary type. The guard cells were structurally ordinary and there were no accessory cells. Underground stems of *Rhynia* and *Horneophyton* were structurally similar to upright stems but bore rhizoids (Fig. 6–3, *D*, arrows). In *Horneophyton* the basal stems showed swellings with rhizoids on their lower surface (Fig. 6–1, *I*). The stem of *Taeniocrada* was ribbon-form, possibly indicating a submerged aquatic habitat. Stems of *Rhynia* contain fugal parts, *Palaeomyces* (Fig. 6–3, *A*), which may have grown inside the healthy plant or may have invaded the plant as it was dying or after it was dead.

Of all the Rhyniales, *Rhynia* and *Horneophyton* are by the far the best known (Kidston and Lang, 1917, 1921). These genera are preserved as essentially complete plants in a hard silicaceous rock, the Middle (possibly Lower)

Banks (1968a)	Present Views
Subdivision: Rhyniophytina	(No subdivisions recognized)
	Class: Rhyniopsida
Order: Rhyniales	Order: Rhyniales
Family: Rhyniaceae	Family: Rhyniaceae
Rhynia	*Rhynia*
Horneophyton	*Horneophyton*
Hicklingia	*Hicklingia*
Eogaspesiea	*Eogaspesiea*
Taeniocrada	*Taeniocrada*
Hedeia	*Hedeia*
Yarravia	*Yarravia*
Hostimella	*Hostimella*
Family: Cooksoniaceae	*Nothia*
Cooksonia	*Cooksonia*
Subdivision: Trimerophytina	Family: Trimerophytaceae
Order: Trimerophytales	*Trimerophyton*
Family: Trimerophytaceae	*Dawsonites*
Trimerophyton	
Dawsonites	

Of the 12 genera listed in the Rhyniales, the anatomy of the stem is known only for *Rhynia*, *Horneophyton*, *Hostimella*, and *Dawsonites*. Each of these four has a more or less terete xylem strand (Fig. 6–2, *C* below a

Devonian Rhynie Chert of Scotland. Their orientation within the rock is often upright, not in bedding planes. Two shoot apices have been described with some cellular detail, although it was not possible to determine the

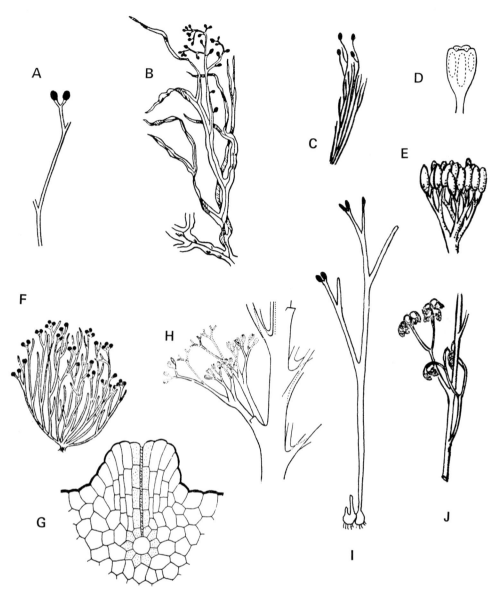

FIGURE 6–1. *A. Cooksonia*, after Croft and Lang (1942). *B. Taeniocrada*, after Kräusel and Weyland (1930). *C. Eogaspesiea*, after Daber (1960). *D.* Synangium of *Yarravia*, after Andrews (1959). *E. Hedeia*, after Cookson (1949). *F. Hicklingia*, after Banks (1968a). *G.* "Archegonium" of *Rhynia Gwynne-Vaughani*, after Lemoigne (1968). *H. Trimerophyton*, after Hopping (1956). *I. Horneophyton lignieri*, after Kidston and Lang (1921). *J. Dawsonites*, after Hueber (1964).

number of initial cells. Several authors have suggested some sort of relatively rapid kill and lithification of the Rhynie Chert plants such as might have occurred if a mineral-laden hot spring flowed into the marsh where they were growing.

The stem of *Rhynia Gwynne-Vaughani* shows bumps along its surface, some of which appear as undeveloped lateral branches. They intergrade with smaller and smaller ones down to small surface eruptions involving relatively few cells. The smaller ones seem to have a

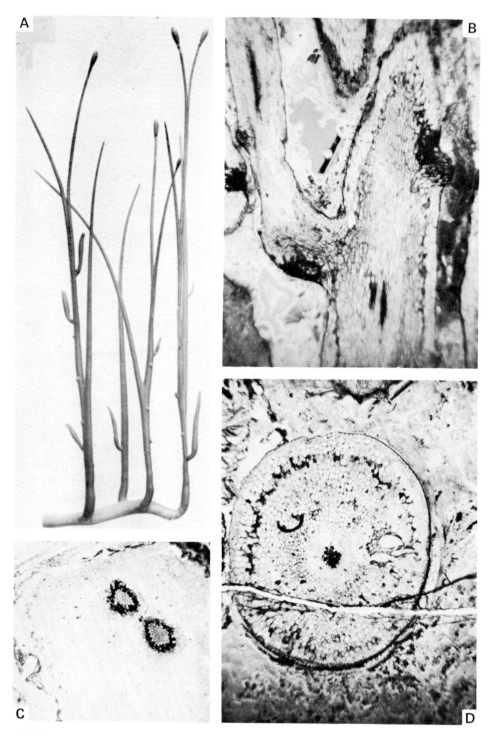

FIGURE 6–2. *A.* Model of *Rhynia Gwynne-Vaughani*, from the 1951 Annual Report of the Chicago Museum of Natural History, by permission of the Field Museum of Natural History. *B. R. Gwynne-Vaughani*, longitudinal section of a branching stem. *C. R. major*, cross section of a stem below a dichotomy. *D. R. major*, cross section of stem.

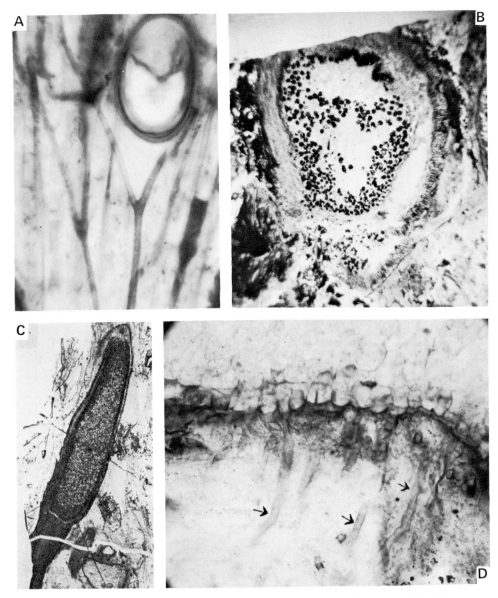

FIGURE 6–3. *A. Palaeomyces* in the stem of *Rhynia major*. *B. R. major*, cross section of a sporangium. *C. R. major*, longitudinal section of a sporangium, after Kidston and Lang (1917). *D.* Rhizoids on the stem of *Horneophyton lignieri*.

central channel leading to a large cell or intercellular space below the surface. Lemoigne (1968) called such structures archegonia and therefore assumed that some of the plants were gametophytes. His diagrammatic reconstruction of one such structure appears in Fig. 6–1, *G*. The so-called archegonia were much more likely hydathodes or secretory

structures of some kind. Several other authors have in the past suggested that some of the rhynialean axes may have been gametophytes; some even said that they "probably were" gametophytes.

There are reasons for the statements but not because of features presented by the axes themselves. The idea may be traced directly to

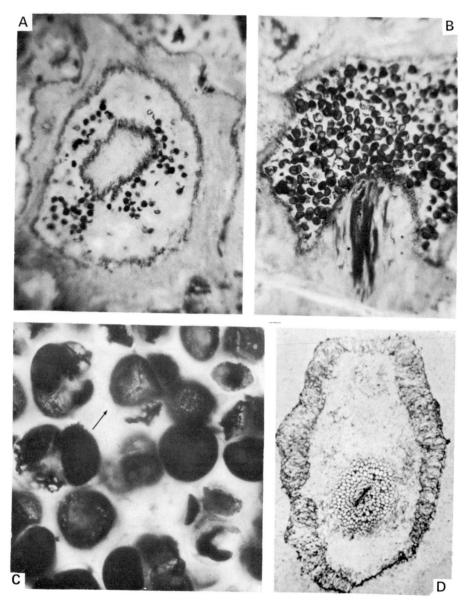

FIGURE 6–4. *A. Horneophyton lignieri*, cross section of a sporangium. *B.* As *A*, but oblique-longitudinal section. *C.* Several spores from *B* enlarged. *D. Dawsonites*, cross section of the axis, after Banks (1968a).

certain morphological implications of the homologous theory, which suggests that the first land plants had essentially indistinguishable gametophytes and sporophytes. The first descriptions of the Rhynie Chert plants and those of the gametophytes of the Psilotaceae appeared at about the same time (1917). The very close morphological correspondence be-tween psilotaceous gametophytes and their subterranean sporophytic counterparts, as well as the superficial similarity of *Psilotum nudum* to the reconstructions of rhyniophytes, stimulated a new train of interpretation given impetus in 1939 by Holloway's description of vascular tissue in the gametophyte of *P. nudum*. More recent information would indicate that the psilotaceous species most indicative of rhynialean affinity (i.e., *P. nudum*) is derived within the family from forms quite unlike the Rhynie Chert plants but more like the flattened *Tmesipteris* species. The question of the ancestral forms of the Psilotaceae is still an open one, as is the question of the nature of the rhynialean gametophyte.

The sporangia of all the Rhyniales were terminal on ultimate axial entities (Fig. 6–1, *A* to *C*, *E*, *F*, *H* to *J*; Fig. 6–2, *A*; Fig. 6–3, *C*). In size they ranged from 1 to several mm long and in shape from globose to somewhat elongate. Various tendencies toward sporangial groupings were expressed in the order, and in *Yarravia* a synangium was developed (Fig. 6–1, *D*). In *Dawsonites* the ultimate sporangia were recurved. In *Trimerophyton* (Fig. 6–1, *H*) and *Dawsonites* (Fig. 6–1, *J*) sporangia occurred on overtopped lateral branch systems. This is the only feature justifying the inclusion of these two genera in the same family, and substantiating information on other features of these plants is sorely needed. Dehiscence was probably longitudinal in most rhynialean genera but seems to have been transverse in *Nothia*, which showed the thickened dehiscence cells at the apex. Some other genera suggest a more general surface distribution of thickened cells (the palisade layer on the right in Fig. 6–3, *B*). Sporangial walls, where known, were a number of cells thick (Fig. 6–3, *B*, *C*; Fig. 6–4, *A*) and the tissue seems to have been a continuation of the stem cortex. In *Horneophyton* the central axial tissue, including the vascular tissue, extended into the sporangial locule as a distinct columella (cross section in Fig. 6–4, *A*, oblique section in *B*). All known species were homosporous and their spores were trilete (Fig. 6–4, *C*).

General Comments on Land Plant Phylogeny

The land plants, which include tracheophytes and bryophytes, are characterized and clearly defined by the possession of the archegonium (except in certain seed plant taxa, where it is lost by reduction), by characteristic spore structure, by a multicellular enclosed embryo, by possession of the stomatal apparatus (except Hepaticae), and by a particular plastid pigment composition (shared by the green algae). These, along with somewhat less distinctive sporangial features, make it difficult to assume anything but a monophyletic origin of the entire Embryophyta. The interpretation of a single origin for tracheophytes from avascular embryophytes is often assumed but is based only upon the common possession of lignified xylary tissue and possibly common features related to sporangial dehiscence.

A group of avascular archegoniates, probably aquatic, which so far has completely escaped detection by those searching the rocks, must be assumed to have given rise to either three or four lines of archegoniates: (1) Anthocerotae, (2) Hepaticae and Musci, and (3) all vascular plants as a single lineage or as two separate ones, whose basal stocks were the rhyniophytes, on the one hand, and zosterophyllophytes, on the other. All vascular plant taxa are readily traceable to either the Rhyniales or the Zosterophyllales. The latter bore fundamentally lateral sporangia which also occur in their presumed derivatives, the lycopods. The Rhyniales bore sporangia terminally on axial entities, and the morphology of all vascular plants except lycopods is readily and logically interpretable in terms of this morphology. So far, these two distinct types of sporangial insertion have never been satisfactorily reconciled one in terms of the other except by speculative exercises in geometry. Reasonable morphological extrapolation stops short in two distinct taxa. From this point, therefore, it is to a large extent speculation.

The common ancestral form of the Rhyniales and the Zosterophyllales may well have had no sporangium in the ordinary vascular plant sense. This ancestral plant may have had scattered about its axes sporogenous tissue in the form of hypodermal patches, large or small, or even single cells. These may have become aggregated or definitized terminally to produce the rhyniophyte sporangium and laterally to produce the zosterophyllophyte sporangium. This concept cannot be defended beyond this point, and it is presented merely to occupy what seems to be knowledge vacuum.

There seems little doubt that from a morphological point of view the sporophyte is ultimately homologous to the gametophyte. The two generations are too similar in many taxa and, after all, the features of the somata of these two generations are determined by the same genome. The greater the differential expression of the genome, therefore, the greater the specialization of the taxon concerned. However, differential expression of the genome in sporophyte and gametophyte has undoubtedly had its phylogenetic ups and downs (see comments at the end of Chapter 16), a point that has to a large extent been ignored by proponents of the classical homologous theory. Algae had been in existence an extremely long time before the first land plants appeared, and to a large extent the fundamental homology between the two generations had been phylogenetically obscured in many lineages by the beginning of Silurian times. The pertinence of this line of reasoning lies in the possible answers to the question: What was the nature of the first vascular plant gametophyte? In habitat it was either subterranean and mycorrhizic, or terrestrial and surface living, or floating aquatic or submerged aquatic. In morphology it was axial, filamentous, thallose, leafy, or without clearly definable form. It can be stated that the first vascular plant gametophytes were not dependent for nutrition upon their sporophytes; their spores demonstrate this. They were either autophytic or saprophytic. Some of the morphological possibilities are less probable than others, but none may be absolutely eliminated. Present knowledge does seem to point out axial morphology as an attribute of the first gametophyte. Evidence from the byrophytes, which likely arose from an ancestral stock reasonably close to the first vascular plants, suggests that the thallose gametophyte of the Marchiantiales represents a flattened axial type that never went through a leafy stage in its phylogeny (Schuster, 1966). The distribution of axial gametophytes among vascular plants (*Lycopodium*, Ophioglossaceae, Psilotaceae, Stromatopteridaceae, *Actinostachys*) allows us to postulate this kind of morphology as a possible common denominator for vascular plants in general. Note that all these examples are subterranean types. It is conceivable that sex went underground as early as Middle Silurian times.

Although the Order Rhyniales includes only relatively simple plants that are not well known, it illustrates certain significant morphological trends toward specialization and constitutes a major center of focus of vascular plant morphologists. The simpler genera are more or less equally dichotomous with others, showing overtopping trends and even pseudomonopodial habit. The overtopped dichotomous trusses of the Trimerophytaceae already strongly suggest the megaphylls of derivative groups such as the Cladoxyales and Protopteridales. There is no evidence that the lateral trusses of *Dawsonites* or *Trimerophyton* had been completely reduced to appendicular status; only ontogenetic studies could show this. Differences between aerial and subterranean axes, however slight, appear in the Rhyniales and in fact may have been apparent in their predecessors. Sporangial recurvature, so prevalent among the sphenopsids, and tendencies toward sporangial grouping or clustering, so very characteristic of most vascular plants, also are apparent within the order. These trends are considered more than mere parallel occurrences. The Rhyniales probably did in reality give rise to all other groups of vascular plants except the Zosterophyllales and the lycopods and did so in Upper Silurian or Lower Devonian times.

7

Equisetum

The genus *Equisetum*, represented in the extant floras, according to Hauke, by 15 species and 5 hybrids all called horsetails or scouring rushes, is the lingering remnant of a taxon similar in antiquity, diversity, and numbers to the lycopods. The living species are herbaceous plants that vary in height from about 15 cm (*E. scirpoides*, Fig. 7–1, *A*) to nearly 10 m (*E. giganteum*). The taller species are spindly herbs, quite incapable of standing when not in dense supporting vegetation. The species vary from sparsely branched (*E. scirpoides* and *E. hyemale*) to branched to the point of being lacy (*E. sylvaticum*). The most conspicuous characteristics of the genus are the jointed nature of the stems, pronounced intercalary growth, whorled leaves and branches, and the sandpapery texture of their surfaces. *Equisetum* is a significant poisonous plant in pastures, it is used medicinally, it is used for polishing tools and reeds of wind instruments, and it is said that it has been used by prospectors as an indicator, as it tends to accumulate gold from the soil. Only the lack of sufficiently cultured taste on the part of man has prevented it from becoming an important ornamental.

Equisetum plants extend themselves prolifically by means of shallow to deep-seated rhizomes that give rise to both upright shoots and adventitious roots at the nodes and in some species to determinate, tuberous storage organs (Fig. 7–1, *C*). A number of species are found growing along exposed banks of streams, where the rhizomes are washed out of the soil, fragmented, and carried downstream to initiate new colonies.

The whorled leaves are regularly connate at their base to form a distinct sheath that is attached to the stem immediately below the transverse intercalary meristem (IM in Fig. 7–2, *A*). The branches originate in the axil of the sheath at its very base but in positions

FIGURE 7–1. *A. Equisetum scirpoides*, habit. *B. E. palustre*, portion of aerial shoot. *C. E. arvense*, portion of rhizome with tubers and roots. *D, E. E. palustre*, portions of aerial shoots with spiral organization.

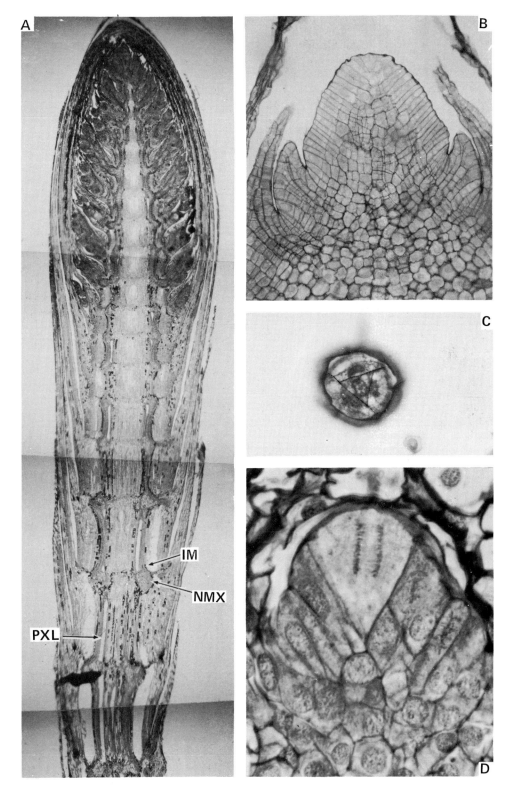

FIGURE 7–2. *A. Equisetum sylvaticum*, the vertical shoot as it is in the underground winter condition in longitudinal section. *B. E. hyemale*, longitudinal section of the vertical shoot tip at the stage when the lower leaf whorls are being produced. *C. E. arvense*, cross section of the shoot tip, showing the apical cell. *D.E.hyemale*, longitudinal section of a lateral bud as seen in a cross section of the parental axis. This is part of Fig. 7–4, *A* enlarged. Apical cell is in division.   IM = intercalary meristem; PXL = carinal protoxylem lacuna; NMX = nodal metaxylem.

alternating with the individual leaves (Fig. 7–1, *B*). They then pierce the sheath and become exposed. Some species show little branching, but sections indicate that resting buds are present at many of the sites (e.g., *E. hyemale*). This species has biennial or triennial shoots and the buds frequently develop as dwarf branches in the second or third year. *Equisetum sylvaticum* and *E. arvense*, at the other extreme, generally express their full capacity for branching in the first year with second-, third-, and even fourth-order branches.

The leaves of *Equisetum* are poorly developed as organs, exposing the photosynthetic surface. Each has a very small, simple, and probably mesarch bundle (Fig. 7–3, *C*; Fig. 7–4, *A*). There is a restricted amount of chlorenchyma and some hypodermal sclerenchyma that is primarily associated with external ridges. The latter are continuous with those of the internode below and number one or two per leaf, depending on the species. Along the line of fusion of individual leaves within the sheath there is often a single row of hook-shaped cells that seem to clamp the adjacent leaves together. The degree of fusion between adjacent leaves of a whorl varies among species and within a single plant body. Most extreme fusion is found in the underground overwintering buds of *E. sylvaticum*, which produce aerial shoots in the following year. In these, the covering whorl or two of leaves are in the form of a complete hood with leaves fused to their very tips. Some species (e.g., *E. hyemale* and *E. kansanum*) produce distinct abscission layers and drop the ends of the free tips of leaves. Subterranean leaves of some species produce rhizoids.

The stem apex of *Equisetum* shows a large apical cell as pronounced and diagrammatic as any among vascular plants (Fig. 7–2, *B* to *D*; Fig. 7–4, *A*). It is broad, pyramidal, and has three cutting faces (Fig. 7–2, *C*). In small stems in which the number of leaves per whorl is three, there is not the constant physical relationship between the leaf position and the cutting face position that is so diagrammatically illustrated in leafy liverworts.

Stem anatomy is very characteristic, with variation sufficient to distinguish species. The stem is externally ridged, with ridge number and position related to leaf number and position at the node above (Fig. 7–3, *B*, *C*). Beneath the ridges are zones of cortical sclerenchyma (CS in Fig. 7–3, *A*). Adjacent to the ridges are areas of cortical chlorenchyma (CCH in Fig. 7–3, *A*) which occur beneath the vertical rows of stomata (ST in Fig. 7–3, *C*). Deeper in the cortex, alternating with the ridges, are schizolysigenous canals that extend essentially the full length of each internode. These are the "vallecular canals," here called cortical canals (CCA on either edge of section in Fig. 7–3, *A*; six in cross section in *B*; three in *C*; two in longitudinal section of lowermost internode in Fig. 7–2, *A*). At the center of the internode is the pith, which is complete only in the very smallest stems and present in others as a cavity surrounded by a few remaining pith parenchyma cells (P in Fig. 7–3, *A*, *B*). Circling the pith is a ring of vascular bundles generally corresponding in number to the leaves in the whorl above (Fig. 7–3, *B*, *C*). There are one or more endodermides associated with the vascular tissue, depending on the species and also on the position of the stem in the plant body. There may be a single endodermis following the stem circumference just outside the ring of bundles (e.g., rhizomes and aerial stems of *E. pratense*, *E. arvense*, and *E. palustre*; aerial stem only of *E. sylvaticum*; and certain smaller rhizomes and aerial stems of *E. variegatum*). There may be an endodermis both inside and outside the ring of bundles (e.g., most rhizomes and aerial stems of *E. variegatum*, rhizomes of *E. sylvaticum*, and aerial stems of *E. hyemale* and *E. kansanum*). Or, finally, there may be a separate endodermis around each vascular bundle (e.g., aerial stems and rhizomes of *E. fluviatile* and rhizomes of *E. hyemale* and *E. kansanum*). The basal, underground part of the vertical stem in each case has the same endodermal condition as the horizontal rhizomes, and when it is different from the aerial portion of the stem it shows transitional conditions at or near the ground level.

Equisetum has a stomatal apparatus of highly specialized structure (Hauke, 1957) and ontogeny in which both guard cells and accessory cells take an active part in opening the stoma. The guard-cell mother cell becomes established after a protoderm cell cuts off

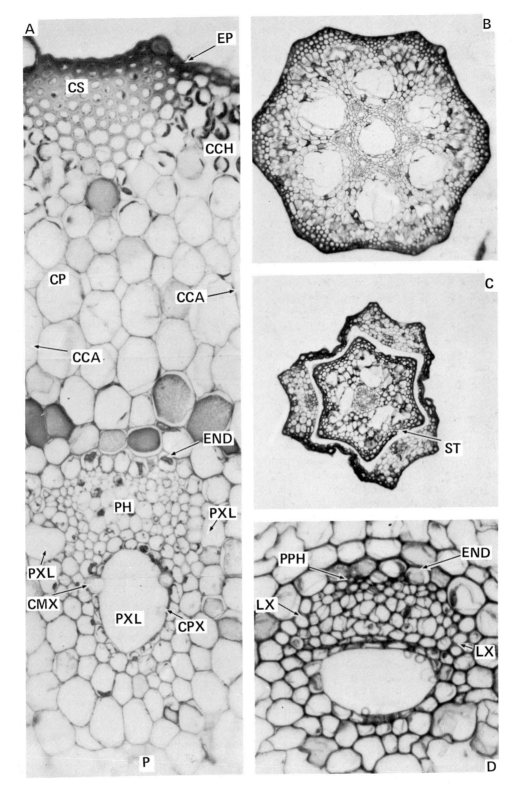

FIGURE 7–3. *A. Equisetum sylvaticum*, sector of a cross section of an aerial stem. *B. E. variegatum*, cross section of aerial stem. *C. E. scirpoides*, cross section of aerial stem just above a node and showing leaf sheath. *D. E. palustre*, cross section of a vascular bundle from the aerial stem. EP = epidermis; CS = cortical sclerenchyma; CCH = cortical chlorenchyma; CP = cortical parenchyma; CCA = cortical canal; END = endodermis; PH = phloem; PXL = protoxylem lacuna; CPX = carinal protoxylem; CMX = carinal metaxylem; P = pith; LX = lateral xylem; PPH = protophloem; ST = stoma.

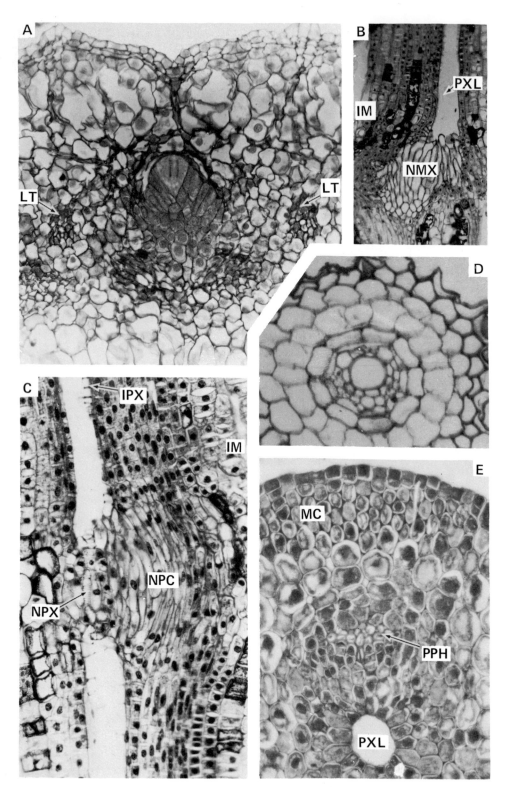

FIGURE 7–4. *A. Equisetum hyemale*, part of a cross section of a stem at the node. A lateral bud situated between two leaves of the sheath is shown. *B, C. E. sylvaticum*, portions of longitudinal sections of two nodes. *D. E. arvense*, cross section of a root. *E. E. kansanum*, cross section of part of a stem through the intercalary meristem. LT = leaf trace; IM = intercalary meristem; NMX = nodal metaxylem; IPX = internodal protoxylem; NPX = nodal protoxylem; NPC = nodal procambium; MC = meristematic collenchyma; PPH = protophloem; PXL = protoxylem lacuna.

two crescent-shaped accessory cells. Following the division to produce the two guard cells, the accessory cells grow over the guard cells such that it appears as if they have divided periclinally. A series of cell-wall ridges develop on the lower surface of the accessory cells and appear to radiate from the stomatal opening.

The vascular bundles of *Equisetum* are unique in structure. Each exhibits an inner group of xylem, the carinal group, which appears at maturity as a conspicuous protoxylem lacuna (PXL in Fig. 7–3, *A*; one shows in each bundle in *B*) with a few peripherally situated xylem elements (Fig. 7–3, *A*, *D*). A mass of phloem appears outside, and in radial alignment with, the carinal xylem (PH in Fig. 7–3, *A*). Protophloem is conspicuous as a line of distorted cells external to the metaphloem (PPH in Fig. 7–3, *D*). On either side of the metaphloem and spatially separated from the carinal xylem are two groups of lateral xylem (LX in Fig. 7–3, *D*) which may have their own protoxylem lacunae (PXL in Fig. 7–3, *A*). The only mature tissues of the stem traceable directly to the apical meristem are the carinal xylem and the protophloem; all others mature from cells produced by the intercalary meristem. Figure 7–4, *E* represents a section transverse to the intercalary meristem. PPH is protophloem and PXL is the carinal protoxylem lacuna. The section has passed through elements between rings of secondary wall so that they do not appear in the photograph. All other cells in the figure are meristematic; MC indicates meristematic collenchyma, which gives rise to the sclerenchyma in the hypodermal region. When lateral xylem matures (occasionally it is absent) above the intercalary meristem it does so in a definite pattern within a horizontal plane; it is endarch with or without protoxylem. It frequently appears to mature synchronously. Under no circumstances is the maturation of the lateral xylem a continuation of that of the carinal xylem.

The maturation pattern of the carinal xylem is not detectable from mature stems. It has in the past been described as endarch, on the assumption that there is uniform maturation within the carinal group and that the lateral xylem represents a continuation of the carinal group. A study of very young internodes of

nine species shows the carinal xylem to be mesarch, but evidence for this is lost by the expansion of the carinal canal. Figures 7–5, *A* to *E* represent younger to older internodes of *E. kansanum*, and *F* and *G* represent older internodes of *E. sylvaticum*. In *A* a single immature tracheid appears. In *B* there are two mature tracheids outside a nearly mature one. In *C* three mature tracheids are outside another that is just recognizably differentiating. In *D* an immature tracheid appears outside a group of five mature ones. In *E* the carinal canal has begun to form by cell separation and some cellular rupture, and at this stage evidence for mesarchy is destroyed, as is certainly the case in *F* and *G*. The radial longitudinal sections shown in Fig. 7–5, *H*, *I* show the earliest matured protoxylem elements, with their rings of secondary wall material greatly separated, bounded on their inner and outer sides by less stretched elements. The beginning of lacuna formation is shown in *I*.

The carinal canal in *Equisetum* is more than a mere intercellular canal. When it reaches nearly its full diameter, the protoxylem parenchyma cells that line it develop thickened walls. In addition, a few adjacent carinal metaxylem elements mature with massive pits in communication with the canal. The canal also comes to have a most intimate connection with the doughnut-shaped mass of metaxylem at the nodes (NMX in Fig. 7–2, *A*; Fig. 7–4, *B*; and its procambial precursor, NPC in Fig. 7–4, *C*). This all indicates the conducting nature of the canal; this may also be shown simply by placing an actively growing shoot in a solution of dye and observing the movement of the dye primarily through the canal.

Treacheary elements of *Equisetum* are specialized in a number of respects. Early-matured elements in parts of the plant body that elongate are generally quite ordinary annular or helical types (Fig. 27–8, *H*, left side). Later-formed annular elements in leaves of some species show vertically to horizontally oriented second-order secondary wall strands interconnecting bars of the first-order framework (Fig. 27–8, *F*). Certain annular elements show rings of wall material that are each in the form of a reticulum (Fig. 27–8, *G*, *J*, *K*). Other elements possess circular bordered pits between adjacent rings (Fig. 27–8, *H*, right

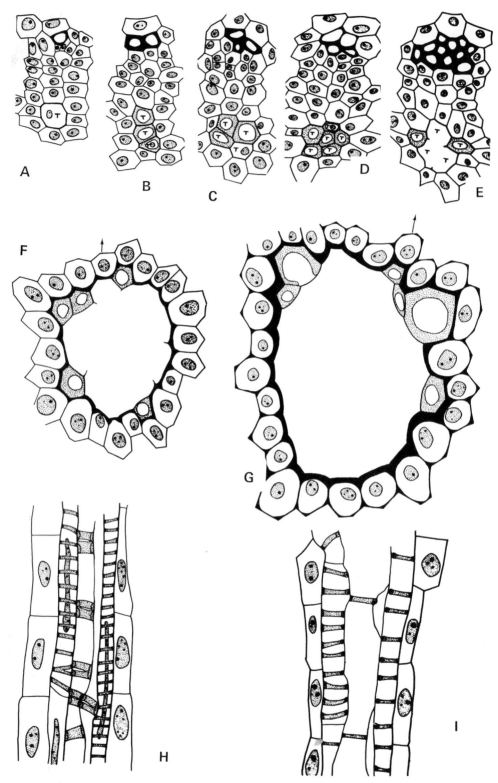

FIGURE 7–5. *A* to *E.* Portions of cross sections of vascular bundles in *Equisetum kansanum.* *A.* Third internode. *B.* Fourth internode. *C.* Fourth internode. *D.* Fifth internode. *E.* Sixth internode. *F, G. E. sylvaticum.* *F.* Seventeenth internode. *G.* Twentieth internode. *H. E. kansanum,* radial section through the carinal xylem in the eighth internode. *I. E. sylvaticum,* radial section through the carinal xylem in the twelfth internode. All after Bierhorst (1958c).

side) or gyres, especially the large peculiar metaxylem elements adjacent to the carinal canal (Fig. 27–8, *I*). Certain metaxylem elements of some species located in the lateral areas of the internodal bundles bear reticulate perforation plates (Fig. 27–10, *E*), but the vessels are apparently only a few cells long. The isodiametric metaxylem elements of the nodal doughnut frequently are perforate at points of contact with the base of the carinal protoxylem lacuna where large tylosoidal outgrowths have ruptured within the canal (Bierhorst, 1958d).

Equisetum shoots show a high degree of radial symmetry and anatomical uniformity in regions where adjacent nodes bear the same number of leaves. This is seen in Fig. 7–3, *C*, which shows a cross section of a whorl of three leaves enclosing a section of the internode above; the latter corresponds in form to the three leaves at the next higher node. Figure 7–6, *K*, is a drawing of three concentric leaf whorls around a stem apex as they appear in a cross section of the terminal bud. Each leaf was measured in terms of the degrees of circumference that it occupied within its whorl. All were expected to approximate 90 degrees and the measured range was 85 to 96 degrees, with a few degrees of experimental error probable. The alternation of leaves from whorl to whorl is also rather precise. A diagrammatic representation of the course of the early protoxylem strands is shown in Fig. 7–6, *A*. Here it can be seen that a carinal strand of xylem extends upward and outward into a leaf, but before leaving the cylinder it branches, sending off traces to both left and right. A pair of such branches come together to form the internodal carinal strand of the next higher internode. The protoxylem strands are continuous and distinct across the node in an old stem, passing on the inner edge of the doughnut of metaxylem (NPX in Fig. 7–4, *C*). Figure 7–4, *A* is a cross section at a level where the leaf traces are turning outward. Two leaf traces (LT) are shown. Toward the inside and on either side of the one on the left are seen a pair of traces that join at a higher level to form another internodal strand. A lateral bud is shown between a pair of leaves.

Equisetum shoots, except in diminutive species, characteristically show changing leaf numbers per whorl. The shoots are overall elongate and cone-shaped. A shoot originates from a bud on a rhizome, experiences an increase in shoot apex size and leaf number per whorl for possibly 3 to 8 plastochrons, then progressively decreases in these values for the rest of its growth period. With these changes come pronounced changes in symmetry and vascular anatomy that may be of particular value in comparing the genus with its presumed relatives and in comprehending morphogenetic factors in operation during ontogeny.

Whenever a change in leaf number occurs, the leaf alternation is altered such that one or more pairs of leaves in adjacent whorls fall within a vertical orthostichy. Figure 7–6, *M* shows a pair of whorls as they appear in cross section in the bud. The outer (older) whorl has seven leaves and the inner (younger) has five. Leaves 1b and 2c are within an orthostichy, as well as 1c and 2e. Note the massiveness of 1b and 1c and the fact that each has a double leaf trace. Figure 7–6, *L* similarly shows three whorls from another bud. The outer whorl has eight leaves, the middle one seven, and the inner one five. The nonalternating leaves, 4f and 5g, 3a and 4a, 3c and 4d, and 3d and 4e, all stand out as size anomalies within their own whorls. In general the following holds: At a point of decrease in leaf number from one whorl to the next younger one, the nonalternating leaves of the younger whorl are larger than anticipated and those of the older whorl are smaller than anticipated if radial symmetry is expected. Conversely, at a point of increase in leaf number, the nonalternating leaves of the older whorl are larger than anticipated and those of the younger one are smaller. The larger-than-anticipated leaves frequently have double traces that vary in their degree of doubleness. Figure 7–6, *N* (corresponding to *M*) and *O* (corresponding to *L*) are reconstructions of the steles showing the carinal xylem strands and leaf traces and how they divide and recombine within the system. Figure 7–6, *J* shows an opened-out reconstructed stele in its entirety. Bundles 1 through 12 correspond to the 12 leaves at the node drawn. Immediately above and alternating with the small leaf-trace stubs are larger ones that supplied the 12 branches at that node.

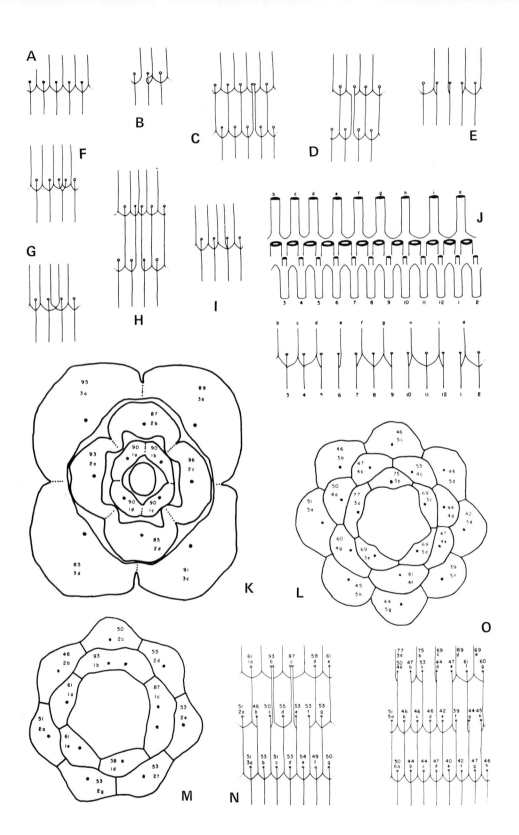

Nine bundles (a to i) extend into the upper internode. Immediately below this diagram is a corresponding diagram showing the course of the protoxylem strands only across the node and into the next internode. The entire range in vascular skeleton variation is indicated in Fig. 7–6, *A* to *I*. *A* is the ordinary condition where no change in leaf number occurs. *B*, *C*, and *D* are anomalous types where no change in leaf number occurs. *E* indicates vascularization accompanying a decrease in leaf number and *F* to *I* an increase. Several of these patterns, if repeated through the stem, would produce very different stelar types similar to those found in other taxa (e.g., the condition in *E*, where a strand is continued vertically in the same orthostichy, if repeated, would produce the pattern found in the fossil sphenopsid *Asterocalamites*).

Occasionally the presence of an anomalously large leaf within a single whorl in *Equisetum* triggers off spiral phyllotaxy (Fig. 7–1, *D*, *E*). Shoots exhibiting this feature are rare, but if one watches large colonies of species such as *E. hyemale* or *E. palustre* regularly from year to year a few will be found. So far only a single early stage in the initiation of spiral phyllotaxy has been seen, and it is the basis for the explanation that follows. A large leaf within a whorl (at a point of decrease in leaf number in the specimen) produces some distortion within the next younger whorl, and it comes to contact laterally not only the leaves within its own whorl, with which it is expected to fuse, but also a leaf in the whorl above. Anomalous interwhorl leaf fusion follows with spatial distortion transmitted up the shoot. In Fig. 7–7 the adjacent whorls are spatially separated for clarity; in reality they are all touching each other. Leaf 10 fused laterally to the large leaf of the next older

whorl; and leaf 1, which normally would have fused with 10, in turn fused with a leaf of younger age; and so the spiral was established. The spirals frequently come to an end and the whorled phyllotaxy again appears. No indication of how this is accomplished was seen. At any one point around a spiral shoot the anatomy is identical to that of shoots with a whorled organization, except for the orientation of the vascular bundles. The intercalary meristem is equally well developed and spirals up the shoot with the continuous leaf sheath.

Equisetum may present itself as a particularly useful tool in the study of nutation movements, as would other plants with varying phyllotaxy and differential leaf development. As a working hypothesis it is suggested that the circular movement of growing shoots is the result of a series of cell elongation spurts immediately below the points of insertion of leaves at a particular stage in development. Successive leaves in a spiral would reach the particular stage at successive times and a circular movement would be observed with time-lapse photography.

Roots of *Equisetum* show all the features normally attributed to such organs. At the root apex is a single apical cell beneath an ordinary type of calyptra. Mature portions show a small cortex (Fig. 7–4, *D*), a stele with a single large centrally placed metaxylem element, and two or three peripheral protoxylem points.

The appearance of roots attached to nodes (Fig. 7–1, *C*) is misleading. Such roots originate in various positions on or in close association with contained lateral buds. In some species a single root forms at the base of the bud, in others two. In *E. sylvaticum* several roots (two to four) are associated with each bud, some on the bud axis, others at the very base on the

FIGURE 7–6. *A*. Ordinary arrangement of carinal protoxylem strands in the node and two adjacent internodes of *Equisetum* where no change in leaf number occurs. *B* to *D*. Variations from the ordinary pattern, still where no change in leaf number occurs. *E*. Pattern of internodal and transnodal protoxylem where a decrease in leaf number occurs. *F* to *I*. Various patterns where there are increases in leaf number. *J*. Node of *Equisetum sylvaticum* opened out and drawn diagrammatically to show the entire vascular skeleton. A change in internodal bundle number from 12 to 9 is shown. The lower diagram shows protoxylem only. *K*. Outline drawing of a cross section of a bud of *E. hyemale* showing three concentric leaf whorls around the stem apex. The degrees of circumference that each leaf occupies is indicated. *L*, *M*. Drawings similar to *K* but of *E. palustre*. *N*, *O*. Diagrams of protoxylem skeletons. *N* corresponds to *M* and *O* to *L*. All after Bierhorst (1959).

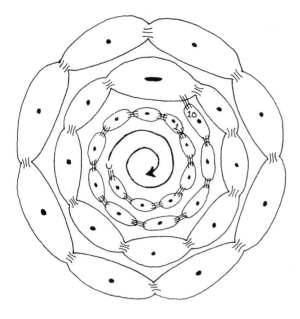

FIGURE 7–7. Diagram of a cross section of a bud of *Equisetum palustre* to show the origin of spiral phyllotaxy. In the actual specimen no space existed between adjacent whorls or gyres.

Equisetum arvense generally shows dimorphic shoots. The fertile ones bear a single terminal cone, are devoid of green color, are unbranched, and die soon after the spores are shed. Variation exists, however, in the expression of dimorphism. On the "typical" fertile shoot, the strobilus is completely formed and meiosis takes place below the soil at the end of a growing season. In certain colonies a high frequency of strobili stop growing at an earlier stage in the fall, and in the spring these grow into intermediate forms between more typical sterile and fertile shoots. The range of intermediacy includes shoots with differing chlorophyll content, degrees of branching, and length of life span.

In some species, a collar or annulus (AN in Fig. 7–8, *A*) is formed at the base of the strobilus. Its form and vascularization indicates that it is a ring of completely fused appendicular organs.

The sporangiophores appear mostly hexagonal from the outside except near the base and apex of the strobilus, where physical factors impose a different shape. They are attached to the strobilar axis by a medianly situated stalk (Fig. 7–8, *A*, *B*). Sporangia are attached to the inner surface around and parallel to the sporangiophore axis (in cross section in Fig. 7–9, *A* and in longitudinal section in *B*). When the sporangia are mature, the strobilar axis and, in some species, the internode above the annulus (AN, Fig. 7–8, *A*) elongate, separating adjacent sporangiophores. The sporangia dehisce along a line parallel to and on the side of the sporangiophore axis.

The strobilar axis shows a stelar structure differing from the vegetative axis in having a greater development of internodal zylem with relatively less xylem at the nodes. This results in a uniform netted appearance of the stele with well-defined gaps (G in Fig. 7–8, *C*). The simple sporangiophore traces arise from the more zigzag nodal ring, and immediately above them there are no gaps. A sporangiophore trace remains undivided until it reaches the end of the stalk, where it dichotomizes

outside of a leaf borne on the bud, and still others immediately below the bud on the tissues of the parental rhizome. Most, if not all, roots are exogenous in origin, although they do not appear so in certain planes of a section.

The sporangia of *Equisetum* are borne on peltate sporangiophores arranged in whorls within a compact terminal strobilus (Fig. 7–8, *A*, *D*). (The term "sporangiophore," literally sporangium carrier, is used in its broad sense without commitment to an interpretation that the organ is a leaf, stem, or other organ. The term "sporophyll," if applied to this or any other plant, implies a foliar interpretation.) The strobili may be borne terminally on the main shoot (e.g., *E. arvense* and *E. sylvaticum*) or on smaller lateral aerial stems (e.g., *E. hyemale* and *E. fluviatile*). In *E. hyemale*, a large terminal strobilus is often produced on a main shoot during its first season, and in the following season smaller strobili are produced on its laterals. In *E. fluviatile* there is often only a single strobilus on a main shoot, but certain less-common segregates produce large numbers of lateral ones as well. Occasionally anomalous indeterminate strobili are produced, especially in *E. arvense*. In these the axis is continued above the strobilus as a vegetative shoot (Fig. 7–8, *E*). This is of interest since certain fossil Equisetaceae exhibit this morphology.

FIGURE 7–8. *A*. Strobilus of *Equisetum palustre.* *B*. Portion of *A* enlarged and with part removed. *C, F*. Portions of strobili of *E. palustre* boiled in 3 per cent phloroglucinol in 95 per cent ethyl alcohol, then immersed in concentrated hydrochloric acid. *D*. Strobili of *E. hyemale*, one split open. *E*. Upper part of a strobilus of *E. arvense* that has continued as a vegetative shoot. AN = annulus; TR = trace to sporangiophore; G = cauline stelar gap.

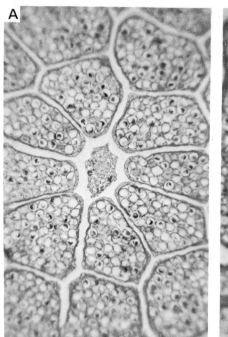
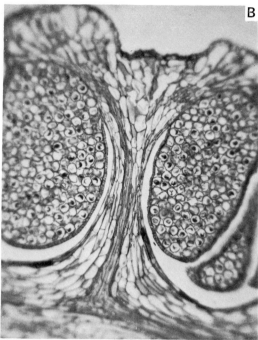

FIGURE 7–9. Transverse and longitudinal section of sporangiophore of *Equisetum palustre*.

(arrows in Fig. 7–8, *F*) several times to establish one ultimate vein for each sporangium.

Sporangiophores originate in whorls at the shoot tip in positions where leaves might be expected to form. The primordia are slightly broader and more dome-shaped than foliar primordia, and they do not possess recognizable single apical cells. There is little ontogenetic evidence in *Equisetum* to indicate a fundamental difference between its leaves and its sporangiophores, but presumably related fossil forms indicate that the organs have been distinct entities within the sphenopsid line since Devonian times.

The sporangia originate from single initials near the center of the sporangiophore apex while it is still a simple dome (Fig. 7–10, *A*). Later the dome expands laterally and the sporangia are pushed to and then beyond the margin to their final position on the lower side of the peltate tip (Fig. 7–10, *A* to *C*, *E*, *G*, *H*). The first division of the sporangial initial is either anticlinal or periclinal. When anticlinal, each of the resultant cells may divide independently in a periclinal plane to establish part of the primary archesporial

tissue, which may be added to again by still later periclinal divisions of outer cells. The sporangium of *Equisetum* differs then from the characteristic lycopod type in originating from a single instead of several sporangial initials and in a less clear-cut early differentiation of wall from sporogenous tissue. The sporangial wall of *Equisetum* eventually comes to be two or three cells in thickness (Fig. 7–10, *G*, *H*), and all but the outer layer disintegrate when maturity is approached. The walls of cells in the outer layer develop thin bands of helicoid secondary wall thickening which are presumably involved in dehiscence.

The early stages in the ontogeny of the *Equisetum* sporangium are not known with the degree of certainty implied in the above account. The uncertainty is due to the variability that exists within the individual species. Fagerlind (1961) states that it is difficult to say if the sporangia originate from one or from more than one initial. He suspects that development of the *Equisetum* sporangium may at first proceed according to the same schedule as is characteristic of the apical meristem of the vegetative shoot. He suggests that possibly

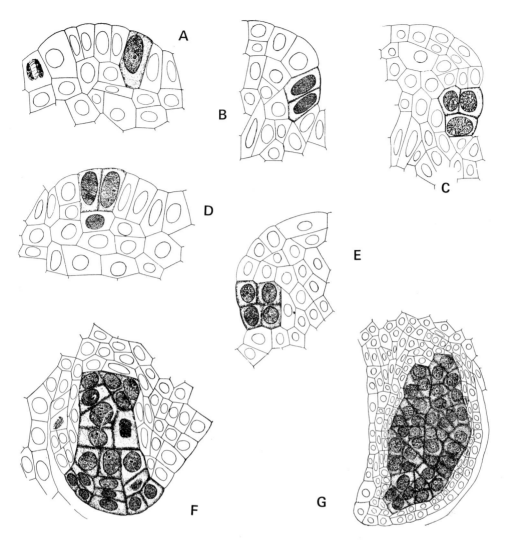

FIGURE 7–10. Sporangial development in *Equisetum hyemale*, after Hawkins (1907).

the apical cell is not seen because of the shape of the young sporangium.

Equisetum spores become spherical early in their development and show neither monolete nor trilete markings. As they mature, four strap-shaped acellular elators are deposited on their outer surface, presumably by the free liquid in the sporangial cavity. When first deposited they are wrapped around the spherical spores, but as the spore mass dries out the elators react by uncoiling (Fig. 7–11, *A*). They continue to respond to humidity changes at and after shedding. Elators have been interpreted as functioning primarily to separate spores, but they more often seem to keep spore groups entangled and to supply lifting power when exposed to external air currents. The viability of the spores is very brief, reported to range from 1 to 48 hours after shedding.

Equisetum spores are green and germinate readily on a wet substratum. The spore expands, sheds its outer coat, and usually divides within 2 days. The first division produces a small rhizoid initial (Fig. 7–11, *C*), which soon elongates (Fig. 7–11, *D*), while its larger sister cell establishes a block meristem (Fig. 7–11, *E*). From the latter a basal pad

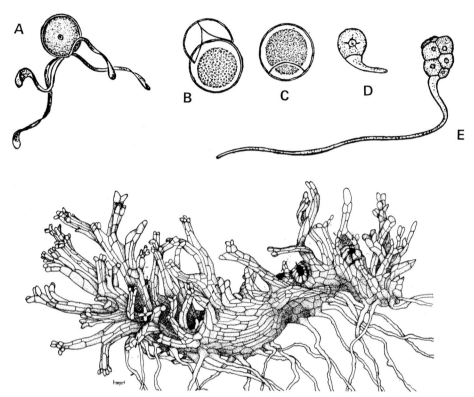

FIGURE 7–11. *A.* Spore of *Equisetum maximum,* after Wettstein (1911). *B–E.* Stages in spore germination of *E. arvense,* after Sadebeck (1902). *F.* Gametophyte of *E. scirpoides,* after Walker (1937).

with upright lobes and ventrally situated rhizoids is eventually produced (Fig. 7–11, *F*; Fig. 7–12, *F*). The gametophyte may continue to grow for some years in cultivation if fertilization and subsequent sporophyte development do not occur. The meristematic behavior of the gametophyte has not been completely described. Mature field-grown gametophytes usually do not exceed a few millimeters, but W. C. Steere in an address to the Botanical Society of America related that he had seen them as "large as half-dollars" on the black muck in subarctic regions of Alaska. Antheridia are most often produced only on the upright lobes (Fig. 7–12, *A, B*), but occasionally they appear on the pad (Fig. 7–11, *F*). Archegonia most often are produced on the pad only, but in at least one species they are intermixed with antheridia on the lobes.

The gametophytes of *Equisetum* are rarely seen in nature. There are several reasons for this. First, to the naked eye the young ones appear as filamentous algal growths or masses of moss protonemata and are also often obscured by other small plants growing in association with them. Second, they often die while quite young, as a result of drying, and in a given season very few, if any, will mature. If young sporophytes are not produced or die while quite young, the gametophyte, even if of mature size, is not likely to be noticed. For a complete life cycle to be realized in a given year in most areas where *Equisetum* grows, the rainfall must be unusually heavy and uniformly distributed chronologically.

The degree of bisexuality or unisexuality various among the species of *Equisetum* from possibly complete unisexuality to variable bisexuality influenced by environmental factors. It is quite possible that incipient or complete heterothallism exists in the genus without accompanying heterospory. This is found among land plants in bryophytes and possibly in a few filicalean ferns as *Ceratopteris*.

The archegonia (Fig. 7–12, *C* to *E*) of

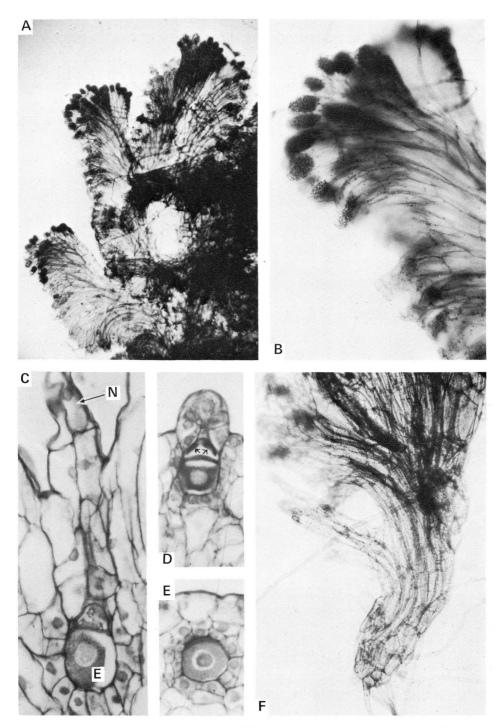

FIGURE 7–12. *A.* Portion of a gametophyte of *Equisetum arvense* showing many antheridia along the margins of the upright lobes. *B.* Portion of *A* enlarged. *C* to *E.* Archegonia of *E. hyemale*. *C.* Mature. *D.* Immature. *E.* Mature and in cross section through the ventor. *F.* Base of the plant in *A* and *B*, showing rhizoids. N = neck; E = egg.

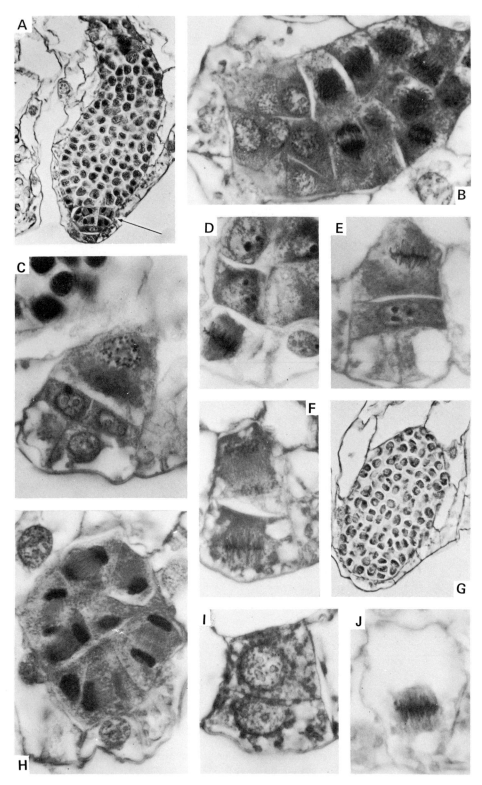

FIGURE 7–13. Antheridia of *Equisetum hyemale* in longitudinal section and in various stages of development. Explanation in the text.

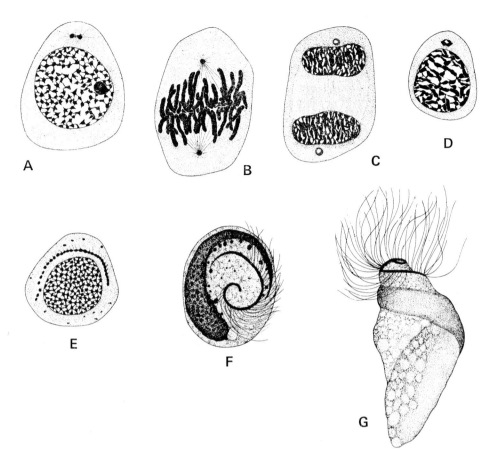

FIGURE 7–14. *A* to *G*. Stages in the development of the sperm of *Equisetum arvense* and the mature sperm, after Sharp (1912).

Equisetum have necks mostly three to five cells long and always four cells in cross section. The axial row consists of egg, ventral canal cell, and generally two neck canal cells that are often aligned side by side (two arrows in Fig. 7–12, *D*). Around the venter is a conspicuous jacket (*C, E*). Cell lineages are as in the lycopods. The cells surrounding the archegonium, as well as those of the archegonial neck, often expand, causing conspicuous stretching of the archegonium and forcing the egg into a deep-seated position (Fig. 7–12, *C*). In *E. bogatense* the terminal neck cells are extremely attenuated and coiled about each other (Hauke, 1968) and appear rhizoidlike. They may well serve to retain capillary water and facilitate fertilization.

The antheridia are slightly elongate structures containing many sperm at maturity (Fig.

7–13, *G*). The wall proper (i.e., that traceable to the antheridial initial) is only a small group of cells at its apical end. Usually a single antheridial initial divides periclinally (Fig. 7–13, *J*) to establish the two-celled antheridium (I). From the outer cell, by anticlinal divisions only, the single-layered wall is formed, and from the inner cell, by a series of quite synchronous divisions (H), the spermatids are established (G). Variation in the ontogenetic pattern exists, at least in *Equisetum hyemale*. In this species many antheridia on gametophytes grown only on mineral nutrients in the laboratory did not show the early separation of wall from spermatogenous tissue at the first periclinal division of the initial cell. Instead they showed recognizably different patches of fertile tissue separately derived from the wall layer at different times. In Fig. 7–13, *A* a

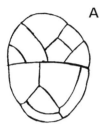 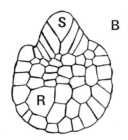

FIGURE 7–15. Two stages in the development of the embryo of *Equisetum arvense*, after Sadebeck (1902). S = stem; R = root.

patch of spermatogenous cells all in telophase is indicated by the arrow; the rest of the cells in the antheridium are advanced spermatids. In *B* two patches of tissue, one in prophase and the other in anaphase or early telophase, are shown. In Fig. 7–13, *D*, *F* periclinal divisions are shown in the surface layer, either initiating a new spermatogenous patch or adding a second layer to the wall, as occasionally occurs. Slightly later stages are shown in *C* and *E*. It is particularly interesting to note that the addition of later-formed fertile patches in the antheridium has its analog in the ontogeny of the sporangium of *Equisetum*.

The antheridial wall is composed of a ring of cells radiating from a point. At this point an intercellular space through which the spermatozoids escape is formed. The cells separate more and more to extend straight up or even outward. As the jacket cells begin to separate, the vigorous sperm crowd near the exit and pop out in single file. The antheridium is empty before the orientation of the jacket cells is changed.

Spermatogenesis proceeds as follows. A centriole, or centriole-like body, appears in the mother cell of two spermatids. It divides

(Fig. 7–14, *A*) and each of the two migrate to opposite poles. Mitosis then occurs (*B*, *C*). Toward the end of telophase the two centrioles begin to enlarge and soon come to appear as a ring of granules (*C*, *D*). The ring appears to open out as a chain, and soon one flagellum is seen associated with each "basal granule" (*E*). The nucleus progressively changes in shape to become helicoid (*F*) and later the entire chain with flagella attaches itself to the sperm. Throughout most of the botanical literature the term "blepharoplast" has been used variously to indicate the string of granules to which the flagella are attached, the ring of granules, and also the single granule in earlier ontogeny.

The embryogeny of *Equisetum*, which is incompletely described and poorly documented, shows variation within individual species. The first division of the zygote is transverse (as indicated in a somewhat later stage in Fig. 7–15, *A*). From the upper cell, after a very few divisions, the pronounced apical cell of the stem (S in Fig. 7–15, *B*) is produced. The first leaf, which comes to be associated with one to three others in a whorl, may be embryonic in origin, or it may form from the stem apex. The first root may originate from the entire lower embryonic hemisphere with its apical cell medianly situated, or from one side (R in Fig. 7–15, *B*). The other side of such a lower hemisphere has been termed a weakly developed foot.

8

Fossil Equisetopsida (Sphenopsida)

The class Equisetopsida is presented here in its classical sense and is equated to the Articulatae or Sphenopsida. The four orders included with their known chronological ranges are the Hyeniales (Devonian), Pseudoborniales (Devonian), Sphenophyllales (Mississippian, Pennsylvanian, Permian), and Equisetales (Upper Devonian to present). The Devonian genera *Climceophyton*, *Sphondylophyton*, *Broeggeria*, *Prosseria*, and *Haspia*, which may be of hyenialean affinity, are not well enough known to be placed. *Protohyenia* has recently been reduced to synonymy with *Pseudosporochnus*. This assemblage of orders seemed until recently a most natural grouping, but since the work of Leclercq and Schweitzer (1965) the position and affinities of the Hyeniales are being reconsidered. The order is only tentatively retained here rather than being discarded and its component genera placed in the Cladoxylales. This further emphasizes the temporal nature of any system of classification of biological forms, especially one that is not based on complete knowledge of all the life cycles and the structure and ontogeny of all component parts.

The Hyeniales includes the poorly differentiated genera *Hyenia* with six species and *Calamophyton* with three. These were rather small plants (Fig. 8–2, *A* is approximately natural size and *B* about one-half natural size). *Hyenia* produced upright, unbranched, or once-forked shoots from a horizontal rhizome. *Calamophyton* produced upright digitately branched shoots. Its rhizome, if it had one, has not been described. Both genera bore imprecisely whorled one-, two-, or three-forked leaves that were three-dimensional in *Calamophyton* (Fig. 8–2, *D*) and planate in *Hyenia* (Fig. 8–2, *A*),

FIGURE 8–1. *A. Pseudobornia*, after Nathorst (1902). *B. Calamites* reconstruction, from Hirmer (1927). *C. Annularia*, after Remy and Remy (1959). *D. Sphenophyllum*, after Stur (1887).

FIGURE 8–2. *A. Hyenia elegans* reconstruction, after Kräusel and Weyland (1932a). *B. Calamophyton primaevum* reconstruction, after Kräusel and Weyland (1926). *C, D. C. bicephalum*, after Leclercq and Andrews (1960). A single sporangiophore is shown in *C* and two sterile appendages appear in *D. E, F. Eviostachya hoegi* sporangiophore, after Leclercq (1957). It is shown artificially extended in *E*.

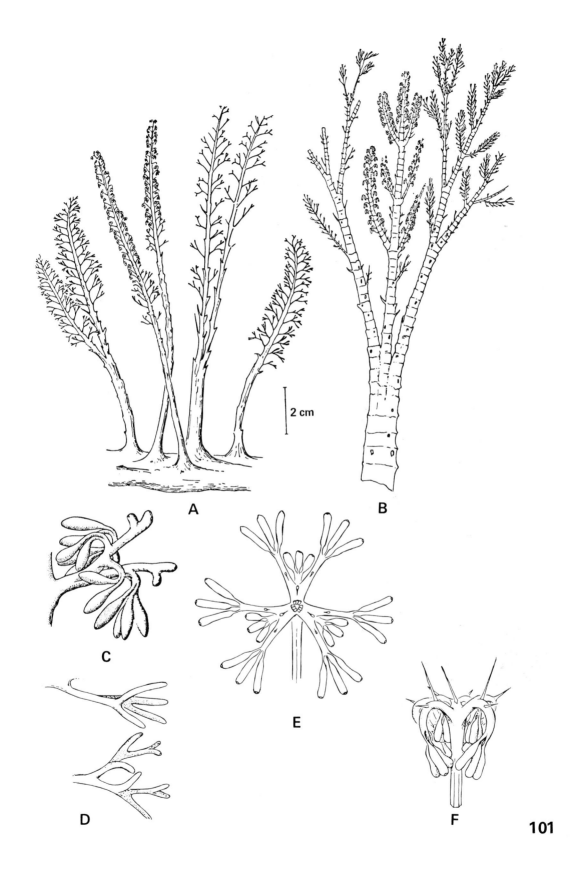

2 cm

A

B

C

D

E

F

and whorled sporangiophores. In some species the sporangiophores occurred in zones alternating with zones of leaves. In others the sporangiophores were in terminal groupings. The stem of *Calamophyton* was originally described as jointed (as appears in the reconstruction of Kräusel and Weyland; Fig. 8–2, *B*), but the joints are inconsistent in occurrence and have been interpreted as fossilization cracks (Leclercq and Andrews, 1960). In *Hyenia* (*Hyenopsis*) *vogtii*, at least, lateral branches of the upright stem were not axillary but, very significantly, took the place of leaves within the phyllotactic series (Høeg, 1942). *Calamophyton bicephalum* is the only species in the order whose stem is know anatomically (Leclercq and Schweitzer, 1965) and it shows a typical cladoxylalean stele (see Chapter 9). This is the prime source of doubt regarding accurate taxonomic placement of the Hyeniales. Some compression specimens of *Hyenia* show striations that may be related to the internal distribution of xylem.

Accurate information on the morphology of the sporangiate fructifications has only recently become available (Leclercq and Andrews, 1960; Leclercq, 1961; Bonamo and Banks, 1966). The sporangiophore of *Calamophyton bicephalum* (Fig. 8–2, *C*) and that of *C. primaevum* were once-forked structures. Each of the two halves bore three lateral branches, each of which terminated in a pair of elongate sporangia and a terminal, sterile tip. In *Hyenia elegans* the sporangiophores occurred in whorls of six on the stem but were inserted as three pairs. Each sporangiophore was similar in morphology to one of the halves of that of *Calamophyton*. It appears that a pair of sporangiophores in *Hyenia* was the morphological equivalent of an entire one in *Calamophyton*, and they may have differed only in the time at which the bifurcation occurred and in the degree of development of the common stalk. This kind of interpretation may be made in this case as well as in analogous instances in vascular plants, as ontogenetic separation of two parts of the same structure has been shown in several extant forms. One well-known instance is the ontogenetic shifting of the sporangium of *Lycopodium* to a distinctly cauline position. Another is the separation of flowers that originate from the same axillary

bud into a line within a vertical pit on the inflorescence axis in certain palms. Still another is illustrated by the false position of the basal ovule in certain dicot carpels where it originates from the base of the carpel but later appears to be inserted directly upon the receptacle with its own independent vascular supply. Such occurrences make it very difficult to interpret structures on which we have no ontogenetic information.

Hyenialean spores, where known, are rather large, globose, and trilete. Sporangial dehiscence was probably longitudinal.

The Pseudoborniales is known only from a single species, *Pseudobornia ursina* of the Upper Devonian (Fig. 8–1, *A*). This was a plant with stems up to 10 cm in diameter. It had distinct nodes each with a whorl of about four leaves. Each leaf forked several times near its base and then was finely pinnate in its distal parts. The plant bore lax strobili, some longer than 30 cm, with whorled bracts and sporangiophores. Even though the plant has been known since Nathorst's description of 1902, the sporangiophores were accurately described only as recently as 1964 (Leclercq). Each sporangiophore was an undivided, horizontally oriented segment that bore more than 30 crowded sporangia. The distal part of the sporangiophore was upturned and divided into two free segments with truncated tips. The affinities of the order are obscure, but it may belong close to the Sphenophyllales.

The Sphenophyllales were relatively small and more or less herbaceous plants. The generic name *Sphenophyllum* is applied to stems, roots, leaves, and a few strobili that have been found in organic attachment. These plants bore thin jointed stems with nonalternating ribs. At each node was a whorl of from 6 to 18 leaves (Fig. 8–1, *D*). Branching was sometimes dichotomous and sometimes by the formation of laterals at the nodes in alternating positions with the leaves. Each leaf was constricted at the base and expanded distally and supplied by a single trace that dichotomized within the lamina (Fig. 8–5, *B* to *E*). One of the largest specimens ever recorded (Seward, 1898) was 85 cm long, 4 mm in diameter, and bore a branch 61 cm long. This suggests a habit that was lax and probably in part prostrate or approaching viny. In overall appearance

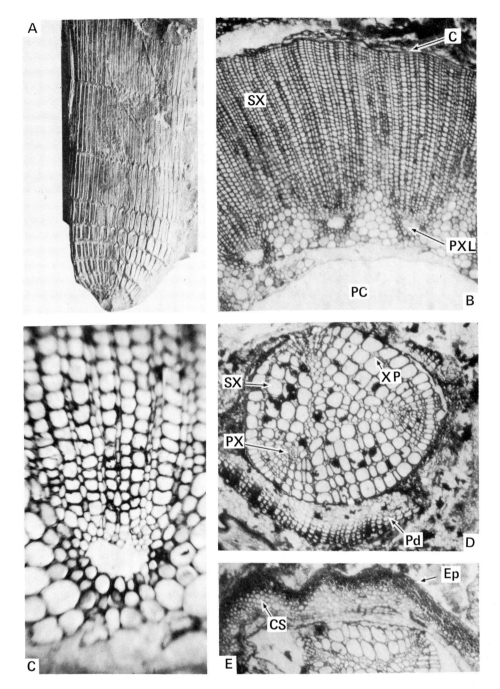

FIGURE 8–3. *A. Calamites suckowi* pith cast, after Jongmans and Kukuk (1913). *B. Calamites* sp., cross section of a portion of the stem. *C.* Portion of *B* enlarged. *D. Sphenophyllum plurifoliatum*, cross section of stem. *E.* As *D*, but of a younger stem. C = cambium; SX = secondary xylem; PXL = protoxylem canal; XP = xylem parenchyma; PX = protoxylem; Pd = periderm; Ep = epidermis; CS = cortical sclerenchyma.

Sphenophyllum probably very closely approximated the extant, rubiaceous genus *Galium*. The structure of the leaf (Fig. 8–5, *A*), with its reduced chorenchymatous tissue and dermal and hypodermal sclerenchyma, may be described as mesomorphic to xeromorphic, but its habitat was within the great coal swamps. One species is reported to have had succulent leaves.

Stems of *Sphenophyllum* had a cortex that was in part sclerenchymatous (Fig. 8–3, *E*) and a central protostele. The primary xylem was triangular in cross section, and at the tip of each arm was one (rarely two) protoxylem pole. In a few instances, protoxylem canals have been reported. The stems produced typical periderm (Pd in Fig. 8–3, *D*) which was deep-seated in origin and resulted in the eventual loss of all external primary tissues. A vascular cambium appeared first in the bays between xylem arms and in older stems came to surround the stele. The secondary xylem contained small tracheids opposite the protoxylem poles and larger ones elsewhere. Vertical strands of small parenchyma cells (XP in Fig. 8–3, *D*) occurred at the corners of the secondary xylem tracheids as they appear in cross section. Tracheary pitting was multiseriate to scalariform.

Vegetatively the sphenophylls are reasonably uniform, in sharp contrast to the broad morphological range exhibited by their sporangiate fructifications. The following is the classification used by Boureau (1964) and followed here:

Sphenophyllalean cones
  Sphenophyllaceae
     Sphenophyllostachys (= *Bowmanites*)
     Peltastrobus
     Sphenostrobus
     Litostrobus
  Cheirostrobaceae
     Cheirostrobus
  Tristachyaceae
     Tristachya

Of the 31 species of *Sphenophyllostachys* listed by Boureau, only three or four have been found in organic connection with *Sphenophyllum*. These are mostly distinct cones with whorls of free or laterally fused bracts and whorls of sporangiophores that were either free or fused in part to the bracts. A part of the morphological range is indicated by the genera described below.

Sphenophyllostachys dawsoni (Fig. 8–4, *D*; Fig. 8–5, *G, H, L*) is the type species of the genus. It was a cone about 20 mm in diameter with 14 to 20 bracts, in a whorl, which were fused at their bases to form a cup. There were 12 to 40 sporangiophores, apparently in a single whorl, but their stalks varied in length and multiple whorls therefore are suggested. Each sporangiophore was fused in part to the cup and bore a single, recurved sporangium.

Sphenophyllostachys aquensis (Fig. 8–5, *J, K*) was a cone about 3 cm long and 0.5 cm in diameter. At each node there was a whorl of free bracts and a whorl of sporangiophores, each of which was axillary, short, and bore a single sporangium.

Sphenophyllostachys majus (Fig. 8–5, *I*) bore a whorl of dichotomized bracts and a whorl of sporangiophores above. Each sporangiophore, although shown separate from the bract in the reconstruction, is described as coalescent to a bract at the base by Boureau. Four sporangia were borne at the tip of each of the extended sporangiophores.

Sphenophyllostachys fertilis (Fig. 8–5, *F*) was a cone 6 cm long and 2.5 cm in diameter. At each node there was a whorl of six groups of three appendages each. The lower two of each group of three seems to have been a single bract divided at its base. The upper appendage of each triad has been called a compound sporangiophore. It had a short axis and bore a cluster of about 16 branches, each ending with a pair of pendant sporangia.

Peltastrobus, known from one species (Baxter, 1950; Leisman and Graves, 1964), represents a further extension of the kind of complexity seen in *Sphenophyllostachys fertilis*. Within the cone of *Peltastrobus* there were superimposed whorls of fertile and sterile bracts. Each whorl contained six free components. Each sterile bract was forked once. Each fertile one subtended a cluster of five peltate sporangiophores with essentially a common attachment. Each sporangiophore bore on its lower surface an outer whorl of eight stalked sporangia and an inner whorl of six to eight sessile ones.

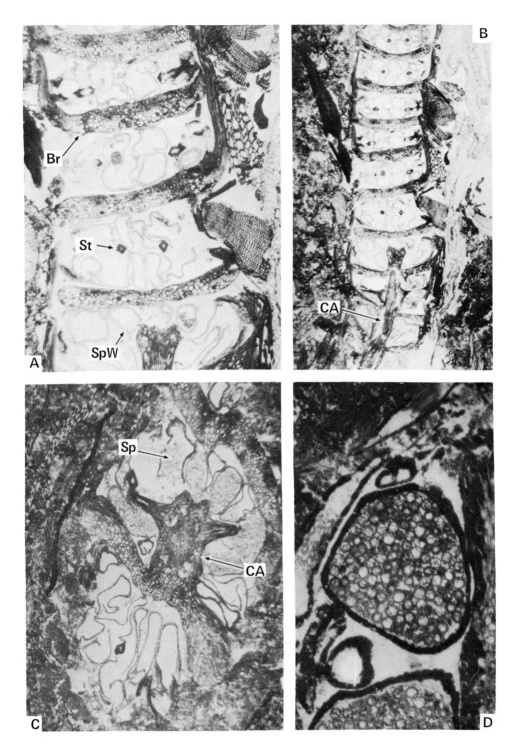

FIGURE 8–4. *A* to *C. Calamostachys binneyana. D. Sphenophyllostachys dawsoni.* Br = bract;
St = stalk of sporangiophore; SpW = sporangium wall; CA = cone axis; Sp = sporangium.

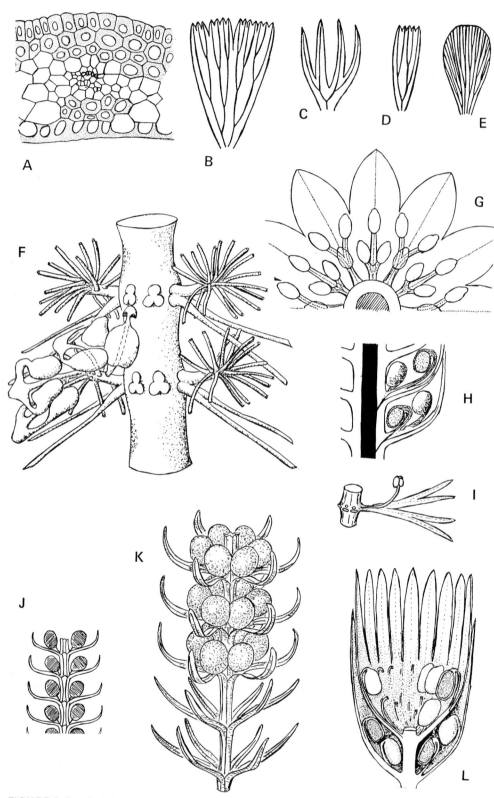

FIGURE 8–5. *A. Sphenophyllum*, cross section of leaf, after Renault (1881). *B* to *E*. Leaves of *Sphenophyllum*, redrawn after Janssen (1939). By permission Illinois State Museum. *B. S. majus*. *C. S. myriophyllum*. *D. S. tenuifolium*. *E. S. verticillatum*. *F. Sphenophyllostachys fertilis*, after Le Clercq (1935). *G, H. S. Dawsoni*, from Hirmer (1927). *I. S. majus*, from Walton (1940). *J, K. S. aquensis*, after Remy and Remy (1959). *L. S. dawsoni*, from Walton (1940).

Litostrobus, known from a single species (Mamay, 1954), was a cone about 3.5 mm in diameter with 12 basally fused bracts and six sporangia at a node. Each sporangium was borne erect on a stalk inserted directly above every other bract. A trace from the axial stele supplied four bracts and two sporangia.

Sphenostachys, also known from a single species (Levittan and Barghoorn, 1948), was a cone about 9 mm in diameter. It bore 16 appendages at a node. There were 16 sporangia attached to the basal disc close to the cone axis. The cone axis is unique among known sphenophyllalean cones in having a tetrarch primary xylem mass instead of a triarch one.

Tristachya, known from two species (Lilpop, 1937; Remy and Remy, 1961), was an axis bearing whorled appendages. In the sterile basal portion there were six wedge-shaped leaves in a whorl. Above these there were whorls of similar leaves in threes, and in the axil of each was a cone. Each cone bore whorls of peltate sporangiophores, each with three rather large (4 to 5 mm diameter) spherical sporangia.

Cheirostrobus, known from one species (Scott, 1898), was described from one cone fragment 4 cm in diameter and 10 cm long. The whole structure was quite compact. At each node were 12 appendages. Each appendage branched in the vertical plane. The lower part then divided into three in the horizontal plane and extended outward, then upward, near the margin of the cone. The upper part of each appendage also divided into three in the horizontal plane and each of its parts became situated directly above one of the parts of the lower branch. Each branch of the upper part was extended outward and bore four very long sporangia that were attached distally and extended back toward the cone axis. There were, therefore, 144 sporangia at each node in the cone.

Mesidiophyton, described by Leisman (1964a), bore a cone similar in structure to *Litostrobus*. It differed from the latter primarily in that the sporangia were in part reflexed, and it appears that the stalk of the sporangiophore was in part fused to its sporangium.

The walls of sphenophyllalean sporangia were one to several cells thick. It is possible that all were more than one cell thick in an early stage of development, but this cannot be demonstrated. In any case, the outer wall layer bore thickenings associated with the dehiscence mechanism. The spores were in some species monolete, in others trilete. Heterospory was reported to have occurred in *Sphenophyllostachys verticillatus*, but this has been challenged.

The monotypic Devonian genus *Eviostachya* (Stockmans, 1948; Leclercq, 1957, is somewhat enigmatic in that the complexities of its sporangiophores and triangular stele suggest the Sphenophyllales, but the absence of sterile bracts in its cone is unknown elsewhere in that order. The cones were up to 5.6 cm long and 8 mm in diameter. Each cone bore a single whorl of six bracts below the fertile region within which were up to 12 whorls of sporangiophores. There were three pairs of sporangiophores in a whorl, one pair situated at each angle of the triangular stele of the cone axis. Each sporangiophore was divided into three parts (shown extended laterally in Fig. 8–2, *E* and in their natural position in *F*), two larger laterals, and a central shorter one, each terminating with three sporangia.

The order Equisetales is a large and diverse group but certainly a natural one. In some taxonomic systems it is considered as two or three orders, but numerous recently described genera emphasize a morphological continuum with no hiatus of ordinal magnitude. The order is important in that it was floristically dominant in parts of the world during Carboniferous and Permian times. Even more significantly, the group illustrates morphological trends, degrees of flexibility as well as conservativeness, and other lessons that have interpretative carryover to other taxa. Boureau (1964) classifies the order as follows:

Order Equisetales
Family Archaeocalamitaceae (five form genera, Upper Devonian and Mississippian)
Autophyllitaceae (5 form genera, Mississippian and Pennsylvanian)
Apocalamitaceae (4 form genera, Pennsylvanian to Cretaceous)

Calamitaceae (20 form genera, Mississippian to Permian)

Sorocaulaceae (3 form genera, Pennsylvanian to Triassic)

Neurophyllaceae (1 genus, Permian)

Phyllothecaceae (6 form genera, Pennsylvanian to Lower Cretaceous)

Schizoneuraceae (4 form genera, Pennsylvanian to Jurassic)

Equisetaceae (*Equisetites*, Triassic, Jurassic; *Equisetum*, Cretaceous to present)

The family Calamitaceae is the best known of the fossil articulates and in many ways the most fascinating. The generic name *Calamites*, is generally applied to the whole plants. Most of the described specimens are fragmentary and are known under one of the following form generic names:

Foliage and small stems (mostly impressions and compressions)
    Asterophyllites
    Annularia
    Dicalamophyllum
Roots
    Asteromyelon and five others
Stems (impressions and pith casts)
    Calamites
Stems (petrified)
    Arthropitys
    Calamodendron
    Arthroxylon
Sporangiate fructifications
    Palaeostachya
    Calamostachys
    Cingularia and six or seven others

The calamites in appearance were much like the extant *equiseta* but were trees (Fig. 8–1, *B*), some more highly branched than others. The longest piece found was about 10 m, but they probably grew to a height of 20 to 30 m. Andrews and Agashe (1965) described a petrified stem 40 cm in diameter. The stems showed conspicuous nodes and internodal ridges (Fig. 8–3, *A*) that alternated across nodes in many species. Leaves were in alternate whorls, inserted in one of the two

patterns in Fig. 8–6, *J*, *K*. Those of *Asterophyllites* were very small and linear (seen in cross section in Fig. 8–6, *C*), while those of *Annularia* (Fig. 8–1, *C*) were up to several centimeters long. In both they were free at the base, although in the latter some basal fusion may have existed. Branches of the stem were nodal and interfoliar, not necessarily occupying all possible positions, as in *Equisetum*. The equisetoid nature of the giant horsetails was also apparent in the internal structure of the stems. Most had a pith cavity formed as the result of the early cessation of growth of a complete pith as the axis continued to expand laterally. A ring of collateral bundles occurred around the pith in the young stems, and in each was a conspicuous protoxylem canal or lacuna. Primary xylem maturation has been described as endarch, but the same problems involved in such designation exists here as in the living *Equisetum*, in which the primary xylem may appear endarch in the mature stem, but ontogeny reveals mesarchy. A cambium appeared between the xylem and the phloem and also in the interfascicular regions, giving the older stem the appearance shown in Fig. 8–3, *B*, *C*. The relatively simple cortex of the young stem is well known; the cortex probably grew uniformly in several dimensions to compensate for the addition of secondary vascular tissues deeper in the axis.

One shoot apex is known with good cellular preservation (Melchior and Hall, 1961). At its summit there is a large and prominent apical cell as in *Equisetum*. Distal to the apical cell there is some evidence of intercalary growth.

It is thought that the calamites were in general rhizomatous plants (Fig. 8–1, *B*). The aerial stems at their points of attachment tapered conspicuously (Fig. 8–3, *A*). The increase in diameter in this region is correlated with an increase in leaves per node, ridges per internode, and internal length. These same features are seen in the extant *equiseta* but to a less conspicuous extent. Eggert (1962) showed that the dimensions of the primary body vary at different levels of the soma. The pith and cortex is larger in larger stems. The larger stems bear larger leaves. The aerial shoot probably developed in a manner

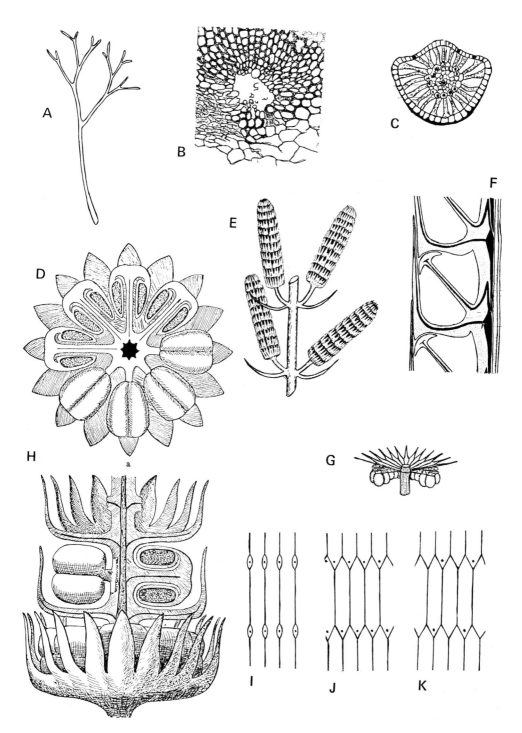

FIGURE 8–6. *A. Archaeocalamites radiatus*, leaf, after Kidston and Jongmans (1917). *B. Proto-calamites pittycurensis*, cross section through the stem at the protoxylary canal, from D. H. Scott (1920–1923). *C. Asterophyllites* cross section of leaf, after H. H. Thomas (1911). *D, H. Calamo-stachys binneyana*, after Zimmermann (1930), by permission of Gustav Fischer Verlag, Jena. *E. Palaeostachya decacnema*, after Delevoryas (1955). *F. P. vera*, after Hickling (1907). *G. Cin-gularia typica*, after C. E. Weiss (1876). *I* to *K*. Diagrams to show stem ridges and leaf trace insertions, from Hirmer (1927). *I. Asterocalamites. J, K. Calamites.*

109

similar to that observed in *Equisetum*, with the establishment of many nodes and internodes in a subterranean bud.

The calamite cone *Calamostachys*, known best in *C. binneyana* (Fig. 8–4, *A* to *C*; Fig. 8–6, *D*, *H*), was relatively compact, 3 to 4 cm long, and up to 7.5 mm in diameter. It was composed of alternating whorls of sterile bracts and very equisetoid sporangiophores. The 12 bracts in a whorl were fused at the base. The tangential section to the cone in Fig. 8–4, *A*, *B* shows the cone axis (CA) in part and the whorls of bracts fused as units. The sporangiophores were six in a whorl and their stalks (ST) were oriented at right angles to the cone axis and inserted midway between two whorls of sterile bracts. There were four sporangia attached to the peltate sporangiophore tip. Some species of *Calamostachys* were heterosporous, usually with megasporangia in one part of the cone and microsporangia in another. Some individual sporangia have been described with microspores at one end and megaspores at another.

Calamocarpon, described by Baxter (1963), is a cone of the *Calamostachys* type, but its megasporangia each contained a single large megaspore (2.7 by 0.7 mm) and its female gametophyte was retained within the cone for some time at least.

Palaeostachya (Fig. 8–6, *E*, *F*) was similar in many respects to *Calamostachys*. Its sporangiophores, however, were inserted in a near-axillary position to the sterile bract whorl and oriented at approximately 45 degrees to the cone axis. In most species the trace to the peltate and equisetoid sporangiophore extended upward in the cortex of the cone axis, then downward and out into the sporangiophore stalk (Fig. 8–6, *F*). It is easy to interpret the sporangiophore stalk as folded downward and in part fused to the cone axis, but it is very difficult to describe this in morphogenetic terms. If, in general, traces to appendicular organs originate as the result of stimili originating in their apices and diffusing proximally the vascular loop becomes a special problem. Such loops are known elsewhere (e.g., in the supplies to the scutellum of certain grasses, in the supplies to flowers in certain palms, and, possibly in a modified form, in the supplies to a "flower" cluster in *Gnetum*).

Each of these may represent a special case in itself and all are not necessarily explainable in the same terms.

In the cone genera *Mazostachys*, *Cingularia* (Fig. 8–6, *G*), and *Stachannularia* the sporangiophores were associated spatially not with the whorl of bracts below, but with the one above. The sporangiophores of these bore two, four, and one pendant sporangia each, respectively.

The Archaeocalamitaceae is the oldest and interpreted as the most primitive family of the Equisetales. Its stem casts (*Archaeocalamites*) showed ridges and grooves of the calamite type and were nonalternating (Fig. 8–6, *I*). Its leaves were also nonalternating and dichotomously branched (Fig. 8–6, *A*), a feature shared with some genera of the Autophyllitaceae. The petrified stem (= *Protocalamites*) was like that of *Calamites* in many regards, but most, if not all, primary xylem matured in a centripetal direction (Fig. 8–6, *B*). It was thus exarch or weakly mesarch; the doubt is retained for reasons that were made clear in the discussion of *Equisetum* and *Calamites*. Tracheary pitting in *Archaeocalamites* was opposite and circular bordered to scalariform, the same range as is found among the calamites. The cone genus *Pothocites* is thought to have been borne on *Archaeocalamites*. It had whorls of equisetoid sporangiophores and no sterile bracts.

It is probable that *Archaeocalamites*, or a form similar to it, gave rise during Mississippian times, as Boureau suggests, to the main calamite line, which had sterile bracts in the cone, and to the *Equisetum* line, which lacked them. The latter line seems to include the Sorocaulaceae, Phyllothecaceae, Schizoneuraceae, and Equisetaceae. The Apocalamitaceae may represent a similar but parallel line.

The Sorocaulaceae were mostly herbaceous plants with small linear leaves that were slightly fused at their bases. Stem ridges were nonalternating, and equisetoid sporangiophores occurred on the axis between leaf whorls.

The Phyllothecaceae (Fig. 8–7, *A*, *B*) bore leaves with various degrees of fusion. In some forms they were fused almost to their tips and extended out at nearly right angles to the stem. Sporangiophores were equisetoid and in

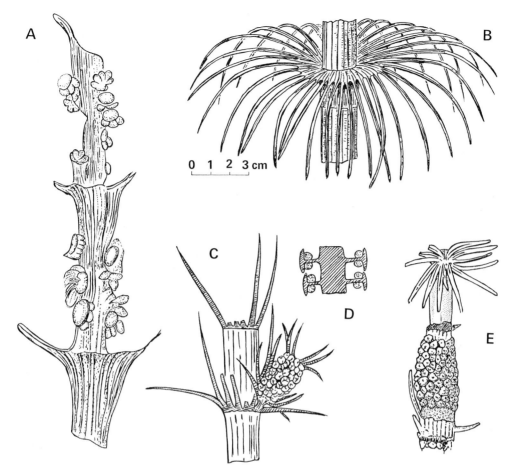

FIGURE 8–7. *A. Phyllotheca delequescens*, after Schmalhausen (1879). *B. P. equisetoides*, after Rasskazova (1961). *C, D. Apocalamites*, after Radczenko (1957). *E. Equisetinostachys*, after Rasskazova (1961).

internodal clusters. They thus resembled the occasional extant *Equisetum* specimen in which the strobilar axis continues vegetative growth. One species is reported to produce a branched sporangiophore, with each ultimate branch having equisetoid sporangiophore morphology.

The Schizoneuraceae showed apparently opposite leaves that were parallel-veined and divided from the tip to various degrees. These may well have been two groups of fused leaves. They bore terminal, catkinlike strobili.

The Apocalamitaceae bore small leaves with slight fusion, nonalternating ridges, and axillary strobili that were bractless and fundamentally equisetoid (Fig. 8–7, *C, D*). The

reconstruction shows leaves at the apex of the cone as occasionally occurs in the living *equiseta*.

A knowledge of only the extant *equiseta* might generate the idea that the Equisetopsida is a specialized and insignificant group. On the contrary, the class represents a major and important segment of the tracheophytes. The articulates diverged during, and have remained distinct since, early Devonian times. They were floristic dominants locally toward the end of the Paleozoic era and then they became progressively reduced and nearly became extinct.

The Hyeniales, whether or not they are to be included within the Cladoxylales, form the main trunk of the articulate line. The leaves of this order are recognizable as appendicular organs but are replaceable by lateral branches of the stem in *Hyeniopsis* and retain the dichotomous branching of a primitive stem system. The latter feature is also shared by primitive members of the Equisetales and is suggested by the venation of the Sphenophyllales. The small and simple leaf of *Equisetum* may therefore be logically interpreted as being reduced from a branch system and not by elaboration of an enation. Transition from dichotomous to lateral branching and degrees of fixation of whorled phyllotaxy are also found within the Hyeniales. The sporangiophores throughout the class Equisetopsida are recognized as simple dichotomous branch systems with consicuous, but interpretable, departures only within the Sphenophyllales.

The Hyeniales also demonstrate the fundamental similarity and homology between leaves and sporangiophores throughout the class. These two structures diverged morphologically before either one was clearly different from a typical branch truss. The application of the term "sporophyll" cannot therefore be used without some qualification. It is suggested that even in the primitive members of the equisetalean line a verticil of primordia within a young strobilus was directed to develop into either a whorl of sporangiophores or a whorl of sterile bracts, not by self-emanating factors, but as the result of influences traceable to the next older whorl. Phylogenetic changes in such morphogenetic interrelationships could readily explain the presence of sterile whorls in some lines and the absense in others without referring to a loss or gain of one kind of morphological entity as such.

The anatomy of the equisetalean stem is not necessarily enigmatic. By loss of most of the xylem in a stem of the *Cladoxylon* type, retaining only the ends of the stelar arms, a stele of the archaeocalamitalean type is readily obtainable. This kind of stelar change is indicated in a number of other lines of vascular plants and would not be peculiar here. The protoxylem lacunae of the Equisetales are interpreted as the homologs of the peripheral loops of the Cladoxylales and *Calamophyton*.

The articulates as a group illustrate a separate and parallel development of heterospory, of strobili, of pronounced intercalary growth, and probably of the root as well.

9

Cladoxylales and Coenopteridales

The cladoxylales are known well enough to generate considerable morphological interest but not well enough to be circumscribed taxonomically with any degree of satisfaction. The group was originally established on the basis of the petrified stem *Cladoxylon*. Later, the petrified stems *Schizopodium*, *Xenocladia*, *Voelkelia*, *Steloxylon*, and *Pietzschia* were added and also a compression fossil, *Cladoxylon scaporium*, which had a small part of its axis petrified was described. *Pseudosporochnus*, known as a compression fossil since 1904, had been placed in another order until Leclercq and Banks (1962) described the anatomy of its stems as cladoxylalean. The family Iridoperidaceae (*Arachnoxylon*, *Iridopteris*, and *Reimannia*) of Devonian petrified stems has been interpreted as having close affinity with the cladoxylaleans (Arnold, 1947), and taxonomic inclusion could be argued. Finally, the description of cladoxylalean stem anatomy in the "hyenialean" genus *Calamophyton* (referred to in Chapter 8) has further compounded the taxonomic problems. Much has been written in recent years concerning the specific taxa under consideration here. The bulk of it, however, represents an argument as to how to record the new information taxonomically. At this evolutionary level of vascular plants we cannot clearly delimit orders and classes, much less subdivisions, but the same information that disallows this adds significantly to our understanding of morphology and phylogeny.

The Middle Devonian *Cladoxylon scoparium* (Fig. 9–1, *K*) was a plant with stems somewhat thicker than 2 cm and possible to 30 cm tall. Its branching was irregular, but dichotomies as well as fascicled (digitate) branches are suggested. On axes that appear to be second through fifth order (the first order on the specimen may not have been the first order on the plant) there were sterile, planate, forked appendages (Fig. 9–1, *G, H*) that were probably spirally arranged. Scars elsewhere on the shoot indicate that they probably occurred over the entire aerial system. The fertile appendages were borne on the ultimate branches and were fan-shaped, dichotomously branched, and bore terminal sporangia (Fig. 9–1, *F*). The stem in cross section (Fig. 9–1, *I*) showed a complex of plates of xylem with most of the ends peripherally situated. Some other species of *Cladoxylon* (petrified stems only) show small circular steles in the center and larger, radiating ones surrounding these (e.g., *C. taeniatum* and in the stem genus *Xenocladia*). Secondary xylem is strongly indicated in several species by radially seriated tracheids situated either around a bundle or primarily toward the inside. Rays were present or absent. Tracheary pitting was mostly multiseriate.

It is not clear how the ultimate appendages of the *Cladoxylan scoparium* type were vascularized. There was some pinching off of the tips of cauline xylem arms, and one arm may have supplied one of the small structures, which suggest leaves. Multiple traces to "appendages" have been described for several Carboniferous species (Fig. 9–1, *J*) of *Cladoxylon*, but it is not clear what these "appendages" correspond to in the one species whose external form is known. The "appendage" whose base is shown in Fig. 9–1, *J* may well have been the equivalent of a branch bearing "leaves" of *C. scoparium*, and the "aphlebiae" (supplied by traces I and IV) may have been basally situated organs equivalent to the "leaves" of the Devonian species. The appendicular traces of some species are reported to be elongate-elliptical in cross section with a protoxylem pole at each end. This feature, together with the presence of peripheral loops and overall stelar form, seem clearly to link the Cladoxylaceae with the Iridopteridaceae and the more specialized coenopterid ferns.

The "peripheral loop" occurs in most cladoxylaceous stem genera. This is an area of "parenchyma" surrounded by protoxylem (white areas included in the blackened xylem in Fig. 9–1, *J*). The loop is generally considered to represent protoxylem parenchyma, but clues to its more specialized nature come from certain extant taxa. In a number of modern ferns the protoxylem is associated with a conspicuous island of "tissue" considered the equivalent of the loop of *Cladoxylon*. In the petiole of *Pteridium*, which this author has studied, the protoxylem tracheids at first mature in a relatively compact group with some parenchyma in association. This takes place at a level in the organ before lateral expansion of all the tissues has been completed. The protoxylem area subsequently expands with the entire organ and, as it does so, the parenchyma cells produce a large number of tyloses completely distorting the early matured tracheids and often making them appear peripheral to the newly formed pseudoparenchyma or cavity parenchyma. Tyloses occur in the protoxylem of most modern fern families and are also reported in coenopterids, but less commonly is a conspicuous mass of pseudoparenchyma produced. In the stem of *Equisetum* the protoxylary canal is formed by a separation of tracheary elements also originally in a compact group. In the rhizomes of some species the canal occasionally becomes filled with cavity parenchyma.

The Devonian stem genus *Schizopodium* has been considered structurally intermediate between cladoxylaceous forms and more primitive ancestors (Banks, 1964). It had a centrally located stelate protostele. Each of the four or more arms of the xylem was again once or twice lobed at its end. The maturation pattern seems to have been exarch, but certain arms of the xylem were surrounded at their ends by cells aligned so as to suggest secondary origin. If these were metaxylem elements, the maturation was, at least in part, mesarch. Tracheary pits occurred in from one to four rows.

The three Middle Devonian stem genera *Arachnoxylon*, *Iridiopteris*, and *Reimannia* had lobed xylem strands and embedded, subperipheral protoxylem areas associated with ill-defined peripheral loops. The steles of the last two of these genera gave off simple leaf traces.

Pseudosporochnus (Figs. 9–1, *A* to *D*), of

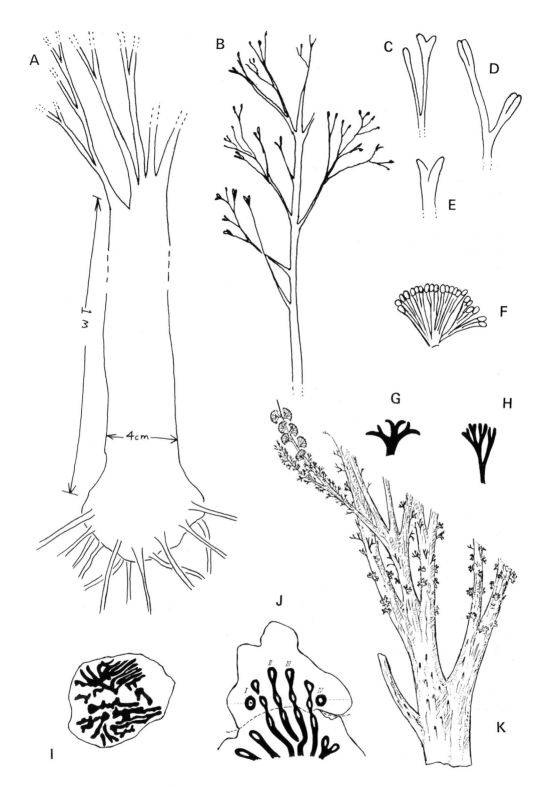

FIGURE 9–1. *A* to *E. Pseudosporochnus*, after Potonié and Bernard (1904). *A.* Main body of the plant. *B.* One branch from *A.* *C, E.* Ultimate sterile portions *D.* Ultimate fertile portion *F* to *I, K, Cladoxylon scoparium*, after Kräusel and Weyland (1926). *F.* Ultimate fertile portion. *G, H.* Ultimate sterile portions. *I.* Xylem outline in stem cross section. *K.* Portion of the plant reconstructed. About one-half natural size. *J. C. mirabile*. Stem and base of an appendage in cross section, from D. H. Scott (1920–1923).

Lower and Middle Devonian age, is kept in its own family. *Pseudosporochnus* was a larger plant than *Cladoxylon*. As far as they are known. The large axis bore a crown of branches some of which were bifurcated. The ultimate branches (fronds) seemed flattened and appendicular in nature and were borne in spiral order on second-order branches. The fronds had a main axis (Figs. 9–1, *B*) that bore laterals. Each lateral, as well as the end of the main axis, underwent several dichotomies, usually three or possibly constantly three, to terminate in eight ultimate ends (the specimen in Figs. 9–1, *B* is probably incomplete). On fertile fronds the tips terminated with paired sporangia (Fig. 9–1, *D*). A dissected xylem strand of the cladoxylaceous type occurred in the roots and stems of the first and second orders. The fronds "appear to have had a single strand of xylem probably in the form of a clepsydroid trace. . . ." (Banks, 1964).

Assigned to the order Coenopteridales are diverse ferns of Upper Devonian, Carboniferous, and Permian rocks. Many were elaborate and specialized plants difficult to describe in classical organographic terms. Many of the simpler ones are difficult to interpret, since they may be either primitively simple or simple by reduction. The possibility exists that coenopterid ferns may be ancestral to all or part (i.e., the Osmundaceae) of the order Filicales, despite the contradictory evidence presented by the Psilotaceae and the Stromatopteridaceae. The coenopterid ferns are considered in terms of four families following the treatment of Delevoryas and Morgan (1954). These are the Stauropteridaceae (Mississippian and Pennsylvanian), Anachoropteridaceae (Mississipian and Pennsylvanian), Zygopteridaceae (Upper Devonian through Lower Permian), and Botryopteridaceae (Mississippian and Pennsylvanian). A fifth family, the Ankyropteridaceae, separated from the Zygopteridaceae to include *Ankyropteris* and "*Tedelia*," should be validated.

The Stauropteridaceae is monogeneric and bispecific. *Stauropteris burntislandica*, of Mississippian age, is the only definitely known heterosporous coenopterid and is antomically very similar to the more recent, homosporous *S. oldhamia* of Pennsylvanian age. *Stauropteris* axes bore four groups of weakly mesarch primary xylem groups that alternated with phloem areas (Fig. 9–4, *E*). The axes bore alternating pairs of branches in different planes (Fig. 9–4, *B*, *G*). Each branch received a pair of traces, one each from two different strands of the parental axis. The two traces then divided to produce four, as in the axis that produced them. The pattern was repeated several times. At the base of each branch pair were two scalelike aphlebiae (Fig. 9–4 *G*). Ultimate parts were more pinnate and planate with essentially no lamina. At the tips of ultimate branches were near-spherical sporangia (Fig. 9–4, *D*; Fig. 9–5, *A*, *B*). Some have considered the axes described above as parts of a three-dimensional frond and, if they are, the stem remains unknown. The sporangial wall was two cells thick, with the inner layer composed of small thin-walled cells. Germinating spores (Fig. 9–4, *J*) have been seen within the sporangium, indicating an initially filamentous gametophyte.

The Zygopteridaceae is the largest of coenopterid families and is known to have existed over the longest time, Upper Devonian to Lower Permian. Its naturalness, however, is questioned (Eggert and Taylor, 1966). Some species had small stems and conspicuously spaced leaves, while others had thicker stems with more compactly arranged crowns. Some may have looked like small trees.

The Upper Devonian stem *Asteropteris* had a stele with about 12 radiating arms of xylem, each with an elongate "parenchyma" loop. "Petioles" were attached in whorls. The appendicular traces were tangentially elongate strands each with two loops, one near each edge. Except for leaf arrangement, it was very similar to the Lower Permian *Asteroclaena* (Fig. 9–4, *A*).

Most zygopterid stems had stelate protosteles similar to the abovementioned genera. Primary xylem maturation was exarch to mesarch. In the illustration of the *Ankyropteris* stem (Fig. 9–2, *A*) the core of each xylary arm, as well as the center of the stele, shows xylem of a different degree of parenchymatization and average cell size. Figure 9–2, *C* shows the tip of one xylary arm enlarged; the two arrows in *A* correspond in position to those in *C*. A deeper portion of the stele is shown enlarged in *B*; the two tracheids marked " × "

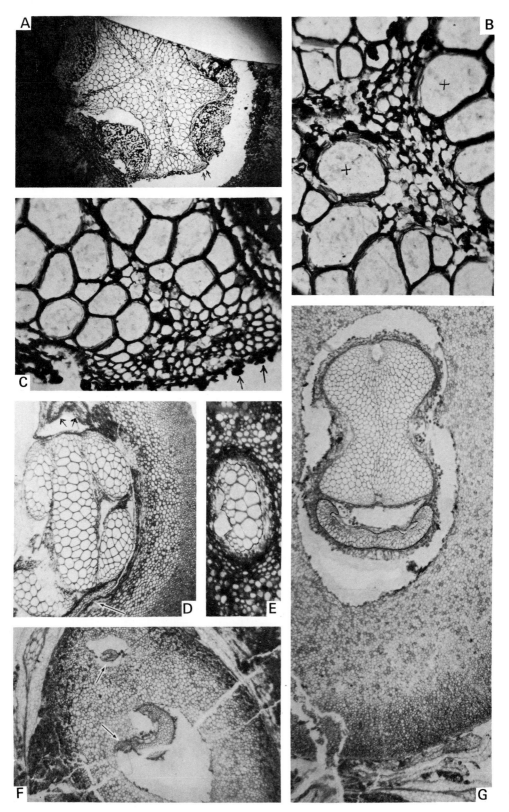

FIGURE 9–2. *A* to *C. Ankyropteris*, cross section of stem stele. *B*, *C* are portions of *A* enlarged. The two arrows in *A* correspond to the two in *C*. The two × 's in *A* correspond to the two in *B*. *D. Etapteris scotti*, cross section of the main foliar axis. *E. Botryopteris ramosa*, cross section of an axis in the foliar truss. *F. Zygopteris duplex*, cross section of a second-order branch of the foliar truss. *G. Z. duplex*, cross section of the main foliar axis.

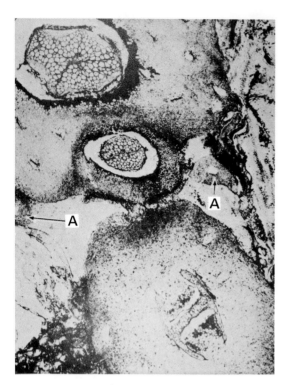

FIGURE 9–3. *Ankyropteris glabra*, after Baxter (1951). The cross section of the stem is in the upper left, that of the axillary branch in the center, and that of the main foliar axis to the lower right.

flattened traces arose singly from the margins of the petiolar strand (lower arrow in Fig. 9–2, *D*; lower part of stele in *G*), having several protoxylem areas in specific locations on the side toward the mother strand. The flat traces then divided into two, as shown in Fig. 9–2, *D* (two arrows at top) and suggested by the median groove within the band in *G*. Subsequent divisions of the second-order stele were mostly at right angles to those shown in *F*. *Ankyropteris* (*Tedelea*) *glabra* was most unusual in having a planate frond (Fig. 9–4, *C*) with two ranks of pinnae, but otherwise it had zygopterid internal anatomy.

Axillary branching occurred in at least several species of the genus *Ankyropteris*. In the section shown in Fig. 9–3, the stem is shown in cross section in the upper left, the axillary branch is below and attached to it at this level, and the petiole with its H-shaped bundle appears to the lower right. Aphlebiae in section are indicated by *A*.

The sporangiate fructifications of the Zygopteridaceae, together with those of other coenopterids, are considered later in this chapter.

The Anachoropteridaceae bore stems with near-terete protosteles with centrarch or mesarch primary xylem maturation. Epipetiolar branches were produced in at least some species of *Anachoropteris*. Most characteristic of the family were the abaxially, however variably, curved petiolar strands. In *Anachoropteris* this reached an extreme in which each arm of the trace was curved away from the stem in nearly a complete gyre. In *Grammatopteris* the trace was almost straight.

correspond to those in *A*. Secondary xylem was reported in limited quantity only in the stem of *Zygopteris*.

Leaves of many zygopterids were three-dimensionally branched structures, and often their basal diameters were as large as or larger than the stem that bore them. The petioles, often called "phyllophores" because they are so unpetiolelike in terms of modern ferns, generally had an H-shaped, anchor-shaped, or hourglass-shaped xylem mass (Fig. 9–2, *D*, *G*; Fig. 9–3, stele in lower right) with four arms or bulges directed toward and away from the stem. Near both margins of the petiole bundle was a loop that varied in shape from circular to very elongate and was usually only in part buried within the metaxylem. Large

FIGURE 9–4. *A. Asterochlaena*, cross section of the stem, after Bertrand (1911). *B. Stauropteris oldhamia*, the branching pattern of the frond as viewed from above, from Hirmer (1927). *C. Ankyropteris glabra*, portion of the frond, after Eggert (1963). *D. Stauropteris oldhamia*, ultimate portion of fertile frond, after Eggert (1964). *E. S. oldhamia*, the stele of the major, known axis, after Tansley (1907). *F. Botryopteris trisecta*, basal part of a frond truss and a small segment of the stem, after Mamay and Andrews (1950). *G. Stauropteris oldhamia*, reconstruction of part of a frond, after Mägdefrau (1967). *H. Botryopteris trisecta*, portion of a frond, after Delevoryas and Morgan (1954). *I. B. trisecta*, ultimate fertile portion of the frond, after Mamay and Andrews (1950). *J. Stauropteris oldhamia*, germinating spores from within a sporangium, after D. H. Scott (1906).

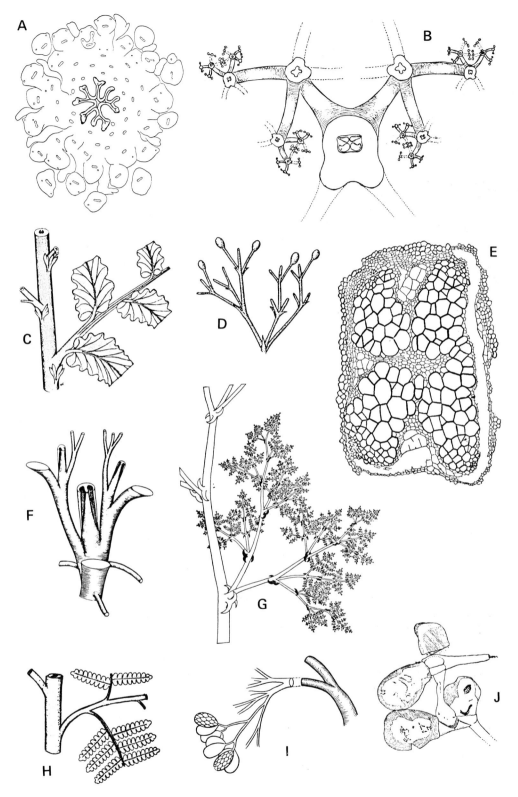

The protoxylem of the petiolar trace occurred as several areas on the concave side toward the stem. The traces to pinnae of the essentially planate frond arose as plates of xylem from the concave flanks of the trace.

Grammatopteris, which was probably a small tree, had a nearly straight petiolar strand. In the center of its stem were broad, short tracheids suggestive of the fossil Osmundaceae. Natural affinities among these forms remain a possibility.

The Botryoperidaceae is represented by the genera *Botryoperis* and *Catenopteris*. The generic name *Botryopteris* may be invalid here, since it was used much earlier for the ophioglossaceous genus *Helminthostachys*. *Botryopteris* had a protostelic stem with near centrally located protoxylem and from it arose spirally arranged fronds. The fronds at their bases showed stemlike steles. They trichotomized (Fig. 9–4, *F*) and the stele of the central axis then assumed a W-shaped form. Each of the two laterals of the triad repeated the trifurcation and anatomical changes. More distal portions of the frond were pinnate (Fig. 9–4, *H*), and some terminated in clusters of sporangia (Fig. 9–4, *I*). In the smaller W-shaped steles of the frond system there were three protoxylem points, one at the tip of each arm (Fig. 9–2, *E*), while in larger ones additional protoxylem points appeared lateral on the concave side of the trace. Fertile fronds produced very large numbers of sporangia, sometimes in spherical masses, apparently as the result of the failure of the fertile frond to uncoil. The peripheral sporangia of the clusters were sterile and without the annulus characteristic of the inner, fertile ones.

Catenopteris (Phillips and Andrews, 1966), of Upper Pennsylvanian age and known only from its stem and leaf bases, is tentatively included here. It showed a protostele in which protoxylem was not recognizable despite good preservation. Appendicular traces were attached in spiral order and each was very similar in cross section to botryopterid frond steles with short arms, as the one in Fig. 9–2, *E*.

Coenopterid sporangia and sori, where present, are unusually variable and some strongly suggest those of extant Filicales. This may indicate an unnaturalness of the order. If the coenopterids, or some of them, are ancestral to modern Filicales, a considerable degree of breakdown of organ integrity and disorganization of the vegetative body must be assumed to have occurred. This assumption would be necessary to account for the peculiar morphology of the Psilotaceae and the Stromatopteridaceae. It is true that in the Coenopteridales, as well as in the two filicalean families mentioned, there is no clear-cut distinction between leaves and branch systems. On the face of it, however, the statement is misleading, since the coenopterid body was of a highly stereotyped and geometric construction, while in the primitive Filicales irregularity is an outstanding feature. The question of whether the filicalean features of coenopterids indicate true affinity with the modern order or parallel developments remains an open one.

The sporangia of *Stauropteris* are strictly terminal (Fig. 9–5, *A*, *B*) and their walls, at least in one species, are multilayered. The heterospory that occurs in this family may be considered parallel to similar developments elsewhere among vascular plants. The megasporangium of *Stauropteris burntislandica* is described as having two large and two apparently aborted spores.

The sporangia of *Botryopteris* (Fig. 9–5, *G*, *L*, *K*) and *Anachoropteris* (Fig. 9–5, *I*, *J*) are similarly terminal and very much like each other. In both the line of dehiscence is indicated by a zone of thin-walled cells and the

FIGURE 9–5. *A. Stauropteris oldhamia*, sporangium, after Eggert (1964). *B. S. burntislandica*, megasporangium, after Eggert (1964). *C. Chorionopteris*, synangium, after Eggert (1964). *D. Etapteris*, sporangia, after Renault (1876). *E. Biscalitheca*, sporangia, after Mamay (1957). *F. Cornepteris*, fertile pinnules, after Eggert (1964). *G, K. Botryopteris glabra*, sporangium from two views, after Phillips and Andrews (1965). *H. Ankyropteris* (*Tedelea*), portion of a fertile frond, after Eggert and Taylor (1966). *I, J. Anachoropteris*, sporangium from two views, after Phillips and Andrews (1965). *L. Botryopteris globosa*, cross section of sporangium, after Eggert (1964). *M. Ankyropteris* (*Tedelea*), sporangium, after Eggert and Taylor (1966).

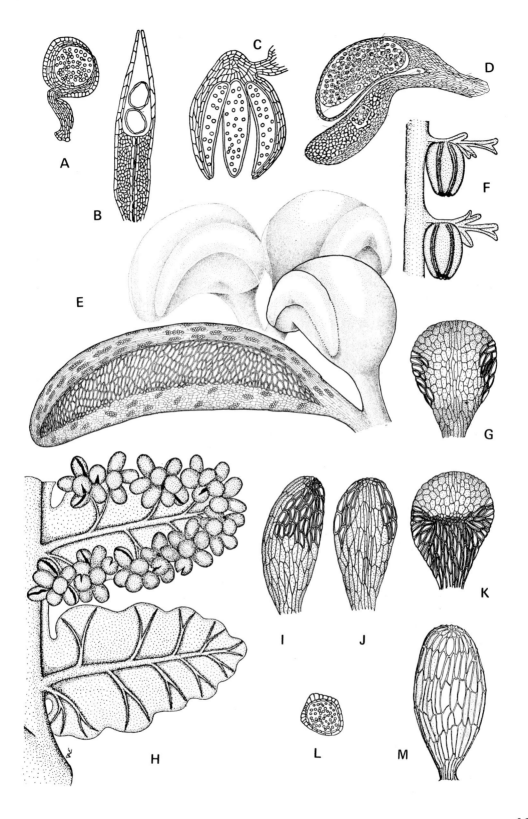

annulus is represented by a broad zone of thick-walled cells. Differences in shape (elongate versus spherical) and annular position (lateral versus subapical) seem insignificant in view of the overall structural similarities. One cannot avoid comparing these with osmundaceous sporangia (Fig. 15–7).

The fructification *Chorionopteris* (Fig. 9–5, *C*) has been referred to the Anachoropteri-daceae. The sporangia were in fours, fused at their bases and covered on the outside by several layers of cells. The entire synangium was in a marginal position on a pinnule. The genus is suspiciously placed here and may be marattialean.

The sporangiate fructifications assigned to the Zygopteridaceae are few in type but represent a confusing lot of heterogeneity. Those attached to *Etapteris* are terminal, elongate structures (Fig. 9–5, *D*) without much detail known. In *Corynepteris* sporangia occurred in closely appressed groups (Fig. 9–5, *F*). A broad, vertical annulus extended over the tip of each sporangium from each side. The sporangia of *Biscalitheca* (Fig. 9–5, *E*) resemble those of *Corynepteris*. There were two elongate and broad annuli. Each sporangium was terminal on an ultimate unit of the frond. The wall at maturity was one cell thick.

Ankyropteris (*Tedelia*) *glabra* is the only species of its genus with attached sporangiate fructifications (Eggert and Taylor, 1966), Fertile pinnules, known by the name *Seftenbergia* and assigned to the Schizaeaceae (Anemiaceae), were likely borne on the same plant. The fertile parts of *Ankyropteris glabra* are so very different from other known zygopterids that the authors proposed a new family, the Tedeliaceae. In the view held here, the generic name *Ankyropteris* should be retained for both the anatomical species as well as for the more complete plant.

The fertile pinnules of *Ankyropteris glabra* bore free sporangia in near-marginal abaxial sori (Fig. 9–5, *H*). Individual sporangia were elongate and presented evidence of longitudinal dehiscence. There was a distal annular area (Fig. 9–5, *M*) composed of more than one tier of cells. At the tip of the sporangium there was a very small cell, surrounded by a ring of slightly larger thick-walled ones, and farther down by more elongate cells of the annular zone. At maturity the sporangial wall was one cell thick, but younger sporangia showed another cell layer on the inside.

The fertile pinnule and the sporangium of *Ankyropertis glabra* are superficially as well as in some detail much like the extant Anemiaceae. Correlated anatomical similarities, however, are not apparent. In view of the high degree of flexibility of sporangial and soral form among extant forms, a close parallelism without close phylogenetic affinity might be assumed.

10

Aneurophytopsida

The class Aneurophytopsida has become reasonably known only during the past decade and now is a major focus of attention of plant morphologists. The special interest in the group dates to 1960, when Beck reported a connection between *Archeopteris* and *Callixylon*, two genera that were formerly thought to be distantly related and placed in different classes. The class Aneurophytopsida was established as the "Progymnospermopsida," but the present author objects to the use of taxonomic names reflecting phylogenetic interpretations, and since the rules of nominal priorities do not apply at the class level, it is not that important. The group is very significant, since within it are possibly the ancestral forms of the pteridosperm–cycadeoid–cycad line, the coniferophyte line, and the Ophioglossales. Three orders are recognized, following Banks (1968a). These are listed below with the better known genera. *Rhacophyton* has been added to those listed by Banks, following the recent studies of Andrews and Phillips (1968). Pairs of generic names separated by a hyphen are those which have been shown to refer to the same plant.

Class Aneurophytopsida
  Order Aneurophytales
    Rhacophyton
    Protopteridium
    Aneurophyton–Eospermatopteris
    Tetraxyplopteris–Sphenoxylon
  Order Archeopteridales
    Archeopteris–Callixylon
  Order Protopityales
    Protopitys

The Upper Devonian *Rhacophyton* until recently was considered a coenopterid fern, but it has been re-

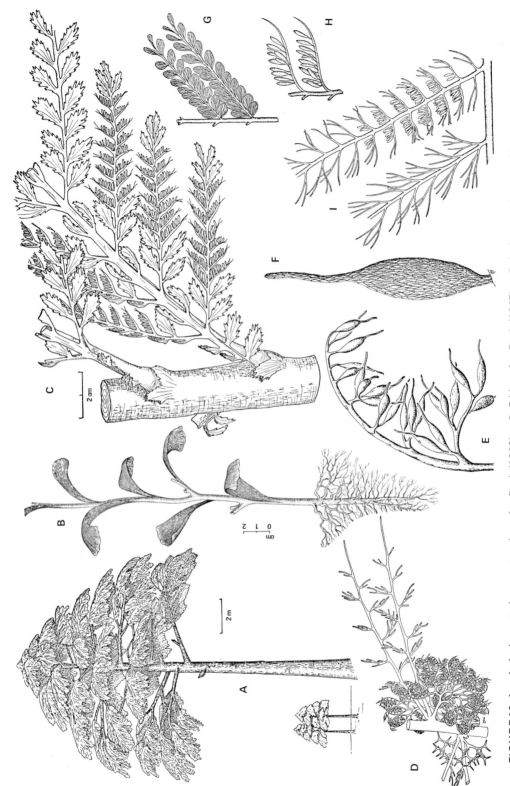

FIGURE 10–1. *A. Archaeopteris* reconstruction, after Beck (1967). *B. Eddya,* after Beck (1962). *C. Archaeopteris,* stem with parts of two fronds and base of a third, based primarily on *A. macilenta,* after Beck (1962). *D* to *F. Rhacophyton,* after Andrews and Phillips (1968). *D.* Portion of a fertile frond showing two tetrads of pinnae. *E.* Portion of a fertile pinna with sporangia. *F.* Single sporangium. *G, H.* Fertile and sterile pinnules of *Archaeopteris latifolia,* after Andrews (1948). *I.* Pinnules of *A. fissilis,* after Andrews et al. (1965).

FIGURE 10–2. Fertile pinnules of *Archaeopteris macilenta* from specimens provided by H. P. Banks. The arrows indicate sporangia.

evaluated since the publication of additional information on *R. ceratangium* by Andrews and Phillips (1968). Its taxonomic inclusion in the Aneurophytales is debatable, but a relationship to more primitive members of the order seems clear.

Rhacophyton was a sparsely dichotomized plant of perhaps 1 to 2 m tall. It bore closely spaced, spirally arranged, planate, bipinnate sterile fronds approximately 30 cm long. In a more proximal position on the axis were three-dimensionally branched, fertile fronds perhaps 20 cm in length which were probably inserted in the same spiral as the sterile ones. The ultimate pinnules of the sterile fronds were unlaminated and dichotomously branched or the larger ones were pinnate. The rhachides of the fertile fronds bore groups of four appendages at a node. The most proximal of the appendicular tetrads was composed of a pair of aphlebiae inserted below a pair of sterile pinnae (left side and below in Fig. 10–1, *D*). The more distal tetrads had fertile pinnae in the lower position (Fig. 10–1, *D*, upper group of four on the right). The sterile pinnae of the fertile frond were similar to those on the sterile frond, but their pinnules were much less branched. The fertile pinnae were bifurcated several times and the branches curved inward so that the entire pinna was a

globose structure approximately 2.5 cm in diameter. Sporangia were borne on ultimate units as shown in Fig. 10–1, *E*. Each of the elongate sporangia (Fig. 10–1, *F*) had a main body 1.2 to 1.4 mm by 0.34 to 0.44 mm in diameter and an attenuated tip of 0.7 to 1.0 mm in length. The tip was probably solid and the body contained several hundred spores of a single kind.

The stems of *Rhacophyton* had a central primary xylem core that in cross section was shaped like a thin bar swollen at both ends, where there is a suggestion of loop development. Primary xylem was very small in quantity and surrounded by secondary xylem in which tracheids were scalariformly pitted.

The significance of *Rhacophyton* lies in its suggestions of trimerophyte affinity (i.e., the grouped appendages on the rachis of the fertile frond, the overall form of the fertile pinna and sporangial form, as well as suggestions of aneurophyte affinity (i.e., form of the sterile fronds, ultimate units of fertile pinnae secondary xylem, and, again, sporangial form).

One additional point is worth bringing out. Andrews and Phillips (1968) described several petrified *Rhacophyton* axes which they thought were pinnae of the fertile fronds. Except for

Aneurophytopsida **125**

the more obvious radial alignment of the secondary xylem, the strands were peculiarly suggestive of those of *Dawsonites*. Even in the latter the "metaxylem" tracheids show some slight indication of radial alignment. Its flattened central core does not seem to represent a fossilization artifact. In these instances as well as in many others the application of the term "secondary xylem" and "primary xylem" without qualification may be misleading. In organs of the extant vascular plants, especially those with endarch primary xylem maturation, there is no distinction between primary and secondary xylem except artificial criteria of restricted taxonomic applicability invented by botanists for convenience. It is quite conceivable that when *Dawsonites* and *Trimerophyton* become better known they will present themselves to be plants very different from that which they now seem to be.

Protopteridium had an axis in which there was a three- or four-lobed protostele and probably mesarch primary xylem maturation. The known axis may have been appendicular upon an axis of a lower order. Upon the known axis were appendages, probably arranged in spiral sequence (Fig. 10–3, *D*). Ultimately the axis dichotomized, as did its apparent appendages. The ultimate units of the system were pinnate, then pinnately lobed. The elongate sporangia occurred on upcurved branches and each sporangium was ultimately terminal (Fig. 10–3, *E*).

Protopitys was a large plant of Mississippian age. Its stem possessed a distinct pith and near-endarch primary xylem with "scalariform" tracheids. This is a particularly ambiguous term when used alone, but in this case it is assumed that it referred to scalariformly pitted tracheids. There was extensive secondary xylem, the tracheids of which bore shorter pits. Its foliage is unknown, but leaf traces were crescent-shaped, colateral bundles arising from the stem stele in such a manner as to suggest distichous leaf insertion. The fertile appendages were supplied by traces similar to those thought to supply vegetative fronds. They dichotomized several times, then were pinnate in the distal portions, much like those of *Protopteridium*. Ultimate divisions bore terminal, fusiform sporangia that dehisced

longitudinally and whose walls were two or three cells thick. Spores showed a very wide range in diameter (82 to 163 μ), which led Walton (1957) to suggest an incipient heterospory.

The stem of *Aneurophyton* possessed a three-lobed mesarch xylem strand that became surrounded by secondary xylem. The latter showed elongate tracheids with multiseriate, bordered pits on all walls and high, mostly uniseriate rays. The stem of *Tetraxylopteris* was similar in structure but its xylem was four-armed. Its secondary phloem is known to have had rays and fibers. Certain larger stems of *Tetraxylopteris*, known as *Sphenoxylon*, showed fossilization gaps in the center of the stele leaving up to nine islands of primary xylem, each with protoxylem in its center. This was originally thought to indicate a pith with medulary strands of a mixed pith, but studies by Matten and Banks (1966) have shown its true nature and identity with *Tetraxylopteris*.

Aneurophyton bore spirally arranged fronds that bore spirally arranged appendages and ultimately small, forked, possibly avascular units. Stelar morphology was the same in all orders of branching of "stem" and "frond." *Tetraxylopteris* bore spirally arranged fronds (Fig. 10–3, *A*) that were then branched in an opposite-decussate manner (Fig. 10–3, *C*) and then dichotomously or pinnately so. The same stelar morphology found in its "stems" was present in all orders of branching of its "frond" except the ultimate ones, which were supplied by small, terete xylem strands.

Sporangia of *Aneurophyton* and *Tetraxylopteris* were fusiform and ultimately terminal. They were borne in clusters on recurved branches (Fig. 10–3, *B*, *C*).

Archeopteris was a large tree. The largest piece found was 28 ft long and 5 ft in diameter. The distinct pith of the stem was encircled by a ring of discrete mesarch bundles. Branch traces were given off in spiral sequence and each one was derived by a tangential splitting of a cauline bundle. The axis (rachis) of the first-order branch (frond) was subtended by a stipule (Fig. 10–1, *C*). At its proximal end its stelar morphology was like that of the parental axis (trunk), but farther out there was a 10- or 12-lobed siphonostele.

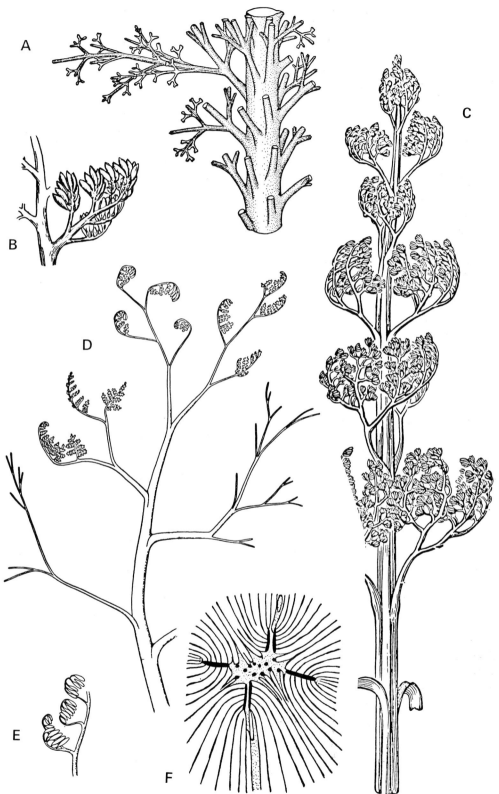

FIGURE 10–3. *A. Tetraxylopteris* stem with first-order branches, from Delevoryas (1962). *B, C. Tetraxylopteris*, after Bonamo (1966). *B*. Portion of *C* enlarged. *C*. First-order branch with opposite-decussate second-order branches. *D, E. Protopteridium*, after Delevoryas (1962), based on Kräusel and Weyland (1923). *F. Sphenoxylon*, cross section of central part of stem, after D. E. Thomas (1935).

The fronds bore pinnate appendages (pinnae) and simple structures (rachial pinnules) (Fig. 10–1, C). The entire frond was nearly planate and its appendages appeared in opposite or subopposite pairs. The pinnae received their vascular supplies from opposite lobes of the rachial stele, but the rachial pinnules (where known) received theirs in spiral sequence. Sterile pinnules of some species were distinctly laminar (Fig. 10–1, C, G), while in others they were not (Fig. 10–1, I). Ultimate fertile pinnules varied in branching complexity (Fig. 10–1, C, H, I; Fig. 10–2) and were not planated. The elongate sporangia were inserted much as were those of *Rhacophyton* (compare Fig. 10–1, E with H, I). Stomata occurred on the sporangial walls as well as on more predictable epidermal exposures. Some species are known to have been heterosporous and it is possible that all were. *Archeopteris* bore well-defined roots, while other aneurophytes may or may not have.

A small plant, *Eddya* (Fig. 10–1, B), was described by Beck (1967), who presented evidence that it was probably a young sporophyte of *Archeopteris*.

The reconstruction of *Archeopteris* (Fig. 10–1, A) is accurate in its details, but the overall form of the crown is "based on that of living conifers" (Beck, 1962). More probably the tree appeared thin and more cylindrical, a form also found among the living conifers in the genus *Araucaria*.

What is or what is not a "leaf" in the aneurophytes is much less a morphological problem than one of terminology. When the question is put as "What is *the* leaf" it is grossly improper. Megaphylls or leaves phylogenetically derived from branch systems (see the end of Chapter 13) are certainly polyphyletic in origin, even within the taxon Pteropsida as used in certain systems. It represents complete reduction to appendicular status of branch systems of different orders. There is abundant evidence to indicate that in the phylogeny of the extant Filicales a megaphyll first evolved from one order of branching; then the branch order that bore these leaves again evolved into another kind of a megaphyll. Complete appendicular status is represented by the condition where the organ primordium is appendicular from its inception and the axial apex (where it is indeterminate) is not appreciably disturbed by its production. In addition, the organ in this ultimate state usually, but not always, has a bilaterally symmetrical apical meristem and a bilateral vascular supply. The latter feature is not restricted to leaves but is also characteristic of many typical stem branches. It is a distinct possibility, if not a probability, that the entire fronds of aneurophytes evolved further to produce well-defined leaves of some taxa, while more distal units of a different branch order are ancestral to leaves of other taxa. To specify the lowest-numbered order of branching that exhibits a stellar form different from the major axis as "the leaf" of an aneurophyte makes little morphological sense.

11

Ophioglossales

The Ophioglossales, considered here as one family, the Ophioglossaceae and three genera, *Botrychium*, *Helminthostachys*, and *Ophioglossum*, are generally called ferns, but their relationship to the ferns is extremely obscure and dubious. Some authors have recognized more than one family and more than three genera, but the assemblage is generally recognized as a very natural taxon. There are approximately 20 to 30 species each of *Botrychium* and *Ophioglossum*, ranging from the tropics nearly to the arctic. There is a single species of *Helminthostachys*, ranging from Australia to the Asian mainland. Some species of *Ophioglossum* are epiphytes.

Botrychium, commonly called grape fern or rattlesnake fern, has a short, fleshy, vertical, subterranean stem bearing adventitious roots, produced one each year, and generally a single aerial structure or complex, at least part of which is leaf (Fig. 11–1, *A*). Generally only one aerial complex is produced per year, but in certain species (e.g., *B. dissectum* and *B. multifidum*) it overwinters and exists in good condition on the plant along with the new one for a time.

In *Helminthostachys* and *Ophioglossum* the stems are horizontal and subterranean and also bear adventitious roots. In the former these are not associated with definite leaves. They produce aerial complexes similar to those of *Botrychium*, each with a sterile laminar portion and a sporangiferous portion, the fertile spike (Fig. 11–2, *A*; Fig. 11–3, *A*). In *Ophioglossum pendulum* and *O. palmatum* (Fig. 11–4, *A*) several fertile spikes are borne on a single complex.

Ophioglossaceous stems are soft and fleshy and, as are all other parts of the plants, devoid of sclerenchyma. In the center of the stem is an ectophloic siphonostele surrounding a prominent parenchymatous pith (Fig. 11–5, *B*; Fig. 11–6, *B*, *C*). The stele is disrupted only

129

130

FIGURE 11–1. *A. Botrychium matricariaefolium*, the aerial complex minus the lower part of the common stalk. *B.* Sporangium of *B. virginianum*, showing the surface cells and line of dehiscence. *C.* Pinna from the fertile spike of *B. virginianum*. *D.* Plant of *B. dissectum*. 67S, 67F, and the common stalk below make up the aerial complex expanded in 1967. The fertile spike of the 1966 complex (66F) aborted before expanding. *E.* Enlargement of the fertile spike from *A.* *F.* Base of the plant shown in *A.* SH indicates the extent of the sheath of the expanded aerial complex, which encloses the bud with its series of younger leaves.

FIGURE 11–2. *Helminthostachys.* *A.* Potted greenhouse plant. *B.* Portion of the fertile spike. *C, D.* Portions of *B* enlarged.

at the prominent leaf gaps (LG). In many species of *Ophioglossum* the gaps are very extensive and overlapping, resulting in a distinct dictyostele (Fig, 11–4, *D*). Each aerial complex receives two traces (LT); these often originate as one that divides in the inner cortex. In some species of *Ophioglossum* more than two traces may be present and they may arise at different levels within the stele and by a circumferential division of a cauline strand (Fig. 11–4, *D*). Primary xylem maturation is mesarch in *Helminthostachys* and endarch in the other genera. Often, especially in the very slow growing stems, there is only earlier metaxylem at a primary xylem pole, and its identification is difficult in sections of mature organs.

Stems of young sporelings are protostelic (base of stele in Fig. 11–4, *D*) and show transitional steles with mixed piths leading to the siphonostelic condition of the older axes. The protostelic portions are described as centrarch in maturation (W. H. Lang, 1912).

In the stems of *Botrychium* secondary vascular tissues and periderm are formed. In this respect the genus is unique among extant ferns and fernlike plants. The phellogen (PG in Fig. 11–5, *C*) originates in the outer cortex and produces cork externally (CK) and phelloderm (PD) internally. The vascular cambium (cambial zone, CZ, in Fig. 11–5, *D*) adds radially aligned tracheids and ray cells that seem quite continuous with the primary tissues toward the inside. The sections in Fig. 11–5, *B* to *D* are from a level in the stem estimated to be approximately 20 years old from the number of roots that were attached in younger regions. There are from 10 to 12 tracheids in a radial row within the secondary xylem and five to six elements in the disrupted phloem rows. External to the recognizable phloem is a region of proliferated endodermis that also probably includes some of the primary phloem (PE in Fig. 11–5, *D*). Sections of stems just a few years old show nearly as much secondary tissue. It seems, therefore, that the cambium is either inactive or nearly so after a relatively short time.

Tracheary elements of the Ophioglossaceae are for the most part highly specialized. Early-matured protoxylem elements (Fig. 27–8, *L* to *N*) are highly suggestive of some found in the Lycopodiaceae, Marattiaceae, and Osmundaceae. In the intermediate protoxylem of all three ophioglossaceous genera circular bordered pits appear between bars of secondary wall material (Fig. 27–8, *O*), and occasionally in some of these the pits themselves are traversed by finer strands (Fig. 27–8, *P*). The last-formed metaxylem elements of *Botrychium* and *Helminthostachys* are uniformly circular-bordered pitted, but in *Ophioglossum* they are scalariformly-bordered pitted. Occasionally in *Botrychium dissectum* a torus occurs composed of primary wall thickening.

The apex of ophioglossaceous stems shows a single pyramidal apical initial that is characteristically long and narrow (Fig. 11–5, *A*) and has three cutting faces. Each segment cut off from the apical cell in *Botrychium* gives rise to a leaf, a condition that was once thought to exist in *Equisetum* and is found regularly in foliose bryophytes. The first division of a segment is by a periclinal wall followed by irregular divisions (D. H. Campbell, 1905). According to Petry (1915) the apical cell divides to produce a segment once each year, corresponding to the one leaf initiated per year.

Ophioglossaceous stems branch frequently or rarely, depending on the species. The branching is dichotomous in some species of *Ophioglossum* (Petry, 1915). In *Helminthostachys* and in *Botrychium* lateral apices are regularly present (Petry, 1915; W. H. Lang, 1915; Gwynne-Vaughan, 1902), but these rarely, if ever in some species, grow. Rather, they tend to be buried, sloughed off, or lose their identity by cell divisions. Lateral buds are described in *Botrychium* (Petry, 1915) as originating regularly on the petiole close to its attachment to the stem.

Roots in the Ophioglossaceae are succulent, sparsely branched, and devoid of hairs. They are mycorrhizal, and it is likely that the fungus provides most of their absorbing surface. Roots in cross section (Fig. 11–5, *E*, *F*) usually show two to five peripheral protoxylem points and frequently a core of parenchyma. The phloem is in the usual position (i.e., alternating with xylem arms) and there is an ordinary endodermis and pericycle from which lateral roots arise.

New plants arise from roots in some *Ophioglossum* species. The new stem apex

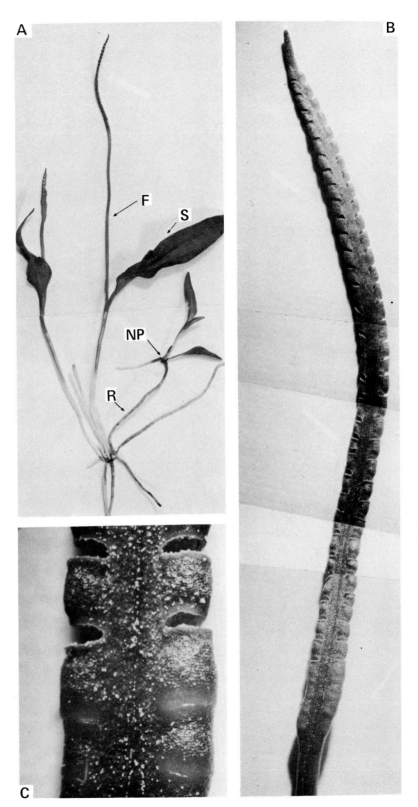

FIGURE 11–3. *Ophioglossum petiolatum*. *A*. Entire plant. F and S indicate the fertile spike and the sterile blade making up one aerial complex. R = root; NP = a new plantlet derived from the tip of a root. *B*. The fertile spike. *C*. Portion of *B* enlarged.

133

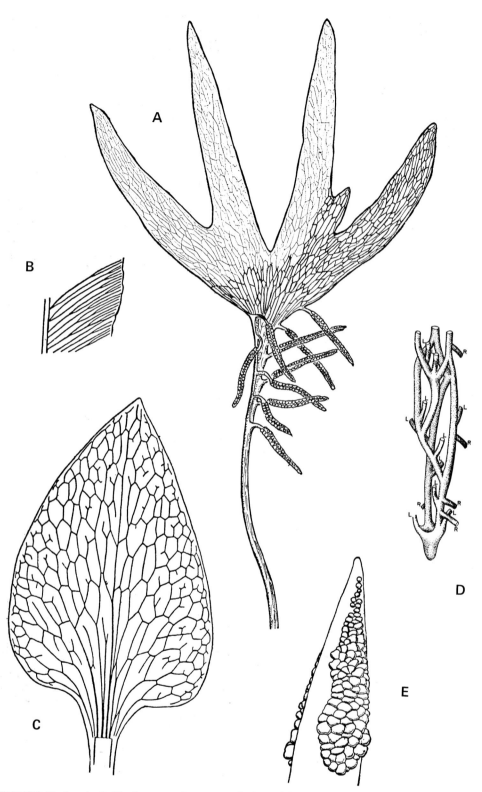

FIGURE 11–4. *A. Ophioglossum palmatum*, a single aerial complex, redrawn from Troll (1937).
B. Venation in the lamina of *Helminthostachys*, after Holttum (1954).   *C*. Venation in the lamina of
Ophioglossum pedunculosum, after Holttum (1954).   *D*. Reconstruction of the stem stele of *O.
lusitanicum*, after Gewirtz and Fahn (1960).   *E*. Primordia of the sporangiferous branches of the
fertile spike of *Helminthostachys*, after Goebel (1918).

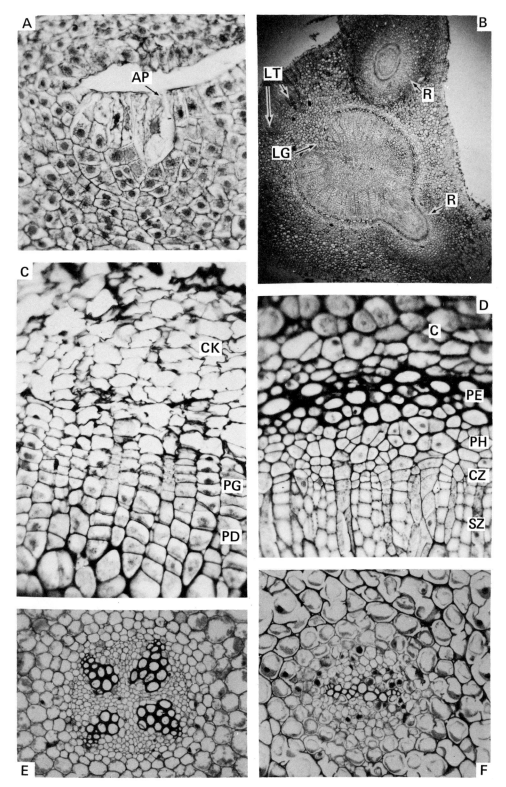

FIGURE 11–5. *A.* Stem apex of *Botrychium dissectum* as seen in longitudinal section. AP = apical cell. *B.* Cross section of the stem of *B. virginianum*. *C.* Peripheral portion of *B* enlarged. *D.* Deeper portion of *B* enlarged. *E.* Cross section of a root stele of *B. virginianum*. *F.* As *E*, but *Ophioglossum pendulum*. LT = leaf traces; R = root; LG = leaf gap; CK = cork; PG = phellogen; PD = phelloderm; C = cortex; PE = proliferated endodermal region; PH = phloem; CZ = cambial zone; SX = secondary xylem.

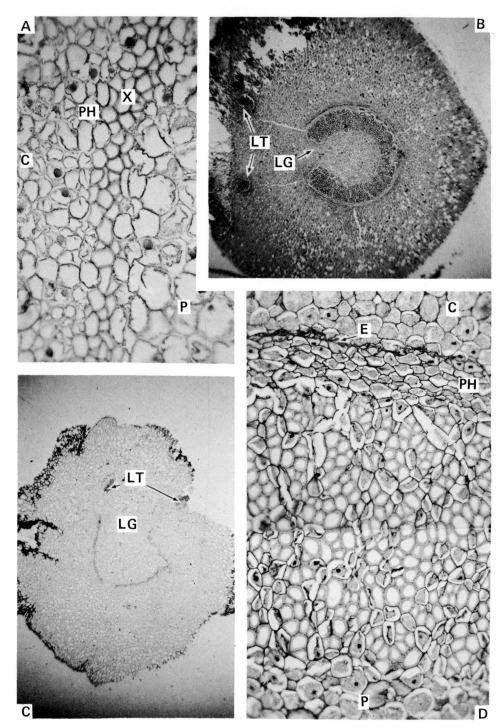

FIGURE 11–6. *A.* Portion of the vascular cylinder from *C* enlarged. *B.* Cross section of the stem of *Helminthostachys.* *C.* Cross section of the stem of *Ophioglossum pendulum.* *D.* Portion of *B* enlarged. C = cortex; PH = phloem; X = xylem; P = pith; LT = leaf trace; LG = leaf gap; E = endodermis.

arises just beneath the root cap from a cell several cells laterally removed from the root apical cell. The root apex continues to grow and the stem apex is shifted to a position some distance proximal, where it ruptures outer tissues of the root and appears to arise endogenously in a more classical manner. Application of the term "endogenous" in this instance, however, is misleading. The cell from which the new stem apex arises is comparable to a surface cell in an apex in which the apical cell does not have a distal cutting face.

The laminar portion of the aerial complex is pinnate in *Botrychium* and *Helminthostachys* Fig. 11–1, *A*, *D*; Fig. 11–2, *A*), but basal pinnae are frequently as large as the entire remainder of the structure so that the blade is overall ternate. Some miniature forms of *Botrychium* (e.g., small specimens of *B. lunaria*, *B. simplex*, and *B. matricaraeifolium*) are only obscurely pinnate. The blades show open dichotomous venation in *Botrychium* and *Helminthostachys* (Fig. 11–4, *B*) and are netted with blind ends in the simple or dichotomously lobed blades of *Ophioglossum* (Fig. 11–4, *A*, *C*).

The fertile spike is pinnate in *Botrychium* with sporangia terminally situated on the ultimate branches (Fig. 11–1, *A*, *D*, *E*). In *Helminthostachys* the sporangia are borne on peculiar lateral branches, radial in organization and symmetrically disposed around the spike axis (Fig. 11–2, *B* to *D*). On each of the branches are one to several sporangia, some of which seem to be terminal on a short stalk, and one to several irregular sterile projections. The spike in *Helminthostachys* is occasionally branched either dichotomously or as one or more of the normally diminutive sporangiferous appendages develop beyond their usual expression. In the latter case the overall branching appears pinnate. The spike of *Ophioglossum* is simple or occasionally equally or unequally dichotomously branched. The sporangia are fused laterally into elongate synangia, but each has an independent vascular supply.

The fertile spike is attached to the laminar portion of the aerial complex at variable distances from the stem. There is a very short common stalk in *Botrychium*, subgen. *Sceptridium* (e.g., *B. dissectum*), and a long one in

other *botrychia* and in *Helminthostachys*, with the spike attached near the level of attachment of the first two pinnae of the laminar part of the complex (Fig. 11–1, *A*). In *Ophioglossum* the fertile spikes, which are single in most species, appear well out on the common stalk or even upon the face of the blade (Fig. 11–3, *A*; Fig. 11–4, *A*; Fig. 11–7, *A*).

The entire aerial complex has often been considered to be a single leaf. Zimmermann (1930) interpreted the division of the leaf into fertile spike and vegetative portion to represent a dichotomy, since the plane of this forking is at right angles to those branchings in the pinnate system above. Chrysler (1910) considered the fertile spike to represent a pair of basal pinnae, reoriented and fused together. His primary evidence was the nature of the vascular supply to the spike in *Botrychium virginianum*. In later publications he agreed with Zimmermann. Nishida (1957 and earlier papers) discusses the history of the various interpretations and accepts, for the most part, Zimmermann's concept.

In *Botrychium virginianum* a pair of opposing C-shaped traces enter the common stalk of the aerial complex. From each of these a smaller trace branches off (Fig. 11–7, *F*). Farther up another pair of small traces branches from the other ends of the larger bundles (Fig. 11–7, *G*); then both swing out and depart to the fertile spike. Within the rachis of the vegetative portion of the aerial complex, the pinnae are supplied by single traces that originate in a manner similar to each of the two supplying the fertile spike. The close similarity between the vascular supply to the fertile spike and that of a pair of pinnae does not extend to all species of *Botrychium*. The vascularization of the aerial complex and of its two major components in *Helminthostachys* is shown in Fig. 11–8, *E* to *N*). A single trace departs from the stem stele in *E*. It divides in the stem cortex in *F*. It enters the stalk of the complex, divides, and the resultant bundles arrange themselves in a ring (*G* to *I*). Branching and reorientation of bundles results eventually in four groups of bundles (*J* to *N*), with the group on the adaxial side (*F* in *N*) supplying the fertile spike and the other three groups supplying the major divisions of the vegetative part of the complex. In *Ophioglossum* a ring of bundles becomes

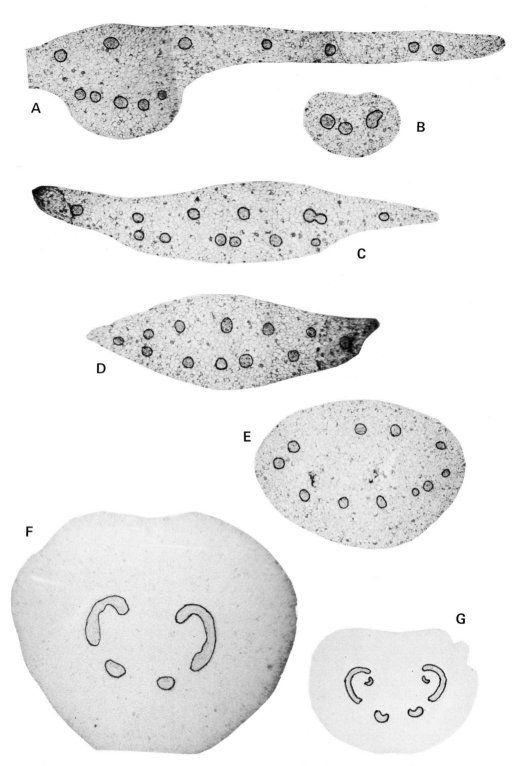

FIGURE 11–7. *A* to *E.* Cross sections of different levels through the aerial complex of *Ophioglossum pendulum. B* is a section of the fertile spike distal to *A. A* shows the blade and the decurrent base of the fertile spike. *C* to *E* are from successively lower levels below *A.* *F.* Cross section of the common stalk of the aerial complex of *Botrychium virginianum.* *G.* As *F,* but of a different one and at a slightly higher level, showing the two small traces on the inside which supply the fertile spike.

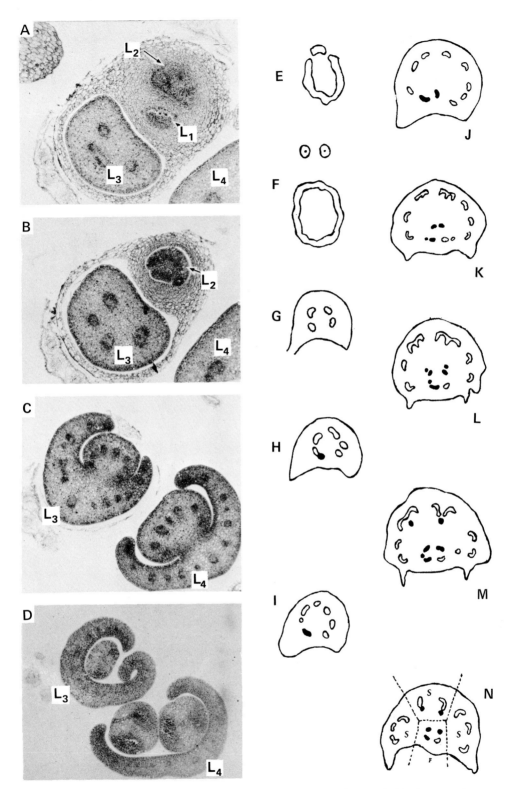

FIGURE 11–8. *A* to *D*. Cross sections from lower to higher levels of a bud of *Ophioglossum vulgatum*. The leaves are numbered from the youngest (L_1) to the oldest (L_4). *E* to *N*. Diagrams of cross sections of *Helminthostachys* from the stem stele, where the appendicular trace arises (*E*), then bifurcates within the cortex (*F*), and then enters the common stalk of the aerial complex to divide further (*G* to *N*) to establish the vascular supplies to the fertile spike (F in *N*) and sterile portions of the complex (S in *N*). Redrawn from Nishida (1956).

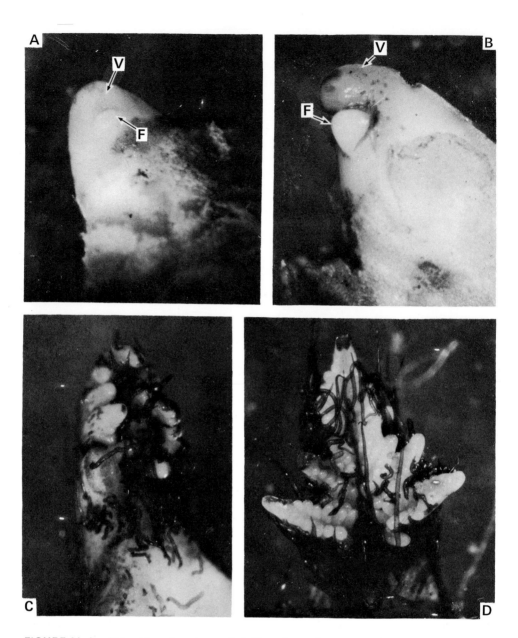

FIGURE 11–9. *Botrychium dissectum. A, B.* Two views of a young aerial complex destined to expand in 1969 as seen in dissection in 1967. F = fertile spike; V = vegetative component of the complex. *C.* Vegetative component of the complex destined to expand in 1968 from the same bud as *A* and *B*. *D.* Young fertile spike from the same complex as the vegetative component in *C*.

organized within the stalk of the complex (Fig. 11–7, *E*; L$_3$ in Fig. 11–8, *A*, *B*). At higher levels the expanded blade is encountered and the ring of bundles comes to outline a lens-shaped zone (Fig. 11–7, *D*, *C*). The bundles on the adaxial side become more closely grouped in the de-

current base of the fertile spike (Fig. 11–7, *A*; Fig. 11–8, *C*) and then enter it (Fig. 11–7, *B*).

The leaflike organs (i.e., the aerial complexes) in *Botrychium* are initiated one per year and take approximately 7 to 8 years to mature. The plant in Fig. 11–1, *D* was collected in the summer of 1967, and the leaflike organ is fully expanded for that year. The one for 1966 wintered over and is still present. Recognizable in the bud were the structures for 1968 (vegetative part shown in Fig. 11–9, C; and fertile part or spike in D), the one for 1969 (in A, B), and the one for 1970. Each young leaflike organ is enclosed in the basal sheath of the next older one, a feature common to all the Ophioglossaceae. The sheath of the current leaf of a *Botrychium* specimen is indicated by SH in Fig. 11–1, F. Other buds show similar numbers of young leaves of very comparable stages in development. From sections and from Petry's descriptions the youngest leaflike organ readily recognizable in dissections is already 2 years old, and there are, within the bud, two even younger ones.

The fertile spike in *Botrychium* is seen when the leaflike organ is about 4 years old as a conical protuberance (F in Fig. 11–9, A, B) overarched slightly by the apex of the vegetative part of the complex (V). According to Petry the spike is first recognizable as an apical cell on the adaxial side of the apical cell of the vegetative structure. The details of the cell lineages between the two apical cells have not been determined and it is important that they should be, especially to determine whether or not an ontogenetic dichotomy is involved. In terms of what is known, the fertile spike in early stages suggests the epipetiolar buds found in certain pteroid ferns and the apex in close association with a "leaf" of *Stromatopteris*. Ontogenetic evidence available seems to completely contradict the suggestion that the spike represents a pair of fused pinnae. Whether the entire aerial complex of *Botrychium* (and the other genera of the family) is leaf or the vegetative portion alone is leaf with the fertile spike only secondarily associated with it remains to be determined.

Following the stage shown in Fig. 11–9, B, the two apices grow and each produces a pinnately branched structure face to face with the other one (the two of a single complex are shown separated in Fig. 11–9, C, D). The vegetative portion later comes to envelop the fertile one within the bud.

The peculiar sporangiferous appendages borne on the fertile spike of *Helminthostachys* are described as originating in two linear clusters (Fig. 11–4, E). By comparison with the other two genera, this might be assumed to be derived from a more simple two-rowed arrangement.

Ophioglossaceous sporangia are massive and, among extant ferns and fernlike plants, larger ones are found only in the genus *Tmesipteris*. The sporangia originate from surface cells, probably each from a single cell in *Botrychium* (Bower, 1896; D. H. Campbell, 1928; Cardiff, 1905) and from a group within the "sporangiogenic band" in *Ophioglossum* (Bower, 1896). A periclinal division establishes the single primary archesporial cell in *Botrychium*. In *Ophioglossum*, on the other hand, later divisions may occur in the outer layers of the sporangium and add additional patches of sporogenous tissue. The wall comes to be multilayered (Fig. 11–10, A to F) and the sporogenous tissue extensive. The latter becomes separated into blocks in *Botrychium* and the premeiotic mitoses may be synchronous within the entire sporogenous mass or within the individual blocks (Fig. 11–10, C). Several of the inner wall layers act as tapetum, the cells of which divide amitotically and become polyploid (Cardiff, 1905; Steil, 1935). The spores throughout the family show triradiate markings. In *Botrychium* the sporangial wall at maturity is composed of about four to seven inner layers and an outer layer of cells with thickened inner and anticlinal walls (Fig. 11–10 A, B). At the line of dehiscence, which is transverse and apical (Fig. 11–1, B, E), the cells of the outer layer are anticlinally short, causing a distinct groove (Fig. 11–1, B; Fig. 11–10, B). Before dehiscence the cells of the inner wall layers break down just beneath the line and those of the outer layer pull apart as a result of shrinkage of cells over the entire surface.

The intersporangial tissue in *Ophioglossum* keeps pace with sporangial growth by cell divisions and cell elongation so that the sporangia are not raised individually above the marginal surface (Fig. 11–10, F). The line of dehiscence is transverse and apical with respect to each sporangium.

The gametophytes of the Ophioglossaceae are homothallic, subterranean, mycorrhizic, and fundamentally axial in organization. In various species they become bilateral in form as they mature and are only obscurely axial.

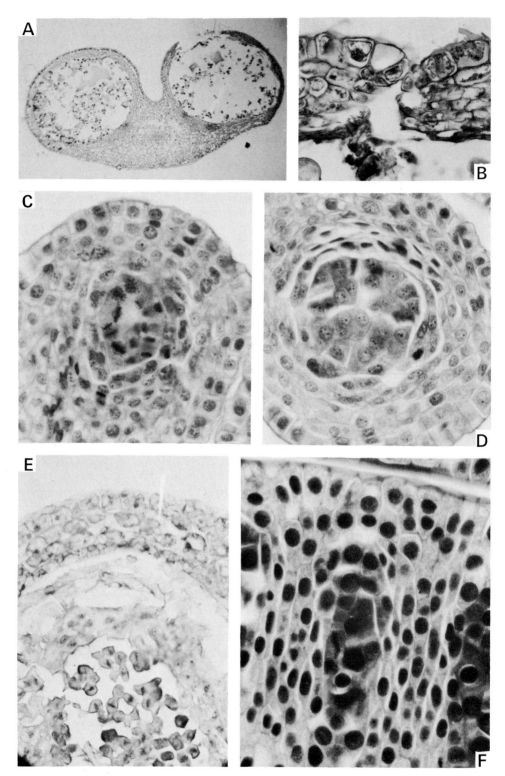

FIGURE 11–10. *A.* Cross section of a unit of the fertile spike of *Botrychium lunaria* showing two sporangia. *B.* Cross section through the line of dehiscence of a sporangium of *B. lunaria.* *C, D.* Cross sections of immature sporangia of *B. lunaria.* *E.* Same of *B. multifidum.* *F.* Longitudinal section through the immature fertile spike of *Ophioglossum vulgatum* cut parallel to its flat side. One sporangium is shown in the center and parts of two others on the edges of the photograph.

142

Ophioglossaceous gametophytes are known for eight species of *Botrychium*, seven of *Ophioglossum*, and the one of *Helminthostachys*: much of the information on these is summarized by Boullard (1963).

Early divisions of the spore and immediate cellular derivatives establish a spherical mass of cells with a distinct apical cell in the very few species that are known at this stage. Jeffrey managed to germinate spores of *Botrychium virginianum* on *Sphagnum*, but the young gametophytes died at about the seven- to eight-celled stage, presumably because at this stage the fungus was required for further growth. In nature the apex expands and the spherical stage is replaced by the teardrop stage. Still later, an axis, branched or unbranched, is maintained with a symmetrical apical meristem in *Ophioglossum* (quite uniform in *O. vulgatum*, Fig. 11–12, *A*, *B*; occasionally somewhat flattened in *O. pendulum*, Fig. 11–11, *C*, *D*, *F*) and in *Helminthostachys* (Fig. 11–12, *D*), in which it is upright and quite stubby. In *Botrychium*, although the apical meristem persists, the gametophyte changes its form considerably after the teardrop stage and becomes bilaterally symmetrical and distinctly dorsiventral.

In species that retain a radially symmetrical, axial organization (Fig. 11–11, *C*, *D*, *F*, *H*; Fig. 11–12, *A*, *B*, *D*), rhizoids and sex organs are distributed uniformly over the surface. Despite some reports to the contrary, all young gametophytes have rhizoids and older ones bear their scars. The rhizoids are septate in *Botrychium* (Fig. 11–11, *G*). Apical branching of gametophytes is apparently general in the family, although rare in *Botrychium* and often very obscured, especially in *Helminthostachys* (Fig. 11–12, *D*), by pronounced lobes that are incompletely described.

Internally, all ophioglossaceous gemetophytes are uniformly parenchymatous. An endophytic fungus is present in all three genera, but it is restricted to a particular zone only in *Botrychium*, where it extends throughout approximately the lower half of the horizontally oriented body.

The gametophyte of *Botrychium*, although quite irregular in form at times and occasionally nearly spherical, has a very definable morphology referable to three distinct meristematic zones. Irrespective of the orientation of the gametophytic axis in the teardrop stage, the axis comes to be essentially horizontal. On assumption of the new orientation, a peripheral thickening meristem becomes active over the lower surface (Fig. 11–11, *G*). Its cells divide in regular planes much like a cambium. It causes a rounding of the lower surface, an upturning of either end of the plant body (Fig. 11–11, *A*), and often causes distinct folds of tissue along the margins which become visible from the top (Fig. 11–12, *E*). The apical meristem, then, more often comes to be situated on the upper side of the body near the apical end (Fig. 11–11, *A*). On the upper surface of the gametophyte, meristematic eruptions occur, traceable to the apical meristem, which tend to form a median ridge or upright keel (Fig. 11–12, *C*; ANR in Fig. 11–11, *A*, *B*). All or nearly all antheridia are borne on these ridges, which are pronounced in species with larger gametophytes, such as *B. virginianum* and *B. dissectum* and often absent in species with smaller ones, such as *B. lunaria*, *B. simplex*, and *B. matricariaefolium*. The archegonia are borne on the more flattened areas of the upper gametophytic surface on either side of the antheridial ridge (Fig. 11–11, *B*; Fig. 11–12, *E*). A sequence of younger to older archegonia may be seen from the apical meristem onto the archegonial plane. Another similar sequence may frequently be seen from near the margin of the gametophyte just inside the upturned edge across the archegonial plane toward the antheridial ridge. This, then, is the position of the third meristem of the body, the marginal meristem (MM in Fig. 11–11, *E*). A more complete account of the growth of the gametophyte is given by Foster (1964).

A peripheral thickening meristem exists near the older ends of gametophytes of *Ophioglossum vulgatum* and probably also of *Helminthostachys*. The meristem, however, does not produce a large amount of secondary tissue, and the overall form of the gametophyte still appears cylindrical.

Although the gametophyte of *Botrychium* has never been seen to branch in the vertical plane, pairs of apices are frequent, one directly above the other (Bierhorst, 1958a). In such a case, the upper one apparently becomes lost in the generalized meristematic eruption to form

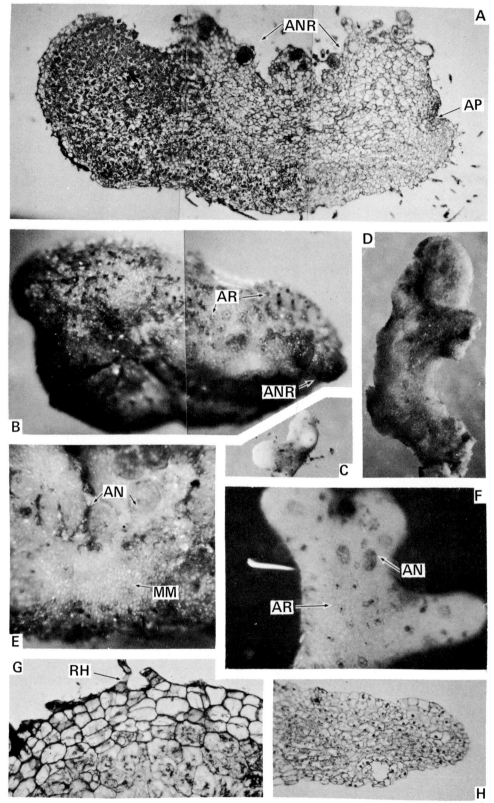

FIGURE 11–11. *A.* Vertical longitudinal section of a gametophyte of *Botrychium virginianum.* *B.* Gametophyte of *B. dissectum* as viewed from the top. *C, D, F.* Gametophytes of *Ophioglossum pendulum.* *E.* Portion of the upper margin of the gametophyte of *B. dissectum.* *G.* Cross section through the lower portion of a gametophyte of *B. dissectum.* *H.* Longitudinal section through a branch of a gametophyte of *Ophioglossum pendulum.* ANR = antheridial ridge ; AP = apical meri-stem ; AR = archegonia ; AN = antheridia ; MM = marginal meristem ; RH = rhizoid.

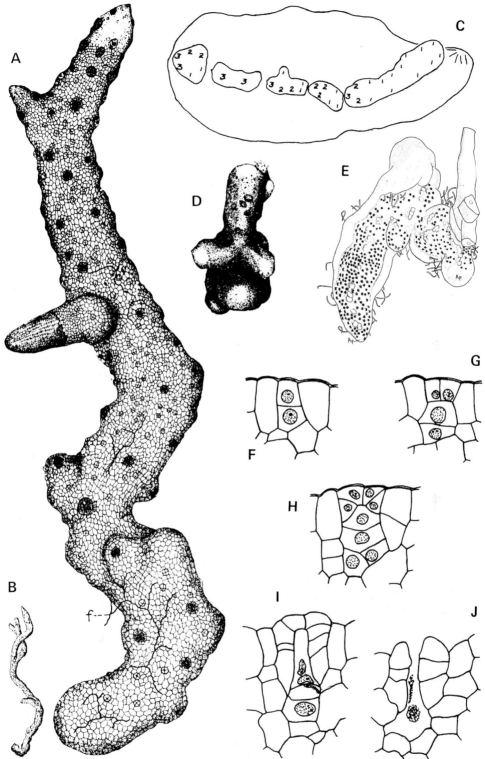

FIGURE 11–12. *A, B.* Gametophyte of *Ophioglossum vulgatum*, after Bruchmann (1904). *C.* Diagram of the upper view of a gametophyte of *Botrychium virginianum*, after Bierhorst (1958a). 1, 2, and 3 are antheridia numbered from younger to older. *D.* Gametophyte of *Helminthostachys*, after W. H. Lang (1902). *E.* Branched gametophyte of *Botrychium virginianum* with a young sporophyte attached proximal to the right-hand apical meristem (Ap), after Bierhorst (1958a). *F* to *J.* Stages in the development of the archegonium of *Ophioglossum pendulum*, redrawn from Campbell (1907).

145

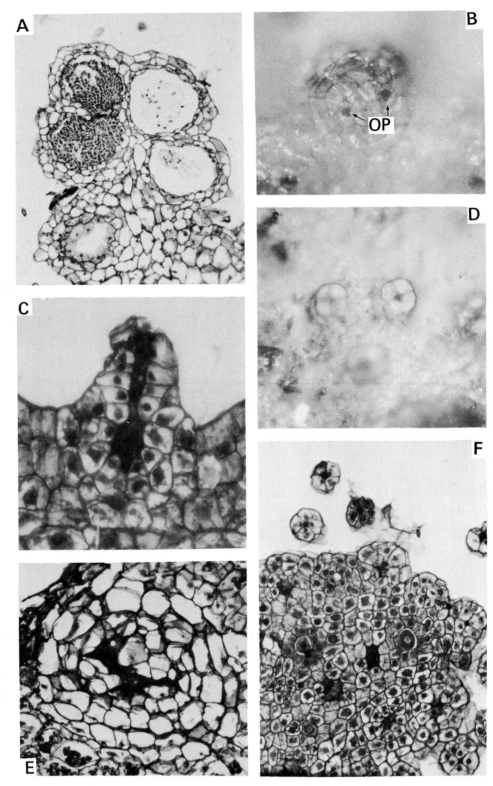

FIGURE 11–13. *A.* Section through the antheridial ridge of *Botrychium dissectum*. *B.* Antheridium of *B. dissectum* showing two opercula (OP). *C.* Mature archegonium of *B. virginianum* in longitudinal section. *D.* Surface view of archegonia of *B. dissectum*. *E.* Cross section through the venter region of an old, postmature archegonium of *B. virginianum*. *F.* Section tangential to the archegonial plane in *B. virginianum* showing sections of several archegonia at various levels.

the antheridial ridge. When the ridge is discontinuous and when the separated segments are relatively young, there is often a developmental series of antheridia from younger to older antheridia within each segment (1 to 3 are younger to older antheridia in Fig. 11–12, C). From these observations it has been concluded that the ridge represents a series of highly modified, determinate, upright branches partly or completely fused to each other.

Ophioglossaceous antheridia are relatively massive, with a size range from mostly under 100 μ in Botrychium matricariaefolium to up to 200 μ in B. simplex. They are almost entirely sunken (Fig. 11–13, A; an empty one in Fig. 11–11, H) and spherical to oblong. Only the jacket exposed at the surface is traceable to the antheridial initial, and here it is two cells thick, except at the opercular cells. The latter are single cells, but there may be from one to four scattered over the surface of the antheridium (two, OP, are shown in surface view in Fig. 11–13, B). In Botrychium breakdown of tissue separating two adjacent antheridia will occur occasionally, and the common contents will exit through the opercula of one (Fig. 11–13, A, the pair of antheridia on the upper left). The first division of the antheridial initial establishes the spermatogenous tissue as the inner cell. The inner cell layer of the jacket on the outside is continuous with a jacket layer on the inside that is derived from cells adjacent to the antheridial initial. The sperm are large, about 10 μ long, and multiflagellate.

Archegonia are large in Botrychium (Fig. 11–13, C) and much less so in Helminthostachys and Ophioglossum (Fig. 11–12, J). The neck is uniformly four cells in cross section at its distal end (Fig. 11–13, D), but in Botrychium additional anticlinal and periclinal divisions occur at the base of the neck (Fig. 11–13, C: cross sections of several archegonia at various levels appear in F). The periclinal division of the archegonial initial establishes the neck mother cell and the mother cell of the axial row (Fig. 11–12, F). The latter comes to be composed of a basal pad cell (Fig. 11–12, G, I) that may divide (H), the egg cell, ventral canal cell, and two neck canal cells or a single one with two nuclei (Fig. 11–12, I). A complete jacket is conspicuous in Botrychium surrounding the venter (Fig. 11–13, C), and it

often proliferates in older unfertilized archegonia after the disintegration of the axial row of cells (Fig. 11–13, E). Archegonial dehiscence in the family is generally accomplished by the separation of the four terminal neck cells, but in one collection of Botrychium virginianum, many archegonia showed separation, then lateral radiation of the four rows of cells, down to about four cells from the distal end.

Embryogeny is outstanding in the high degree of variability that it exhibits within the Ophioglossaceae, and even within certain genera (Table 11–1). The variability is expressed in a differential growth of the zygote before division, the orientation of the first division wall, the relative sizes of the cells in the two-celled stage, the presence or absence of a suspensor, exoscopy and endoscopy, origin of organs in the quadrant zones, the relative orientation of embryonic organs to each other, degree of development of the foot, and the relative time of appearance of each organ. Although such features have in general been considered fundamentally conservative in most other taxa, similar broad ranges in variation are now suggested for at least two families of filicalean ferns, the Schizaeaceae and the Hymenophyllaceae, and the list may very well increase as embryologically unknown species are described.

The first division of the zygote tends, throughout the family, to be nearly transverse to the archegonial axis with variation of as much as a 35-degree tilt (Fig. 11–14, B, E; in B the lower of the two transverse walls is the first one). In Helminthostachys and three species of Botrychium, the first division results in the formation of a conspicuously smaller hypobasal cell (that deeper within the archegonium) and a larger epibasal cell (the cell toward the neck canal). In all but one of these species, B. matricariaefolium, the zygote elongates before division and the epibasal cell develops into a suspensor while the hypobasal cell is the proembryonic cell. In all other embryologically known species of the family, the first division of the zygote is more or less equal (Fig. 11–14, E, M) and both cells are proembryonic and no suspensor is formed.

Early divisions of the proembryo generally result in a quadrant stage (Fig. 11–14, F), but

TABLE 11–1. Embryological characteristics of Ophioglossaceae.

	Zygote Elongation	Suspensor	Two-Celled Embryo	Stem Origin*
Helminthostachys	+	Two-celled filament	Small hypobasal and large epibasal cell	Endoscopic
Botrychium dissectum	+	One- or two-celled filament	Small hypobasal and large epibasal cell	Endoscopic
B. japonicum	+ · (probably)	Cell mass	Small hypobasal and large epibasal cell	Endoscopic
B. matricariaefolium	None or slight	None	Small hypobasal and large epibasal cell	Endoscopic
B. virginianum	None or slight	None	Two (±) equal cells	Exoscopic
B. simplex	None or slight	None	Two (±) equal cells	Exoscopic
B. lanceolatum	None or slight	None	Two (±) equal cells	Endoscopic
B. lunaria	None or slight	None	Two (±) equal cells	?
B. lanunginosum	None or slight	None	Two (±) equal cells	?
Ophioglossum	None or slight	None	Two (±) equal cells	Exoscopic

* Exoscopic, derived from an epibasal quadrant zone ; endoscopic, derived from an hypobasal quadrant zone.

frequently, as intraspecific variation, the second division is parallel to the first. Organs of the embryo (i.e., stem, leaf, root, and foot) may not be referred to specific quadrants, and they are not clearly recognizable until the 100- to 200-cell stage (Fig. 11–14, *O*). The organs in certain species, however, have been traced approximately to quadrant zones such that some at least may be described as exoscopic (the stem from an epibasal quadrant zone) or endoscopic. There is some differential growth and shifting orientation of parts during later embryogeny so that the stem position in older embryos is only crudely indicative of its initial position. This can be visualized by following the sequences in Fig. 11–14; *A-B-C-J = Botrychium dissectum*, *A-B-C-I = Helminthostachys*, *D-E-F-H-K*, and *L-M-N-O = Botrychium virginianum*.

The two embryological extremes in the family might be represented by *B. dissectum* (Fig. 11–15, *B, C*) and *B. virginianum* (Fig. 11–15, *A*). In *B. virginianum* the stem is exoscopic (i.e., it is traceable to an epibasal quadrant zone that also produces the first leaf). The root originates in a central position between two quadrant zones, one epibasal and one hypobasal. The foot is massive and most of the hypobasal region (two quadrant zones) takes part in its formation. The final orientation of parts is indicated in Fig. 11–14, *K* and Fig. 11–15, *A*. The section in Fig. 11–15, *A* is longitudinal to the embryonic axis and shows the root (R) in cross section.

In *B. dissectum* (Fig. 11–14, *J*; Fig. 11–15, *B, C*) the stem is endoscopic (i.e., hypobasal in origin), the leaf is epibasal in origin, the root is probably mostly hypobasal in origin, and the foot is in part hypo- and in part epibasal. In Fig. 11–15, *B* the section is longitudinal to the embryonic axis. The root is shown in longitudinal section after it grew straight down, through, and out the lower side of the gametophyte. The foot (F in Fig. 11–15, *C*, which is part of *B* enlarged) does not appear as a protrusion but merely as a half-girdle of tissue with the characteristic contents and staining reactions of foot tissue. The bump on the right side of the embryo just above the foot and almost on the leaf base represents the point of attachment of the suspensor.

The origin of the Ophioglossales and its

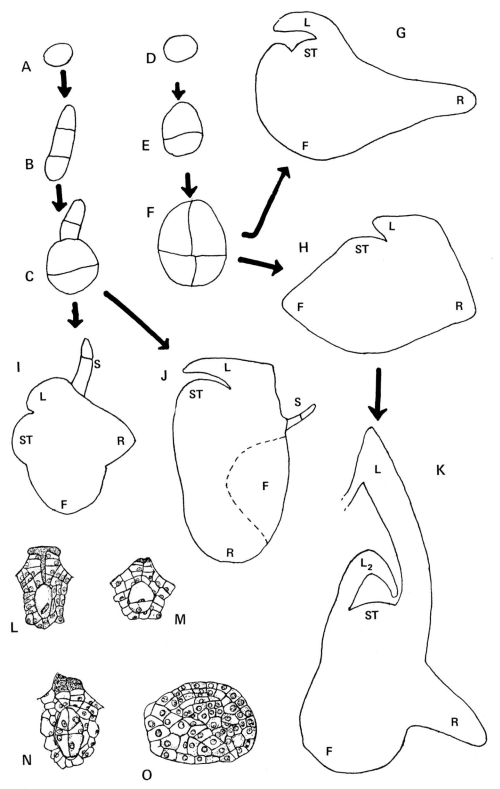

FIGURE 11–14. Embryogeny of the Ophioglossaceae. The series are read as follows : *A* to *B* to *C* to *J*, *Botrychium dissectum*, based on H. L. Lyon (1905) ; *A* to *B* to *C* to *I*, *Helminthostachys*, based on W. H. Lang (1914) ; *D* to *E* to *F* to *G*, *Ophioglossum vulgatum*, based on Bruchmann (1904) ; *D* to *E* to *F* to *H* to *K*, *Botrychium virginianum*, based on Jeffrey (1896). *L* to *O*. *B. virginianum*, after Jeffrey (1896).

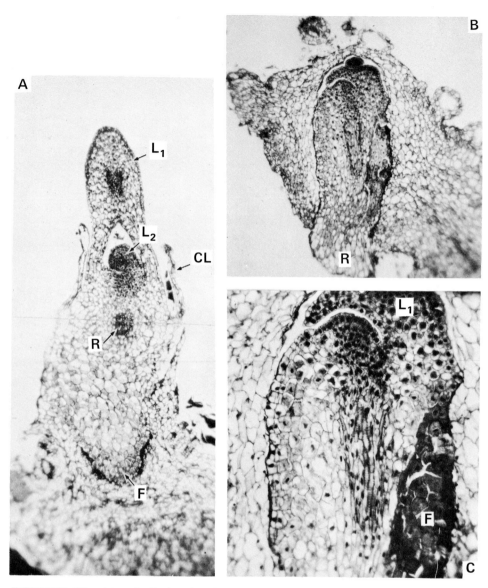

FIGURE 11–15. *A.* Longitudinal section of a young sporophyte attached to its parental gametophyte in *Botrychium virginianum. B.* As *A,* but *B. dissectum. C.* Portion of *B* enlarged. L = leaf ; CL = calyptra ; R = root ; F = foot.

relationship to other known taxa are very obscure. Various authors in the past have suggested derivation from rhyniophytes, coenopterid ferns, bryophytes, and lycopods. Ophioglossaceous morphology suggests that the taxon is rather primitive and probably very antique, but its fossil history is unknown. Most commonly the group has been considered to represent an early offshoot of the phylogenetic line that eventually gave rise to the Filicales, but recently obtained information on the Psilotaceae, Stromatopteridaceae, Schizaeaceae, and Hymenophyllaceae seems to suggest that the "higher ferns" are in most respects more primitive than are the Ophioglossales. At present there is room for considerable speculation, and it is likely that only the fossil record can supply the answers.

In the view held by the present author, the Ophioglossaceae are most likely derivatives of the Protopteridales in the Aneurophytopsida or some form in a linage between the Trimerophytaceae and the Protopteridales. In support of this interpretation, one can cite the double leaf traces with some traces originating by circumferential division of strands of the cauline stele, the secondary vascular tissues and periderm of *Botrychium*, the stipular sheaths, circular pits in tracheary elements between massive bars of a reticulum, sporangial trusses with terminal sporangia, and centrarch protostele in the young sporophyte. All these characteristics are found in the Ophioglossaceae with counterparts in the suggested ancestors.

The next-most-plausible view is that the Ophioglossaceae represent derivatives of the coenopterids or botryopterids. Most suggestive of this is the globose sporangium, with apical and transverse dehiscence and a multilayered wall, and the axillary buds of *Botrychium*, as Petry (1915) has suggested. There is, however, a single report of coenopterid spores (D. H. Scott, 1906) that germinated within a sporangium and produced filaments initially.

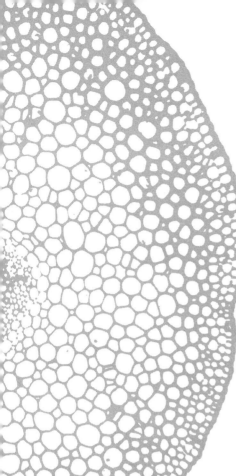

12

Psilotaceae and Noeggerathiaceae

The Psilotaceae is a small family of no economic importance that constitutes a very inconspicuous element of the world flora. Its morphology, however, along with that of several presumably closely related families, suggests that it may present clues to the fundamental nature and origin of plant organs. From what is known of the Psilotaceae, the Stromatopteridaceae, the Gleicheniaceae, and the Schizaeaceae, it might be suggested that among these families there exist gradate series of organs, from stem systems to leaves and from stems to roots. The series that suggest themselves may be present not only in a structural and in a physiological sense but, more significantly, in terms of progressively more elaborate and fixed morphogenetic events (determining factors) that occur during their ontogeny. The many experiments performed during the 1940s and 1950s that had as their goal an elucidation of those ontogenetic events which determine form were performed on species in which the organs are clearly definable and fixed in their morphology early in ontogeny. In the Psilotaceae and Stromatopteridaceae, however, "organs" retain the potential to develop along various morphological pathways until rather late in ontogeny, and even after seeming determination may change by further development. There seems to be a potential for experimental studies, yet undeveloped, within these two families that does not exist elsewhere.

The seemingly excessive treatment of the Psilotaceae in this volume is given not only because of the very special interest it generates and the unusual significance it bears, but also because of the particular mistreatment it has received in many general texts in the past and

FIGURE 12–1. Fronds or parts of fronds of *Tmesipteris* species. *A. T. forsteri* from New Zealand. *B. T.* sp., a terrestrial New Caledonian species. *C.* Part of *B* enlarged. *D, E. T. lanceolata* from New Caledonia. *F.* Polynesian form of *T. tannensis*. *G. T.* (cf. *vieillardi*) from New Caledonia.

because of the amount of original material that must be presented and sufficiently documented.

The Psilotaceae consists of two genera, *Tmesipteris* with about 10 species and *Psilotum* with 2 or 3. Although the two genera appear externally quite different from each other, in most details they intergrade, and they certainly do not represent two separate families as some researchers have suggested.

Tmesipteris is a tropical, Asiatic, and Far Eastern oceanic genus. Most species are epiphytes, "rooted" within the root mantle of palms or trunked ferns or in collections of organic debris within the trees. There are two terrestrial forms, *T. vieillardi* (Fig. 12–1, *G*) and *T.* sp. (Fig. 12–1, *B*, *C*) both of which may actually have been included in the type collections of the former described from New Caledonia by Dangeard. The "aerial shoots" or "fronds" of most species are unbranched or rarely branched (Fig. 12–1, *B*, *D* to *G*). *Tmesipteris forsteri*,[1] of which a small portion of a "frond" is shown in Fig. 12–1, *A*, is probably consistently highly branched.

The "fronds" of some species of *Tmesipteris* are quite flattened, with two rows of subopposite pairs of pinnae and a terminal one [e.g., *T. lanceolata* (Fig. 12–1, *D*, *E*: Fig. 12–15, *E*) and *T. tannensis* (Fig. 12–1, *F*)]. At the other extreme lies *T. vieillardi* (Fig. 12–1, *G*), with apparent radial symmetry of the frond and pseudospiral arrangement of pinnae. The pinnae themselves have a distinct tip (the equivalent of the entire *Psilotum* pinna), which matures early in its ontogeny, and a basal part (the bulk of the pinna), which is of later origin. Pinnae of *Tmesipteris* occurring at the bases of fronds are of the psilotoid type in their entirety (Fig. 12–1, *G*) and occasionally on fronds of *Psilotum* pinnae develop the tmesipteroid base (Fig. 12–2, *C*). Smaller pinnae of *Tmesipteris* at the base of the frond are avascular; the larger, later-formed ones are supplied by a single vein.

Psilotum, presumably the more specialized genus of the family, is tropical or nearly tropical in its distribution and is well known to botanists by the widely cultivated tetraploid *P.*

---

[1] The "legal" name of this species is still probably *Psilotum forsteri* Endl. No evidence of recombination was discovered.

---

nudum (Fig. 12–2, *A*). This species exhibits a decussately dichotomous frond with spirally arranged distal pinnae but with some subopposite pairing of many pinnae at the very base of the frond. The pinnae of *Psilotum* are minute in general and only occasionally are vascularized and then with a very small, often incompletely developed trace. *Psilotum complanatum* (Fig. 12–2, *E*) is a small form, with fronds up to 6 or 8 inches long. Branches of the frond are flattened and have pinnae inserted along the edges in subopposite pairs. *Psilotum flaccidum* is a long (to 3 ft), pendulous epiphyte with flattening and appendage insertion on fronds as in *P. complanatum*, from which it is often not recognized as a distinct species (Fig. 12–2, *B*: Fig. 12–15, *F*). The branching of the frond in *P. complanatum* and *P. flaccidum* is mostly within a single plane.

The subterranean parts of the plant body are quite similar throughout the Psilotaceae. They are branched, appendage-less, rhizoid-bearing axes, probably growing without any relationship to the gravitational direction. The "rhizomes" tend to be in a definite clump in *Psilotum nudum* (Fig. 12–2, *A*), but in other species they seem to be more runnerlike in disposition.

The rhizoids are distributed uniformly over the surface, are situated medianly upon an epidermal cell from which they are separated by a cross wall, and are from one to three cells in length (Fig. 12–3, *A*, *D*, *F*). They are covered by a cuticle, as is the surface of the epidermal cells. Probably the major absorbing surface of the subterranean system is presented by the mass of fungal hyphae that occur within the cells of the cortex and extend out through the rhizoids and into the substratum. In *Psilotum nudum* the tips of some of the rhizoids when in an immature stage, proliferate to produce a small mass of tissue (a gemma or brood body) that is capable of regenerating another subterranean axis and subsequently an entire plant (Fig. 12–3, *B*, *C*).

Branching of the subterranean axes ranges from equal and dichotomous to quite lateral or it may be irregular, owing to injuries and to variable, multiple, meristematic center regeneration. When an equal dichotomy occurs, the single apical cell with its three cutting faces divides equally, establishing two new apical

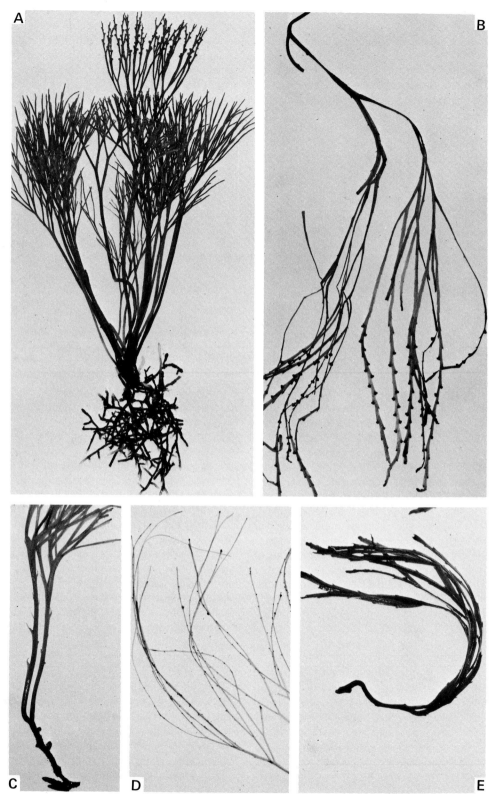

FIGURE 12–2. Plants, or portions, of *Psilotum* species. *A.* Tetraploid *P. nudum*, a greenhouse plant. *B. P. flaccidum* from Fiji, sun form. The shade form bears fewer sporangia and is longer. *C. P. nudum* from the same clone as *A*, showing pinnae with tmesipteroid bases. *D.* Diploid form of *P. nudum* from Fiji. This is reproduced at the same scale as *A*. *E. P. complanatum* from Hawaii.

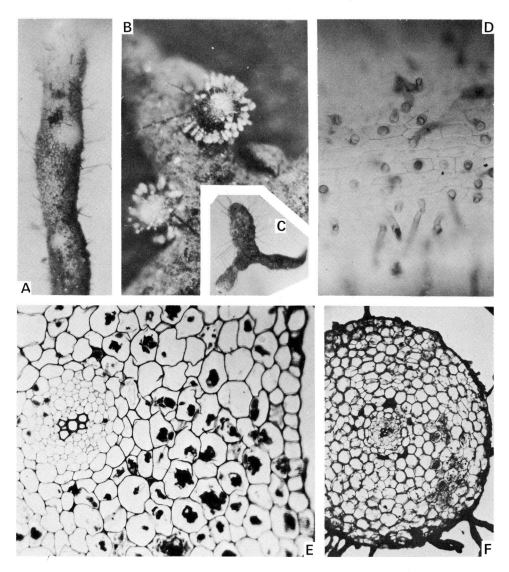

FIGURE 12–3. Subterranean axes or rhizomes of the sporophyte of *Psilotum nudum*. *A* to *C*, *E*, *F* from the tetraploid race ; *D* from the diploid. *A*. Surface view showing two lateral apices. *B*. Brood bodies on tips of rhizoids. *C*. Entire plantlet grown from a brood body. *D*. Surface view, showing rhizoids and their attachments. *E*. Cross section. *F*. Thick hand section. *A* to *C* after Bierhorst (1954c).

cells and subsequent meristematic centers, instead of unequally, as it usually does, to produce a small cell and a large one that remains the apical cell (Fig. 12–4, *C*). In lateral branching, a small area on one side of the apical meristem seems to be left behind as a residual meristem, while cells around it differentiate and mature. Often the meristematic center of the rhizome becomes lateral and subapical by differential growth; here it divides in a plane transverse to the axis, a phenomenon also seen in *Stromatopteris*.

Apical injuries are common in *Psilotum* when the plant is grown in a sandy substratum. The naked apices are apparently mechanically injured to various degrees as they grow

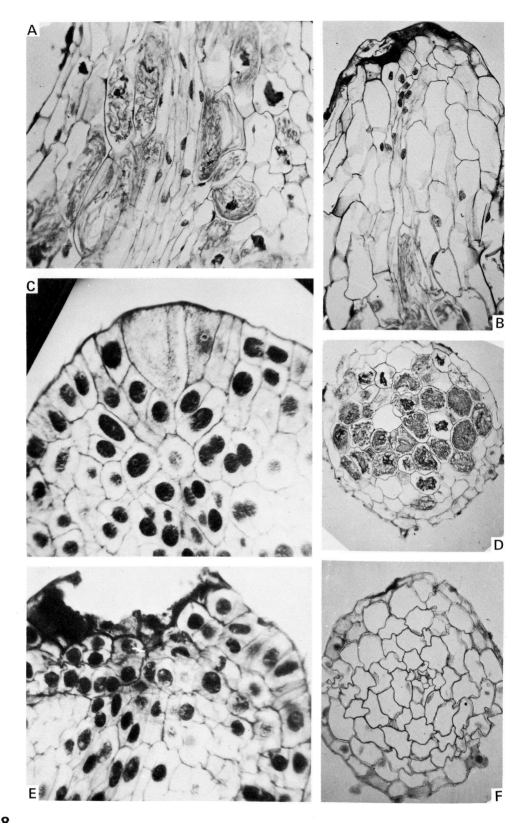

through the soil. If regeneration occurs (Fig. 12–4, *E*), from one to several new centers of meristematic activity, and subsequent new apices, are formed. There is apparently considerable apical dominance, and often well-organized apices do not grow out to produce new branches (Fig. 12–3, *A*).

↙ The internal anatomy of the rhizome of all psilotaceous species varies with the diameter. The smaller ones in *Psilotum nudum* (mostly less than 1 mm in diameter) are avascular, and in cross section one sees only uniform parenchyma with the endophytic fungus (Fig. 12–4, *D*). In slightly larger rhizomes a central core of undifferentiated but elongate cells occurs (Fig. 12–4, *A*, *F*). In still larger ones a complete stele, the complexity of which again varies with axial diameter, is present. The smaller steles show one to several centrally placed tracheids (all metaxylem) surrounded by sieve cells that are very difficult to distinguish in cross section from the pericycle, which surrounds them (Fig. 12–3, *E*, *F*). A diagrammatic endodermis clearly delimits the stele. In larger rhizomes (2 to 3 mm in diameter) the xylem mass becomes dissected in various degrees by the differentiation of parenchyma among the tracheids. In these steles, unlike the smaller ones, certain of the smaller tracheids mature earlier than the others, but their position varies. The cortical cells of *Tmesipteris* rhizomes frequently bear rather diagrammatic collenchymatous thickenings. Collenchyma in the clearly definable sense, such as occurs in *Tmesipteris*, is particularly rare outside of seed plants and occurs to this author's knowledge elsewhere in the "vascular cryptogams" only in the intercalary meristem of certain species of *Equisetum* and in underground axes of *Stromatopteris*. Collenchymatous thickenings of a different nature do occur in such foliose structures as the "leaves" of liverworts and gametophytes of many ferns.

In addition to the mere presence or absence of a vascular strand in the smaller subterranean axes of *Psilotum*, there are occasionally longitudinal interruptions of the stele where vascular differentiation took place, stopped, and then resumed again. This phenomenon has also been observed in the gametophyte of *Psilotum nudum*. The cessation of vascular differentiation is correlated with a reduction in the total bulk of the apical meristem, although the intensity of meristematic activity may also be involved, as was suggested by Wardlaw (1944). A reduction in bulk often seems to be the direct result of apical injury and an increase in bulk to regeneration. If such shifts in size are above and below the "critical limit," a vascular interruption will be observed subsequently. Figure 12–4, *B* shows the tip of a subterranean axis in *Psilotum* that was avascular at its proximal end, produced a procambium, and was then injured. The procambium ended abruptly and some of its cells enlarged to take part in the regeneration. If complete regeneration had occurred, procambium might have again been differentiated from the new apex (or apices).

The aerial fronds of the Psilotaceae are formed from the tips of subterranean axes, the causative factors being in part unknown. Light striking an apex will cause it to turn up and develop into a frond. However, occasionally an apex as deep as 10 cm below the soil surface will turn upward and initiate the aerial axis. The process of frond formation can be reversed, with the production of a new subterranean axis directly from the frond apex. This can be done by burying the tip at any time before ultimate ontogenetic determination of the frond. In *Tmesipteris* it is not uncommon to find, near the surface of the substrate, underground axes that had "turned on and turned off" pinna production several times.

FIGURE 12–4. Rhizomes of the tetraploid *Psilotum nudum*. *A*. Longitudinal section showing central stele, devoid of xylem, and cortex with fungus. *B*. Longitudinal section of an apex. The lower portion is astelic. In the younger portion, a procambial strand was produced, then the apex was injured and some regeneration began. *C*. Apex with a pronounced apical cell. The procambium begins about three cells below the apical cell, but it is in very oblique section. *D*. Cross section of a completely avascular portion. *E*. Large apex that was injured and is regenerating. The bulge about four cells to the right of the injury is a new center of meristematic activity becoming organized. *F*. Cross section, showing a mature stele with only undifferentiated, elongated, thin-walled cells. *B* to *F* after Bierhorst (1954c).

When the tip of a *Psilotum* frond is buried, the apex will swell and many rhizoids will develop on the already formed but immature parts, including the pinnae. Pinnae production next ceases, and the axis from this point on is typical of the "rhizome." The burying of the growing frond tip is a method of obtaining fungus-free plants, since the fungus does not invade the aerial green parts and the production of a "rhizome" from them can be accomplished in a sterile medium.

In both *Psilotum* and *Tmesipteris* the "rhizome" apex, after it begins to grow upright and even after several pinnae have been formed, produces one to several lateral apices, which most often remain dormant or grow only slightly. The minute spot at the arrow in Fig. 12–5, *B* is one such lateral apex. The small stele in Fig. 12–5, *D* supplies another. (See also Fig. 13–3, *C*, *D*.)

The "phyllotaxy" or, better, pinna arrangement varies within the Psilotaceae. Observations on mature fronds have been misleading. Studies of relative positions of pinnae and also their relative stages of development on the meristematic apex provides more accurate information.

Pinna arrangement along the triquetrous, ultimate, aerial axis of *Psilotum nudum* can be described as spiral and, quantitatively, as having a one-third "phyllotaxy." The pinnae are inserted along the three ridges of the axis. Nowhere else in the family does spiral "phyllotaxy" occur.

In the flattened species of *Tmesipteris* the pinnae originate in subopposite pairs (1–2, 3–4, and 5–6 in Fig. 12–5, *E*). Pinna 2 is more nearly like 1 in size than it is 3; 3 is more like 4 than 2; and so on. Although the insertions along the axis are on two sides of the flattened frond, they are not in two precisely vertical lines but in two pairs of lines. Each member of a pair of vertical lines ("orthostichies") is very close to the other member, so that the two "orthostichy" condition is closely approached.

In *T. vieillardi* the frond appears to be radially symmetrical, but, again, spiral "phyllotaxy" does not exist here. The pinnae are produced in subopposite pairs as above, but there are from six to nine "orthostichies" (Fig. 12–6, *B*).

The frond of the flattened species of *Psilotum*

clearly shows two-ranked pinnae, which, in fact, originate in this relative position. Much of the morphology of *P. complanatum* and *P. flaccilum* may be specialized in terms of flattening and pinna insertion, and a comparison with other species may only add confusion.

In *P. nudum*, after the first appendage on a frond originates (Fig. 12–5, *A*), subsequent ones appear in relative positions very similar to those in *Tmesipteris* species. Subopposite pairing is readily detectable (Fig. 12–5, *C, F*) until approximately 12 to 15 pinnae have been formed, at which time irregularities or branching of the frond occur. In *P. nudum* the first pinna does not have an opposite member in about 30 per cent of the cases.

The often symmetrical, decussately dichotomous, frond system in *Psilotum nudum* is preformed by a chronologically closely spaced series of apical branchings. The first pinnae produced on a frond are relatively far removed from the center of the meristematic dome; there is a very clear separation of pinna and frond apex. Later-formed pinnae are formed successively closer to the frond apex (cf. Fig. 12–5, *A*, *C*, *F* and Fig. 12–6, *A*, which are successively later stages in frond formation). Shortly after the stage shown in Fig. 12–5, *F*, the first dichotomy of the apex occurs. It and the set of subsequent dichotomies are each subtended by an "angle leaf." Up to 32 apices may be present in a "bud" which shows little or no external manifestation of branching and is completely covered by pinnae attached below it. In Fig. 12–6, *A* each " × " marks an "angle leaf" and the two lines extending from the " × " indicate the apices associated with that dichotomy. A dichotomy of the frond apex (or one of its apices) is shown in section in Fig. 12–6, *C*. Each apex bears a pronounced, single apical cell (reconstructed in Fig. 12–6, *D*). No evidence has been found to suggest that dichotomy of the frond results from the equal division of a single apical cell; more probably the old apical cell looses its identity and two new ones appear. Trichotomies commonly appear in the frond, and in each of the three axils there is an "angle leaf."

The "angle leaf" is generally shifted out of position by differential growth, so that on an old frond it may appear above, below, or to the side of a dichotomy.

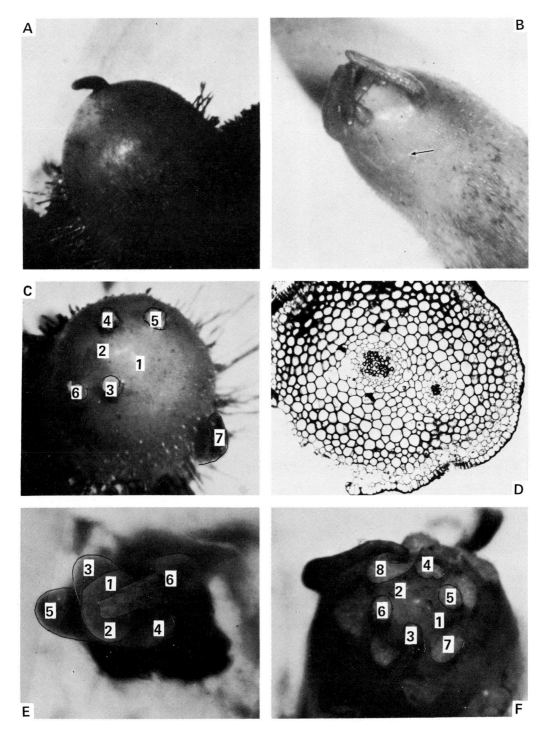

FIGURE 12–5. *A.* Beginning of frond formation in *Psilotum nudum*. The apex has produced the first pinna. *B.* Young frond of *P. nudum* that has produced about seven pinnae. The arrow indicates the position of a minute patch of residual meristem. *C.* Frond of *P. nudum* after seven pinnae have been produced. The meristematic center is situated between pinna primordium 1, the youngest, and 2. *D.* Cross section of a frond of *P. nudum* near the ground level. The small lateral stele supplied one of the undeveloped branches. *E.* Apex of a frond of *Tmesipteris lanceolata*. The meristematic center is located between pinna primordium 1, the youngest, and 2. *F.* Apex of a frond of *P. nudum* after about 20 pinnae have been produced and before the first signs of bifurcation. The eight most recently produced pinnae are numbered from the youngest to the oldest. *A, C, E, F* after Bierhorst (1968b).

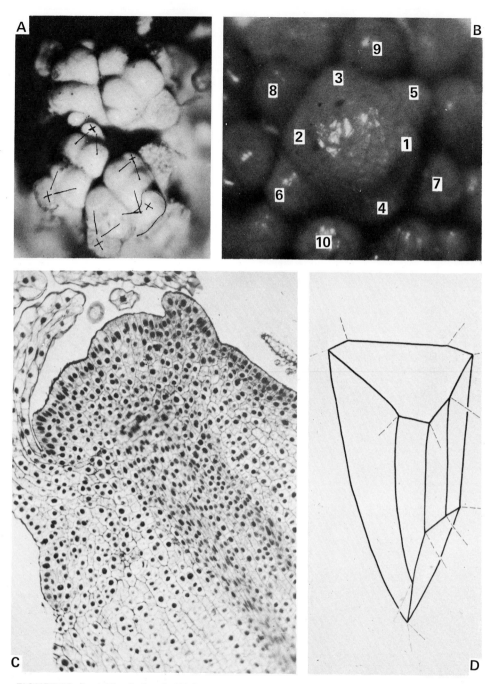

FIGURE 12–6. *A.* Tip of a frond of *Psilotum nudum* after most of the fourth-order bifurcations have been established. The mass of apices are seen from above after removal of the overlapping pinnae. "X" marks an individual "angle leaf" and the pair of apices with which each leaf is associated is indicated by the lines. *B.* Apex of a frond of *Tmesipteris vieillardi* in the growth phase when only fertile appendages, numbered from the youngest to the oldest, are being produced, after Bierhorst (1968b). *C.* Longitudinal section of a recently bifurcated frond apex of *Psilotum nudum*. *D.* Apical cell of a frond of *P. nudum* as reconstructed from 10 serial cross sections, after Bierhorst (1954b).

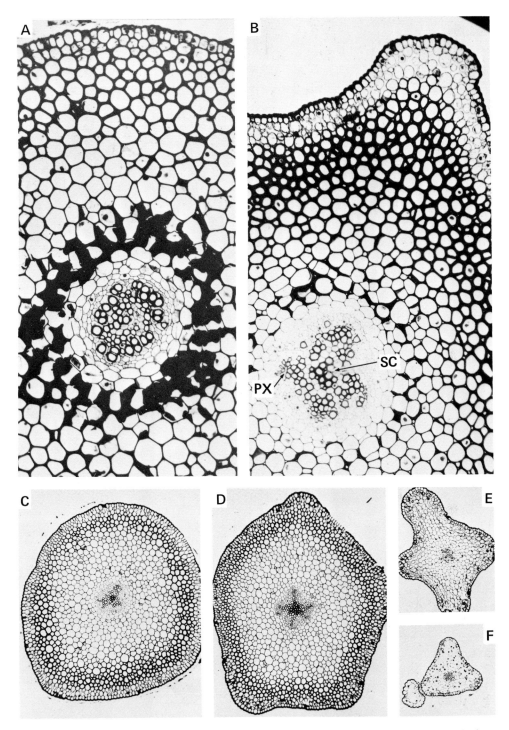

FIGURE 12–7. Cross sections at various levels of the frond axis of *Psilotum nudum.* *A.* Just below the ground level. *B.* About 1 cm above the ground level. *C.* About 3 cm above the ground level. *D.* About 7 cm above the ground level and about halfway between it and the first bifurcation. *E.* Above the fourth-order bifurcation. *F.* Above the sixth-order bifurcation.

163

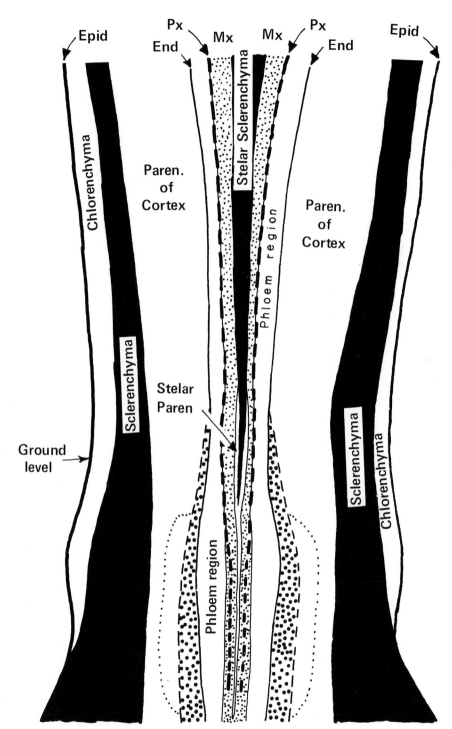

FIGURE 12–8. Diagrammatic reconstruction of a longitudinal section at the base of a frond of *Psilotum nudum.* Epid = epidermis ; End = endodermis ; Paren = parenchyma ; Px = protoxylem ; Mx = metaxylem.

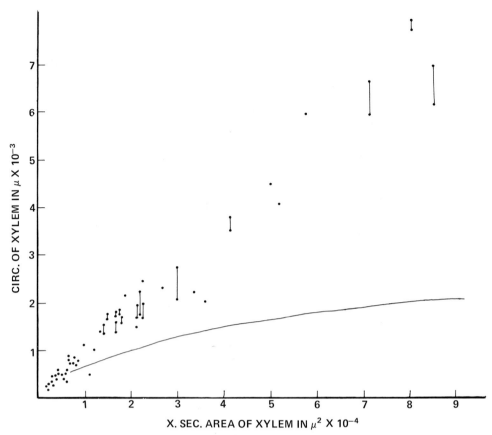

FIGURE 12–9. Relationship between circumference and cross-sectional area of the xylem in various axes of the sporophyte of *Psilotum nudum*. This shows the relationship between surface area (circumference times unit vertical distance) and volume (cross-sectional area times unit vertical distance) of the xylem.

Rouffa (1968) described a race of *Psilotum nudum* which he called appendageless. It was, in the sense that the characteristic pinnae were not present. On the plant, however, were a number of lateral branches similar to those which occasionally develop on ordinary plants of the same species, where pinnae develop beyond their normal expression.

Roth (1963a) recently described cell lineages associated with apical dichotomy in the distal regions of the frond of *P. nudum*. She described a new apical cell as arising lateral to the old one. Both apical cells, one old and terminal and one new and lateral, continue as separate centers, each producing an axis as if the parental axis had dichotomized. This description is in particular agreement with the general inter-

pretations presented in this chapter. Compare this description of pseudodichotomy with that occurring in *Schizaea dichotoma* in Chapter 14.

The anatomy of the frond axes in *Psilotum nudum* varies throughout their lengths. The underground part of the frond (Fig. 12–7, *A*) is anatomically quite similar to larger "rhizomes" of the subterranean system. It has a mychorrhizal cortex of parenchyma cells with somewhat thickened cell walls and a relatively simple stele either with some stelar parenchyma intermixed with the centrally placed tracheids or with an ill-defined pith. Within the inner cortical cells are massive deposits of phlobaphenes (black around the stele in Figs. 12–7, *A*) or tannin anhydrides. At least some, or possibly all, of the deposits are irregular wall thickenings. The stele at this point is triarch, with the three early metaxylem poles near the outside of the xylem mass but in a distinctly mesarch position. At successively higher levels (Fig. 12–7, *A* to *F*; Fig. 12–8) the following changes occur: The xylem becomes more stellate in outline and forms distinct protoxylem which attains the exarch position usually 1 to 3 cm above the soil level (mesarchy may exist in some fronds to above the second dichotomy). The protoxylem points increase in number up to a level just below the first dichotomy, then progressively decrease in number to three in the distal branches. The pith region becomes more distinct, with nucleated sclerenchyma cells maturing in the center and most often clearly separated from the xylem by stelar parenchyma (Fig. 12–7, *B*). The sclerenchyma core is progressively diminished at higher levels and its magnitude depends on the size of the frond. The cortex becomes zonated with an outer region of chlorenchyma, a middle zone of sclerenchyma, and an inner one of parenchyma. At still higher levels the cortex becomes uniformly chlorenchymatous. Stomata occur at the surface between the ridges of the axis.

Protoxylem elements of the Psilotaceae range from annular to helical with occasional irregular forking among the system of thickenings (Fig. 27–8, *S*, *T*). Early metaxylem elements exhibit thin sheets of additional wall thickenings between the bars, and in them there are rather broad simple pits. These intergrade into the later-formed elements, which show predominantly scalariformly bordered pitting but also some circular bordered pitting.

By examination of steles of *Psilotum nudum* throughout the sporophyte, the conclusion reached by Bower that increasing complexity of the xylem mass accompanies increasing size becomes apparent. This was investigated by Bower's student, Wardlaw, who demonstrated that the ratio of surface area of the xylem bordering on parenchyma to volume of xylem tends to be maintained. Throughout vascular plants Bower describes the kinds of xylem change as "medulation" (pith formation), "vitalization" (differentiation of parenchyma among tracheary elements), and "stellation" (production of extended xylem arms). The illustrations (Fig. 12–7) clearly show that all three types of change occur in *P. nudum*, differentially and to various degrees at different levels. The amazing precision with which the surface area/volume ratio is maintained with increasing xylem complexity is illustrated in Fig. 12–9.[2]

The phenomenon described above can be demonstrated (as Wardlaw did) just as well in a variety of taxa (e.g., *Lycopodium* stem and angiosperm roots). Its significance in morphology is obvious. Its significance in the understanding of xylem function is strongly inferred. It has been thought by many that parenchyma cells associated with tracheary elements were concerned in some way with movement of liquid, but a definite role has not been demonstrated.

Rhizomes and basal axes of fronds of *Psilotum flaccidum* and *P. complanatum* are anatomically much like those of *P. nudum*. A stellate, exarch xylem mass occurs shortly above the substratum level (Fig. 12–10, *A*);

[2] The data were collected as follows: Cross sections of various levels of three fronds and some associated rhizomes were made. The xylem in each was drawn in outline with the aid of a camera lucida on paper that had a uniform weight per unit area. The linear contact of all xylem cell walls bordering on parenchyma cells was measured for each section. This figure, when multiplied by the magnification factor, gave the circumference of the xylem bordering on parenchyma at that level. This is a linear measure of surface area per unit vertical distance. The xylem mass in each section was carefully cut out and weighed. This value, multiplied by a magnification factor, gives the cross-sectional area of xylem, which is a linear measure of the volume of the xylem per unit vertical distance at this level. Of the two points of each pair connected by a vertical line, the upper includes the xylem to sclerenchyma contact, while the lower excludes it for that level. Note that the points describe a reasonably straight line; when the points from each frond were plotted separately the three lines had nearly the same slope.

To emphasize the effect of xylem configuration changes with increasing xylem cross-sectional area, the lower line was added. This is a theoretical line derived from only one of the small simple, rhizome steles and assuming that it increases in size but maintains its unelaborated xylem. The distance from this line up to one of the real points would give a measure of the xylem change with increasing xylem bulk.

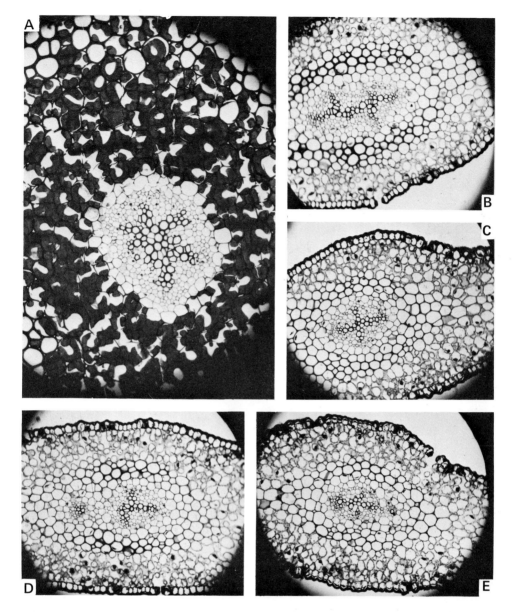

FIGURE 12–10. Cross sections at various levels in the frond of *Psilotum flaccidum*. *A*. About 2 cm above the level of the substratum. *B* to *E*. Sections of the more distal, flattened portions. *B* is just below a bifurcation. In *D* the smaller trace supplies a fertile pinna. In *E*, at right, the very small trace goes to, but not into, the base of a sterile pinna.

below this is a more rounded, triarch, and mesarch mass with some centrally placed stelar parenchyma. Stelar sclerenchyma is absent or poorly developed. The phlobaphene deposits are more numerous, thicker (Fig. 12–10, *A*), and are extended to a much higher level in aerial axes. The distal frond axes of the flattened species bear tetrarch xylem cores with two larger arms corresponding in position to the wings of the axis (Fig. 12–10, *C*). Below a dichotomy, the stele widens and new primary xylem arms appear (Figs. 12–10, *B*). Traces to

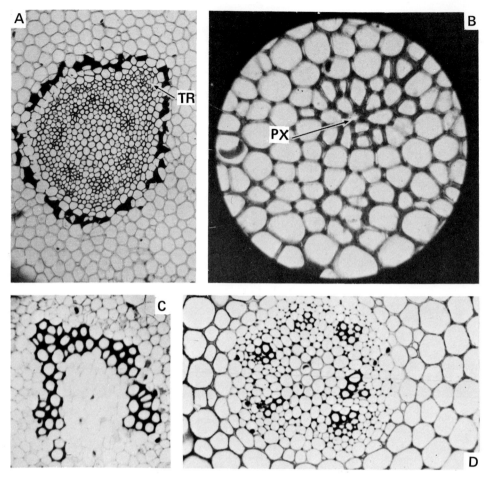

FIGURE 12–11. Cross sections of *Tmesipteris* fronds. *A*. Stele about halfway up the frond in *T. tannensis*. The trace, TR, supplies a sterile pinna. *B*. Portion of *A* enlarged to show a mesarch xylem group with centrally located protoxylem, PX. *C*. Stele at the base of the frond of the *Tmesipteris* species shown in Fig. 12–1, *B*. *D*. Stele about halfway up the frond in the same species as *C*.

fertile pinnae (Fig. 12–10, *D*) pinch off the long arms, taking with them the entire protoxylem area, which becomes replaced in the main stele by further differentiation above. Traces to sterile pinnae (Fig. 12–10, *E*) may be present or absent; when present they are quite small and rarely extend all the way to the base of a pinna.

The lower part of the frond axis in *Tmesipteris* is similar to its counterpart in *Psilotum*, although it differs in several respects. The parenchymatous pith is usually more distinct and the one to three groups of tracheids are, for the most part, more compact without intermixed parenchyma. There are three protoxylem points appearing in a mesarch position at about the substratum level. In *Tmesipteris vieillardi* the stele is radially organized and, just above the ground level, the xylem breaks up into five or six mesarch strands arranged in a ring that extends up into the axis and from which pinna traces originate. In the flattened *Tmesipteris* species the stele is U-shaped at the base, with the opening of the U toward a flat side of the frond (Fig. 12–11, *C*). In *T. lanceolata* nearly all stomates on the pinnae are on the side of the frond opposite the side toward which the U of the stele opens. As the xylem mass breaks up at higher levels, the U is sometimes still apparent (Fig. 12–11, *D*) but is often lost (Fig. 12–11, *A*). Figure 12–11, *B*

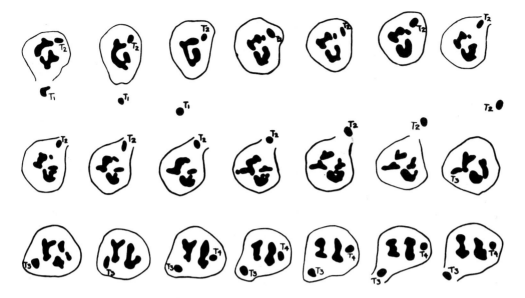

FIGURE 12–12. Serial outline drawings of the xylem in the frond of *Tmesipteris tannensis*. Pinna traces (T) are numbered. After Bierhorst (1968b).

shows one of the mesarch xylem strands from Fig. 12–11, *A* enlarged.

The form of the entire frond in the flattened *Tmesipteris* species, it should be noted, conforms internally and externally in its fundamental features (i.e., pinna form, pinna insertion, terminal pinna, stomate distribution, and the U-shaped stele) to a more typical fern frond. The frond apex, however, maintains a more radial symmetry throughout its active existence, having an apical cell with three cutting faces, a condition that occurs also in at least one species of *Osmunda*.

An additional similarity to be added to the above list is the manner in which pinna traces depart from the stele of the frond axis. The divisions of the xylem strands are not radial but more tangential. This can be seen if one follows the serial diagrams in Fig. 12–12.

Certain cytological features of the Psilotaceae are particularly worthy of note. The entire family exhibits nucleoli that persist during mitosis until late telophase (shown at metaphase in Fig. 12–14, lower right). This feature is not peculiar to the Psilotaceae but also occurs irregularly in *Stromatopteris*, probably in various other ferns, and sporadically in some angiosperm species (e.g., *Canna*).

In *Psilotum*, nucleoli are often seen, one at each pole of the achromatic figure, during nuclear division and could easily be mistaken for centrioles. They apparently are trapped within the spindle and are pushed outward to these positions (interpretation of C. H. Uhl, personal communication).

The chromosome numbers found in the Psilotaceae are approximately 100 (*Psilotum complanatum, P. flaccidum*), 104, 156, 208 (*P. nudum*), and 400 to 500 (*Tmesipteris*). Designations of ploidy in the Psilotaceae are relative to the lowest "*n*" number in the family, which is 52. The "*x*" number is interpreted to be 13 (Chiarugi, 1960; Ninan, 1956); hence the diploid *Psilotum nudum* with 104 chromosomes is considered an octaploid with respect to some unknown ancestor. Chromosome numbers in multiples of 13 are also found in *Stromatopteris, Gleichenia*, and *Matonia*, which may be comparatively significant.

Associated with the high chromosome numbers in the family are abnormalities in mitosis and meiosis. *Tmesipteris vieillardi* rarely produces normal spores (see Fig. 12–19, *H, I*), and extensive search has failed to turn up any gametophytes. Meiosis in the high-chromosome race of *Psilotum nudum* becomes irregular at low temperatures.

There is strong evidence that the tetraploid

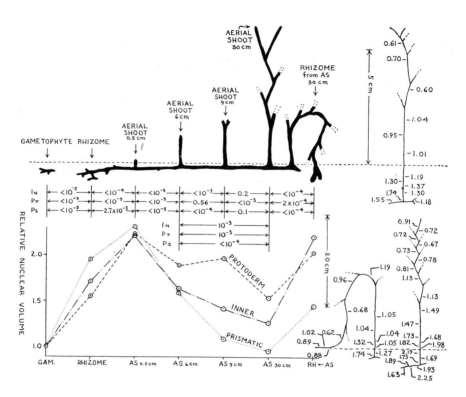

FIGURE 12–13. Changes in relative nuclear volume and tracheid diameter in various axes of the tetraploid *Psilotum nudum*. The three diagrams to the right indicate tracheid diameters at various levels of three fronds and associated rhizomes. The diagrams in black across the top correspond to the levels plotted across the bottom. Probabilities indicative of significance between means are shown as dimension lines. See the text for further explanation. After Bierhorst (1958b).

($2n = 208$) *P. nudum* has reached its maximum limit in polyploidy. It seems to have gone through a cytological history, unlike polyploids in general, reflective of its inability to experience a reduction in cell and nuclear volume in successive generations following a step up the polypoid ladder. Throughout the life cycle of *P. nudum* there are progressive changes in cell and nuclear volume (Fig. 12–13). This is illustrated for the nuclei of the cells of the prismatic layer (adjacent to apical cell), cells of the protoderm about 8 to 10 cells from the apical cell, and cells of the still meristematic cortex ("inner"). The values for nuclear volume are shown relative to that of the gametophytes, arbitrarily set at one. The underground sporophytic axes (rhizomes) show a near-gigas (i.e., $2X$ gametophyte) relationship, but as they grow out of the soil to become fronds ("aerial shoots") they experience a

dramatic increase in cell and nuclear volume. Later, as the frond continues to grow, the volumes are progressively reduced. If a frond is buried and reverts to a rhizome, the volume is again increased. The cell volumes are also reflected in the cross-sectional areas of mature tracheids at various levels of the frond (the three diagrams on the right in Fig. 12–13).

The emergence of the young frond from below the soil represents a critical point in the life cycle. At this point the cell and nuclear volumes are at their highest and the cross-sectional area of cells at its relative lowest in proportion to nuclear and the chromosomal volume. Here octoploidy frequently originates and results in complete abortion of up to 5 per cent of all fronds. An octoploid apex with numerous cytological abnormalities appears in Fig. 12–14.

It seems significant that the spores are pro-

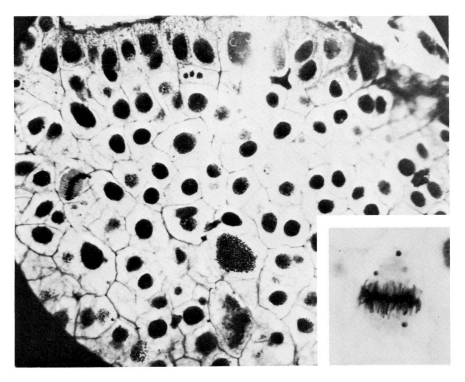

FIGURE 12–14.   Apex of an octoploid frond of *Psilotum nudum*.   Inset : Metaphase mitotic figure showing persistent nucleoli. After Bierhorst (1958b).

duced on the frond in that growth phase of the entire life cycle which is cytologically most stable. Natural selection may very well have been responsible, in part at least, for this special spacing of ontogenetic events.

The sterile pinnae of *Psilotum* originate as follows:

A bump appears near the frond tip (Fig. 12–16, *A*). Across the mound, a single row of anti-clinally elongate cells, continuous with the prismatic layer of the frond apex and oriented parallel to the frond axis, is present. According to Roth (1963b) the pinna initially arises from three such cells vertically aligned at the surface. In these respects it is, therefore, comparable to an ordinary fern pinna. The pinna soon as-sumes a more radially symmetrical growth, its cells elongate, and the entire structure matures and stops growing quite precociously (Fig. 12–16, *A* to *E*).

The *Tmesipteris* pinna grows in much the same way as that of *Psilotum*, but before com-plete maturation a basal zone in the organ becomes meristematic (Fig. 12–15, *A* to *C*). The psilotoid tip is pushed outward as the tmesipteroid base is increased in length by intercalary growth and also in width by mar-ginal meristematic activity.

The tmesipteroid base is occasionally pres-ent in *Psilotum* pinnae (Fig. 12–2, *C*) and the pinna is regularly entirely psilotoid and avas-cular at the bases of fronds in *Tmesipteris*. The most complete series of intermediates is found in *T. vieillardi* (Fig. 12–1, *G*: Fig. 12–15, *D*).

There is a terminal pinna in *Tmesipteris* developed directly from the last of the frond apex (Fig. 12–15, *E*), whereas in *Psilotum* the frond apex, after ceasing growth, remains and is represented by a mass of differentiated cells.

The fertile pinnae of *Psilotum* and of *Tmesip-teris* are inserted on the frond axis in the same "phyllotactic" series as are the sterile ones. In *Psilotum* the fertile pinnae are formed as a series in the distal parts of the frond divisions (Fig. 12–2, *A, B*). In *Tmesipteris* their positions vary with species, being either near the base

Psilotaceae and Noeggerathiaceae   **171**

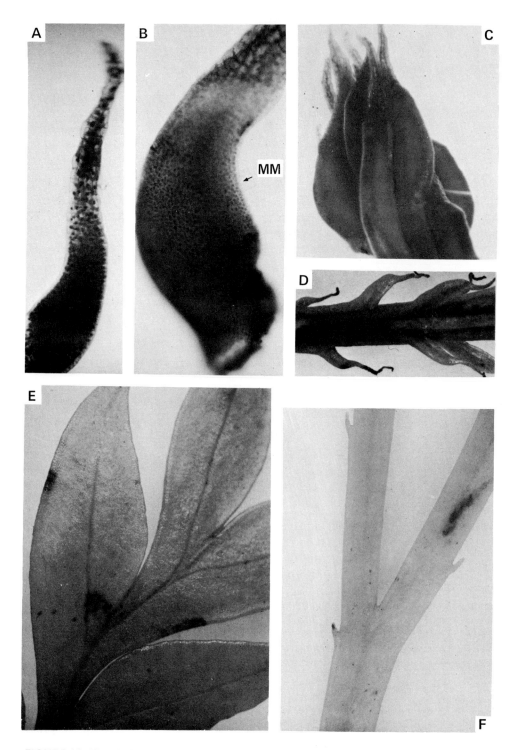

FIGURE 12–15. *A, B.* Young sterile pinnae of *Tmesipteris lanceolata.* MM = marginal meristem. *C.* Number of sterile pinnae enclosing the growing tip of the frond of *T. lanceolata.* *D.* Sterile pinnae on the frond of *T. vieillardi* in the region of transition from psilotoid to tmesipteroid pinnae. *E.* Four terminal sterile pinnae on a frond of *T. lanceolata.* *F.* Portion of a frond of *Psilotum flaccidum* at a birfurcation.

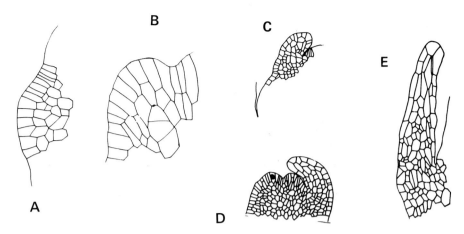

FIGURE 12–16. Development of sterile pinnae in the tetraploid *Psilotum nudum*. After Bierhorst (1956).

(*T. lanceolota*, Fig. 12–1, *D*; Fig. 12–17, *B*), within one or more zones along the length of the frond (*T. tannensis*, Fig. 12–1, *F*; *T. forsteri*, Fig. 12–1, *A*), or terminal in a strobiloid cluster (*T. vieillardi*, Fig. 12–1, *G*; Fig. 12–17, *A*).

A fertile pinna of *Psilotum* has a basal stalk, which often is nearly absent, so that the pinna appears sessile on the frond axis (Fig. 12–2, *B*; Fig. 12–20, *F*, *G*). Occasionally the stalk is well expressed (Fig. 12–21, *E*, *F*, *K*). On the side of the pinna away from the frond axis is a structure bearing two sterile extensions, each of which is quite like an entire sterile pinna. At a relatively young age this entire structure is quite like a half-cup (Fig. 12–20, *C*, *D*), but the tissue connecting its two distal extensions stops growing in length quite early while continuing to extend laterally somewhat, so that, in the mature fertile pinna, there is often little indication of its unity. More than two (up to five) sterile extensions are present in up to 20 per cent of all fertile pinnae on some fronds, and when this is so, the unity of the half-cup is more obvious.

Distal to the insertion of the half-cup with its two (or more) extensions is another short axis. It may be so short as to be entirely hidden by the slight downward folding of the sporangia above (Fig. 12–22, *D*); in other cases (less common) it is better developed (Fig. 12–21, *E* to *G*).

Three fused sporangia usually terminate each fertile pinna (Fig. 12–20, *F* to *H*; Fig. 12–22, *D*), but occasionally there are more or fewer (Fig. 12–21, *I* to *L*). Free sporangia are very uncommon, but in one New Zealand collection a pinna with three completely separate sporangia was found (Fig. 12–21, *C*) in addition to several pinnae that had two fused and one free sporangia (Fig. 12–21, *D*).

The *Tmesipteris* fertile pinna is quite similar to that of *Psilotum*. The basal stalk is generally better developed (Fig. 12–17, *A*; Fig. 12–19, *A* to *C*). The two sterile extensions of the pinna are relatively large, with a base added in the same way as the tmesipteroid base is added to the sterile pinna (Fig. 12–19, *F*). Occasionally, the basal stalk develops a marginal meristem as well and becomes vertically winged (Fig. 12–19, *A*).

A great range in variation exists in form and degree of development of both sterile and fertile pinnae throughout the Psilotaceae. The sterile ones, although most commonly undivided, bear up to four distal "teeth" in *Psilotum* and occasionally are divided to the base in *Tmesipteris*.

The fertile pinna not only shows degrees of expression of different parts of its axis, but varying numbers of parts, both fertile and sterile. The entire pinna is occasionally forked at the base (Fig. 12–19, *E*). When the pinna axis above the insertion of the half-cup outgrowth with its two tips grows beyond its normal expression, it may produce either an

FIGURE 12–17. *A*. Strobilus of *Tmesipteris vieillardi*. *B*. Fertile region on a frond of *T. lanceolata*.

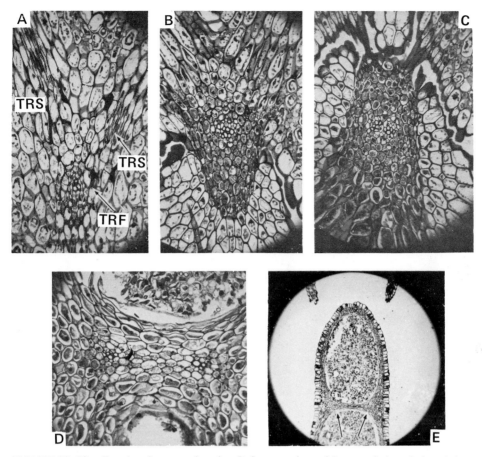

FIGURE 12–18. *Tmesipteris tannensis.* *A* to *D*. Cross sections of the vascular supply from below the base of the two sporangia and into the septum separating them. In *A* the two branches, TRS, are the traces to the two sterile wings or lobes of the fertile pinna and TRF extends up into the fertile portion, *B*, where it divides at the base of the septum separating the two sporangia, *C, D*. *E*. Lower magnification just above the level of *D*. Two traces within the septum are indicated by arrows.

entire branch of the frond or a smaller one with a variable number of sterile parts and sporangia (Fig. 12–21, *F, G*: Fig. 12–19, *D*). Finally, there are occasionally no sterile outgrowths on the fertile pinna below the sporangial attachment (Fig. 12–21, *H, I*).

The pinna of *Tmesipteris* illustrated in Fig. 12–19, *G* shows the form of a fertile pinna, but the distal axial extension has no sporangia.

The wide range of variation in form and structure of psilotaceous pinnae is reflected in their ontogeny. It is suggested that the larger and more axially organized the pinna is, the greater will be its eventual development. It also appears that there is some range in variation in terms of size and apical organization among

primordia that develop into essentially the same kind of pinna. This variation seems to account for some of the discrepancies in the descriptions of ontogeny in earlier literature (e.g., the presence or absence of an apical cell in the fertile pinna at various stages in ontogeny). The gradate range of structures from avascular to vascular, from toothlike to quite pinnalike, and from sterile pinnae to elaborate fertile pinnae to branches of the frond occasionally makes accurate specification of a primordian in terms of its probable mature form difficult. The ontogeny of only the most ordinary pinnae is known with any degree of accuracy, and these are described from frond apices that were still growing and producing a

Psilotaceae and Noeggerathiaceae **175**

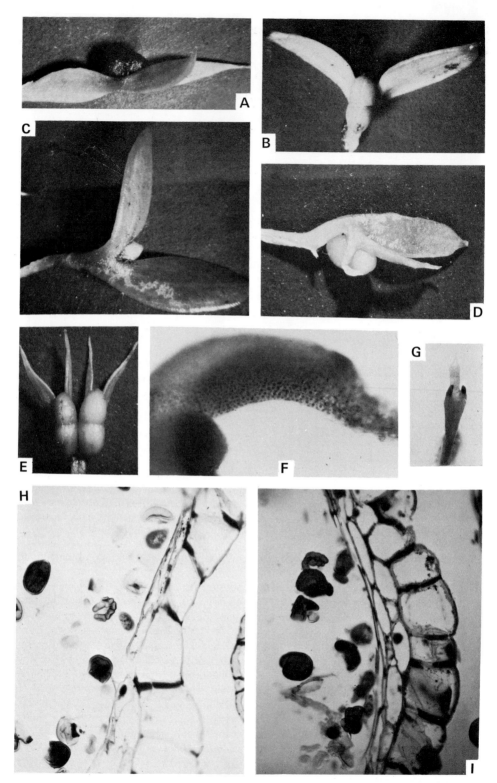

FIGURE 12–19. *Tmesipteris.* *A*. Fertile pinna of *T. forsteri* in which the stalk has developed a marked wing. *B, C.* Ad- and abaxial views of a fertile pinna of *T. lanceolata.* *D, E.* Anomalous types of fertile pinnae in *T. forsteri.* *F.* One of the two sterile lobes of the fertile pinna in *T. lanceolata* showing the precociously matured tip (at right and cut partly off) and the still meristematic base. *G.* Pinna of *T. forsteri* having the general form of a fertile pinna, but the normally sporangiate portion is sterile. *H, I.* Cross sections through the outer portion of a mature sporangium of *T. vieillardi.*

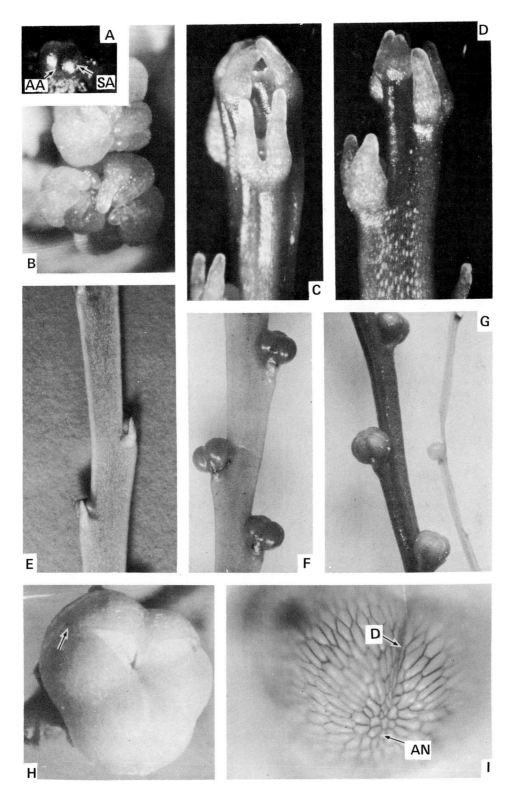

FIGURE 12–20. *A.* Apex of a frond, SA, and apex of a fertile pinna, AA, shortly after initiation in the tetraploid *Psilotum nudum.* *B.* Two branches of the frond of the tetraploid *P. nudum,* each covered with a number of fertile pinnae. *C, D.* Young fertile pinnae on a frond of the tetraploid *P. nudum.* *E, F.* Younger and older fertile pinnae on a frond of *P. flaccidum.* *G.* Portions of a frond of the tetraploid (left) and the diploid (right) *P. nudum.* *H.* Trisporangiate synangium of the tetraploid *P. nudum* during dehiscence. The arrow indicates the annulus. *I.* Portion of surface of *H* stained and enlarged. AN = annulus ; D = line of dehiscence.

177

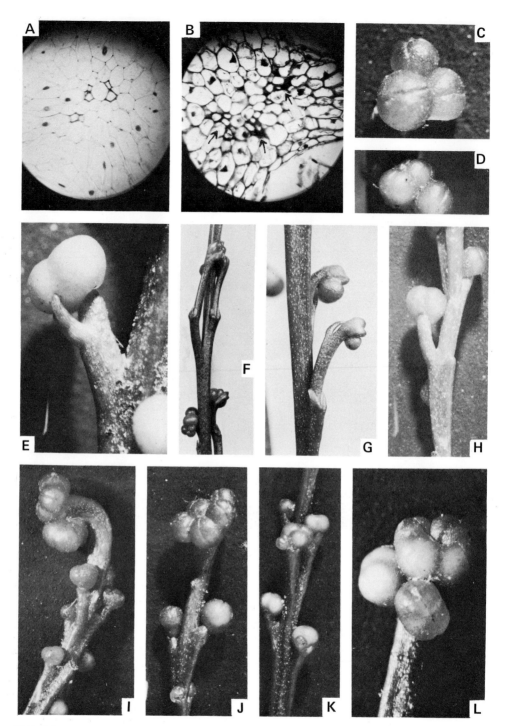

FIGURE 12–21. *A.* Cross section through the central portion of a trisporangiate synangium of *Psilotum nudum* showing the three sporangial traces. *B.* As *A*, but *P. flaccidum*. *C.* Three completely free sporangia from a fertile pinna of *P. nudum*. *D.* Three sporangia from a fertile pinna of *P. nudum*. Two make up a bisporangiate synangium, the other is free. *E.* Fertile pinna of *P. nudum* in which the stalk supporting the synangium distal to the sterile lobes is relatively well developed. *F, G.* Fertile pinnae of *P. nudum* in which the axial entities below and above the sterile lobes are well expressed, after Rouffa (1967). *H.* Fertile pinna of *P. nudum* in which the sterile lobes are absent. *I* to *L.* Fronds of *P. nudum* showing terminal clusters of synangia, each with a variable number of sporangia.

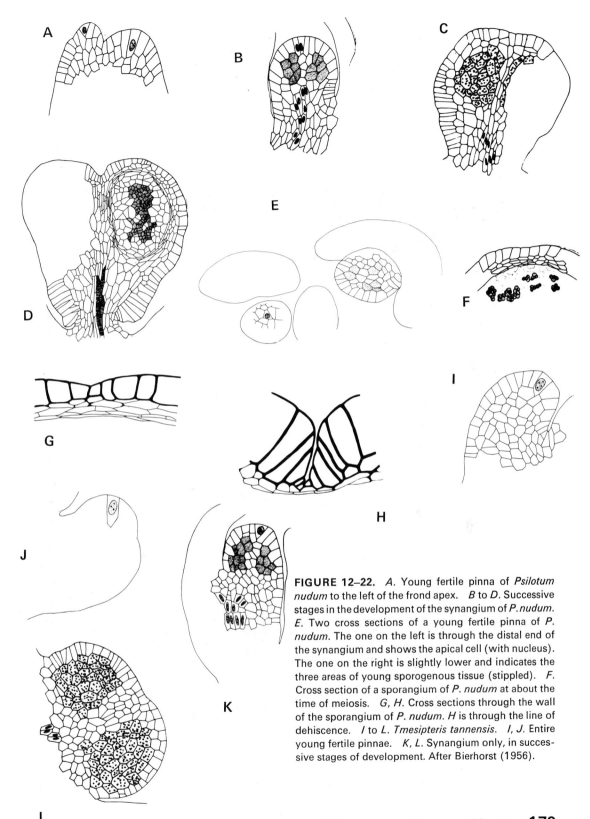

FIGURE 12–22. *A.* Young fertile pinna of *Psilotum nudum* to the left of the frond apex. *B* to *D.* Successive stages in the development of the synangium of *P. nudum.* *E.* Two cross sections of a young fertile pinna of *P. nudum.* The one on the left is through the distal end of the synangium and shows the apical cell (with nucleus). The one on the right is slightly lower and indicates the three areas of young sporogenous tissue (stippled). *F.* Cross section of a sporangium of *P. nudum* at about the time of meiosis. *G, H.* Cross sections through the wall of the sporangium of *P. nudum. H* is through the line of dehiscence. *I* to *L. Tmesipteris tannensis.* *I, J.* Entire young fertile pinnae. *K, L.* Synangium only, in successive stages of development. After Bierhorst (1956).

very uniform series of pinnae, either all sterile or all fertile.

The youngest primordia of fertile pinnae in *Psilotum* (Fig. 12–20, *A*, *AA*) are nearly the same size as the apex that continues the growth of the frond (Fig. 12–20, *A*, *SA*). This was constant in a number of apices dissected, such as those shown in Fig. 12–20, *B*. The pinna at this stage has a recognizable apical cell with three cutting faces (Fig. 12–22, *A*). There is, presumably, a range in variation at this point in terms of the relative size of the pinna and of the frond apex, and this would account for intermediate forms. A ridge of tissue, which soon comes to be two-lobed, forms on the "abaxial" side of the pinna primordium (Fig. 12–22, *A*). These lobes develop precociously and soon grow over the rest of the pinna (Fig. 12–20, *B* to *D*). Immediately below the apex of the pinna the three (usually) groups of sporangial initials are soon established and divide periclinally. This division for the most part blocks out the wall (outer cells in Fig. 12–22, *B*) from the inner sporogenous and tapetal (stippled cells in Fig. 12–22, *B*) areas. The apical cell of the pinna is occasionally recognizable (its two daughter cells are shown with nuclei in Fig. 12–22, *B*) even after the sporangia are initiated. Further growth of the sporangia is primarily in an outward direction and perpendicular to the plane of division of the sporangial initials. This enables one to specify the position of the annulus as apical (Fig. 12–20, *H*, *I*). Figure 12–22, *E* shows two cross sections of a fertile pinna comparable in age to the one shown in longisection in *B*.

The internal cells of the sporangium divide and redivide to produce a mass of cells that becomes differentiated internally as the sporogenous tissue (stippled cells in Fig. 12–22, *D*) and externally as a massive tapetum. The sporogenous mass becomes highly lobed, and, in a given section, it may falsely appear that there is some mixing of sporogenous and tepetal tissue. The central cell mass becomes broken up into small groups at about the time of meiosis and, more or less synchronously, the tapetum decomposes (Fig. 12–22, *F*).

The outer cell derivatives of the sporangial initials divide to increase the number of wall layers (Fig. 12–22, *C*, *D*) until, at maturity, the wall is four to six cells thick (Fig. 12–22, *F* to *H*). Occasionally a cell will be added to the inner mass of the sporangium by outer cells which ordinarily form wall only, and vice versa.

The wall becomes differentiated into an outer cell layer with thickened (especially radially) walls and inner ones. The surface cells are mostly anticlinally elongate except at the line of dehiscence (Fig. 12–22, *H*; Fig. 12–20, *I* at *D*) and across the sporangium below the annulus (Fig. 12–22, *G*). The inner wall cells also thicken somewhat, primarily on their radial walls.

The nonfunctional annulus (Fig. 12–20, *H* dark spot at arrow; *I*, AN) is represented by a patch of thicker walled cells at one end of the line of dehiscence (apical on the sporangia). Compare Fig. 12–20, *H*, *I* and Fig. 15–34, *B*, *C*, which show sporangia of the genus *Mohria* of the Anemiaceae.

Dehiscence in *Psilotum* begins at the center of the three-sporangiate synangium (Fig. 12–20, *H*) and proceeds to the annulus. The entire synangium is torn open at the center as surface cells shrink and fold.

The fertile pinna of *Psilotum* is supplied by a single trace from the stele of the frond axis. It differentiates upward into the base of the synangium (Fig. 12–22, *D*) without giving off branches to the sterile entity on the fertile pinna below the sporangia. Within the synangium it fades out, but often before doing so it divides into three parts, corresponding in position to the three sporangia (Fig. 12–21, *A*, *B*).

The fertile pinna in *Tmesipteris* develops much as it does in *Psilotum*. In *Tmesipteris*, although the primordium is larger than it is in *Psilotum*, it is smaller in proportion to the frond apex, so it appears much more "appendicular." Its apex is well organized (Fig. 12–22, *I*). As in *Psilotum* the sterile outgrowth appears as a half-cup which is soon two-parted, although occasionally, even at maturity, especially in *Tmesipteris lancelata*, the continuity at the base in the same plane as the "wings" is recognizable (Fig. 12–19, *C*).

Sporangial development and structure (Fig. 12–22, *J* to *L*: Fig. 12–19, *H*, *I*) is much the same in *Tmesipteris* as in *Psilotum*. There is, however, some breakdown of inner wall layers as the structure matures (Fig. 12–19, *H*).

Massive sporangia have been mentioned in most earlier literature as a diagnostic feature of the Psilotaceae. In *Tmesipteris* they are frequently over 2 mm long and in *Psilotum* up to about 1.5 mm, but in the diploid race of *P. nudum* sporangia are mostly less than 0.5 and most fall well within the size range typical of many filicalean ferns.

The spores are very uniform in structure throughout the Psilotaceae, being bean-shaped, with a slit on the concave side that is surrounded by a ridge of wall thickening.

In *Tmesipteris* the fertile pinna is supplied by a single trace that gives off a branch to each of the two lobes of the sterile part of the pinna (Fig. 12–18, *A*, TRS), then continues up into the septum, separating the two sporangia. At the base of the septum, it most commonly divides into two traces, each of which continues up one edge of the septum (Fig. 12–18, *A* to *E*). In several species there is an occasional third branch located in the center of the septum but it extends upward only a very short distance. In *T. vieillardi* more branching of the vascular system frequently occurs within the septum, forming a dichotomous truss of up to five ultimate branches, all in the plane of the septum.

Psilotaceous gametophytes known are those of *Psilotum nudum* (from both tetraploid and diploid sporophyte races), *P. flaccidum*, *Tmesipteris tannensis*,[3] *T.* sp. from New Caledonia (corresponding to sporophyte in Figs. 12–1, *B*, *C*), and another *Tmesipteris* species from Australia that was described under the vague, all-inclusive name *T. tannensis*. All these gametophytes are subterranean, branched, axially organized, and extremely similar in form to the underground sporophytic axes.

Psilotaceous gametophytes have well-organized apical meristems with single apical cells (Fig. 12–23, *A*, *B*; Fig. 12–24, *B*; Fig. 12–25, *B*, *C*). They branch by equal or unequal dichotomies or irregularly as a result of apical injuries. Superficial buds originating independently of the growing point have been de-

[3] This New Zealand material was referred to as *T. tannensis* var. *lanceolata* by Holloway, but the illustrated sporophyte was not this species, recognized as *T. lanceolata* here, but the more typical *T. tannensis*.

scribed, but these may well be patches of residual meristem left behind by the apex. Projecting from the surface and distributed more or less uniformly are rhizoids (Fig. 12–23, *A*, *C*), antheridia (Fig. 12–23, *A*, *B*; Fig. 12–24, *E*), and archegonia (Fig. 12–23, *B*; Fig. 12–24, *B*). A more distinct distribution pattern of gametangia is seen in the New Caledonian *Tmesipteris* sp. (Fig. 12–24, *A*, *B*), where they occur in definite zones along the axis. The surface cells within the fertile zones are relatively shorter than those in the infertile areas.

The internal anatomy of the gametophyte is mostly simple, with only mycorrhizal parenchyma present (Fig. 12–25, *A*; Fig. 12–26, *C*). The endophytic fungus, which essentially fills most of the internal cells, is nonseptate and locally quite vesiculate; it has been described as *Chladochitrum tmesipterides*. The endophytic fungi of most, if not all, non-seed-bearing vascular plants seem to be phycomycetes. Although they are incompletely known, their hyphal morphology falls within the range existing in the Mucorales.

In larger individual gametophytes from the tetraploid sporophytic race of *Psilotum nudum* a central stele is often present. It may be complete with one to three tracheids, surrounded by phloem and endodermis (Fig. 12–26, *B*, *D*), or merely composed of a few elongate and undifferentiated cells (Fig. 12–26, *E*). An apical meristem producing a procambial strand is shown in Fig. 12–25, *B*: it is from a gametophyte but is, in all qualitative aspects, identical to that of a subterranean sporophytic axis. The minimal axial diameter necessary for gametophytic stelar differentiation is approximately 1 mm, just as it is for sporophytic axes. The gametophytic steles are often discontinuous; the causes for this longitudinal interruption are probably the same as for the similar phenomenon in the sporophyte.

The entire surface of the gametophyte is covered by slightly thickened cell walls and a pronounced cuticle, including rhizoid surfaces. When stained with Sudan IV the cuticle appears striate in surface view and may not present a complete barrier to water intake. The cuticle does make the surface, with all its rhizoids and gametangia, resistant to decomposition, and intact "shells" of gametophytes are frequently recovered from the soil. This suggests a very

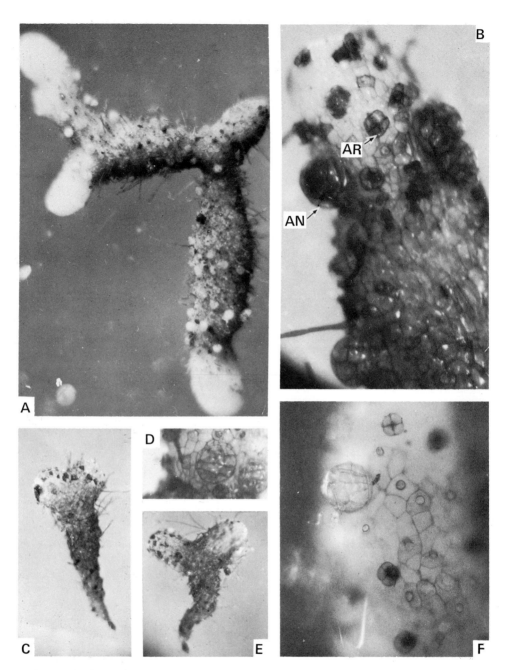

FIGURE 12–23. *A.* Diploid gametophyte of the tetraploid race of *Psilotum nudum.* *B, D.* Portions of gametophytes of the tetraploid *P. nudum* enlarged. *C, E.* Young sporophyte (*C*) and gametophyte (*E*) of the tetraploid race of *P. nudum* of gemma origin. In each, the mother gemma can be seen at the tip of the "tail." *F.* Surface view of a haploid gametophyte of the diploid race of *P. nudum* showing one antheridium and several archegonia. AN = antheridium; AR = archegonium. *A* to *E* after Bierhorst (1953).

FIGURE 12–24. *A* to *D*. Gametophytes or portions of gametophytes of *Tmesipteris* sp. (corresponding to the sporophyte in Fig. 12–1, *B*). The one in *D* is complete and is of spore origin. *E, F.* As in *A*, but *T. tannensis.* These are specimens of Holloway's collection and sent to Eames some years ago. *B, C* after Bierhorst (1968b).

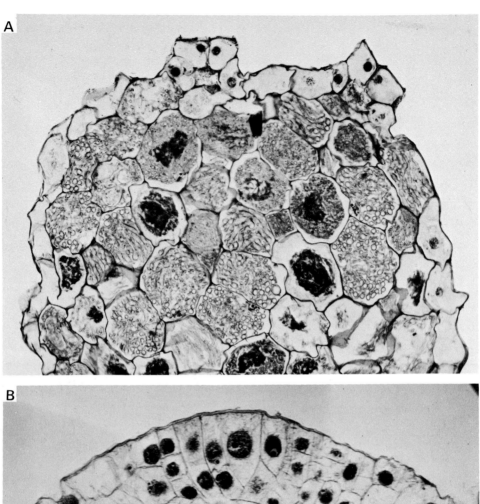

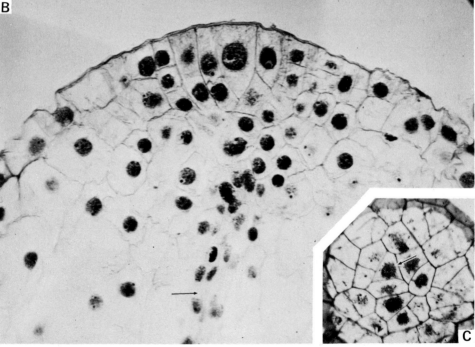

FIGURE 12–25. *A*. Cross section of a diploid gametophyte of the tetraploid *Psilotum nudum*. Two archegonia are shown at the top. *B*. Longitudinal section of the apex of a diploid gametophyte of the tetraploid *P. nudum*, showing pronounced apical cell and procambium (arrow) below. *C*. Cross section of an apex of a diploid gametophyte of the tetraploid *P. nudum*, showing apical cell (arrow). After Bierhorst (1953).

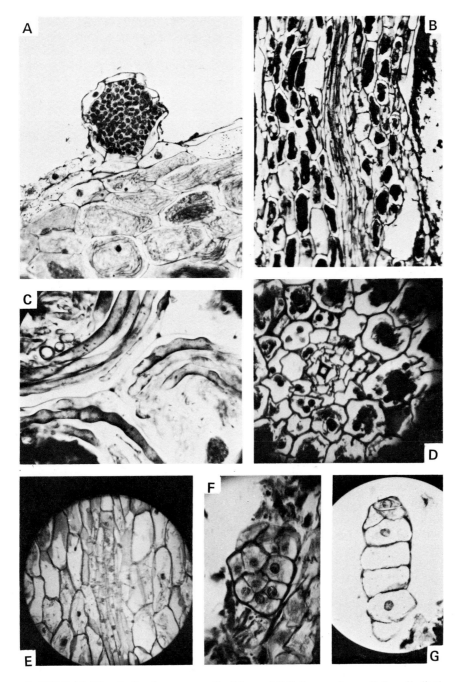

FIGURE 12–26. *A.* Nearly mature antheridium of *Psilotum nudum. B.* Longitudinal section of a vascularized, diploid gametophyte of the tetraploid *P. nudum. C.* Fungal hyphae in three adjacent cells of the gametophyte of *P. nudum. D.* Cross section of a stele from a diploid gametophyte of the tetraploid *P. nudum. E.* Longitudinal section of a diploid gametophyte of the tetraploid *P. nudum*, showing a central core of undifferentiated, elongate cells. *F, G.* Gemmae from the gametophyte of *P. nudum*. After Bierhorst (1953).

reasonable possibility that someday fossil gametophytes will be found in macerated rock preparations.

Gemmae or brood bodies are produced on the gametophytes of *P. nudum* and are qualitatively indistinguishable from those on the sporophyte (Fig. 12–26, *F, G*). The plantules produced from them are similarly indistinguishable. Of the two such plantules in Fig. 12–23, each of which still has the gemma attached to its "tail," the one in *C* is sporophytic, as evidenced by lack of sex organs and a nuclear volume of nearly twice that of the one in *E*, which has several antheridia.

Several gametophytes of other races or species with a diameter of 1 mm or slightly greater have been found, but none showed the slightest indication of a stele.

Psilotaceous antheridia are relatively large and almost completely above the epidermal surface (Fig. 12–23, *A, B, D, F*; Fig. 12–24, *C, E, F*; Fig. 12–26, *A*). Their size varies considerably within individual collections, owing to variability in total cell number comprising each antheridium. Plotting measurements of antheridial diameter against gametophytic axis diameter of *P. nudum* produces a straight line of considerable tilt. At the upper end of the series, large antheridia on large gametophytes approach 120 μ in diameter and may be seen with the naked eye. Smaller antheridia on smaller gametophytes are in the range 50 to 70 μ.

An antheridium originates from a single surface cell that divides periclinally. The outer of the two resultant cells goes on to produce the jacket, while the inner one gives rise to the spermatogenous tissue. A three-celled antheridium is shown in Fig. 12–27, *A*, in which the inner cell has divided once.

At maturity the antheridium is composed of an inner mass of 128, 256, or 512 cells (an even power of 2, since the derivatives of the inner cell divide synchronously) and a jacket one cell thick (Fig. 12–27, *B*). The cells beneath the spermatogenous tissue, which appear to continue the jacket, are cut off from cells that were below the antheridial initial. Cells of the jacket, when seen from the surface, tend to be particularly aligned in rows across the entire structure (Fig. 12–23, *D*, two cell rows on the left antheridium are oriented transversely in the

figure; Fig. 12–24, *F*, the end of two rows are seen from the side). The opercular cell is single, laterally situated, and breaks down to allow sperm exit (Fig. 12–27, *C*). In the New Caledonian *Tmesipteris* sp. the jacket cells are again divided such that in surface view a number of pairs of cells are seen, each about twice as long as broad (Fig. 12–24, *C*).

Archegonia arise from initials not distinguishable from antheridial initials. The archegonial initial divides periclinally to block out the neck (outer cell) and the axial cell row (inner cell). The neck mother cell divides anticlinally and its two daughter cells do the same at right angles to the first division. In Fig. 12–27, *D* a four-celled archegonium is shown in which the axial row mother cell is bulging up among four neck-tier mother cells, only two of which can be seen in the section. The neck-tier mother cells divide parallel to the surface (transversely to the archegonial axis) to produce ultimately a neck about six cells long. The axial-row mother cell divides, also transversely to the archegonial axis, to produce the mother cell of the egg and ventral canal cell below and of the neck canal cell above (Fig. 12–27, *E*). Karyokinesis takes place in the neck canal cell but rarely accompanied by cytokinesis. The basal one or two cells in each neck tier develop thickened walls separating them from more distal neck cells (Fig. 12–27, *F*), which become lost by cellular disintegration (Fig. 12–23, *F*; Fig. 12–25, *A*).

Spore germination, known only for *Psilotum nudum*, is delayed for some time after the spores are placed in a suitable environment. Darnell-Smith (1917) reported a delay of about 3 months, Bierhorst (1955) a delay of about 18 months, before the first cell division. The spore swells, extends well out of the exine (Fig. 12–28, *A*) and then divides (Fig. 12–28, *B*). After very few divisions an apical cell is established (Fig. 12–28, *C*) and axial growth commences. A young "teardrop" stage of *Tmesipteris* sp. is shown in Fig. 12–24, *D*.

Within the Psilotaceae, the embryogeny of only *Psilotum nudum* (tetraploid race) and *Tmesipteris tannensis* is known. In both, the first division of the zygote is transverse (Fig. 12–29, *A*); in *Tmesipteris* this is preceded by some zygote elongation (Fig. 12–30, *A*). At the first division, a foot (proximal cell) and an

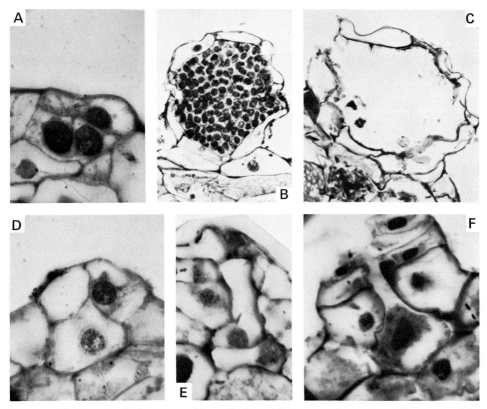

FIGURE 12–27. *A* to *C*. Younger to older antheridia of *Psilotum nudum.*   *D* to *F*. Younger to older archegonia of *P. nudum.* After Bierhorst (1954a).

outer hemisphere (distal cell) are established. After several divisions in the foot initial and its derivatives (Fig. 12–29, *C*: Fig. 12–30, *B*, *C*), individual cells, and later strands of cells, project and extend from the surface of the foot into the gametophytic tissue (Fig. 12–29, *D*: Fig. 12–30, *D*). There is also some proliferation of adjacent gametophytic tissue.

In the outer hemisphere, after a few divisions, an apical cell is established and subsequently an entire growing point (Fig. 12–29, *D*), which ruptures the calyptra (Fig. 12–29, *D*, *E*, which are of the same embryo; Fig. 12–30, *D*) and grows into a typical subterranean sporophytic axis. The apex frequently divides while still contained within the

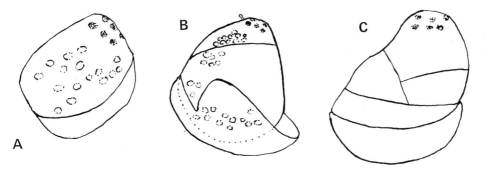

FIGURE 12–28.   Stages in spore germination of *Psilotum nudum,* after Darnell-Smith (1917).

Psilotaceae and Noeggerathiaceae   **187**

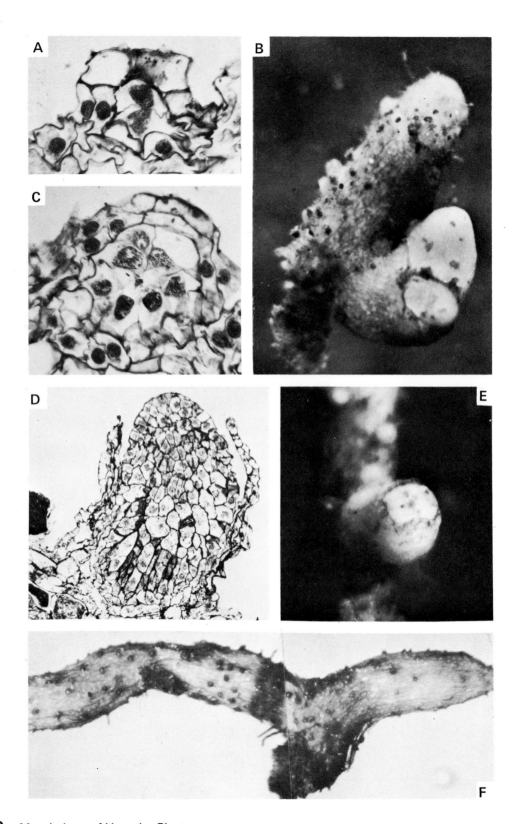

FIGURE 12–29. *A*. Two-celled embryo of *Psilotum nudum* within the archegonium. *B*. Gameto-phyte of *P. nudum* with an attached embryo. The two apices on the lower right are sporophytic and have only recently broken out of the calyptra. *C*. Young multicellular embryo of *P. nudum* contained within gametophytic tissue. The three upper cells of the embryo constitute the outer or distal hemisphere from which the rhizome apex develops. The lower cells of the embryo constitute the inner or proximal hemisphere from which the foot develops. *D, E*. Both are of the same embryo of *P. nudum*, *D* in longitudinal section. The sporophyte has just broken out of the calyptra and is composed of apex (exposed) and foot (embedded). *F*. Young sporophyte of *Tmesipteris tannensis* from Holloway's collection. The darker portion in the center at bottom represents the embryonic foot with a fragment of the gametophyte remaining. The two branches going to the left and right are of the young sporophyte. *A* to *E* after Bierhorst (1954a).

FIGURE 12–30. Embryos of *Tmesipteris tannensis*, after Holloway (1918).

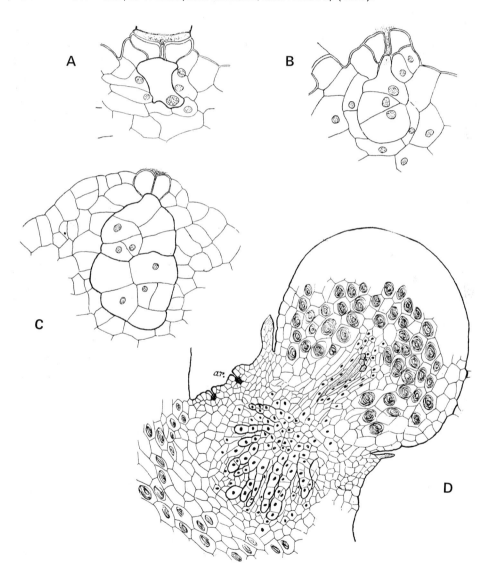

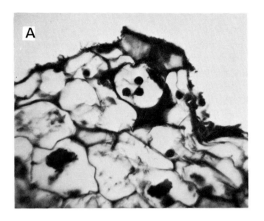

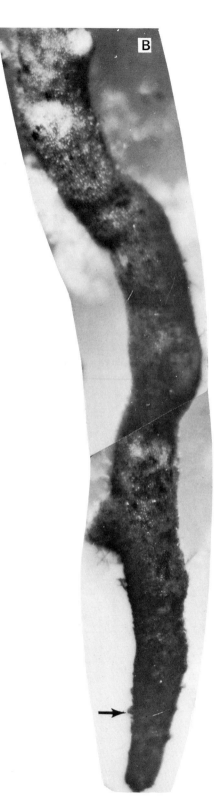

FIGURE 12–31. *A*. Three-celled diploid embryo contained within a diploid gametophyte of *Psilotum nudum*. A presumed case of apogamy. *B*. Subterranean axis of *P. nudum* which began as a gametophyte and continued as a sporophytic rhizome. The entire axis is diploid and was derived from a tetraploid sporophytic clone.

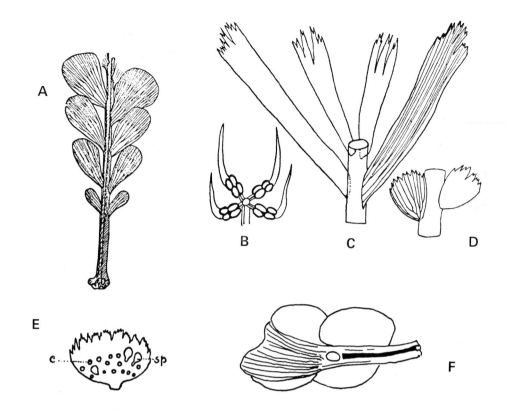

FIGURE 12–32. Noeggerathiales. *A. Noeggerathia foliosa,* after Stur (1885). *B* to *D. Tingia,* from Browne (1933). *E. Noeggerathiostrobus bohemicus,* after Stur (1887). *F. Tingia,* lower view of a fertile appendage, after Browne (1933).

gametophyte (Fig. 12–29, *B*) or it is possible that two apices originate independently. The young sporophyte of *Tmesipteris* shown in Fig. 12–29, *F* apparently branched just after it grew out of the calyptra. The dark basal part in the figure is a remnant of the gametophyte.

Green aerial parts of the sporophyte are apparently produced early in the life in *Tmesipteris,* but in *Psilotum* the sporophyte may survive for some time, possibly several years, as a subterranean saprophyte.

Apogamy occurs in the tetraploid race of *P. nudum.* The three-celled embryo in Fig. 12–31, *A* is clearly diploid, as are the surrounding gametophytic cells (the diameter of the embryonic nuclei are nearly the same as that of the gametophytic nuclei). Compare this figure with Fig. 12–29, *A, B,* in which the tetraploid sporophytic nuclei of embryo are

conspicuously larger than the surrounding gametophytic ones.

Another case of apogamy is illustrated in Fig. 12–31, *B.* This is a diploid subterranean axis associated with a tetraploid clone. At the basal end are a number of antheridia (one at arrow). The axis is vascularized throughout, but shortly above the arrow it bears no more antheridia and has expanded to a diameter far out of the range of diameters of gametophytes. A considerably more complex stele, of a type characteristic of larger subterranean axes of the sporophyte, was found in the upper part. There was complete axial continuity throughout the structure. The same apical meristem apparently continued its activity, producing the same axis with fundamentally the same morphology. It is guessed that some quantitative rather than qualitative factor was involved in the transition.

Noeggerathiaceae

The Noeggerathiaceae is a poorly known extinct family from Upper Palaeozoic and Triassic rocks and is the only family included in the order Noeggerathiales. Only the external morphology is known, but this strongly suggests that the family may be tmesipteroid in affinity, as suggested by Browne (1933).

Two ranked, vertically inserted, suboppositely arranged appendages have been seen on axes of *Noeggerathia* (Fig. 12–32, *A*). Distinct verticillate arrangement and stem jointing also occur (Fig. 12–32, *B*). The appendages show dichotomous venation, branching from a single trace (Fig. 12–32, *A*, *C*, *D*, *F*). Sporangia occur scattered on the upper surface of fertile appendages (Fig. 12–32, *E*) or fused to form synangia (Fig. 12–32, *B*, *F*). The region of attachment of a synangium is a small circular area (Fig. 12–32, *F*).

Although some have considered this family to have sphenophyllalean affinity, in terms of the present and very limited knowledge of the Noeggerathiales, the most likely place to insert it in taxonomic systems is somewhere near the base of the filicalean line in the vicinity of the Psilotaceae.

Summary and Discussion

The psilotaceous sporophytic plant body exhibits a conspicuously poor degree of differentiation among its parts. The terms "stem" and "leaf," in their classical senses, are only dubiously applied. An entire aerial branch of a flattened species of *Tmesipteris* has essentially the form and structure of a fern frond but is not reduced to appendicular status on something that could be called a stem. In these respects it is quite similar to *Stromatopteris*, with which it shares many other features (see Chapter 13). In *Psilotum* and in the radially organized *Tmesipteris vieillardi* the aerial axes (single or branched trusses) are more shootlike and less leaflike, but even in these the "phyllotaxy" suggests the more flattened forms.

The Psilotaceous sporangium is a clearly definable entity, distinct in its origin and vascularization and occasionally quite free of fusion with other sporangia. It cannot be considered a locule of a three-parted (*Psilotum*) or two-parted sporangium (*Tmesipteris*). The sporangium is lateral near the tip of an axis that is represented in *Psilotum* by a part of the central tissue among the three sporangia. Each one may be interpreted as being terminal on a lateral axial entity that has been lost, but evidence for this could come only by comparison with other forms, which might be presumed to be related or ancestral (e.g., *Rhyniaceae* and *Trimerophytaceae*). It does seem that one of these two families gave rise to the *Psilotaceae* or to their immediate predecessors.

There is no root in the Psilotaceae. This has, in the past, been considered a primitive feature, because the embryo also lacks a root and because the presumed ancestral forms, the Rhyniales, are similarly rootless. Since the discovery of rootless embryos in *Stromatopteris* and *Actinostachys*, which produce roots later in ontogeny, the evidence favoring primitive rootlessness in the Psilotaceae is considerably diluted. Similarly, new information on the Psilotaceae, particularly about the nature of fronds and "phyllotaxy," tends to point at a higher degree of specialization in the Psilotaceae and weakens the interpretation of direct descendence of the family Psilotaceae from the Rhyniales.

13

Stromatopteridaceae

Stromatopteridaceae is a monotypic family, represented only by *Stromatopteris moniliformis*, which is restricted to New Caledonia. The species has been known for many years but primarily from a few dried and very incomplete specimens. Until recently the information available clearly called for assigning it to the Gleicheniaceae, where it was often placed within its own subfamily. New information on various aspects of the life cycle, however, while still supporting the gleicheniaceous affinity of this most interesting genus, necessitates familial separation and brings out previously unexpected similarities to the Psilotaceae.

Stromatopteris is a very primitive fern with some ecological specializations imposed upon its histology and morphology. It looks like a fern (assuming most of us have a generalized concept of how such a non-taxonomic entity appears) with once-pinnate aerial "leaves" (Fig. 13–1, *B*). The plant shows obvious xeromorphic features in "leaf" texture and is adapted to survival in a tropical habitat that is very exposed, has extremely good subsurface drainage, and is subject to frequent fires. Within its range, it is also common in shaded forests growing on humus to almost pure clay.

Most distinctive of *Stromatopteris* are its ill-defined organs, which are held in common with Psilotaceae. The descriptions that follow, therefore, may appear somewhat awkward, since our morphological terminology was not devised to fit such a plant.

If one follows what appear to be petioles down to the underground parts of an old plant, one sees that they are part of a verical truss of coarse, tough, scaly axes appearing dichotomously to laterally branched with many arrested apices (AAP) (Fig. 13–1, *A*, *F*; Fig. 13–2, *D*). One arrested upright branch is shown in Fig. 13–1, *G*; the white areas on its apex represent residual

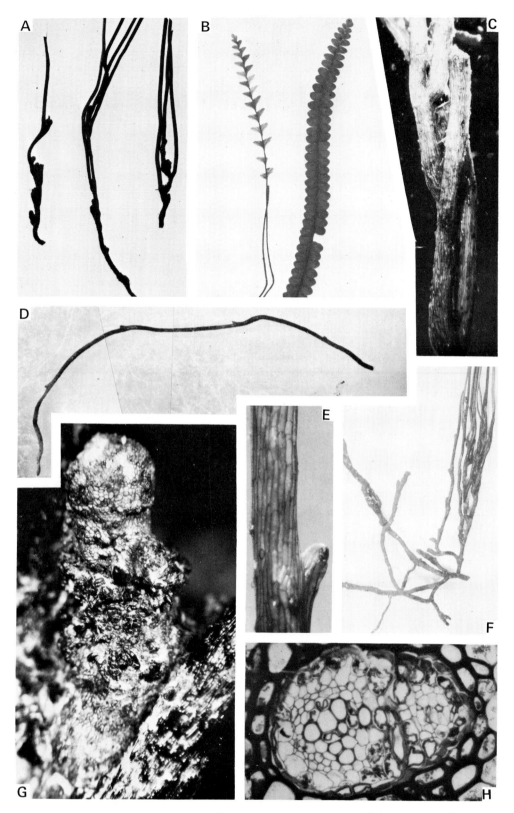

FIGURE 13–1. *Stromatopteris.* *A.* Portions of three vertical trusses and attached "petioles" from old plants. *B.* Entire "leaf" from a small plant and a portion of one from a large plant. *C.* Part of a vertical truss from a small plant. *D.* Primary subterranean axis with a series of laterals. *E.* Part of *D* enlarged. *F.* Vertical truss (upper right with several attached rhizomes and two roots, one in the lower left extending downward from a rhizome. *G.* Short vertical axis from the vertical truss; it has an inactive apex. White areas are residual meristem. *H.* Cross section of steles of a primary axis and a smaller attached lateral. *A* to *C, G* after Bierhorst (1968b); *D, E* after Bierhorst (1969a). (Other figures in this chapter from these two sources are not indicated.)

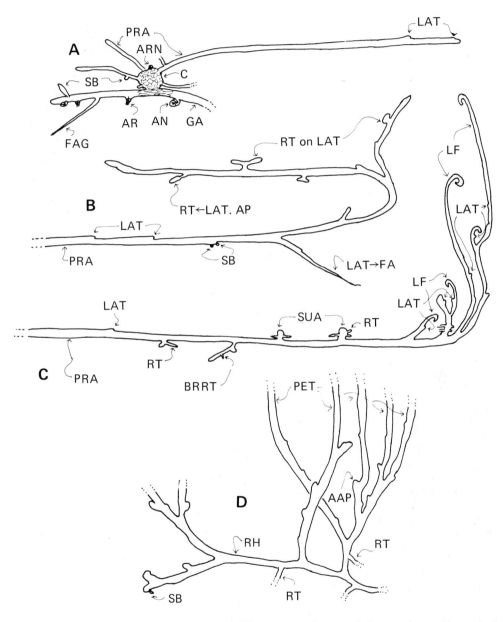

FIGURE 13–2. *Stromatopteris*, diagrams of different types of axes. *A.* Gametophyte with attached young sporophyte. *B, C.* Primary axial systems and derivative parts. *D.* Underground system of an old plant. PRA = primary axis; LAT = lateral; ARN = archegonial neck; C = calyptra; SB = superficial bud; FAG = filiform axis of gametophyte; AR = archegonium; AN = antheridium; GA = gametophytic axis; RT←LAT.AP = root derived directly from apex of lateral; LAT→FA = lateral becoming filiform; SUA = stubby upright axis; RH = rhizome; PET = "petiole"; AAP = arrested apex; LF = "leaf"; BRRT = branch root.

195

meristem. The surface outgrowths range from irregular trichomes to scales and undefined epidermal eruptions. The parts of the sporophytic body from which the petioles of an old plant extend constitute the *mature vertical truss*.

Arising from apices near the base of the *mature vertical truss*, and giving rise to new such trusses, are horizontally to irregularly oriented axes called *rhizomes* (RH in Fig. 13–2, *D*; Fig. 13–1, *F*). The rhizomes branch in ways similar to the individual axes of the vertical truss but less frequently. Rhizomes bear some septate rhizoids.

The subterranean part of the sporophyte also has what are called *primary subterranean axes*. These are rather thin (most being from 0.5 to 2 mm in diameter but with a few < 0.3 mm), are naked or bear septate rhizoids, and are oriented irrespective of gravity. They occasionally branch dichotomously but frequently and regularly in a peculiar lateral manner (Fig. 13–1, *D*, *E*; Fig. 13–2, *A* to *C*). The *primary subterranean axes* are traceable directly to the embryo (Fig. 13–2, *A*) and arise as branches from other similar axes or as superficial buds from other similar or dissimilar subterranean axes (SB in Fig. 13–2, *A*, *B*, *D*).

In addition, the plant body bears a limited number of true roots. These arise from rhizomes, from the bases of subterranean vertical trusses, or from the laterals on primary subterranean axes (RT in Fig. 13–2, *B* to *D*).

Within the body of *Stromatopteris* it is not possible to designate "leaves" as appendicular organs upon a "stem," as can clearly be done with most other ferns and nearly all seed plants. However, this confusion in many ways adds to our comprehension of and supports our interpretations of the interrelationships of the more fixed vegetative organs of other ferns. The two families, Psilotaceae and Stromatopteridaceae, therefore, along with a few much less known extinct families, constitute focal points in any theoretical consideration of the nature of vascular plant organs.

The growing tips of the primary axes of *Stromatopteris* show a slight recurvature with the meristematic center somewhat subapical (Fig. 13–3, *A*, *B*). It divides to produce a pair

of axially aligned apices, the more distal of which remains the primary axis apex and divides again and again in the same way. The more proximal apex is a "lateral" on the primary axis. The division of the apex of the primary axis appears to be an equal dichotomy, but the precise cell lineages have not been ascertained. The arrangement of laterals is often uniform and uniseriate (Fig. 13–1, *D*), reflective of a relatively unchanging position of the apex of the primary axis. Within each meristematic center of the apices of the primary axes, as well as the laterals, there is a single apical cell with three cutting faces.

The counterpart of the lateral branching on primary axes of *Stromatopteris* is found in all species studied in the Psilotaceae (Fig. 13–3, *C*, *D*), where the branching is, however, less regular and grades insensibly into what appears to be equally dichotomous branching. Roth (1963a), however, described branching in the aerial axes of *Psilotum* as being fundamentally lateral, with one of the two apical cells arising not directly from an old one but within the prismatic layer several cells removed from the apical cell. The same ontogenetic pattern exists in part in the pseudodichotomously branched leaf of *Schizaea dichotoma*.

Anatomical complexity of the primary axis varies with its diameter. Those with diameter < 0.3 mm are avascular and composed entirely of uniform fungus-containing parenchyma. Larger axes contain simple protosteles with centrally placed xylem, surrounded by phloem, which in turn is surrounded by pericycle and endodermis (Fig. 13–3, *E*). In the figure the inner cells of the cortex stand out conspicuously because of thickened, phlobaphene-impregnated walls. The bulging cells seemingly adjacent to the cortex make up the pericycle. The endodermis is composed of excessively narrow cells just outside the pericycle and is not obvious in the photograph. Larger primary axes show large central xylem masses with some dissection (Fig. 13–1, *H*, left-hand stele) and suggestions of either mesarchy or exarchy. There is no protoxylem in the sense of presence of stretchable elements.

Stelar anatomy in the laterals is comparable to that of primary axes of similar diameter (Fig. 13–1, *H*, right-hand stele).

Most laterals produced on primary axes

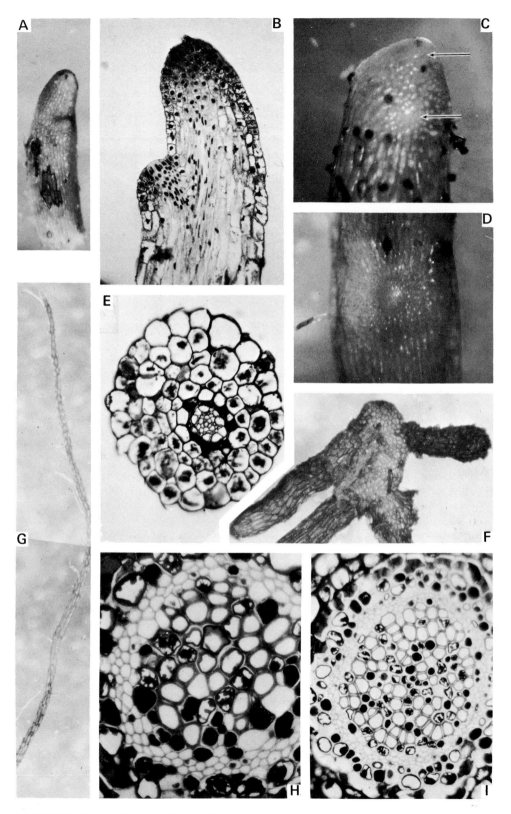

FIGURE 13–3. *A*. Tip of a primary axis with a new lateral in *Stromatopteris*. *B*. Object in *A* in longitudinal section. *C*. Type of lateral branching on an underground axis in *Tmesipteris* sp. Arrows indicate the two new apices. *D*. Lateral apex on an underground axis of *Psilotum flaccidum*. *E*. Cross section of a primary axis in *Stromatopteris*. *F*. Upright stubby axis with three roots in *Stromatopteris*. *G*. Primary axis of *Stromatopteris* tapering down to filiform. *H*. Cross section of the stele of an upright stubby axis in *Stromatopteris*. *I*. Cross section of a rhizome in *Stromatopteris*.

become determinate (Fig. 13–1, *D*, *E*), although in section they seem to possess a residual meristem on their adaxial surface. Other laterals grow to produce a primary axis like the one that produced them. Still others grow but are progressively reduced in diameter all the way down to a uniseriate filamentous state (Fig. 13–2, *B*, Lat → FA; Fig. 13–3, *G*). Within such an axis, the stele dissappears at an axial diameter of about 0.3 mm.

The tips of primary axes or laterals may turn upward and change into another growth phase: the upright, stubby axes (Fig. 13–2, *C*; Fig. 13–3, *F*). The change in growth pattern is expressed by changes in the apex to a broad flat dome with a medianly situated growth center on which there is a medianly located cell with three cutting faces and by a conspicuous lack of cell elongation proximal to the apex (Fig. 13–3, *F*). The upright stubby axes regularly produce one to several roots near their attachment to the primary axis and then proceed to branch and produce the vertical trusses.

Anatomically, the upright stubby axes are protostelic with a mycorrhizic, parenchymatous cortex. The stele is more complex in terms of xylic dissection and intertracheidal parenchymatization than the small primary axes but represents merely an extension in degree of the complexity in the latter (Fig. 13–3, *H*). There is no protoxylem, and only occasionally is a poorly defined pole of early metaxylem differentiation discernible. The perixylic phloem is continuous.

Branching in the vertical trusses is in part dichotomous and in part lateral. This is reasonably clear in young plants (Fig. 13–2, *C*) but much less so in older plants (Fig. 13–1, *A*, *F*; Fig. 13–2, *D*).

The rhizomes (RH in Fig. 13–2, *D*) arise within the branching region of the vertical truss, near its base. Their massive apices have a high dome, usually with a medianly situated three-sided apical cell. They branch both dichotomously and laterally, but the apex is only slightly displaced before lateral branching. Although rhizomes are similar to the axes of the mature vertical truss in diameter, they bear septate rhizoids and no scaly outgrowths. The rhizome stele shows a further increase in the xylic complexity exhibited by the stubby upright axes and is in many ways nearly indistinguishable from the stele of a gleicheniaceous stem (Fig. 13–3, *I*). Protoxylem is absent and poles of early metaxylem maturation are either absent or very obscure. When discernible they indicate mesarchy.

The first leaflike structures produced by *Stromatopteris* originate when the plant is already composed of a mass of subterranean axes. In relatively young plants the "leaf" may be ontogenetically derived from a lateral, from the tip of a primary axis, or from a branch within a vertical truss from an upright stubby axis. In each case, the apex produces a last lateral just before it itself begins to assume what may be called leaf form (Fig. 13–4, *A* to *C*). The lateral branching is seen in Fig. 13–4, *A* just after the two new centers are separated. In Fig. 13–4, *B* the more distal of the two apices has been elevated by further growth and has begun to show the circinate coil, which is always toward the lateral. In Fig. 13–4, *C* the coil is more obvious (arrow indicates lateral apex). At this stage uniseriate trichomes appear on both the "leaf" apex and that of the associated lateral. The constant relationship of the "leaf" apex and last-formed lateral suggests that together they may be considered some sort of morphological unit in the interpretation of *Stromatopteris* in more classical fern terminology. The regularly occurring elpipetiolar buds found in several pteridaceous genera

FIGURE 13–4. *Stromatopteris*, all except *G*. *A* to *C*. Young "leaf" and the associated lateral. In *A* the apical division has just occurred and both apices are on the slanted surface to the left. In *B* the lateral has been left behind by growth of the "leaf." In *C* the lateral is indicated by an arrow and the "leaf" has begun to coil. *D* to *F*. Sections of the vertical truss below (*D*), through (*E*), and above (*F*) the division of the stele to produce the "leaf" trace (LT) and another axial stele. *G*. Cross section through the stele of a frond just below the ground level of *Psilotum nudum*. *H*. Primary axis with attached lateral. The lower bulge on the lateral is the first external indication of root formation. *I*. Later stage in the development of a root from a lateral. The root points downward from near the tip of the lateral. *J*. Root derived by direct transformation of the apex of a lateral. *K*. Root showing a conspicuous short cell zone in the center of the photograph.

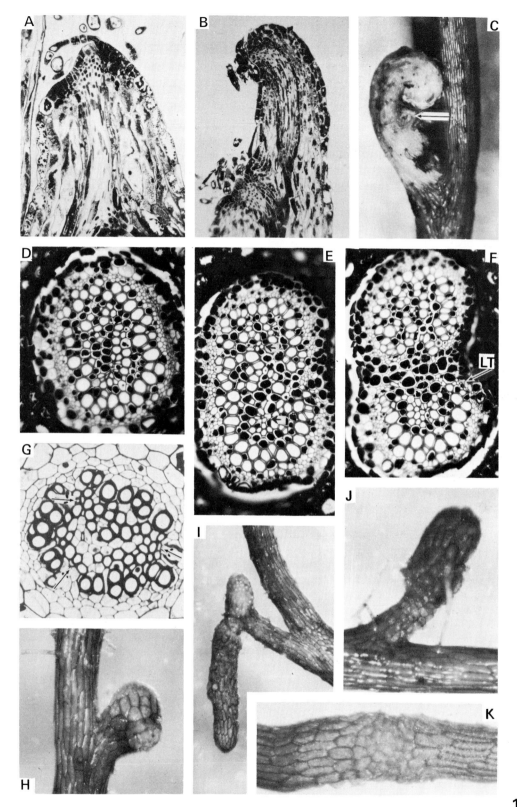

199

and in *Botrychium* might be considered in this context.

The leaf apex at the stage shown in Fig. 13–4, *C* still has an apical cell with three cutting faces. Those slightly more advanced, however, show a linear prismatic layer in which there is an apical cell with two cutting faces and are, therefore, at this stage, like other fern leaf apices. The pinnae, which are in a series of subopposite pairs, originate as lateral bulges several cells below the apical cell.

What one might take to be a petiole of *Stromatopteris* is anatomically much like that organ in many more typical ferns. It shows a U-shaped stele with a protoxylem point at each open end and a third one near the center and on the inside of the U (Fig. 13–4, *F*, LT). The similarity does not extend to the manner in which the "petiole" originates from subterranean axes, however.

A cross section of an axis within the vertical truss shows a protostele surrounded by an often highly sclerenchymatous cortex. The configuration is different from that in the protosteles elsewhere in the plant body. It shows a peripheral ring of large metaxylem elements (Fig. 13–4, *D*) surrounding an ill-defined mixed pith within which are smaller metaxylem elements and two poles of early metaxylem maturation (arrows in Fig. 13–4, *E*). While this stele is gleichenaceous in several respects, much closer comparison may be made with cross sections of psilotaceous axes, also from just below the ground level (Fig. 13–4, *G*).

In following such an axis up through the branching and into a petiole in *Stromatopteris*, an equal division of the stele is observed. Figure 13–4, *E* shows the two steles nearly separated. The two steles produced are essentially like the one below. A short distance up (Fig. 13–4, *F*) the stele that enters the "petiole" becomes bilateral and leaflike. The "petiole" of *Stromatopteris* thus can be described as having "stem anatomy" at its base and "leaf anatomy" farther up.

The root of *Stromatopteris* arises very late in the life of the plant, and, in fact, many well-established young sporophytes with several "leaves" are completely rootless. The roots arise endogenously (Fig. 13–4, *H*, lower bump on the lateral; *I*, the axis extending downward

from the lateral) or by direct continuation of a lateral on a primary axis (Fig. 14–4, *J*)!

The tissues of the root are traceable to a single prominent apical cell. Its distal derivatives in some roots go on to produce root cap only (Fig. 13–5, *A*), but in other roots, cells of similar origin also contribute to epidermis and cortex (Fig. 13–5, *B*).

The internal structure of *Stromatopteris* roots is, for the most part, much like that of other ferns (Fig. 13–5, *C*). The figure shows an ordinary diarch stele with a protoxylem point at top and bottom, two arcs of phloem (left and right in the stele), a pericycle, an endodermis, and a parenchymatous, mycorrhizic cortex.

Close to the points where roots are attached to the stubby upright axes their stelar anatomy is somewhat more stemlike with obscure protoxylem points (the arrow in Fig. 13–5, *D* indicates the only clearly recognizable one in this section) and more xylic dissection.

Externally the roots are hairless (some knobs at the distal ends of surface cells may be interpreted as reduced trichomes) and are covered by a cuticle over thick epidermal cell walls. The fungal mycelia do not extend out from the roots into the substratum as they do from other subterranean axes of *Stromatopteris*. The root, therefore, is not an absorbing organ. The root grows downward and penetrates deeper than the other organs of the plant, and it is possible that it serves to regenerate plants after serious fires.

Subterranean axes, roots, primary sporophytic axes, and gametophytes of *Stromatopteris* all show periodic zones of short cells along their lengths (one is shown in the center of the root in Fig. 13–4, *K*). In the root, various degrees of vascular interruption occur at the short-cell zone. In certain specimens the interruption is complete such that throughout the axis at that point there will be only isodiametric parenchyma. In others complete steles in the long-cell zones are connected by undifferentiated but elongate parenchyma. In still others an endodermis and a pericycle, surrounding a few undifferentiated cells, are present.

The pinnae of *Stromatopteris* are mostly about as long as broad, semielliptic, and entire with revolute margins (Fig. 13–1, *B*;

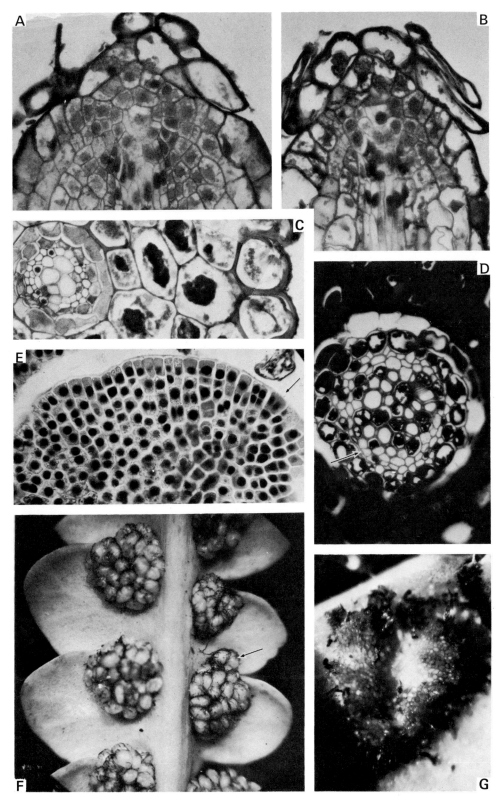

FIGURE 13–5. *Stromatopteris.* *A, B.* Longitudinal sections of root tips. *C.* Cross section of a sector of a root. *D.* Cross section of a root near its point of attachment to an upright stubby axis. *E.* Paradermal section of part of a young pinna. *F.* Abaxial view of a frond with fertile pinnae. The arrow indicates a small second sorus on one of the pinnae. *G.* Receptacle (dark V-shaped area occupying most of the figure) with sporangia removed.

Fig. 13–5, *F*). In some shade forms pinnae are longer and closely approximate gleicheniaceous (dicranopteroid) pinnules. Small "leaves" of juvenile plants bear pinnae that are obliquely deltoid with a shorter region of attachment (Fig. 13–1, *B*, left; Fig. 13–7, *D*); the very first to be produced, however, are extremely decurrent and less distinct from each other. Pinnae are occasionally lobed, and when they are there is usually a very small lobe on the distal edge adjacent to the rachis (Fig. 13–7, *A*, *C*). This is the position of origin of the sorus when it is present, and the lobe is interpreted as that structure undeveloped.

Regardless of whether they are entire or lobed at maturity, all young pinnae show at least three slight but recognizable lobes, each with a meristematic center containing a single apical cell with two cutting faces connected by a continuous marginal meristem (Fig. 13–5, *E*). The particular lobe from which the sorus develops is always recognizable in very young stages.

The sorus at maturity is exindusiate and appears as a cluster of sporangia on the abaxial side of the pinna close to the distal edge (Fig. 13–5, *F*). The arrow indicates a second sorus on one of the pinnae in a similar position but near the proximal edge. If the sporangia are removed, the receptacle is revealed as a V- or Y-shaped mound (Fig. 13–5, *G*), paralleling a forking in the vein system. Among the sporangia are a number of uniseriate paraphases (Fig. 13–5, *F*; stubs shown in *G*).

A cross section of a leaf, including the sorus, reveals that beneath each arm of the sorus there are two parallel veins (Fig. 13–6, *E* and *G* arrows), which can be traced backward to dichotomies within the vein system at right angles to the plane of the pinna.

The sporangiferous receptacle, Re, is first recognized during ontogeny as a slight lobe covered with precocious paraphases on the distal edge of the pinna adjacent to the rachis, RA (Fig. 13–6, *A* adaxial, *B* abaxial). The application of the terms "abaxial" and "adaxial" to the *Stromatopteris* "leaf" requires elaboration, since the "leaf" is not appendicular upon a stem. The "leaf" is vertically oriented, so "upper side" and "lower side" are not descriptive. The direction of the circinate coiling in all ferns, except during later stages of growth in *Schizaea* and *Actinostachys*, is adaxial, and this is used as the primary reference direction in *Stromatopteris*. In addition, the *Stromatopteris* "leaf" shows revolute margins toward, and bears stomates only on, what is referred to as its "abaxial" surface.

The margin of the lobe on which the receptacle originates divides transversely to its plane to produce an obscure three-dimensional branching of the apparently planar structure (Fig. 13–6, *D*). The procambium within also divides, and the pattern of two vertically aligned veins below the receptacle is laid out. Further growth extends the receptacle as well as the leaf margin but is more extensive in the latter, so that the receptacle comes to lie on the abaxial surface of a flattened pinna. During this final lateral extension, the last dichotomy of the vein system and of the receptacle occurs (Fig. 13–6, *F*, paradermal section).

The pinna margin above the sorus frequently becomes extended as a definite lobe or finger (Fig. 13–7, *B* arrow).

Over the surface of the receptacle a number of sporangial initials become established (SI in Fig. 13–8, *A*) by enlargement and change in pattern of segmentation. They divide, as do single apical cells of stems to produce first the sporangial stalks (Fig. 13–8, *B*, *C*), which in mature sporangia are terete and four to five cells across (Fig. 13–8, *F*). The terminal cell then divides to produce a flat cell toward the distal end of the whole structure and an inner, completely enclosed cell. The two-celled stage of the sporangium proper is established.

Historically the term "sporangial initial"

FIGURE 13–6. *Stromatopteris. A, B.* Both sides of a young fertile pinna attached to a piece of the rachis. *C.* Group of fertile pinnae on the coiled tip of the frond. *D.* Cross section through the tip of a young fertile pinna. The abaxial surface is up. *E.* Cross section through both branches of the forked receptacle on an older pinna. Abaxial surface is up. *F.* Paradermal section through a young fertile pinna. The two branches of the forked receptacle are shown. *G.* Cross section through one branch of the receptacle showing the pair of parallel veins (arrows) below the external ridge. The abaxial surface is up. RE = receptacle; RA = rachis; LM = lamina margin.

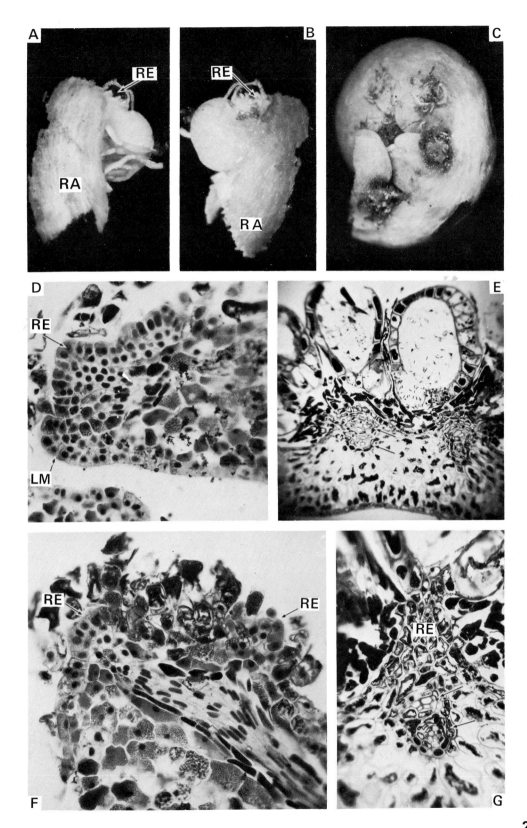

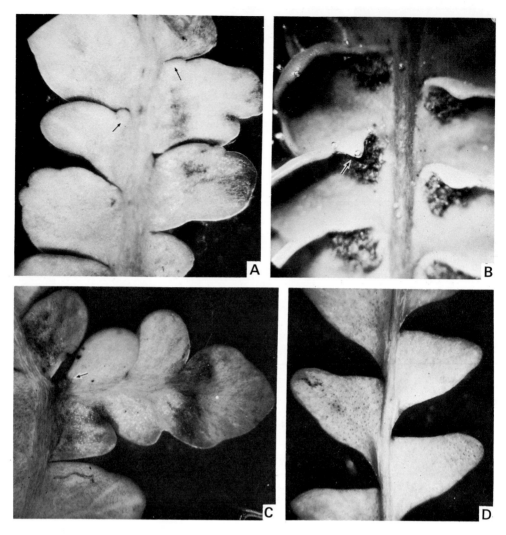

FIGURE 13–7. *Stromatopteris.* *A.* Portion of a frond with lobed pinnae. The arrows indicate the position of the most frequently present extra lobe. *B.* Fertile pinnae in which the margins have extended themselves as conspicuous lobes over the receptacles. One is indicated by arrow. *C.* More highly developed pinna. The arrow indicates a diminutive lobe. *D.* Portion of a frond from a young plant.

has been applied in filicalean ferns to indicate the initial cell before the stalk cells are cut off, and this is what has been above. For comparative purposes, however, the terminal cell just before the two-celled sporangium is produced might best be likened to the sporangial initials in most other groups of ferns and fernlike plants.

The outer (distal) cell of the two-celled sporangium undergoes a series of anticlinal divisions, establishing the outer wall layer (Fig. 13–8, *B* to *G*). The inner cell divides three or four times, each time more or less parallel to the outer surface, thus cutting out a single central cell, the primary sporogenous or archesporial cell, surrounded by a layer of cells between it and the outer wall (Fig. 13–8, *C, D*).

The cells of the middle layer of the three-layered sporangium (Fig. 13–8, *D*) all divide periclinally (Fig. 13–8, *E*). Of the two new layers thus produced, the outer one, after some anticlinal divisions, matures into the inner

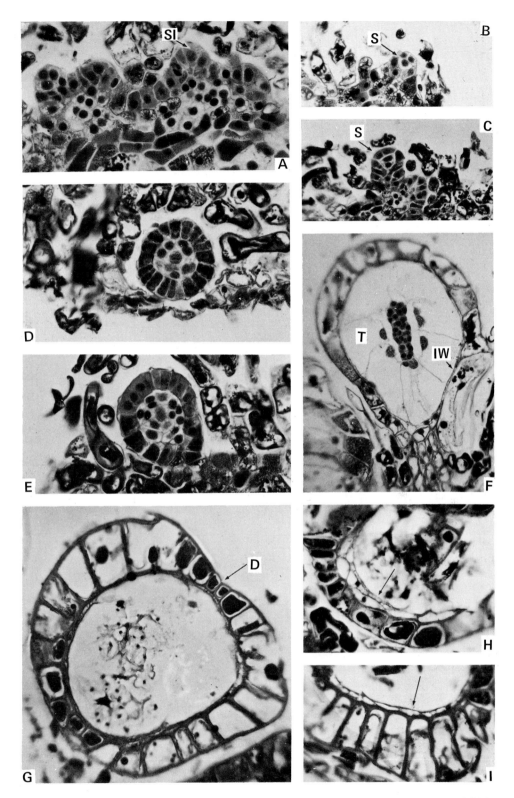

FIGURE 13–8. *Stromatopteris*. Sporangial development and wall structure. SI = stalk initial; S = sporangium; T = tapetum; IW = inner wall; D = line of dehiscence; arrows in *H, I* indicate inner wall.

205

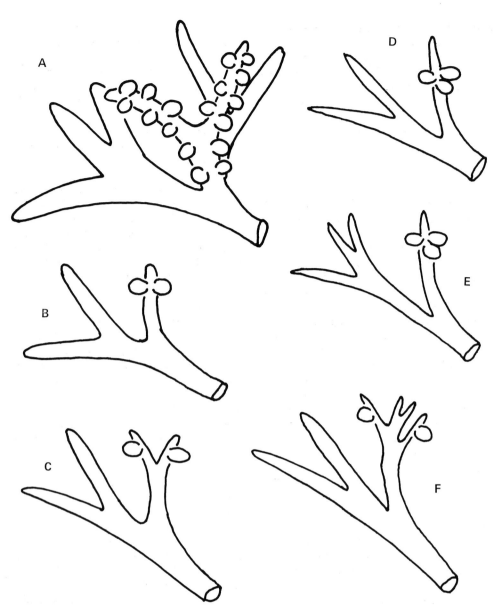

FIGURE 13–9. *A*. Diagram of the fertile pinna of *Stromatopteris* as it appears with presumed fusions removed. *B* to *F*. Diagrams of psilotaceous fertile pinnae as they appear with presumed fusions removed. *B, D, E, Psilotum; C, F, Tmesipteris.*

wall layer (Fig. 13–8, *F, I* arrow), while the inner, the tapetum, expands anticlinally with the whole sporangium. The tapetal nuclei become variably polypoid as nuclear divisions and fusions occur. Additional periclinal divisions occur here and there in the inner wall layer (Fig. 13–8, *H*), so that the entire wall ranges from two to five cells thick. Inner wall cells develop radial thickenings and persist throughout the life of the sporangia.

Divisions in the sporogenous tissue continue until approximately 64 spore mother cells are produced. The cellular integrity of the tapetum is lost as meiosis proceeds to produce the approximately 256 monolete, bean-shaped spores (Fig. 13–8, *G*). G. Erdtman informs the author that some years ago he was struck by the fact that the spores of *Stromatopteris* were very similar to those of *Psilotum* and *Tmesipteris* and that, according to his opinion, the latter two genera should be referred to the Filicineae. His conclusion is now substantiated by evidence from nearly all parts of the life cycles of the three genera concerned.

During increase in volume, the sporangium assumes its bilateral form and the uniseriate annulus is differentiated in the surface layer. The annulus is obliquely oriented and is not interrupted by the stalk. Dehiscence results from separation of slightly elongate cells of the outer layer and tearing of the inner layer along a predetermined line (Fig. 15–35, *A*, *B*).

The dehiscence and postdehiscence trigger mechanism is like that in most filicalean ferns. Because of the thickening and consequent greater rigidity of radial and inner walls, the annular cells shrink on drying by a pulling together of the outer ends of their radial walls. The sporangium is then torn open along the line of dehiscence (D in Fig. 13–8, *G*). The dehiscence is thus completed and the sporangium is forcibly held in the open position by the tensile strength of a shrunken column of liquid in each annular cell. The trigger is thus set and on the rupturing of the liquid columns the spores are forcibly ejected. The mechanism may be repeated a number of times in the same sporangium and works in preserved as well as living material.

The fertile pinna of *Stromatopteris* can be interpreted as a fusion product of three-dimensionally branched entity corresponding to its pattern of vascularization, presented diagrammatically in Fig. 13–9, *A*. This interpretation is supported by evidence from its ontogeny. Note that the sorus is a digit or a branched digit with sporangia uniformly distributed. As will be seen later, the sorus of most of the relatively primitive filicalean fern families may be similarly interpreted.

If fertile pinnae of the Psilotaceae are diagrammed by extending all parts and removing presumed fusions, their appearance (Fig. 13–9, *B* to *F*) becomes noticeably similar to those of *Stromatopteris*. The diagrams represent the total range observed in *Psilotum* (*B*, *D*, *E*) with the exception of the multisporangiate structures and in *Tmesipteris* (*C*, *F*).

The gametophyte of *Stromatopteris* is subterranean and of a true axial type. The gametangia and septate rhizoids are distributed uniformly over its surface (Fig. 13–10, *A* to *C*). The gametophyte axis, which branches dichotomously (Fig. 13–10, *B*, *D*) and by superficial, lateral budding (Fig. 13–10, *E*), is, except for the presence of sex organs, indistinguishable from the thinner primary sporophytic axes (Fig. 13–11, *A*, *B*, gametophyte; *C*, sporophyte).

In the gametophytic apex (Fig. 13–11, *I*, *J*) there is a medianly situated apical cell with three cutting faces. Some gametophytic axes, however, grow in length with progressive diminution of the apex until a filament having an apical cell with a single cutting face is formed, just as in some sporophytic axes.

The internal tissue is uniformly parenchymatous with the cells containing the same fungus as in the sporophyte (Fig. 13–11, *D*, *G*).

Each surface bud is traceable to a single cell (Fig. 13–11, *E*). The buds often occur in clusters that are derived from a residual meristematic zone surrounding the archegonial neck.

The entire gametophyte is extremely brittle, since most of its branches are attached by single cells and very few entire gametophytes are found. The few that have been seen ranged upward to 2 cm long and were highly branched in a plane corresponding to the grain of rotten wood in which they occurred. The axial diameters ranged upward to about 0.8 mm.

The antheridia are relatively large, spherical, and completely superficial. Their attachment is usually by a single cell, which is occasionally elongated to produce a definite stalk (Fig. 13–10, *C*; Fig. 13–11, *G*). The cells of the uniseriate jacket are slightly elongated over the top of the antheridium such that in one section many small cross sections of cells are seen (Fig. 13–11, *L*), and in the plane perpendicular to it fewer and longer cells are seen (Fig. 13–11, *G*). These cells converge on one side of the antheridium as the hair at a granny knot on the back of a lady's head.

On one of the faces of the antheridium parallel to the long cells across the top, is the single opercular cell (Fig. 13–10, *I*; Fig. 13–11, *H*) adjacent to its C-shaped sister cell and surrounded by several rings of cells. Sperm output is high, as indicated in Fig. 13–11, *G*, *L*.

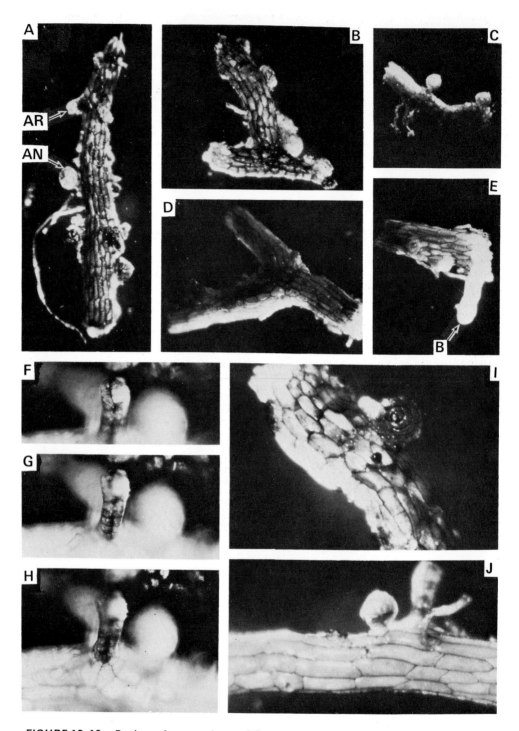

FIGURE 13–10. Portions of gametophytes of *Stromatopteris*. *F* to *H* are different focal planes of the same archegonium. AR = archegonium; AN = antheridium; B = a branch of superficial bud origin.

FIGURE 13–11. *Stromatopteris*. *A*. Portion of a gametophyte. *B, C*. Primary sporophytic axes. *D*. Longitudinal section of a gametophyte. *E*. Section through the attachment of a bud cluster on the gametophyte. The arrow shows the tenuous connection of one bud. *F, G, L*. Cross sections of gametophytes. An archegonium appears in *F*, two archegonial necks and an antheridium in *G*, and an antheridium in *L*. *H*. Surface view of the opercular and adjacent cells of an antheridium. *I, J*. Longitudinal sections of gametophytic apices. *K*. Longitudinal section through a rhizoid.

208

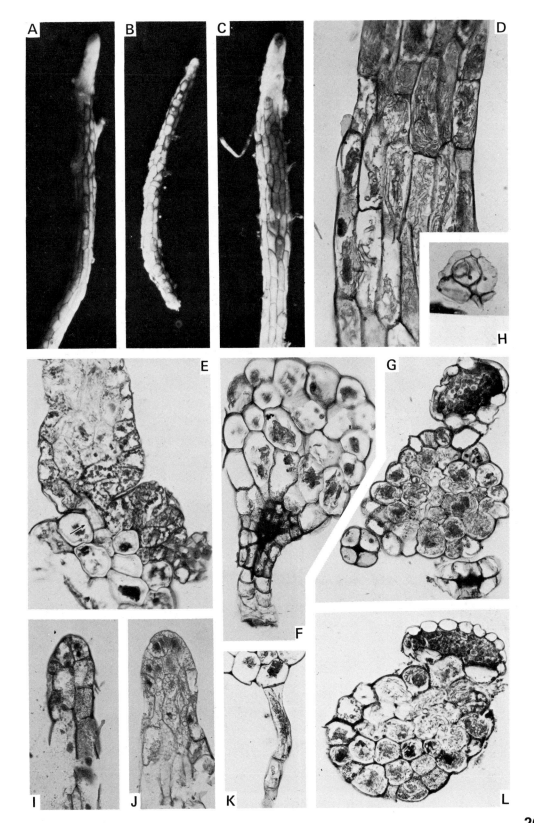

209

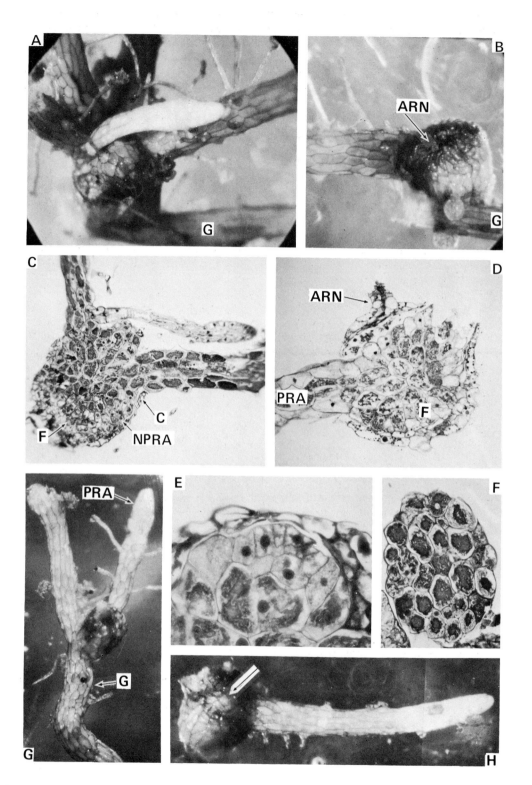

The antheridia thus are essentially identical to those of the Gleicheniaceae. There is some suggestion of similarity also to antheridia of *Tmesipteris* and *Psilotum*, although the jacket rows are less pronounced and less regular in the latter genera.

The archegonial necks are four-celled in cross section (Fig. 13–11, *G*) and six to nine cells long (Fig. 13–10, *F* to *H*; Fig. 13–11, *F*). Walls of the basal neck cells are thickened up to a particular plane across the neck (Fig. 13–11, *F*), where the archegonium frequently decapitates, as in the Psilotaceae. Around the base of the archegonia cell divisions result in two to four rings of cells (Fig. 13–10, *H*), a feature also found in *Actinostachys* and to a lesser extent in some other ferns (e.g., *Psilotum*). The necks are frequently curved, but not in the regular manner characteristic of more advanced filicalean ferns.

Although the embryo of *Stromatopteris* is unique in certain respects, it also subjects itself to comparison with that of the Psilotaceae and of *Actinostachys*. The early stages are unknown, but in later development it is a spherical mass of tissue completely enclosed within the calyptra of gametophytic origin (Fig. 13–12, *A* to *D*, *G*, *H*). The proximal (inner) hemisphere constitutes the foot (F in Fig. 13–12, *C*, *D*); the figure shows an irregular periphery that results from differentially extending radial cell lineages, which causes some intermixing of sporophytic and gametophytic tissue. Whereas in *Psilotum*, *Tmesipteris*, and *Actinostachys* the entire upper hemisphere becomes organized as one (or occasionally two) axial meristems, this does not occur in *Stromatopteris*. In the latter a number of primary axes originate superficially over the surface of the upper hemisphere and grow directly out through the calyptra. Figure 13–12,

A shows an old embryo with a cluster of primary axes attached to the embryonic sphere, which is enclosed within the calyptra and in turn attached to the gametophytic axis (G) below. The axis whose apical meristem is shown arose by budding from another primary axis, as seen in longitudinal section (Fig. 13–12, *C*). All the primary axes of a particular embryo are not of the same age, but they apparently originate over a period of time. A new one arising is shown in Fig. 13–12, *C*, NPRA, and enlarged in *E*. The embryo in Fig. 13–12, *H* shows one extended primary axis and another (at arrow) producing an external bulge on the surface of the calyptra.

The embryonic primary axes are all avascular (Fig. 13–12, *F*), but they progressively increase in diameter and then differentiate the small protostele. Also at about this stage (Fig. 13–2, *A*) the apical meristem shifts from the symmetrical form with a medially situated apical cell to the asymmetrical form with a subapical center and begins to produce the sequence of laterals.

General Considerations of the Leaf

Plant morphologists have been characterizing vascular plant taxa as microphyllous or megaphyllous (same as macrophyllous) for many years, especially since the work of E. C. Jeffrey in the early part of this century. Some of the concepts involved became more solidified in the context of the "telome" theory outlined by W. Zimmermann in 1930 and considerably elaborated in later years.

Zimmermann set as a starting point (frame of reference) the simple undifferentiated plant body such as occurs in the Rhyniaceae. In this he defined "telomes," either fertile or sterile,

FIGURE 13–12. *Stromatopteris*. *A*. Young sporophyte attached to its parental gametophyte. The bulbous mass directly on the gametophyte contains the embryonic sphere, the upper part of which has produced a group of primary axes. *B*. Young sporophyte attached to its parental gametophyte. A single primary axis is shown. Two antheridia appear on the gametophyte. *C*. Longitudinal section of the structure shown in *A*. *D*. Longitudinal section of the structure shown in *B*. *E*. New primary axis from the structure in *A* and pointed out in *C* enlarged. *F*. Cross section of a primary axis from the structure in *A*. *G*. Young sporophyte still attached to the gametophyte. *H*. As *G*, but gametophyte broken off. The arrow indicates the external bulge produced by a new primary axis still beneath the calyptra. G = gametophyte; ARN = archegonial neck; C = calyptra; F = foot; NPRA = new primary axis; PRA = primary axis.

as the ultimate axial portions beyond the most distal dichotomies and "mesomes" as the interdichotomy axial units. By changing angles between branches of dichotomies, by introducing a differential developmental potential between two axes produced by a dichotomy, and by allowing differential axial determination within the system one can, within the bounds of theory, derive, on the blackboard at least, essentially any vascular plant from a rhyniaceous body. Similarly, within a rather specialized plant body one can designate telomes and mesomes. The theory was too simple and too easily applicable, and unfortunately its excessive use greatly diminished its value. In not a single taxon were the reductions and elaborations that occurred in the phylogenetic history of its soma illuminated. One cannot, however, underestimate the influence that the telome theory had and is having on morphological thought.

The *microphyll* is considered to represent an enation upon a stem (i.e., a simple outgrowth of that stem arising *de novo* and not by phylogenetic modification of another organ occupying that position). In some of the literature a sharp distinction is drawn between an enation as the avascular predecessor and the microphyll as the vascularized derivative, but this distinction can only be made with excessive subjectivity and with differential applicability in various taxa.

The microphyll has in the past been interpreted to be present in the Equisetales, the Psilotaceae, certain genera now placed in the Trimerophytaceae [e.g., *Psilophyton* (in part)], and in all lycopods. There are, however, indications that the *Equisetum* leaf is reduced from something more elaborate (e.g., a megaphyll), as evidenced by the morphology of *Hyeniopsis* and *Asterocalamites*. Within the Psilotaceae one cannot selectively interpret the avascular appendages on the aerial axis in *Psilotum* out of context of the spectrum of organs in which they fall. This leaves only the interpretation of the lycopod leaf standing unquestioned.

The *megaphyll* is defined as a type of leaf phylogenetically derived by modification of a branching stem system or stem truss. Historically the megaphyll has been interpreted as being represented by leaves of ferns, gymnosperms, and angiosperms. The derivation of a megaphyll in a phylogenetic sequence starting with a dichotomously branched plant body would seem to involve the following:

1. Overtopping, which is the differential development of two axial units above a dichotomy such that one seems to continue the main axis and the other is subordinate.

2. Planation, which is the changing of a three-dimensionally branched stem truss so that the successive forkings occur in a single plane.

3. Webbing, which is the introduction of tissue (mesophyll and epidermal extension) between the units of the branched truss.

The effects of overtopping may be observed in a variety of extant and extinct species. The living lycopods are illustrative: In *Lycopodium* and *Selaginella* a range from equal dichotomous to pseudomonopodial branching occurs. The overtopping in *Lycopodium* is finely gradate, and often (e.g., in *L. complanatum*) the extremes reflect differences in the sizes of the two primordia at the point of dichotomy. The ultimate in overtopping would seem to be the complete relegation of one of the two primordia to appendicular status and as well as to a fixed position in a phyllotactic arrangement of a series of similar organs. This end would seem to have been reached in nearly all presumably megaphyllous taxa except the Psilotaceae and the Stromatopteridaceae.

The reference to the above two families must be further qualified, for in each the pinnae have achieved full appendicular status upon a rachis, even though the latter has not done so upon the stem. Furthermore, the entire range from equal dichotomous branching to lateral branching, resulting either in indeterminate lateral axes or in organs with appendicular status, occurs in the Psilotaceae. A similar range in variation of apical branching also occurs within a linear meristem in the leaf of *Schizaea dichotoma* and very possibly of many other ferns. These facts all suggest a modified interpretation of the megaphyll in the main phyletic line of ferns: The leaflet as such arose before the leaf. In other words, the various steps outlined in these paragraphs which presumably led to the megaphyll occurred within different orders of branching at different times. This interpretation does *not* specify that the primitive leaflet was either simple or compound. Further indication of such phyletic change occurs among the aneurophytes, where one finds different orders of branching each suggesting a degree of appendicular status, which has led various authors to designate different entities as "the" leaf.

Planation similarly seems to have been complete in the megaphylls of most taxa. The extinct Coenopteridales are outstanding exceptions. In that order what otherwise might be considered a leaf was in reality a three-dimensional, bushy structure. There are also strong indications that the fertile pinnae of *Stromatopteris* retain a minimal degree of three-dimensional branching, as well as do their presumed homologs, the fertile appendages on the aerial axes (fronds) in the Psilotaceae.

Webbing involves the introduction of marginal meristematic growth. The progression of mature leaf forms, which is assumed to represent to some degree phylogenetic reality, would begin with a flattened organ with open dichotomous venation dissected to the base of each dichotomy, go through leaves with progressively less dissection, and ultimately end with a simple entire leaf. It is generally accepted that the phylogeny of webbing has involved dewebbing as well, and many species seem to be less webbed (i.e., more dissected) by reduction (e.g., many aquatic angiosperms). It seems significant, however, that a much greater proportion of fern and fernlike foliage of Devonian and Mississippian age shows conspicuous dissection than does that of Pennsylvanian and Permian age.

The ferns, which show a more generalized plant body than do seed plants, present several examples of intermediacy between stem systems and leaves, which tend to confirm the interpretation of one in terms of the other. In two families in which leaves are reasonably well-defined, the Osmundaceae and Schizaeaceae, the young leaf primordium has an apical cell with three cutting faces. This is replaced later in ontogeny by a cell with two cutting faces, except in one species of *Osmunda*, in which it persists in its original form. In the Stromatopteridaceae, the obvious homolog of the leaf develops from a primordium that apparently does not "make up its mind" until very late in ontogeny. The structure that

appears to be the homolog of the fern leaf in the Psilotaceae is so shootlike (especially in *Psilotum*) that the application of the term "frond" will certainly be objected to. Among extant forms we seem to have a relatively complete sequence of forms from shoot systems to leaves.

Intermediates between apical meristems and marginal meristems frequently have several centers of growth, each with an apical cell that has two cutting faces. These may be readily interpreted as derivatives of more radially symmetrical axial meristems. However, to apply a similar interpretation to marginal areas, which are more active without morphological distinctness, is certainly treading on soft ground.

The general bilateral nature of the leaf is expressed in terms of its flattened external form, its linear meristem, and the bilateral nature of its vascular supply. It is these features, together with its fundamental appendicular status from the time of its initiation, which have defined the organ. The bilateral nature of the leaf has been considered as a consequence of the reduced, appendicular status of the leaf primordium on the side of the stem apex. This concept was developed particularly as a consequence of Wardlaw's experiments on the stem apex of the fern *Dryopteris*.

In *Dryopteris*, as in almost all vascular plants, the phyllotaxy is so regular that the position of the next leaf to arise may be readily specified ("the presumptive leaf position"). If this site is partially isolated by a surgical slit between it and the center of the stem apex, then a stem instead of a leaf will develop at the site. The interpretation readily arising, therefore, is that a primordium develops into a leaf because of its position relative to the stem apex; in other words, the more dominant stem apex imposes a bilateral appendicular nature upon the leaf. New evidence from the morphology of the Psilotaceae and Stromatopteridaceae definitely clouds the issue and indicates that an organ may have essentially all the attributes of a leaf without being reduced to appendicular status. This emphasizes the major importance of these two families as future sources of information necessary to any real understanding of the fundamental nature of the leaf.

14

Schizaeaceae

The Schizaeaceae, as recognized here, includes two genera that are, unfortunately, rather obscure to most botanists. The genus *Schizaea* now contains approximately 28 widely distributed tropical species and one North Temperate species, *S. pusilla*. The other genus, *Actinostachys*, which has approximately 13 species, is nearly as widely distributed but a high concentration of its known species are found in New Caledonia. One species is known to occur in the continental United States but only in southern Florida. A listing of the known species and their distribution is misleading. The plants are highly inconspicuous in the field, and many of the known, relatively distantly related species closely simulate each other in appearance. It is very likely that there are still a number of undescribed ones.

Recent information has, in the writer's opinion, made it necessary to exclude from the Schizaeaceae the genera *Anemia*, *Mohria*, and *Lygodium* as well as all the fossil forms previously assigned here with the exception of several Cenozoic spore species. There is a validly published familial name available for each of the three excluded genera, or they all may be placed within the Anemiaceae, this name having priority if the three are kept together.

Actinostachys species are small plants living either in shaded forests or in quite zeric habitats. They have a very short underground stem that bears adventitious roots and leaves in a spiral sequence. In some species only one leaf is present at a time (Fig. 14–1, *A*), and it may be as short as 2 cm or, in the more robust forms, as long as 25 cm. The petiole ranges from triangular in cross section to broadly winged (Fig. 14–1, *A*, *B*; Fig. 14–2, *C*). The wing is derived ontogenetically from a distinct marginal meristem.

Distally on the fertile leaves there are from 1 to

215

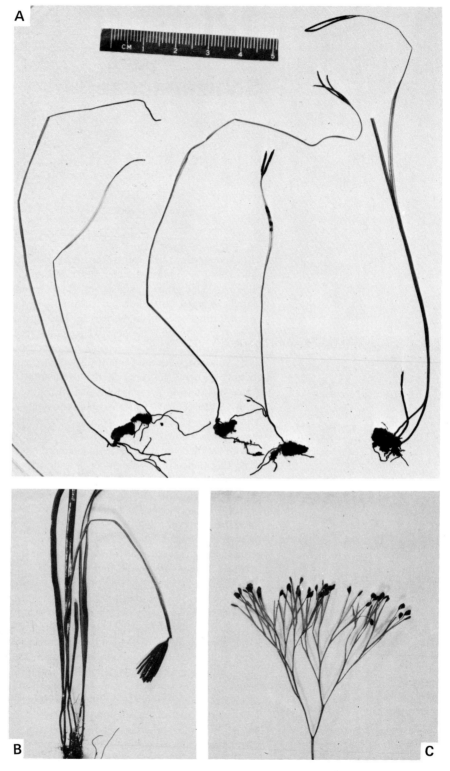

FIGURE 14–1. *A.* Five complete sporophytes of *Actinostachys oligostachys*, each with a gameto-phyte attached. The two on the left each have a single terminal fertile digit on the leaf. *B. Actino-stachys melanesica*. The upper part of the stem is shown with several leaves attached. The leaf that is bent over bears a number of fertile digits. *C.* Single leaf of a small form of *Schizaea dichotoma*. Figures in this grouping and elsewhere in this chapter taken from Bierhorst (1966, 1967, 1968a, 1969b) are not specifically indicated.

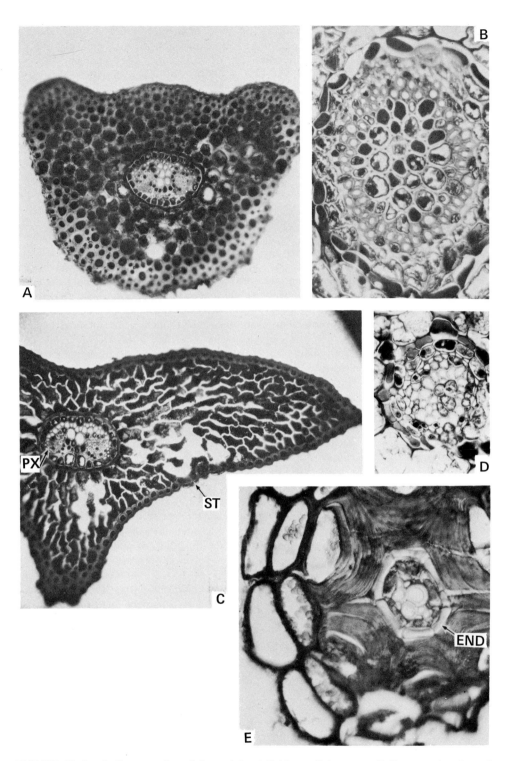

FIGURE 14–2. *A*. Cross section of the petiole of *Schizaea dichotoma*. *B*. Cross section through the stem stele of *Actinostachys melanesica*. *C*. Cross section through the petiole of *Actinostachys intermedia*. ST = stoma. *D*. Cross section through the stem of *Schizaea fistulosa*. *E*. Cross section through the root of *Actinostachys intermedia*. END = endodermis.

approximately 10 thin, fingerlike extensions that bear the sporangia and are arranged in what superficially appears to be a digitate manner (Fig. 14–1, *A, B*; Fig. 14–4, *C*).

The major feature distinguishing the sporophyte of *Schizaea* from that of *Actinostachys* is the arrangement of the foliar sporangiate fructifications, which are distinctly pinnate in *Schizaea* and digitate in *Actinostachys*. The terminal clusters of *Schizaea* are shown in Fig. 14–1, *C* and one very young one appears in Fig. 14–4, *J*.

Actinostachys and *Schizaea* are generically separated primarily on the basis of differences in their gametophytes and embryos, and before these were known both were justifiably included within *Schizaea*.

Within the genus *Schizaea* there are species with simple leaves (e.g., *S. pusilla*); species with one or a few forkings in the leaf (e.g., *S. bifida*); species with flattened, dichotomously (falsely) branched leaves (e.g., *S. dichotoma*; Fig. 14–1, *C*); and species with simple but deeply lobed, fan-shaped leaves (e.g., *S. elegans*). *Schizaea dichotoma* occasionally produces single leaves as tall as 50 cm and as broad as 25 cm, while the leaves of *S. pusilla* are generally only about 3 to 7 cm in length.

Stems of *Schizaea* and *Actinostachys* are covered with numerous, stiff, simple trichomes one or two cells long (Fig. 14–3, *A*). When the young leaves extend beyond the hairy covering of the stem apex, they are reflexed; the circinate coil does not appear until they are approximately 1 cm in length. The stem stele (Fig. 14–2, *B, D*) shows a central core of parenchyma surrounded by a cylinder of xylem; this, in turn, is completely encircled by phloem, then by pericycle and endodermis. A small amount of internal phloem has been described as occurring in one species. A solid core of xylem is found at the oldest end of the stem, where it was attached to the foot of the embryo, and occasionally just beyond this is a very short region where there is alternation of pithed and pithless regions until the mature form of the stem is attained. Protoxylem is not found in the stems and, in fact, there are no clearly recognizable primary xylem poles. Regularly, however, cauline xylem matures first below a leaf attachment.

In the development of the stem, late stages of procambial growth are characterized by periclinal divisions producing radial series of cells (shown in the young sporeling stem in Fig. 14–16, *E*). The regularity is peculiarly unfernlike and among fernlike plants in general resembles *Botrychium*.

The leaf trace is single and C-shaped. In small stems it is often as large as the rest of the stele at the point of departure, giving the impression of a dichotomy, to which this branching conceivably could be homologous. Within the petiole the trace more or less maintains its form with a protoxylem point at each end in the cross section (Fig. 14–2, *A, C*). The bulging metaxylem in the center of the trace makes it appear W-shaped.

There is hypodermal sclerenchyma in the leaves and a relatively compact chlorenchyma with some air chambers, which are mostly associated with the stomata. The latter occur on the abaxial side in two rows on either side of the vein (ST in Fig. 14–2, *A*).

The surfaces of the roots show characteristic longitudinal rows of cells. Within each row, long cells alternate with shorter trichoblasts (shown at T in Fig. 14–3, *B* before it has produced a root hair). Over the tip of the root, the outer cells of the root cap are arranged so as to form a characteristic dissected umbrella (RC).

In the root apex there is a single, broad apical cell, as is typical of ferns in general (Fig. 14–3, *C*).

In certain species of *Actinostachys*, which appear as dense tufts of leaves in the field, the root apex may turn up and grow directly into a stem. There is at first a slight swelling of the tip (Fig. 14–3, *A*, RS, *D*). This is followed by a loss of the distal cutting face of the apical cell and a sloughing off of the calyptra. In Fig. 14–3, *E* a stem apex is well organized beneath a remnant of the calyptra. The first stele to mature in the new stem is nearly identical to that in a young sporophyte of sexual origin. This kind of organ transformation has been reported to occur in several higher ferns (see McVeigh, 1937).

The highly branched leaf of *Schizaea dichotoma* is of special interest in an overall concept of fern-leaf branching patterns. It appears to be a uniform dichotomous truss at maturity. (Fig. 14–1, *C*), but its ontogeny is otherwise.

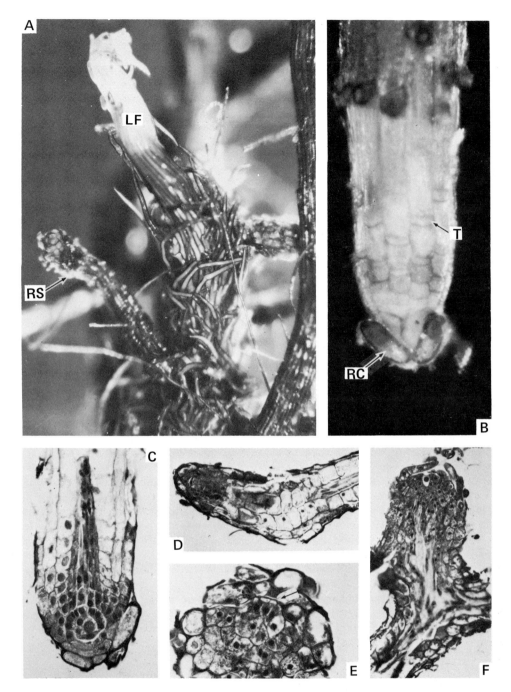

FIGURE 14–3. *A.* Stem of *Actinostachys intermedia.* LF = a young leaf with reflexed tip; RS = root tip that is in a transitional stage to becoming a stem. *B.* Root tip of *A. intermedia.* T = trichoblast; RC = root cap. *C.* Longitudinal section of the root tip of *A. intermedia.* *D.* Tip of a root in *A. intermedia* which is turning upward and becoming swollen proximally. *E.* Tip of a root of *A. intermedia* which has already assumed characteristics of a stem apex (arrow) but is still beneath the old root cap. *F.* Stage following *E* in which the cap is gone and typical stem trichomes have been produced. No leaf primordia have yet appeared.

The first fork is a true dichotomy; that is, two new apical cells (Fig. 14–4, *A*) are directly traceable to an equal division of a pre-existing one. The next several apices to appear become organized around new apical cells that originate within the prismatic layers of the older apices and on the sides away from the axil of the first dichotomy (one shown in Fig. 14–4, *A* to the far right). Soon a continuous marginal meristem is formed in which there are major and minor centers of growth (Fig. 14–4, *B*) and in which there are some true dichotomies and a number of laterally originating centers, often in rows of two or three on one side of a major center. At the young stage shown in Fig. 14–4, *B* the entire leaf appears as two-lobed and cup-shaped masses all within the circinate coil. There is some evidence that the apparently different types of branching actually do intergrade, depending on the proximity of a new apical cell to the one closest in cell lineages. In the strict sense of our terminology, if it is the sister cell of another apical cell, then a dichotomy has occurred; if a derivative of an apical cell divides one or more times before a new apical cell is established, then lateral branching has occurred. It seems apparent that a sharp distinction between the two types of branching is unnatural in this case and possibly in a number of other ferns as well, where we observe frequent dichotomies in an otherwise pinnate system. Nothing is known of the ontogeny of the simple fan-shaped leaves of the genus *Schizaea*.

The entire terminal cluster of fertile digits on the leaf of *Actinostachys* is referable to one pair of lateral pinnae and a terminal one (Fig. 14–4, *C*), which branch dichotomously to produce the total number of digits. The apex of a young frond before pinna formation is shown in Fig. 14–4, *D*. As development proceeds, the two lateral pinnae appear as two lateral flanges (LP in *E*; LA is the leaf apex). Further development is shown in *F*, where the pinnae are beginning to divide and the terminal pinna (TP) can be recognized. Two further stages are seen in *G* and *H*. The leaf apex proper develops directly into the terminal pinna and, as it does so, it reverses its direction of coiling (F). This is clear by comparing Fig. 14–5, *A* with *B*. At an early stage the lateral pinnae appear as broad flat outgrowths (Fig. 14–4, *F*; Fig. 14–5, *C* and *D* in two planes of section). This appearance becomes lost later, however, as a result of differential growth of the entities involved.

In *Schizaea* the fertile digits arise as an acropetal succession of pinnae just as their mature disposition suggests (Fig. 14–4, *I, J*). A few dichotomies occur, but not with so high a frequency as in *Actinostachys*. The leaf apex also becomes the terminal pinna.

The vascular anatomy at the tip of the *Actinostachys* fertile leaf is indicative of its ontogeny. A massive trace supplies each of the two lateral pinnae and one trace extends to the terminal one. This is seen in the series of photographs taken at progressively higher levels shown in Fig. 14–7, *A* to *D*. LP goes to a lateral pinna, TP to a terminal one.

Once a fertile digit of *Schizea* or *Actinostachys* is readily recognizable as a distinct outgrowth (as the older ones in Fig. 14–4, *I, J*) it possesses an apical meristem composed of two linear and parallel initial zones (IZ_1 and IZ_2 in Fig. 14–5, *E*). One zone (IZ_1) is abaxial and the other adaxial (see Fig. 14–6, *B*). In *Schizaea* the digit apex is more asymmetrical and "turned over" such that both zones appear in face view from the abaxial side as in Fig. 14–5, *E*.

At the time of initiation of the digits, each grows by means of a lens-shaped apical cell (seen in its broad aspect in each of two young

FIGURE 14–4. *A.* Tip of a young leaf of *Schizaea dichotoma*. An initial dichotomy took place to establish the two large apical cells. Then a small lens-shaped apical cell became differentiated on the outside of each of the larger apical cells (only one, on the right, is shown). *B.* Tip of a somewhat older growing leaf of *S. dichotoma*. The young petiole is shown in cross section below. When dissected, this leaf appeared as two cup-shaped structures with a lobed or crenate outline with a number of large and small apical cells as the two in *A*. *C.* Truss of terminal digits on the leaf of *Actinostachys melanesica*. The structure has been flattened out at the base and therefore there is a tear in the tissue. *D.* Apex of a young leaf of *A. laevigata*. *E* to *H*. Development of the fertile digit truss in *A. laevigata*. *I, J.* Young fertile leaf tip of *Schizaea dichotoma*. *K.* Part of a fertile digit of *Actinostachys melanesica*. LP = lateral pinna; TP = terminal pinna; LA = leaf apex.

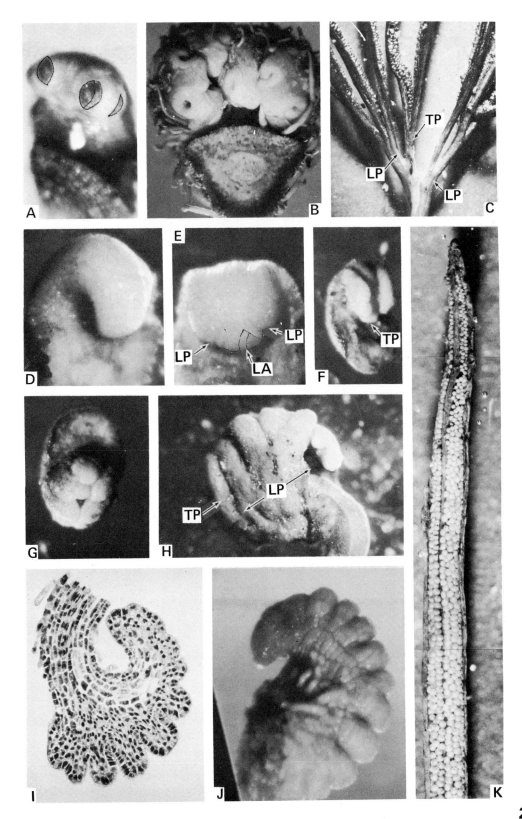

221

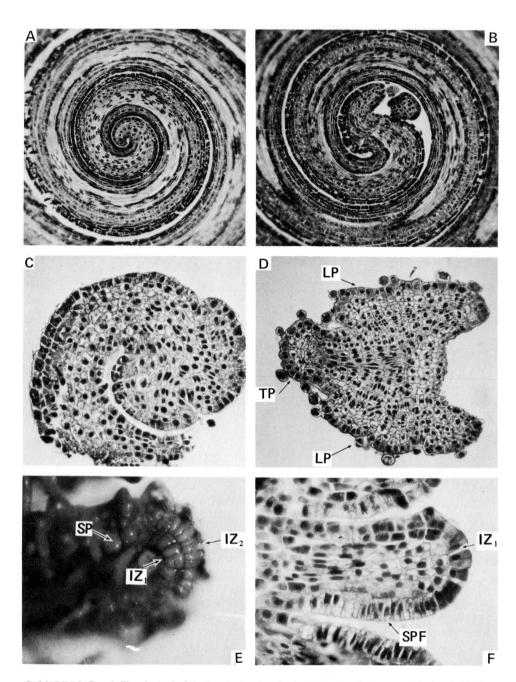

FIGURE 14–5. *A.* Tip of a leaf of *Actinostachys laevigata* within the circinate coil before initiation of the sporangiate fructification. *B.* Stage later than in *A,* showing two of the three fertile pinnae. A lateral one is shown in cross section and the terminal one in longitudinal section after it has reversed its direction of coiling. *C.* Longitudinal section of a young fertile leaf of *A. intermedia,* showing a lateral pinna in paradermal section. *D.* Tip of a young fertile leaf of *A. melanesica* cut in such a way that the three fertile pinnae are seen in cross section. TP = terminal pinna; LP = lateral pinna. *E.* Adaxial side of a young fertile pinna of *Schizaea dichotoma.* *F.* Young fertile pinna of *S. dichotoma* in paradermal section. SP = sporangium; IZ = initial zone; SPF = sporangiferous file.

digits projecting from the cross section of a very young rachis in Fig. 14–6, *A*). Details of the establishment of the two initial zones following this stage have not been worked out. By the time the two zones are established, they and their linearly arranged surface derivatives are continuous down the sides of each digit and up the next one.

The cells of IZ_2 divide anticlinally and transversely to the line of the meristem to produce smaller cells around and over the apex of the digit, as seen in Fig. 14–5, *E*. The larger sister cells then appear to maintain the linearity of IZ_2. The smaller cells eventually give rise to the epidermis over the adaxial side of the digit (i.e., the surface not visible in Fig. 14–5, *E*). The larger cellular derivatives of IZ_2 (i.e., those which seem to maintain its integrity at the surface down the sides of the digit) now constitute a marginal meristem which later gives rise to a flap of tissue that protects the sporangia. This is the indusium (I in Fig. 14–6, *D, E* and much extended in *F* to *H*). When apical growth of the digit ceases, the indusium also forms over the apical portion.

The divisions in IZ_1 are anticlinal and both transverse and parallel to the meristem, as well as periclinal or oblique to produce inner tissue of the digit. Ultimately all the inner tissues are traceable to IZ_1. Despite the various planes of division, IZ_1 seems to maintain its surface continuity and is continuous with the line of sporangial initials. The file of surface cells in which sporangial initials will be differentiated is shown in paradermal section in Fig. 14–5, *F*. In *Schizaea* the sporangia are much more precocious in development, appearing close to the digit apex, so the structure SP in Fig. 14–5, *E* is already a multicellular sporangium.

The marginal meristem, which produces the wing of the petiole in *Actinostachys*, is continuous with IZ_1 of the most proximal digit. This fact, in addition to the fact that IZ_1 produces all the internal digital tissue, allows the interpretation of IZ_1 as the equivalent of the marginal meristems in leaves of other ferns and, as a corollary, the interpretation that the sporangia themselves are fundamentally marginal in position.

In previous literature the sporangia were interpreted as marginal on the basis of a study of cross sections of developing digits. In some schizaeaceous species the sections show the sporangia becoming established before the indusium actually grows out as a definite flap (Fig. 14–6, *C*). The different chronology of events in other species, had they been studied, may have resulted in a different interpretation. The description presented here is based on a study of *Schizaea pusilla*, *S. dichotoma*, *S. fistulosa*, *Actinostachys melanesica*, *A. intermedia*, *A. laevigata*, *A. oligostachys*, and *A.* sp.

Within the sporangiferous file of cells (Fig. 14–5, *F*; Fig. 14–6, *C, E, F*) conspicuously bulging cells are seen at a varying distance from the apex of the digit, much closer in *Schizaea* than in *Actinostachys*. These are the sporangial initials in the more classical sense, although in this text the sporangial initial is considered that cell occurring later in ontogeny of the more typical filicalean sporangium, which divides to produce the wall initial and the first included cell. By the time the cells bulge they have already divided anticlinally both transverse to the sporangiferous file such that they are separated from each other by one to several thin flat cells, and also parallel to the file to produce one to several cells laterally. They have also divided at least once periclinally, producing a cell beneath the surface. The first cells produced around and under the bulging cell remain unelevated and at maturity are not obviously a part of the sporangial stalk. The bulging cell then divides several times in the manner of an apical cell before the sporangial initial is established (Fig. 14–6, *D*). Following this the events are similar to those described for *Stromatopteris* and most other filicalean ferns. The two layers between the sporogenous tissue and the surface layer both appear tapetal and decompose, as contrasted to *Stromatopteris*, in which the outer of the two is an inner wall layer.

The mature sporangia are urn or bottle-shaped, showing slight bilateral symmetry due to a slight bulge outward along the longitudinally oriented line of dehiscence and a slight tilt backward from the line (Fig. 15–34, *C, D, G*). The nearly apical transverse annulus ceases its circumferential growth before the rest of the sporangium, especially in *Schizaea*, so that an apical constriction results (Fig. 15–34, *G*). The annulus is most commonly composed of

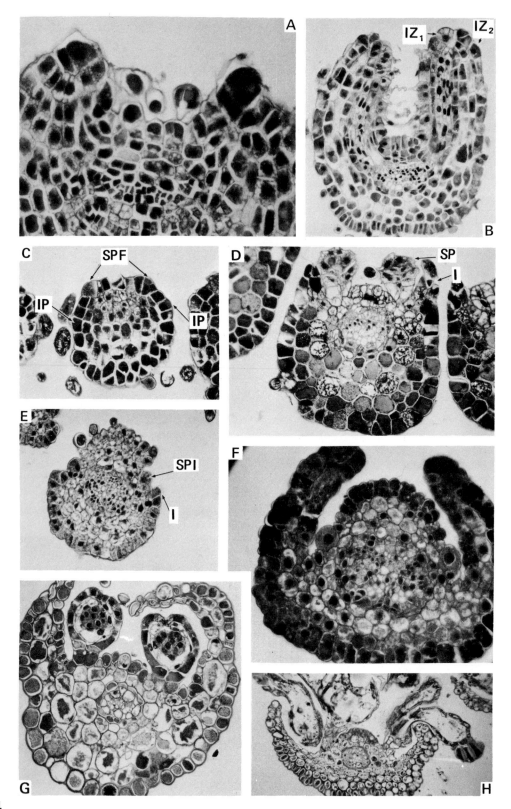

224

one ring of elongate thickened cells, but a second or a third ring, complete or incomplete, is occasionally present. Along the line of dehiscence the cells are specialized in some species (Fig. 15–34, *G*) but not in others; there is, in fact, a complete specialization series in these regards in both *Schizaea* and *Actinostachys*. At the apex of the sporangium (the "distal plate") there is generally a single thin-walled cell enclosed by the annulus, but in individual species of *Schizaea* the range is from one to six.

The line of dehiscence is predetermined by the shape of the distal plate and the distribution of wall thickenings adjacent to it rather than by a line of weakness down the side of the sporangium. The plate is triangular in surface view with one angle at the distal end of the line or dehiscence, where the wall thickening is slightly less extensive. The opening is analogous to tearing a piece of cloth that has been notched slightly.

The gametophyte of *Actinostachys*, which is known for six species,[1] is subterranean and is of a true axial type. That is, it has a well-organized, multicellular apical meristem in which there is a single apical cell with three cutting faces (Fig. 14–8, *A*, *B*; Fig. 14–9, *A*, *D*, *E*). The young axes bear uniformly distributed antheridia and rhizoids. The internal tissue is entirely parenchymatous and mycorrhizal (Fig. 14–10, *A*). Branches are produced at the surface from single cells (Fig. 14–10, *D*).

The rhizoids, when young but seemingly mature, are one or two cells long and separated

[1] Descriptions of four have been published (Bierhorst, 1965, 1966, 1968a). The fifth is undescribed and belongs to a yet-undescribed sporophyte. The sixth is a single tuberous gametophyte found attached to a sporophyte of *A. spirophylla* (col. Brass, 23552, New Guinea) in the Gray Herbarium, Harvard University.

by a distinct cross wall from a bulging epidermal cell. In older gametophytes, however, extra transverse divisions occur near the base (Fig. 14–10, *C*), and many of these new short cells grow out to produce new rhizoids, so that peculiar rhizoid tufts occur.

The gametophytic axis grows secondarily by means of a peripheral thickening meristem (note the recent periclinical divisions at and near the surface in Fig. 14–10, *B*). This type of growth continues, becomes differential within the surface, and eventually a tuberous body is produced (Fig. 14–8, *C* to *E*; Frontispiece). The peripheral thickening can be seen at the base of the gametophyte in Fig. 14–8, *A*; from here it progresses toward the apex, where it may eventually result in some distortion of apical growth (Fig. 14–9, *C*). Following this stage, where the apex seems almost in danger of being buried, there is often a change in relative growth rates so that the apex produces a thinner axial extension from the tuber (Fig. 14–9, *B*).

Old tuberous gametophytes branch by surface budding to produce new primary axes (Fig. 14–8, *E*, PA), or in some species the tips of the rhizoids or necks of archegonia may similarly reproduce vegetatively. The archegonium in Fig. 14–10, *F* has mushroomed out at its apex, and on the new tissue several antheridia have formed. On other such eruptions new apices may become organized.

Differential thickening of the tuberous gametophytes results in many valleys and ridges (Fig. 14–8, *C* to *E*). The rhizoid tufts are located on the ridges and the archegonia in the valleys (Fig. 14–10, *E*).

Sporangia have been found attached terminally to gametophytic rhizoids on some individuals of *Actinostachys oligostachys*. All had dehisced and none showed contents. Sporangia so extremely adventive are unusual but not

FIGURE 14–6. *A.* Cross section of the young rachis of *Schizaea fistulosa* showing longitudinal sections of two fertile pinna primordia projecting at the top of the photograph. *B.* Cross section of the young rachis of *S. dichotoma* at a later stage than the one in *A*, showing longitudinal sections of two fertile pinnae. IZ = initial zone. *C.* Cross section of a young fertile pinna of *S. fistulosa* before the indusium has grown out. IP = indusial position; SPF = sporangiferous file. *D.* As C, but a later stage in development. SP = sporangium; I = indusium. *E.* Section similar to *D*, but of *Actinostachys melanesica*. The sporangia, however, are much less developed as compared to those in *D*. SPI = sporangial stalk initial. *F.* Section of *Actinostachys intermedia* similar to *E*. Sporangial stalk initials are seen bulging from the sides of the midvein region beneath the indusium. *G.* Later stage in fertile digit development in *A. intermedia*. *H.* Cross section of a mature fertile digit of *A. laevigata*.

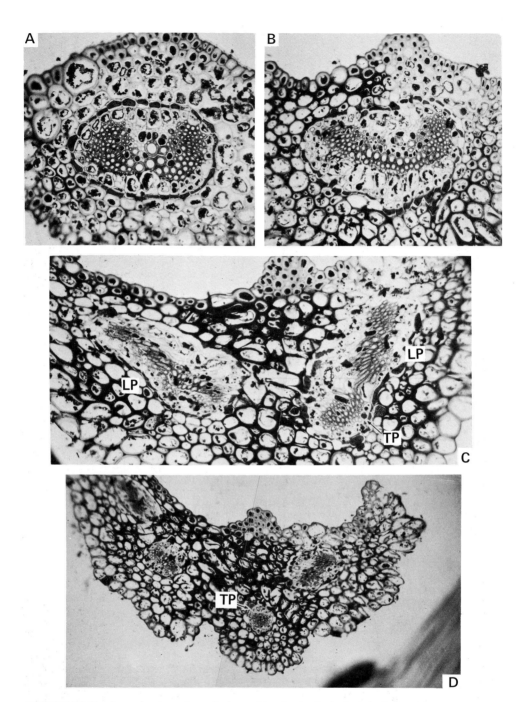

FIGURE 14–7. Cross sections through the rachis of a fertile leaf of *Actinostachys laevigata*. The sections are at successively higher levels from *A* to *D*. The rachis trace has broadened in *B*. The trace to one lateral pinna has diverged in *C* and the other one nearly so. The separate supplies to the three pinnae are shown in *D*.   LP = trace to lateral pinna; TP = trace to terminal pinna.

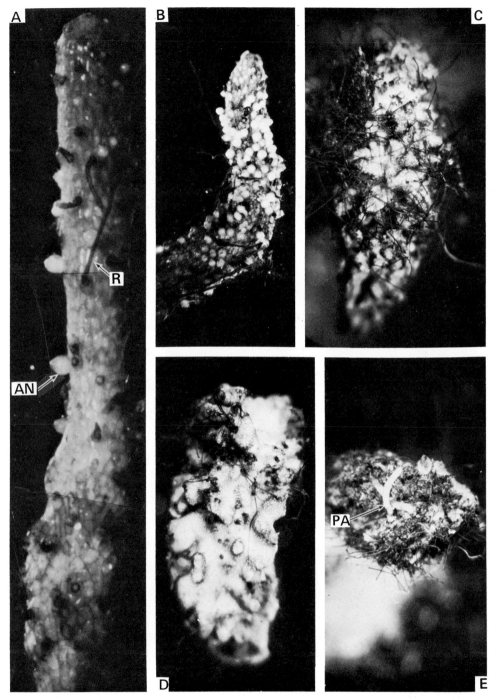

FIGURE 14–8. Gametophytes of *Actinostachys*. *A.* Primary gametophytic axis of *A. melanesica*. AN = antheridium; R = rhizoid. *B.* Primary gametophytic axis of *A. intermedia* with many antheridia. *C.* Older tuberous gametophyte of *A. intermedia*. *D.* Tuberous gametophyte of *A. oligostachys* with rhizoids brushed off. *E.* Tuberous gametophyte of *A. oligostachys* with several primary axes, PA, attached.

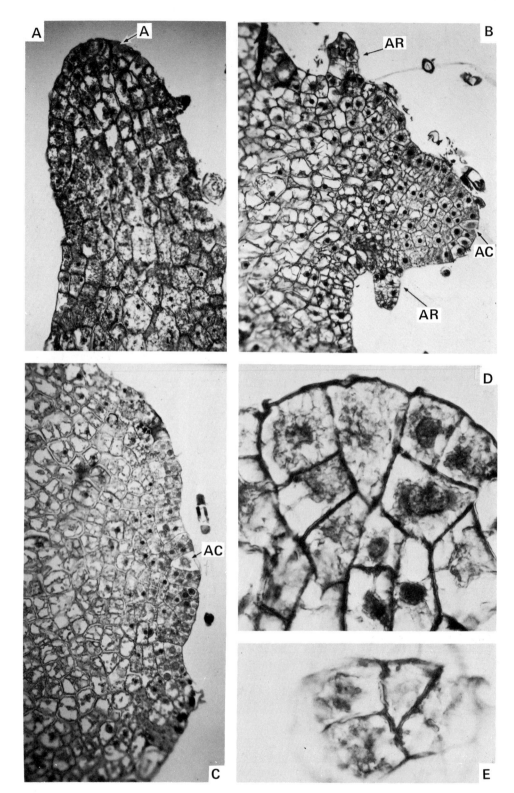

FIGURE 14–9. *A.* Longitudinal section through a primary gametophytic axis of *Actinostachys intermedia.* A = apex. *B.* Apex of a tuberous gametophyte of *A. melanesica.* AC = apical cell; AR = archegonium. *C.* Apex of a tuberous gametophyte of *A. intermedia.* AC = apical cell. *D, E.* Apical cell and adjoining cells of a primary gametophytic axis of *A. melanesica* in longitudinal and cross sections.

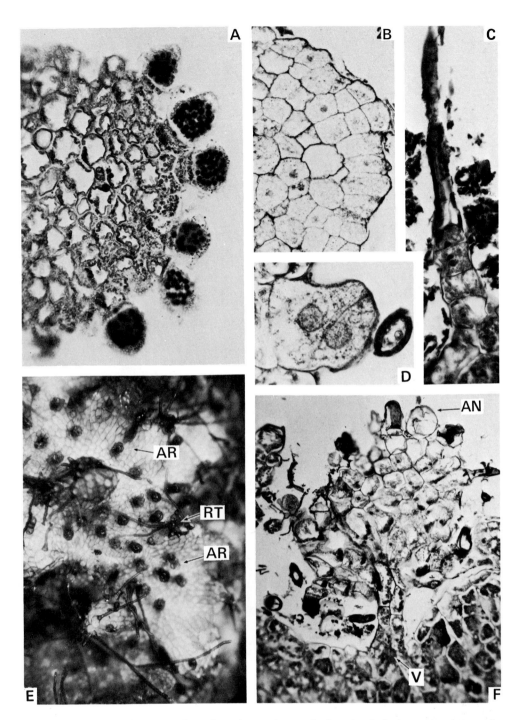

FIGURE 14–10. *A.* Cross section of a primary gametophytic axis of *Actinostachys intermedia,* showing a number of antheridia. *B.* Cross section through a primary gametophytic axis of *A. mela-nesica,* showing the beginning of meristematic activity resulting in peripheral thickening. *C.* Gameto-phytic rhizoid and its base in *A. intermedia. D.* Two-celled surface bud on a gametophyte of *A. melanesica.* At the right is a cross section of a thick-walled rhizoid containing a cross section of a fungal hypha. *E.* Surface of a tuberous gametophyte of *A. oligostachys.* AR = archegonium; RT = rhizoid tuft. *F.* Archegonium of *A. intermedia* the neck of which has proliferated to produce a crown of tissue on which are a number of antheridia. AN = antheridium; V = venter.

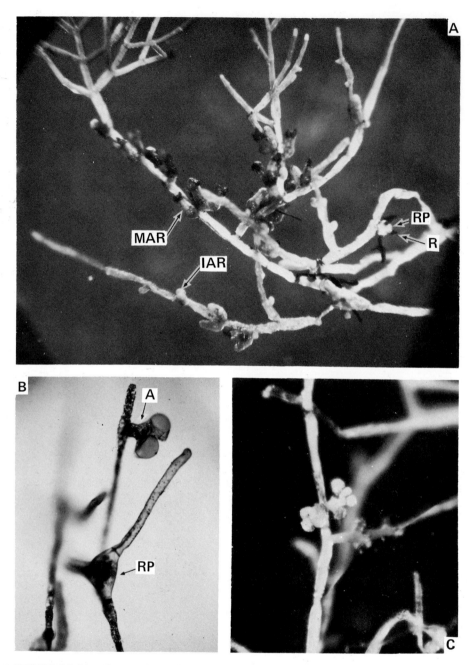

FIGURE 14–11. Gametophyte of *Schizaea fistulosa.* MAR = mature archegonium; IAR = immature archegonium; RP = rhizoidophore; A = antheridiophore; R = rhizoid.

previously unknown in ferns. More significant than their occurrence on the wrong generation is their form (Fig. 14–14, *A*; 15–35, *H*), which is gleicheniaceous.

One of the two sections of the genus *Schiz-*

aea, the one previously known as *Euschizaea* (the name of which is invalid according to the international rules of nomenclature, and the section does not contain the type species of the genus as the name might suggest),

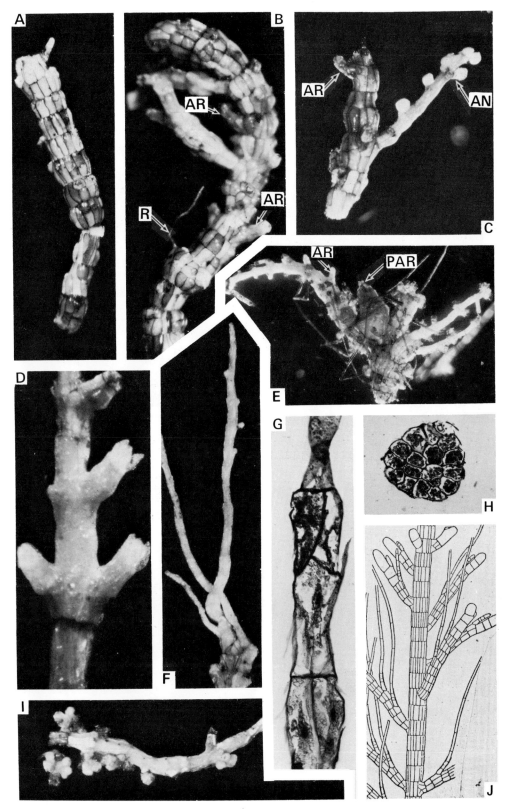

FIGURE 14–12. *A* to *I*. Gametophyte of *Schizaea dichotoma*. AR = archegonium; R = rhizoid; AN = antheridium; PAR = pregnant archegonium. *J. Sphacelaria hystrix*, a brown alga, after Oltmanns (1922), by permission of Gustav Fischer Verlag, Jena.

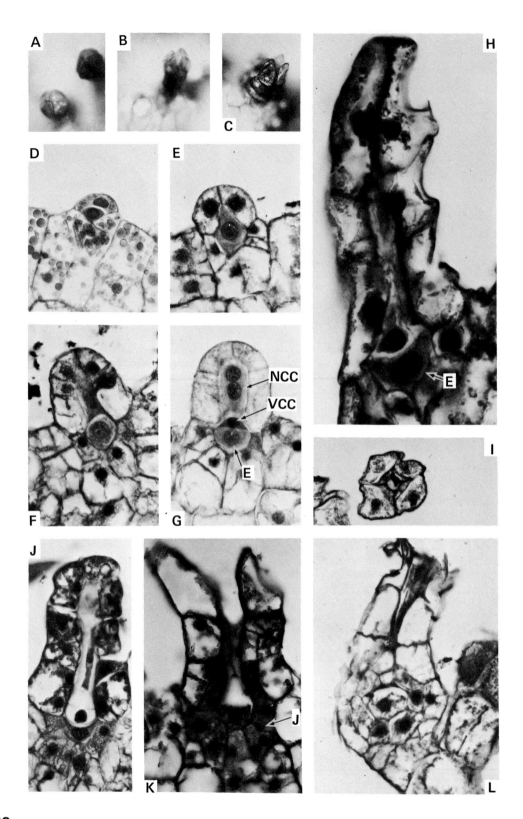

produces filamentous, partly exposed, partly green gametophytes. The known gametophytes of the section are those of *Schizaea pusilla, S. robusta, S. fistulosa, S. bifida*, and *S. rupestris.*

The gametophytes and sporophytes of this section tend to grow in much wetter habitats than do those of other members of the family, and frequently on wet overhanging banks the gametophytes and sporophytes may be found in profusion. When growing on wet more or less barren clay, the gametophytes tend to be compact, almost entirely on the surface and green. When on looser, better drained organic substrata they are more loosely packed, partly to entirely subsurface, white, and saprophytic. In general there is a degree of filament dimorphism with runner filaments and bush filaments. The former are composed of longer cells, are horizontally to irregularly oriented, and bear most of the rhizoidophores and antheridiophores. The bush filaments tend to form upright tufts, are mostly exposed at the surface, and bear most of the archegonia. An endophytic fungus is present in all cells of the nongreen parts of the body but tends to be restricted to the rhizoidophores and rhizoids in exposed green parts. The rhizoidophores are single bulbous cells laterally inserted on a filament and attached to it by a single stalk cell (Fig. 14–11, *A, B,* RP). Usually two to five rhizoids are attached to each rhizoidophore (R in *A*). The antheridiophores are short lateral structures (A in Fig. 14–11, *B, C*) that bear one to several antheridia. The first antheridium is produced terminally, and subsequent ones develop from single cells at the bases of earlier formed ones. The archegonia are attached singly to a parental filament but often occur in whorls of up to four, and there are often a number of whorls close together on the bush filaments (Fig. 14–11, *A*). Except for the four terminal neck cells of the archegonia and the rhizoids, the entire gametophytic body is highly cutinized and resistant to movements of solvents and solutes. The antheridial cap cells are intermediate in cutinization.

The second section of the genus *Schizaea* is widely known as *Lophidium* (but according to the rules should be the section *Schizaea,* since it contains the type species of the genus, *S. dichotoma*). This section includes the forms with much branched leaves and those with simple fan-shaped leaves. Gametophytes of two species within the section are known, those of *S. dichotoma* and *S.* sp., a yet-undescribed species. To date, gametophytes belonging to none of the species with fan-shaped leaves have been described or, presumably, seen.

The gametophyte of *Schizaea dichotoma* is a subterranean, modified filamentous or pseudo-axial type (Fig. 14–12, *A* to *I*). Its growing tips are unicellular filaments (Fig. 14–12, *F*), each with a single apical cell with a transverse cutting face such as occurs in the unmodified filamentous types. The cells cut off from the apical cell, however, go on to divide and redivide to produce packets of cells recognizable as distinct joints in the older pseudoaxial body (Fig. 14–12, *A* to *C, G,* and *H* in cross section). This is the only occurrence of this type of body among vascular plants, but it closely simulates certain sphacelarealean algae (Fig. 14–12, *J*). Rhizoids much smaller than the vegetative filaments are initially cut off by a division wall from the distal ends of cells elsewhere on the body (Fig. 14–12, *B, E*). Vegetative branches originate as larger cellular bulges than do the rhizoids but in a similar manner. Antheridia occur singly or in clusters on short lateral branches (Fig. 14–12, *C, I*) similar in origin and in structure to their counterparts on the unmodified filamentous forms. The archegonia are lateral and often in whorls, but their regions of attachment are multicellular.

The archegonia of *Actinostachys* have rigid, persistent projecting necks (Fig. 14–9, *B*; Fig. 14–10, *E*; Fig. 14–13, *A* to *C*). The shape of the neck characterizes some species and varies

FIGURE 14–13. *A.* Unopened archegonia of *Actinostachys oligostachys. B, C.* Opened archegonia of *A. oligostachys* and *A. melanesica. D* to *G, J, K.* Stages in the development of the archegonium of *Actinostachys. D* to *G. A. laevigata. J, K. A. intermedia. H, I.* Longitudinal and transverse sections through the archegonium of *Schizaea dichotoma. L.* Longitudinal section through an archegonium of *S. fistulosa.* E = egg; NCC = neck canal cell; VCC = ventral canal cell; J = jacket.

from cone-shaped to club-shaped and cylindrical. One species has a ring of elongate neck cells just below the four terminal ones.

The archegonial initial is established by a characteristic and specific set of cell divisions. As seen in longitudinal section a surface cell divides obliquely, cutting off a small cell that is triangular in shape. This cell then divides by cutting off a flat cell on the side opposite its grandmother cell. The sister cell of the flat cell then acts as the archegonial initial. In Fig. 14–13, *D* the archegonial initial has divided periclinally to produce the neck mother cell (outer cell) and the axial row mother cell (inner cell). The small cell immediately to the right of the two-celled archegonium is the sister cell of the archegonial mother cell, which is often still recognizable in mature archegonia if they are sectioned longitudinally in the proper plane. The neck mother cell divides anticlinally and the two daughter cells do the same, so that the mother cells of each of the four vertical rows of the neck cells are established. They later divide to produce the neck, which is eventually four to six cells long. The axial row mother cell elongates and divides along with the growing neck (Fig. 14–13, *E* to *G*, *J*, *K*). Its first transverse division establishes the single neck canal cell and the egg-ventral canal-cell mother cell (Fig. 14–13, *F*). Karyokinesis later occurs in the neck canal cell to produce from two to four nuclei, and the ventral canal cell and egg are established by a transverse division of their mother cell (Fig. 14–13, *G*). A jacket layer, formed by divisions of adjacent cells, completely surrounds the venter and the lower part of the neck (Fig. 14–13, *J*, *K*).

The archegonia of *Schizaea dichotoma* (Fig. 14–12, *D*; Fig. 14–13, *H*, *I*) are different in external shape but in most other respects similar to those of *Actinostachys*. The archegonial initial in *Schizaea* is established by a transverse division of a bulging surface cell, but from that point on its ontogeny is more or less as in *Actinostachys*. The archegonial jacket is more uniform within the neck in *Schizaea dichotoma* (the four small cells lining the neck canal in the cross section shown in Fig. 14–13, *I*) but does not extend the full length.

The archegonia on the filamentous types of *Schizaea* gametophytes are borne on the tips of short stalks usually one cell long and two cells in thickness; this accentuates their superficiality and bulging venter (Fig. 14–11, *A*; Fig. 14–13, *L*). The neck canal, uniformly narrow down to its base, does not flare out into the venter (Fig. 14–13, *L*), which is lined by a layer of jacket cells.

The antheridium is particularly uniform throughout the Schizaeaceae; the major variation is intraspecific in certain *Actinostachys* species. The antheridium typically contains a central mass of spermatogenous tissue surrounded by three cells (Fig. 14–14, *B*, *C*): the cap cell, C, a single ring cell, R, and a basal coin-shaped cell, B. In one species of *Schizaea* the cap cell is divided.

The antheridial initial is formed by a transverse division of a bulging surface cell (Fig. 14–14, *E*). Usually the coin-shaped cell is then produced by the inner cell (i.e., the sister cell of the antheridial initial); however, there are indications that sometimes it results from a transverse division of the outer cell. Next the primary spermatogenous cell is cut off as a thin lens against the inner wall of the outer cell and soon bulges up into its covering sister cell (Fig. 14–14, *F*). Later the cap and ring cells are formed by division of the primary cover cell, and by a succession of divisions the spermatids are established from the primary spermatogenous cell. The sperm output is relatively high, as may be ascertained from the number seen in the longisection in Fig. 14–14, *B*. When the antheridium is ripe, the inner wall

FIGURE 14–14. *A*. Sporangium borne at the tip of a gametophytic rhizoid in *Actinostachys oligostachys*. *B*. Longitudinal section of an antheridium of *A. oligostachys*. *C*. As *B*, but tangential section. *D*. Tangential, transverse section of an antheridium of *A. oligostachys* showing the operculum. *E*. First division of the antheridial initial in *A. intermedia*. *F*. Three-celled antheridium of *A. melanesica*. *G*. Antheridium of *A. melanesica* in which the cap cell became a rhizoid. *H* to *J*. Successive sections of an antheridium of *A. intermedia* in which the ring cell has undergone additional divisions. *K*. Sunken antheridium of *A. melanesica*. *L*. Tip of an antheridiophore of *Schizaea dichotoma*. C = cap cell; R = ring cell; B = basal cell; A = antheridium; AI = antheridial initial.

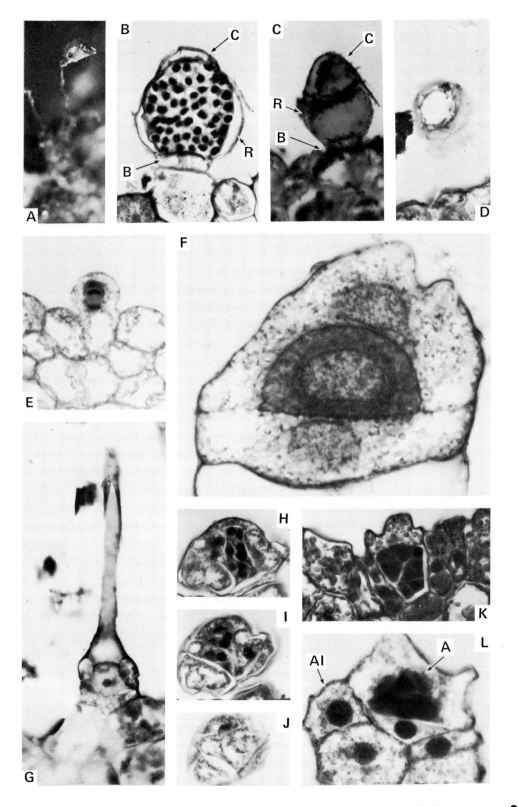

of the cap cell decomposes completely, leaving the ripe sperm separated from the external environment only by a single thin cell wall. When conditions of moisture are proper, this wall ruptures, leaving the gaping hole seen in Fig. 14–14, *D*. Remnants of the outer cell wall of the cap are visible around the opening in this figure.

Additional cells, similar to the basal coin-shaped cell, are produced in species of *Schizaea* that produce groups of antheridia on an antheridiophore (as in Fig. 14–11, *C*). One of these will grow out laterally and act as the initial of another antheridium (Fig. 14–14, *L*, *AI*).

Several rather rare variations in antheridial structure and development occur in *Actinostachys*. In early development, the antheridium may stop growing as an antheridium while its cap cell elongates as a typical rhizoid (Fig. 14–14, *G*). In others, additional divisions may occur in the ring cell, resulting in a multicellular jacket more nearly like that of antheridia in the Stromatopteridaceae, Gleicheniaceae, Hymenophyllaceae, and a few other families. Another variation occurs when the mother cell of the antheridial initial does not protrude and divides periclinally below the surface. This results in a sunken antheridium lined by a jacket of cells produced by divisions of all adjacent cells in a manner similar to that in which the single coin-operated cell is cut off from the sister cell of a bulging antheridial initial (Fig. 14–14, *K*). If, in this antheridium, the cap cell were to divide to produce several cells, the overall structure would be essentially identical to antheridia found in the Marattiaceae, Ophioglossaceae, Equisetaceae, and Lycopodiaceae.

The embryogeny of four species of *Actinostachys* is known, and among these it is particularly uniform and corresponds closely to that of the Psilotaceae. Following fertiliza- tion the zygote elongates into the gametophytic tissue as it does in *Tmesipteris*. In Fig. 14–15, *B* the same elongate zygote is encountered twice in the same section (*Z*). The first division is transverse to the long axis of the zygote, which, during its initial elongation, may have become curved and changed its orientation relative to the archegonial axis. In Fig. 14–15, *C* a two-celled embryo is seen. Cell 1 is curved sufficiently that it appears as two cells; only one edge of cell 2 is shown. The inner cell (cell 2) gives rise to foot only. Its initial divisions, all longitudinal and thus establishing several semielongate cells at the base of the embryo, occur before the first division of the distal cell (1). At maturity around the base of the massive foot, strands of cells, appearing as packets in the cross section in Fig. 14–16, *A*, extend into and intermix with the gametophytic tissue below. The outer or distal cell of the two-celled embryo enlarges considerably; then it, and its immediate derivatives, go through three (probably) oblique divisions to establish the apical cell of the stem. The young embryo shown in Fig. 14–15, *A* shows the stem apex and foot in median longitudinal section. The entire distal half, beneath the neck of the archegonium (*N*), is organized into a stem apex and the entire lower half is foot, which shows the beginnings of cellular extensions into gametophytic tissue below. An older embryo is shown in Fig. 14–15, *F*. Its stem apex (*A*) is protruding from within the massive calyptra (*C*). The same embryo in longitudinal section (Fig. 14–15, *D*) shows it to be still composed of stem apex (*A*) and foot (*F*). There is, at this older stage, a procambial strand (*PC*) extending from just beneath the apex into the foot. At an older stage (seen in cross section in Fig. 14–16, *B*) the foot end of the strand becomes branched with two or three free ends. The two strands in the foot shown in *B* contain no tracheary elements, but slightly closer to the stem end of the embryo tracheids

FIGURE 14–15. Embryogeny of *Actinostachys intermedia*. *A*. Longitudinal section of a young embryo. *B*. Archegonium with an elongate, curved zygote seen in two pieces. *C*. Two-celled embryo. Cell number 1 is curved around and encountered twice in the section. *D*. Embryo slightly older than the one in *A*. The calyptra has torn open. This same embryo before sectioning is shown in *F*. *E*. Embryo slightly older than the one in *D* and *F*. Trichomes now cover the protruding apex of the young sporophyte. *G*. Longitudinal section near the proximal end of the stem-foot axis of the embryo in *E*. *H*. Longitudinal section of the protruding portion of the embryo in *E*. *N* = archegonial neck; *C* = calyptra; *A* = stem apex of young sporophyte; *F* = foot; *Z* = zygote; *PC* = procambium; *S* = stele; *CO* = cortex; *G* = gametophytic tissue; *R* = root.

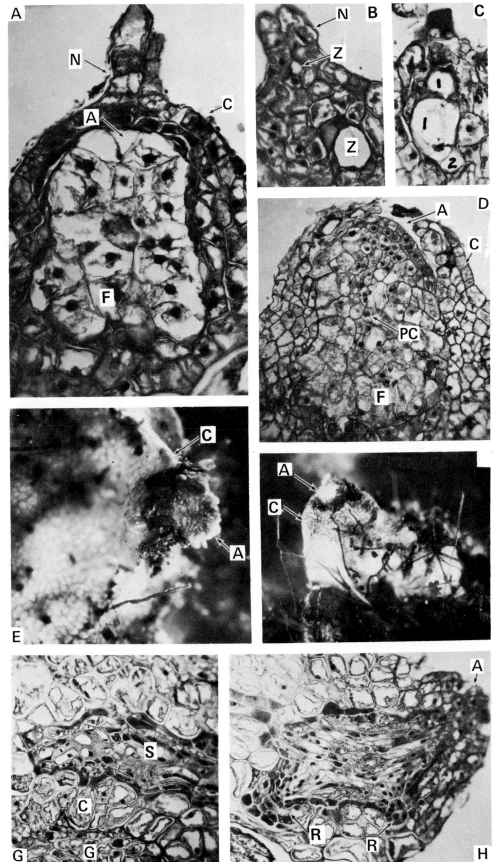

237

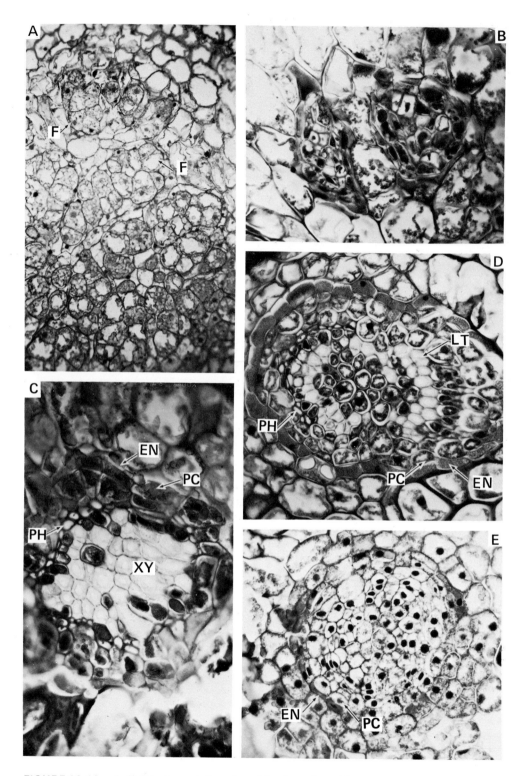

FIGURE 14–16. *A.* Section through the edge of the foot of an old embryo of *Actinostachys intermedia*. F = patches of foot tissue; the less-rounded cells between foot areas are gametophytic. *B.* Cross section of a branched stele within the foot of *A. intermedia*. *C.* Cross section of the sporeling stem stele of *A. intermedia* at about the level where it emerges from the gametophyte. *D.* Cross section through the first node of a young sporophyte of *A. intermedia*. *E.* Cross section through the procambial strand of a young sporophyte of *A. intermedia*. EN = endodermis; PC = pericycle; PH = phloem; XY = xylem; LT = leaf trace.

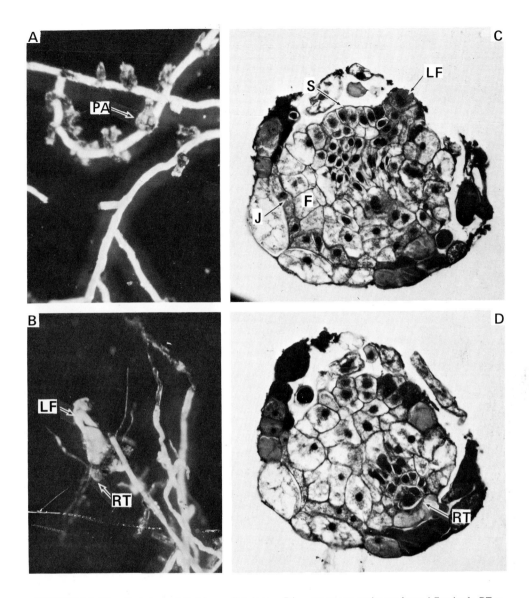

FIGURE 14–17. Embryos of *Schizaea fistulosa*. PA = pregnant archegonium; LF = leaf; RT = root; S = stem; F = foot; J = jacket.

occur in a central position (Fig. 14–16, *C*) and still closer to the apex a central core of parenchyma appears within the xylem (Fig. 14–16, *D*). Occasionally the pith may disappear and reappear in the young sporeling axis.

Roots and leaves are of later origin in the young sporophyte of *Actinostachys*. The embryo shown in Fig. 14–15, *E* is slightly older than the one in *F*. The simple trichomes that

characteristically cover the stem apex of older sporophytes now cover the apex of the embryo (at A). In section this embryo showed the first leaf as a primordium on the stem apex and the first two roots, which had originated endogenously on the young stem (R in Fig. 14–15, *H*). A longitudinal section of the foot end of this embryo is shown in Fig. 14–15, *G*.

The traces to the first leaves of the young

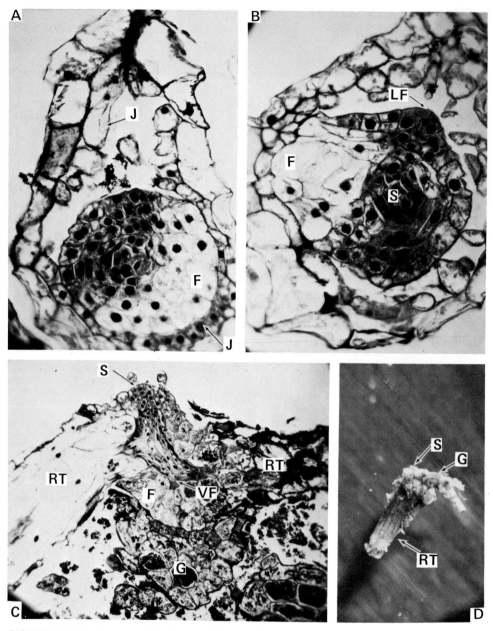

FIGURE 14–18. Embryos of *Schizaea dichotoma*. *C* is a section of the same embryo shown un-sectioned in *D*. J = jacket; F = foot; S = stem; LF = leaf; RT = root; G = gametophyte; VF = a bump on the vascular system associated with the foot.

sporophyte are usually massive in proportion to the rest of the stele, and at their point of departure (Fig. 14–16, *D*) a nearly equal dichotomy of the stele is suggested.

Of the species of *Schizaea* with filamentous gametophytes, the embryogeny of *S. fistulosa* is partly known and that of *S. pusilla* slightly less so. As compared to *Actinostachys* their embryos are precocious in development, be-coming established as independent plants at a very small size. Their organs, leaf, stem, root, and foot all originate early and are considered primary parts of the embryo. This is in contrast to *Actinostachys*, in which only the stem apex and the foot are primary embryonic organs. The embryo of *Schizaea fistulosa* shown in Fig. 14–17, *B* with its first leaf (LF) exposed and green and its first root (RT) projecting below is quite minute, as can be realized by comparing its size with the uniseriate gametophytic axis to which it is attached. The embryo contained within the archegonium in Fig. 14–17, *A* was composed of a total of approximately 15 cells and in a stage of development not much different from the one in *B*, which shows leaf (LF) and root (RT) protruding.

In *S. fistulosa* the first division of the zygote is oblique. The more proximal cell seems to form foot only. When the tissue derived from the distal cell is composed of approximately eight cells, the apical cells of the first stem, the first leaf, and the first root may be recognized. The foot is small and is not vascularized; the embryonic procambium is composed of a single once-branched strand with one of its free ends at each of the other three embryonic organs.

The whole embryo is nearly spherical at about the time of calyptral rupture (Fig. 14–17, *C*, *D*, which are sections of the same embryo). The foot (F) is relatively small. The stem apex (S) conforms to the surface of the sphere. The leaf (LF) is the most rapidly growing part of the embryo and soon dominates all other organs in size. The root (RT) grows into the substratum shortly after elongation of the leaf.

The embryogeny of *Schizaea dichotoma*, although incompletely known, seems similar to that of *S. fistulosa*. The organs do not reach a functional stage as early as those in the latter species, and relative sizes are slightly different. In *S. dichotoma* the foot is more prominent (Fig. 14–18, *A*, *B*) and has associated with it a very slight vascular extension of the main embryonic stele (VF in Fig. 14–18, *C*). The embryo shown in section in Fig. 14–18, *A*, *B* is the one contained within the pregnant archegonium of Fig. 14–12, *E*, the inner cavity of which was occupied to a large extent by loosely packed tissue of archegonial jacket origin. The jacket also forms a complete lining of compact tissue where the embryo contacts the base of the venter (J in Fig. 14–18, *A*), as it also does in *S. fistulosa*.

Certain embryos of *S. dichotoma* and apparently all of those of the undescribed *S*. sp. are completely leafless. One such embryo is shown in Fig. 14–18, *C*, *D*, where G indicates the gametophyte, S the stem apex, and RT the root. In older plants of *S. dichotoma*, where the entire sporophyte is still present, the oldest leaf is commonly attached at a distance of 1 to 3 mm from the end of the stem, indicating its status as a non-embryonic organ.

General Interpretations

The Schizaeaceae, although certainly specialized in certain respects, exhibit several very primitive (i.e., generalized), features of filicalean ferns. The true axial gametophyte of *Actinostachys* is probably the basic type for the entire order. The simple, rootless, and leafless embryo of *Actinostachys*, held in common with *Psilotum*, *Tmesipteris*, and *Stromatopteris*, is readily interpreted as the fundamental type from which advanced embryos with early organ determination arose. Intermediate types of embryos occur in *Schizaea* and in the Hymenophyllaceae. Presumed primitive features of the sporangium are the transverse annulus, occasional multiple rings of annulus, relatively large size, high spore output, lack of differentiation of the line of dehiscence, and initiation and development in acropetal succession. Sporangial position on a more axial extension of the leaf rather than on an entity within the blade also seems primitive. The entire leaf is more stem-like in early ontogenetic stages, because of the presence of an apical cell with three cutting faces, a feature shared with the Psilotaceae, Stromatopteridaceae, and Osmundaceae. Within the genus *Schizaea* a series of intermediates occur between pinnate and dichotomous branching. And finally, the family produces only monolete spores, as do the Psilotaceae, Stromatopteridaceae, and Gleicheniaceae (in part).

The Schizaeaceae can be interpreted as an early offshoot from the filicalean stock at nearly the same level of primitiveness as the Psilotaceae and Stromatopteridaceae. Other relatively early derivative families (i.e., the Gleicheniaceae, Anemiaceae, and Osmundaceae) probably each represent separate lines of specialization in terms of degrees of organ fixation and differentiation, gametophyte development, and embryogeny.

15

Filicales: Selected Significant Families

Osmundaceae

This family, which is known in terms of the extant genera *Osmunda* (6 spp.), *Leptopteris* (6 spp.), and *Todea* (1 sp.) and several fossil ones, probably became differentiated during early Permian times. The Osmundaceae have been considered for many years to exhibit much of the fundamental or generalized morphology of the Filicales and to be ancestral to the other families of the order (see Bower, 1923; Eames, 1936). So very many new facts have been uncovered since this hypothesis was put forward (many quite contradictory to it) that it must now be discarded. It seems most logical now to consider the Osmundaceae as a very early offshoot of the filicalean line and as a phylogenetic dead end. Despite this, the Osmundaceae presents features and illustrates trends that are fundamental in understanding filicalean morphology and phylogeny.

The stems of the Osmundaceae are upright and up to 3 or more cm in diameter. *Leptopteris* has the overall form of a small tree to several feet tall and with a crown of leaves. In gross appearance it suggests a cyatheoid, a dicksoniad, a cycad, or a blechnoid. *Osmunda* and *Todea* have short stems and do not appear treelike. *Osmunda* produces a massive mantle of persistent roots along its stem, and a plant that may be a century or more old appears as a large crown perched upon a spherical, conical, cylindrical or flattened, spongy mass of roots. If the wiry roots are cut away, the plant looks like *Leptopteris* but usually with several dichotomies in the often vertical trunk.

Although a few poorly preserved fossil specimens have been misidentified, the anatomy of osmundaceous stems is highly distinctive. The bulk of the stem is represented by cortex that is not distinguishable from the mass of leaf bases. Each of the many leaf traces within the cortex, as well as each root trace, is surrounded by a very tough sclerenchymatous sheath. The leaves are attached in a spiral order and the roots are inserted two at the base of each leaf.

In the extant species the stele in cross section shows a ring of vascular bundles around a central pith (Fig. 15–2, *A*). The bundles mostly appear slightly elongate in the radial direction and are in close pairs or single. The single ones are elongate, terete, U-, O-, or S-shaped. The cross-sectional shape of a bundle for the most part is reflective of its position relative to a leaf-trace insertion. The U-shaped bundles generally are located immediately below the level of leaf-trace departure (Fig. 15–2, *B* and *D*, at a higher level) and the O-shaped ones immediately below the U-shaped ones. In other words, the leaf gap extends through the xylem and into the pith as well as deeper into the xylem bundle at a level where it does not communicate with the pith. In Fig. 15–3, *I, J*, the gaps are shown in surface view (below) and in longitudinal view (above). The lowermost portion of the gap in the upper figure of the pairs shows the vertical extension. In each U- or O-shaped bundle, a single protoxylem pole is usually present in the position indicated in Fig. 15–2, *B, E*, left, with an occasional additional protoxylem pole in one of the two xylem arms extending toward the pith. When the leaf trace departs (Fig. 15–2, *D*), the entire median protoxylem strand usually goes with it, leaving the two radially aligned arms of the U generally without a protoxylem strand. In some instances, the median protoxylem strand will divide circumferentially (i.e., in a plane transverse to the radius of the stem) before departing with the leaf trace and thus leave a protoxylem pole in one of the cauline bundles. In any case, the remaining cauline bundles all come to possess protoxylem poles at a higher level as new ones differentiate either internally within the strand or peripherally as in Fig. 15–2, *E* (center). All strands are probably mesarch,[1] although those in which

the pole is peripheral often appear not to be so. Adjacent xylem strands from adjacent U-shaped bundles come together at a higher level to form another solid, terete strand, then an O-shaped one, then another U-shaped one, and so to the next leaf-trace departure around the genetic spiral. The stele is further complicated by irregularities, especially in species with long leaf gaps. The gap occasionally opens and closes and opens again in its vertical course. There are rare gaps not at all associated with leaf departure. The poles of primary xylem differentiation, whether they be protoxylem poles or merely early metaxylem poles, are thought to form a continuous system within the osmundaceous stem, but their identification is difficult as it is in some stems of the Psilotaceae, Stromatopteridaceae, Schizaeaceae, Gleicheniaceae, Anemiaceae, and Lygodiaceae.

The phloem forms a thin, continuous band around the xylem and dips in and becomes more extensive between the bundles (see between left and middle bundles in Fig. 15–2, *E*). Rarely there is a bit of internal phloem and internal endodermis (e.g., *Osmunda cinnamomea*). Immediately above the level of separation of the leaf trace, the phloem becomes continuous between the trace and the two cauline strands it has left behind (Fig. 15–2, *D*).

The first stele produced in a young *Osmunda* sporophyte has a relatively simple solid core of xylem and the first leaf trace is similar (Fig. 15–3, *B*). As the stem apex expands, in the subsequently produced, larger portions of the stem, the stele becomes progressively more complex (Fig. 15–3, *C* to *F*) and the leaf traces similarly approach their characteristic mature form. The course of the protoxylem in the young plant is undescribed. The leaves of the young sporophyte appear sheathing, as they are much broader in proportion to the stem diameter than are such organs borne on older plants (Fig. 15–3, *F*).

Among fossil stems referred to the Osmun-

---

[1] Endarchy has been reported as occurring in the Osmundaceae, but the accuracy of these reports is questioned. An internally situated primary xylem pole does not indicate endarchy unless the first xylem element in the group matured on the inside. In all apparently endarch bundles examined by the author, weak mesarchy was detectable.

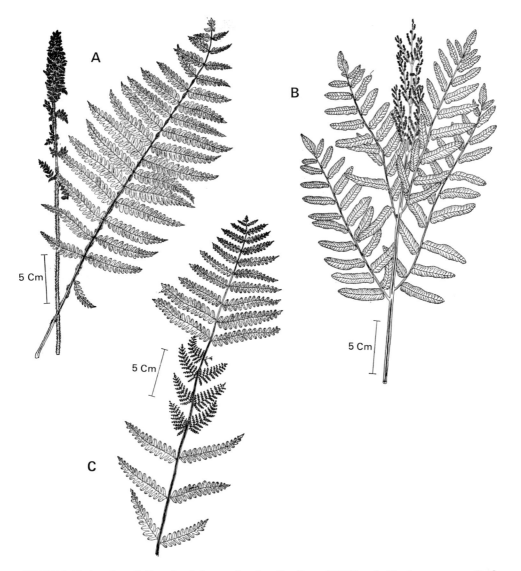

FIGURE 15–1. *A* to *C*. Fronds of *Osmunda*, after Hewitson (1962). *A. O. cinnamomea. B. O. regalis. C. O. claytoniana.*

daceae, a series of types is found, suggesting the manner in which the stele has evolved within the family. In *Thamnopteris* (Fig. 15–3, *G, K*) the cauline xylem and that of the leaf trace at its point of departure are solid. A core of parenchyma appears in the petiolar trace, which farther out opens up and becomes C-shaped, with an increased number of proto-xylem poles. In *Osmundites*[2] (H) the paren-

[2] *Osmundites*, according to Miller (1967), is an invalid name and is replaced by *Osmundacaulis.*

chymatous area of the petiole is extended to within the cauline xylem mass and forms an incomplete gap. This differs from *Osmunda* (*Osmundacaulis*) *kolbei* (I), in which the gap is complete but vertically inextensive and from *O. regalis* (J) and other extant species with a more extensive gap. Some fossil osmundaceous stems possess a complete zone of internal phloem and are stelically more elaborate than modern ones, and it is possible that extant species have been reduced.

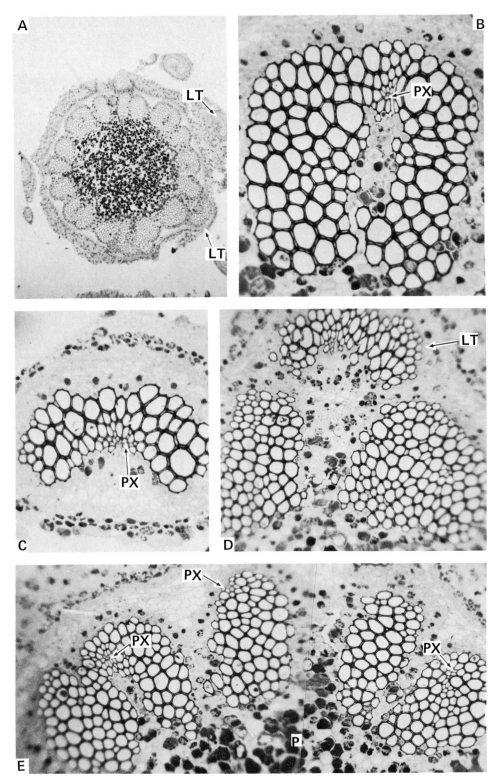

FIGURE 15–2. *Osmunda cinnamomea.* *A.* Cross section of the stem. *B* to *E.* Portions of *A* enlarged. *B, E.* Bundles of the cauline ring. *C.* Leaf trace in the stem cortex. *D.* Two cauline bundles and a leaf trace slightly separated.

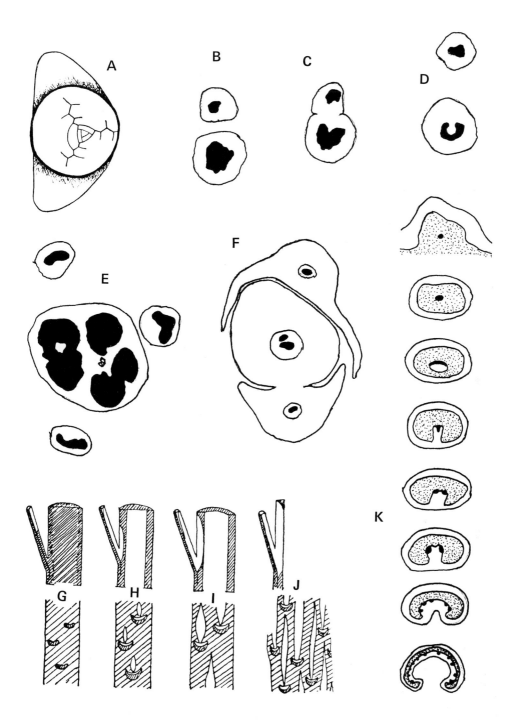

FIGURE 15–3. *A.* Apex of a young leaf of *Osmunda*, after Bower (1926). *B* to *D*. Cauline xylem and a leaf trace (above in each) as seen above the third, fifth, and eighth nodes, respectively, in *O. cinnamomea*, based on Faull (1909). *E, F.* Stem and leaf outlines with xylem blackened in young plants of *O. cinnamomea*, but older than *B* to *D*, after Faull (1909). *G* to *J*. Steles in various osmundaceous genera in longitudinal sectional view and in surface view, showing degrees of development of the leaf gap and the possible way in which it may have evolved, after Emberger (1944). *G. Thamnopteris.* *H. Osmundites dunlopi.* *I. O. kolbei.* *J. Osmunda regalis.* *K. Thamnopteris schlectendalii*, progressive changes in the leaf trace from its origin in the stem stele, after Kidston and Gwynne-Vaughan (1907). *G* to *J*, by permission of Masson et C^{le} Editeurs, Paris.

Osmunda arnoldi (Miller, 1967) from Paleocene rocks shows in its cauline stele a pair of xylem strands below each point of leaf-trace departure. Embedded in each near the outside is a primary xylem pole but without protoxylem. Slightly higher, protoxylem appears at each pole along with an island of associated parenchyma.[3] Then the islands become confluent with the parenchyma between the bundles, which now appear in cross section to be hooked, with protoxylem poles within the eye of the hook in an "endarch" position. The two adjacent bundles then fuse to form one, with a pair of poles on the inside of the now U-shaped bundle with its opening toward the pith. The leaf trace then splits off, carrying with it two primary xylem poles.

In the osmundaceous genus *Itopsidema* of Upper Triassic age (Daugherty, 1960) there is an ectophloic, mesarch siphonostele without leaf gaps, and in its pith there are a very few isolated, reticulate-pitted tracheids (as seen also in *Osmunda kolbei*) as well as a number of pith cells with one pointed end and one truncated end. *Thamnopteris* shows a solid protostele, but the tracheids in the center are short. D. H. Scott (1920–1923) considered these tracheids to be primarily water-storage cells, which were formed by transverse divisions of prosenchymatous elements of the procambium. Daugherty considers the pith parenchyma cells of *Itopsidema* to be the homologs of the pith tracheids of *Thamnopteris* and to have been formed in the same manner. He points out that these genera indicate that the pith in the Osmundaceae originated as the result of tracheids in the center of the protostele becoming modified into parenchyma.

The leaves of the Osmundaceae are relatively large, to approximately 1 m long, and primarily once or twice pinnate (Fig. 15–1, *A* to *C*). Many of the ultimate divisions in the more finely divided *Leptopteris* species appear

[3] Such islands of parenchyma are common in higher ferns and often quite conspicuous. Where well known, they represent an area of protoxylem parenchyma with a few remnants of early-formed protoxylem elements. Commonly also, the area is enlarged and complicated while the bundle is still expanding laterally by the formation of a number of protoxylem tyloses, forming what is known as pseudoparenchyma or cavity parenchyma.

dichotomous (Fig. 15–5, *D*, *E*). The venation in all species is open dichotomous (Fig. 15–1, *B*: Fig. 15–5, *C*, *E*). In the primordial stage the leaves are relatively massive and are first recognizable some distance from the center of the also massive stem apex (Fig. 15–4, *B*: the apical cell of the stem is outlined). The young leaf has an apical cell with three cutting faces (Fig. 15–3, *A*). Steeves and Briggs (1958) report that the leaf of *Osmunda cinnamomea* arises from a group of cells of the apical meristem but that a single pyramidal apical cell is soon set off which then functions throughout the period of apical growth of the leaf. The stemlike nature of the *Osmunda* leaf, as evidenced by the form of its apical cell, a feature shared by leaf primordia of *Stromatopteris* and *Actinostachys*, is brought out still further by the work of Kuehnert (1967). He found that primordia as old as those in the P$_3$ position still had not reached the irreversible state and could revert to stems. When P$_3$ primordia were excised and grown in synthetic medium in isolation, 75 per cent developed into shoots and 25 per cent into leaves. When P$_3$ primordia were grown in pairs 33.3 per cent became leaves and 66.7 per cent shoots. But when the P$_3$ primordia were grown in contact with P$_{10}$, the percentages shifted to 64.5 per cent leaves and 35.5 per cent shoots, and with P$_{12}$ the percentages were 75 per cent leaves and 25 per cent shoots. From these data Kuehnert questioned the concept that primordia develop into leaves as a result of the influence of the stem apex upon them, an interpretation derived from Wardlaw's experiments on *Dryopteris* (see the end of Chapter 13). He goes on to propose that it is a morphogenetic factor produced by older leaves, which have a determining effect on the younger ones. This hypothesis has its merits, particularly when trying to rationalize the leaflike nature of the *Tmesipteris* frond or that of *Stromatopteris*, where a physical relationship to a stem apex is difficult to understand. The first leaf or leaflike organ, however, stands alone on embryos, on buds from callus, on lateral branches, and excised shoot tips may be grown with only young primordia. It is possible that both the hypothesis of Kuehnert and that of Wardlaw hold to a certain extent and possibly are differentially valid from taxon to taxon.

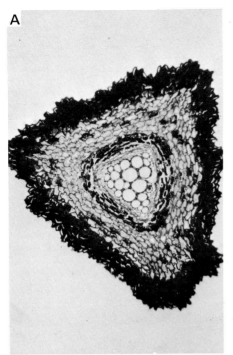

FIGURE 15–4. *A.* Cross section of a root of *Osmunda claytoniana*. *B.* Stem apex and young leaves of *O. cinnamomea*, apical cell outlined.

The roots of the Osmundaceae are larger than those of most ferns and frequently possess more than two protoxylem points (Fig. 15–4, *A*). The surface contour frequently conforms with that of the xylem mass, a very rare feature in roots in general but common in stems. The roots are tough and resistant to decay and are thus useful as a culture medium for various orchids and plants of similar growth requirements.

The sporangia of *Leptopteris* are relatively sparse and are borne on the undersurface of ordinary leaves along the veins (Fig. 15–5, *D*, *E*). Those of *Todea* (Fig. 15–6, *A* to *C*) are more crowded and are borne on pinnae with slightly less laminar extension than sterile pinnae, but they are still along veins. Those of *Osmunda* are usually borne on nonlaminated pinnae (Fig. 15–1, *A* to *C*) and an entire leaf or only a portion of a leaf may be fertile. The ultimate units of the fertile pinnae show sporangia clustered and disposed radially (Fig. 15–5, *A B*). Pinnae are frequently only partially fertile in *Osmunda* (Fig. 15–5, *C*), and

when so some sporangia are marginal at the tips of veins on poorly laminated portions of the pinna. Note in Fig. 15–5, *C* that the sporangial clusters on the right side of this pinna fall opposite, or nearly so, to the major vein trusses in the laminated portion on the left.

The sporangial arrangement and insertion as occurs in *Leptopteris* and *Todea* is interpreted here as representing the primitive condition within the family, with the tasseloid condition of *Osmunda* derived. Many other authors have considered the reverse to be true. Neither interpretation may be defended vigorously in view of the variable expression of the lamina on sporangiferous leaves of many ferns and the apparent "ups" and "downs" that this feature has experienced in the phylogeny of various families.

The sporangia of the Osmundaceae are relatively large, with a spore output of up to 512. They often appear globose, but there is a high degree of structural asymmetry (Fig. 15–7, *A* to *E*; Fig. 15–34, *F*). The annulus is represented by a band or patch of thickened cells

Filicales: Selected Significant Families **249**

FIGURE 15–5. *A* to *C*. Portions of fertile pinnae of *Osmunda regalis*. *D*. Portion of a fertile frond of *Leptopteris superba*; *E*. of *L. hymenophylloides*.

FIGURE 15–6. Portions of a fertile frond of *Todea barbera*. *A* is an abaxial (lower) view and *B* adaxial. *C* is part of *A* enlarged.

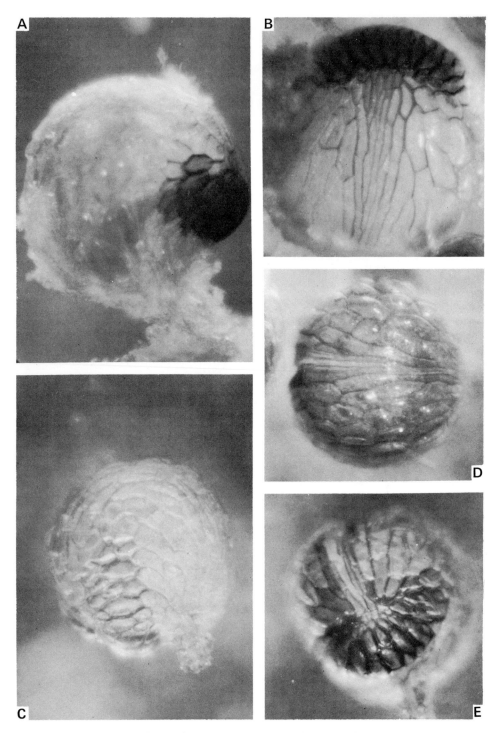

FIGURE 15–7. Various views of osmundaceous sporangia. *A, B. Osmunda cinnamomea. C to E. Leptopteris superba.*

that in the mature sporangium is quite lateral (Fig. 15–34, *F*; Fig. 15–7, *A*, *C*), but it assumes this position as the sporangium twists over as a result of asymmetric growth during development. This may be visualized by noting the orientation of the cell lineages on the sides of the sporangia in Fig. 15–7, *A*, *C*; Fig. 15–34, *F*. The actual apex of the sporangium is in the notch of the annulus at the end of the line of dehiscence, which then is fundamentally longitudinal but has come to assume a transverse and apical disposition during ontogeny. The cells are conspicuously elongate and often thickened along the line of opening and the rows converge in the direction away from the annulus (Fig. 15–7, *B*, *D*).

The initial point of cell separation during dehiscence is not at the annulus but several cells removed from it. Separation proceeds from this point in two directions until the sporangium gaps widely (Fig. 15–7, *D*, then *E*; then Fig. 15–6, *C*). Cells on the flanks of the sporangium shrink conspicuously along with the cells of the annulus and facilitate opening. The postdehiscence snapping action is, however, a function of the annulus alone. In these regards, the osmundaceous sporangium is similar to those of the Anemiaceae and Schizaeaceae and seems intermediate between the more common fern type, in which the dehiscence and snapping action is entirely a function of the annulus and in which dehiscence occurs at a line of interruption across the annulus and the psilotaceous condition in which there is no snapping action, in which the annulus is apparently functionless and in which dehiscence begins at a point far removed from the annulus.

In the ontogeny of the osmundaceous sporangium, the cell-division pattern leading to the establishment of the sporangial initial is inconsistent and irregular. A large cell may divide obliquely and unequally as an apical cell, then divide periclinally (at this point it is called the sporangial initial) to establish the inner tissue of the sporangium and the initial cell, which will eventually give rise to the outer wall of most of the sporangium. In other cases the division patterns previous to the establishment of the sporangial initial are less regular, even on the same plant, and to refer to a cell that divides like an apical cell is difficult (Fig. 15–8, *A*). Even when lateral segments are produced, they divide in various planes close to their large sister cell so as to distort cellular patterns. The stalk of the sporangium comes to be massive (Fig. 15–7, *A*; Fig. 15–34, *F*) and its tissue derivation is only partly related to the large cell that preceded the sporangial initial [i.e., that cell which is called the sporangial initial in earlier fern literature (see the discussion in Chapter 13)].

The primary inner cell of the sporangium, derived by a periclinal division of the sporangial initial, cuts off a layer of cells (probably four) on its outside (t in Fig. 15–8, *B*), and the remaining central cell (stippled in the figure) proceeds to produce the fertile tissue. The layer then surrounding the initial fertile cell divides to produce two to four layers. Of these,

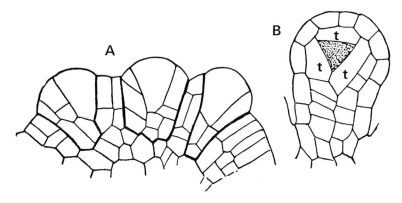

FIGURE 15–8. *Osmunda regalis*, after Bower (1889). *A*. Sporangial stalk formation. *B*. Young sporangium. t = tapetum.

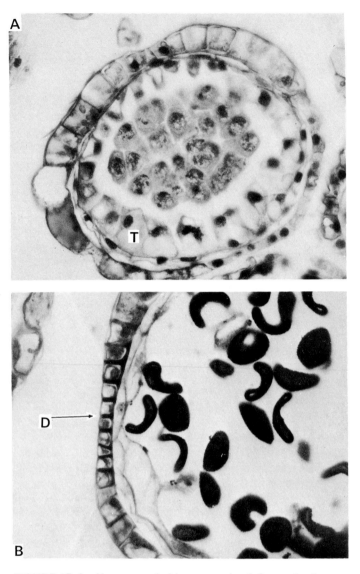

FIGURE 15–9. Younger and older sporangia of *Osmunda clayton-iana*. T = tapetum; D = line of dehiscence.

the innermost is the tapetum (T in Fig. 15–9, *A*), which becomes radially enlarged. The outer of these layers come to be thin and circumferentially enlarged, with an occasional radial wall thickening, and either remains or breaks down before the sporangium matures. In these final regards, therefore, the osmundaceous sporangium is comparable to that of the Stromatopteridaceae and the Psilotaceae. The spores of the Osmundaceae, unlike those of the other families mentioned, are uniformly trilete.

The gametophytes of the Osmundaceae (D. H. Campbell, 1928; Stokey and Atkinson, 1956c) are surface living, green, thalloid, often up to 5 cm long, and have a pronounced midrib. The margins often become very irregular with age and the midrib may even be devoid of the marginal wings here and there. They thus may appear in part axial, but still these portions of the body apparently do not originate from a radially organized apical meristem but from a linear meristem, as thalloid gameto-

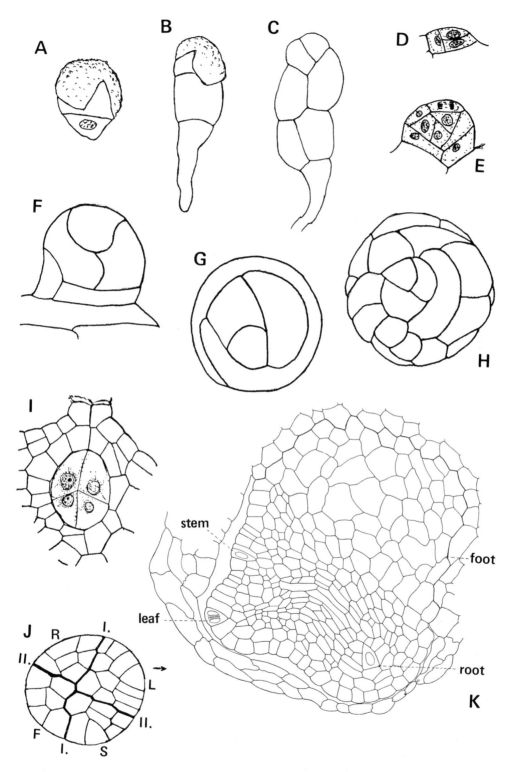

FIGURE 15–10. *A* to *C.* Stages in spore germination of *Osmunda claytoniana*, redrawn from D. H. Campbell (1928). *D, E.* Two stages in the development of the antheridium of *Todea barbara*, after Stokey and Atkinson (1956c). *F, G.* Two views of the antheridium of *Leptopteris superba*, after Stokey and Atkinson (1956c). *H.* Top view of an antheridium of *Osmunda javanica*, after Stokey and Atkinson (1956c). *I* to *K.* Younger to older embryos of *Osmunda*. *I, J. O. claytoniana*, after D. H. Campbell (1928). *K. O. cinnamomea*, after Cross (1931).

phytes do in general. Rhizoids develop on the lower surface and sometimes they are septate, a feature shared with the Psilotaceae, Stromatopteridaceae, Schizaeaceae, and some Ophioglossaceae. The antheridia are either marginal or on the lower surface near the margins. The archegonia are on, or lateral to, the midrib.

The archegonia are of an ordinary type for ferns in general, with a neck five to seven cells long and four cells in cross section and an axial row composed of an egg, a ventral canal cell, and a binucleate neck canal cell. All the cells are related by cell lineages in the same manner as in most archegonia. The necks are bent back and point away from the apical notch of the gametophyte, as is the case in the majority of higher ferns. An indistinct and usually incomplete jacket of cells lines the venter. Longitudinal divisions of neck cells are absent or very rare.

The antheridia are relatively large, comparable in size to those of the Psilotaceae. Stromatopteridaceae, and Gleicheniaceae, with a sperm output sometimes of over 100. The antheridial wall is highly complex in surface configuration (Fig. 15–10, *F* to *H*), with an apical opercular cell. The turban effect that one sees in antheridia of *Stromatopteris*, *Gleichenia*, and to a lesser extent in the Psilotaceae is not at all apparent in the Osmundaceae. In the establishment of the antheridial initial, a pair of oblique divisions occurs in a surface cell (Fig. 15–10, *D*). An intermediate stage in development of the antheridium is shown in *E*, in which the jacket and the spermatogenous tissue are already distinct.

The manner of germination (Fig. 15–10, *A* to *C*) of the spore is peculiar among ferns. The spore first enlarges, projects out of the spore coat, and then divides transversely to produce a small distal cell (the rhizoid cell). The basal cell then divides in one of various planes and, after several divisions, either a two-dimensional plate or a three-dimensional mass of cells is formed at this end of the young gametophyte. A linear meristem with an apical cell is eventually formed, and it comes later to lie within the notch of the thallose gametophyte. The complete reversal of polarity is the significant feature of the above pattern. In other ferns with thalloid gametophytes the

rhizoid is basal and the apical meristem is apical or distal.

The first division of the zygote in the Osmundaceae is longitudinal to the axis of the archegonium, as it is in most of the more advanced fern families, and also parallel to the long axis of the gametophyte. The second division (or pair of divisions) is transverse to the first (Fig. 15–10, *I*) and either parallel or transverse to the first. The next division (set of four) results in the octant stage. The embryonic organs (Fig. 15–10, *J*, *K*) seem related in origin to quadrants or at least approximate quadrant zones as follows: the leaf and the stem from each of the two outer quadrants (toward the neck of the archegonium) and the root and foot from the two inner quadrants. The apical cell of the root does not arise at the surface. The foot is relatively large as compared to higher ferns and it has an irregular haustorial surface. The foot then is comparable to a degree to that of the Psilotaceae, Stromatopteridaceae, and Schizaeaceae.

Gleicheniaceae

The Gleicheniaceae is a family seemingly closely related to the Stromatopteridaceae, as evidenced by sporangial structure, spore structure, chromosome number, antheridial structure, stem anatomy, pinna form, and rachis anatomy. It is represented in the extant floras by a single genus, *Gleichenia*, with approximately 130 species of tropical and South Temperate distribution. In less conservative treatments, the genus is split into the genera *Gleichenia*, *Sticherus*, *Dicranopteris*, and *Hicriopteris*. The family suggests itself to be ancestral to several exindusiate families of higher ferns, and its antiquity, dating back possibly to Upper Carboniferous times, is in conformance. Eggert and Delevoryas (1967) have, however, recently shed doubt on the validity of assigning *Oligocarpa* and other genera of sporangia to the Gleicheniaceae.

The sporophyte of *Gleichenia* has an above- or below-ground rhizome which is frequently a number of meters long and relatively large fronds. The fronds are usually two or more times pinnate, with the ultimate divisions being merely pinnatifid (Fig. 15–11, *B*; Fig. 15–12,

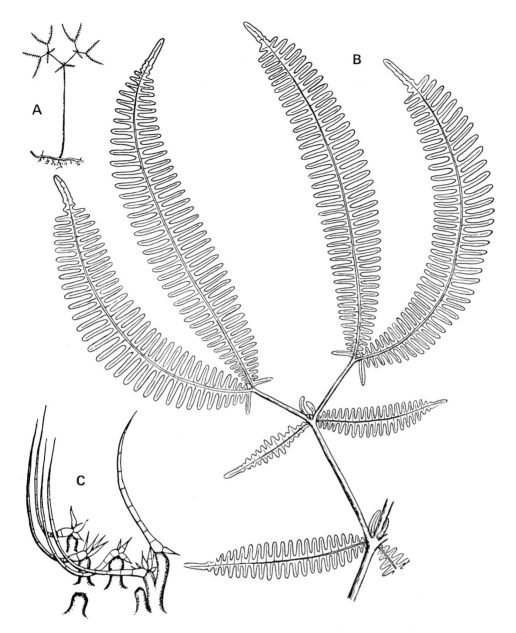

FIGURE 15–11. *A, B.* Frond and piece of rhizome and portion of frond enlarged of *Gleichenia linearis,* after Pichi-Sermolli (1962). *C.* Hairs from the leaf base of *G. pectinata,* after Bower (1923).

1). Arrested apices commonly occur in fronds of many species, and immediately below a pair of pinnae grow out to produce a false dichotomy (Fig. 15–11, *A, B*). This pattern is often repeated a number of times in the rambling species, and the very extensive leaf systems give the plant the aspect of a vine. This growth pattern is quite common among species that inhabit semixeric areas such as the dry savannahs of South America or grasslands that are frequently burned on islands of the South Pacific.

The stem of *Gleichenia* branches dichotomously and, at least in *G. caudata,* has an

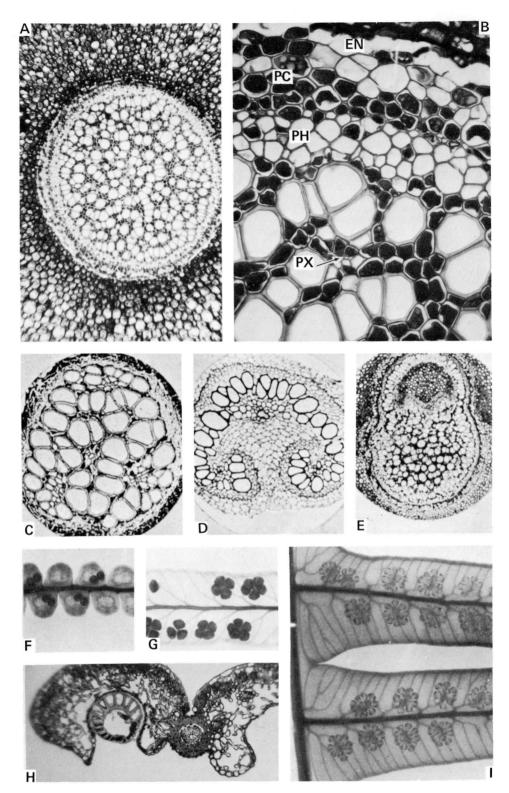

FIGURE 15–12. *A*. Cross section of the stem stele of *Gleichenia caudata*. *B*. Portion of *A* enlarged. EN = endodermis; PC = pericycle; PH = phloem; PX = protoxylem. *C*. Leaf trace in *G. polypodioides*. *D*. Leaf trace in *G. boryi*. *E*. Leaf trace at its departure from the cauline stele in *G. intermedia*. *C* to *E*, after Chrysler (1943, 1944). *F*. Portion of a fertile pinnule of *G. dicarpa*. *G*. Portion of a fertile pinnule of *G. caudata*. *H*. Cross section of a fertile pinnule of *G. dicarpa*. *I*. Portions of two fertile pinnules of *G. linearis*.

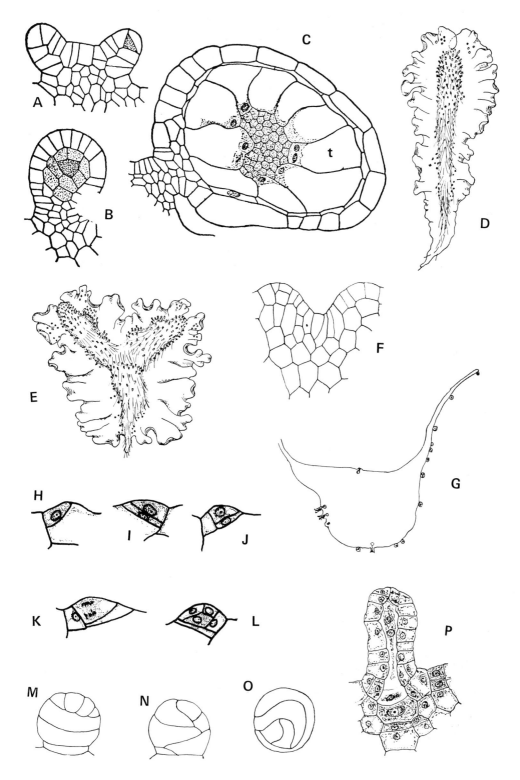

FIGURE 15–13. *A* to *C*. Stages in the development of the sporangium of *Gleichenia flabellata*, after Bower (1926). *D*. Gametophyte of *G. bifida*. *E*. Gametophyte of *G. glauca*. *F*. Apical notch with apical cell of *D*. *G*. Diagrammatic cross section of a gametophyte of *G. glauca*. *H* to *L*. Stages in antheridial development. *H, I, L. G. palmata*. *J. G. glauca*. *K. G. bifida*. *M* to *O*. Antheridia of *Gleichenia*. *M. G. volubile*. *N. G. glauca*. *O. G. volcanica*. *D* to *P*. After Stokey (1950).

apical cell with two cutting faces. Among the various species the stem produces simple hairs, branched hairs (Fig. 15–11, *C*), pedicillate hairs or scales or some combination of these.

The apical meristem of the stem of *G. caudata*, *G. linearis*, and *G. dicarpa* is subapical and situated on the upper side of the organ. The leaf primordia are produced in acropetal succession and in the first two species are in a single row on the upper side of the stem. In *G. dicarpa* the leaves are alternately in two rows, each about 30 degrees to 40 degrees to the left and right of the upper side of the stem. In each of the three species most of the leaves remain dormant in a primordial stage. Thus the "stem" with its "leaves" in *Gleichenia* suggests the "primary axes" with its "laterals" in *Stromatopteris*. In the latter, however, the laterals show various developmental potentialities. The stem is protostelic (Fig. 15–12, *A*). There is a uniform distribution of scalariformly pitted tracheids in the central core and much intermixed stelar parenchyma. The protoxylem occurs as small near-peripheral islands (Fig. 15–12, *B*), and the maturation is therefore mesarch. A continuous zone of phloem, pericycle, and endodermis is external to the xylem (Fig. 15–12, *B*).

The petiolar strand is either C-shaped with inrolled ends in cross section (Fig. 15–12, *D*) or nearly a solid mass of xylem. In both cases there are three protoxylem points (*C*). The parenchymatous core within the C-shaped trace extends back to the cauline xylem mass (Fig. 15–12, *E*) and there seems comparable to the incomplete gap of *Osmundites* (Fig. 15–3, *H*).

Leaf venation is of the open dichotomous type, with a few anastomoses (Fig. 15–12, *G*, *I*) in some species.

The root of *Gleichenia* is much like that of higher ferns both in calyptral structure and mature tissue organization.

The sporangia are usually borne in a single ring inserted upon a slight moundlike receptacle. When the sporangial number is high (i.e., 10 to 15) several often appear out of the ring and on the center of the receptacle. Sori occur on the lower (abaxial) sides of essentially unmodified pinnules or pinnatifid segments and over, or at the end of, a vein (Fig. 15–12, *G*, *I*). The sori are sometimes slightly sunken,

and in *Gleichenia dicarpa* (Fig. 15–12, *F*, *H*), in which the sporangial number per sorus is 1 to 3, the pinna is highly reduced and cup-shaped. Note that the outer edge of the cup in Fig. 15–12, *H* appears as the incurled edge of the pinna, but the inner edge seems otherwise. In Fig. 15–12, *F* it appears that the entire margin of the cup was likely produced by the same meristem, but on its inner edge it is attached to the midvein of the pinnule-bearing axis. A complete description of the ontogeny of the pinnule and how (if this is so) the marginal meristem of the pinnule came to be an apparent extension of the pinna axis should be illuminating.

The sporangium of *Gleichenia* is much like that of *Stromatopteris*. A surface cell of the receptacle divides obliquely, left and right, as an apical cell. The then-elevated sporangial initial (Fig. 15–13, *A*, left) divides periclinally to establish the initial cell of the wall (the distal cell) and an inner cell. The latter then goes on to produce the primary archesporial cell, the mother cell layer of the tapetum, and the inner wall layer. In appearance these layers (Fig. 15–13, *C*) are particularly suggestive of *Stromatopteris*. The inner wall layer mostly breaks down before the spores are produced. The sporangial stalk is relatively massive and has a nondistinct origin, as in the Osmundaceae. For a description of the mature sporangium see below under Anemiaceae and Lygodiaceae.

The sporangiferous receptacle originates much later in *Gleichenia* than in *Stromatopteris* and seems to form essentially in its final position. That is, there does not seem to be the ontogenetic shifting from a marginal to abaxial position as occurs in the latter genus. There are, however, conflicting reports on this in the literature.

The spores of most species of *Gleichenia* are trilete, but a few are monolete.

The gametophyte of *Gleichenia* is surface living, green, and thalloid. It has a conspicuous midrib or central cushion (Fig. 15–13, *D*, *E*, *G*), is occasionally branched, and often has an irregular margin. It possesses an apical cell with two cutting faces in the terminal notch (Fig. 15–13, *F*), and this, as in other thallose gametophytes, is continued laterally as a marginal meristem. Rhizoids and archegonia are

FIGURE 15–14. *A*. Frond of *Anemia phyllitidis*. *B*. Portion of the fertile region of *A* enlarged. *C*. Part of a fertile frond of *Lygodium reticulatum*. *D*. Part of a fertile frond of *Mohria caffrorum*.

borne on the lower surface along the midrib; antheridia are mostly on the lower surface of the wings, but a few also occur on the upper surface above the midrib (Fig. 15–13, *G*).

The archegonia are relatively long-necked and straight (Fig. 15–13, *G*, *P*). There is an incomplete jacket around the venter, and a single binucleate neck canal cell.

The antheridia are complex and relatively large. The jacket cells give the turban effect and the operculum is lateral (Fig. 15–13, *M* to *O*). Early stages in antheridial ontogeny (Fig. 15–13, *H* to *L*) are more or less as in the Osmundaceae and certain Pteridaceae.

Anemiaceae and Lygodiaceae

As considered here, the Anemiaceae consists of two genera: *Anemia*, with its approximately 90 species mostly of the American tropics, and *Mohria*, with its three species of Africa. The genus *Lygodium*, which has 39 pantropical species, is kept in its own family. Some authors have recognized a separate family for each of the three genera. Still others maintain *Anemia Mohria*, and *Lygodium* within the Schizaeaceae along with *Schizaea* and *Actinostachys*. The differences of opinion are only relative, as it is generally accepted that five genera mentioned have had a common origin. This hypothesis, although appearing reasonable at our present state of knowledge, should be periodically re-examined as new information is gathered. This is especially true since what were formally considered "characteristic schizaeaceous sporangia" cannot reasonably be distinguished from sporangia occurring in the Gleicheniaceae, Stromatopteridaceae, or in the coenopterid complex.

Lygodium and *Mohria* each have a dichotomously branched, subterranean rhizome (Fig. 15–15, *A*). The branching in *Anemia* appears lateral, but bud origin should be investigated. The rhizomes bear adventitious roots, leaves, and dermal appendages that are scales in *Mohria* but simple hairs in the other two genera. The leaves are basically pinnate (Fig. 15–14, *A*; Fig. 15–15, *B*) except in *Lygodium*, in which dichotomies and intergradations occur. Venation is open dichotomous in *Mohria*, the same with a few anastomoses in *Lygodium* (Fig.

15–14, *C*) and open dichotomous to reticulate among the various species of *Anemia*. The leaf of *Lygodium* maintains active apical growth for a long period and may reach a length of more than 20 m.

The stem of *Lygodium* has a protostele much like that of *Gleichenia*, with a terete, central, uniformly parenchymatized xylic mass. The poles of primary xylem maturation are, however, peripheral, and the pattern is therefore exarch. At a pole there is no protoxylem, but the earlier-formed metaxylem is distinct. The leaf trace does not disturb the cauline xylem mass at its point of departure, and it is simple with some adaxial curvature.

The stems of *Mohria* and *Anemia* have ectophloic siphonosteles that are dissected at a given cross-sectional level in *Mohria* and in those species of *Anemia* that bear crowded leaves. The leaf traces approximate the simple "C" that seems the basic condition of the entire Filicales.

The roots of the *Anemiaceae* and *Lygodiaceae* illustrate features that are recurrent in many filicalean families (i.e., a sclerenchymatous inner cortex, an outer cortex of pseudoperiderm, a narrow endodermis, a pericycle of enlarged cells, and two peripheral protoxylem points; Fig. 15–16, *A*).

In *Mohria* the sporangia are borne on the lower surface of ordinary laminae in a submarginal position closely associated with veinlets. They are partially protected by a revolute margin (Fig. 15–14, *D*). In *Anemia* the sporangia are borne in two rows along the ultimate veins on a fertile pinna, and the lamina, which is nearly extinct in many species, partly overarches them. The fertile pinnae are frequently the basal pair of a frond (Fig. 15–14, *A*) but not consistently. There are frequently great masses of sporangia produced, completely masking the laminate nature of the fertile pinna (Fig. 15–14, *B*).

Lygodium is highly distinctive in the disposition and grouping of sporangia and in their associated components. The sporangia appear in marginal strobiloid or spikelike masses (Fig. 15–14, *C*). A single sporangium appears near the end of one of the veinlets and each sporangium is covered by a flap. The latter is generally called an indusium and one sporangium an entire sorus. The sporangium

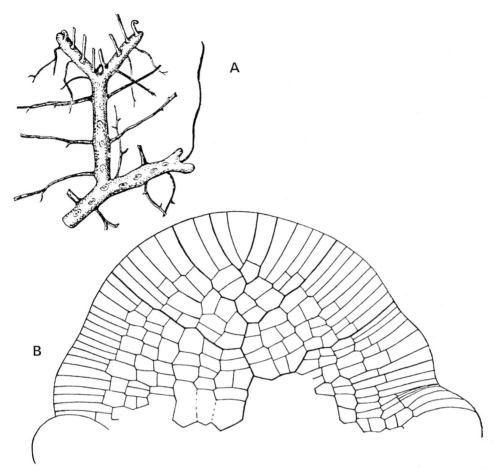

FIGURE 15–15. *A.* Dichotomized rhizome of *Lygodium scandens*, after Velenovsky (1905). *B.* Frond apex and developing pinnae of *Anemia rotundifolia*, after Kupper (1906).

of *Lygodium* originates as an outgrowth of the marginal series of cells directly continuous with the prismatic layer of the apical cell of the leaf segment. The "indusium" in its ontogeny seems to be a lip of the lamina which has grown around as a flap on the lower side of that part of the leaf (see Binford, 1907, for illustrations).

In the Anemiaceae and the Lygodiaceae sporangial ontogeny begins with the differentiation of an enlarged surface cell, which divides transversely (this may or may not be consistent) before dividing obliquely as an apical cell. The two arrows in Fig. 15–16, *C* mark the plane of the first division; the resultant basal cells have divided several times later. From this stage the terminal cell goes on to divide and

ultimately produce the sporangium as in most other filicalean families. The sporangial initial comes into being after the stalk is produced; it divides periclinally at the apex to establish the outer wall initial and the inner cell. The latter ultimately produces the tapetum and the inner wall layer and the sporogenous tissue in the usual filicalean manner (Fig. 15–16, *D*). The inner wall layer disappears completely before sporangial maturation (Fig. 15–16, *B*).

Spores of *Lygodium*, *Anemia*, and *Mohria* are all trilete, and those of the last two bear coarse ridges very similar to those found on spores of certain *Actinostachys* species and of *Ceratopteris*.

The gametophytes of *Lygodium*, *Anemia*, and *Mohria* begin as filaments that soon

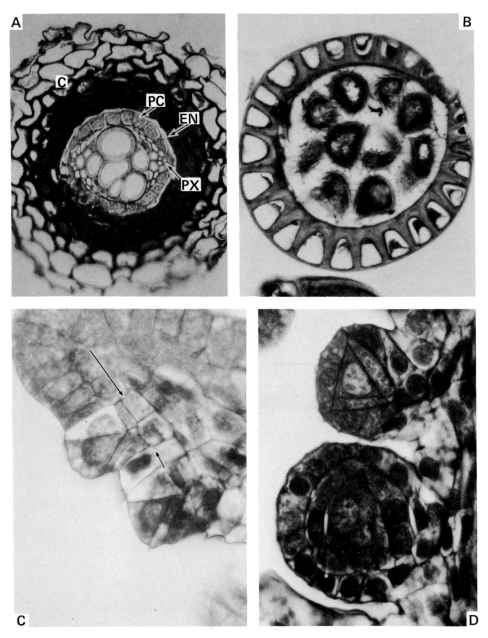

FIGURE 15–16. *A.* Cross section of a root of *Anemia phyllitidis.* *B.* Cross section of a mature sporangium of *A. phyllitidis* through the annulus. *C, D.* Stages in the development of the sporangium in *A. phyllitidis.*

expand into cellular plates. The first rhizoid is lateral. In each the apex originates in a subapical position and the gametophyte, although flat and cordate, is lopsided. According to Stokey (1951) similar asymmetrical growth

also occurs in gametophytes of the three pteridaceous genera *Actinopteris, Onychium,* and *Acrosticum.* The apical meristem comes to be situated in a notch. Figure 15–17, *A* is cut transverse to the gametophyte and tangential

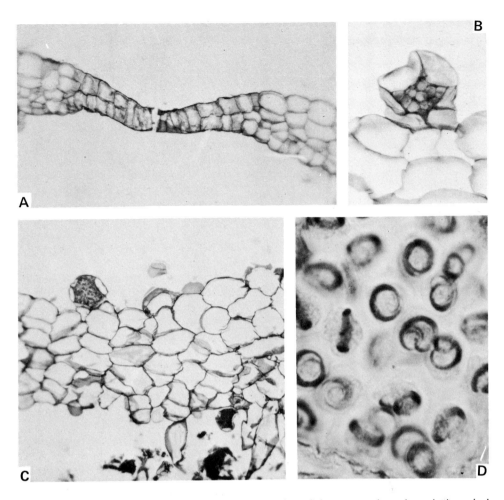

FIGURE 15–17. *Lygodium scandens.* *A.* Cross section of the gametophyte through the apical meristem in the notch. *B.* Antheridium. *C.* Cross section through the gametophyte showing an antheridium on the upper surface and one on the lower surface (lower right, contents uniformly dark). *D.* Nearly mature sperm.

to the notch meristem. Antheridia are borne on the lower cushion or lateral to it and occasionally on the upper surface as well (Fig. 15–17, *C*). Archegonia appear on the cushion. There are occasional unisexual gametophytes in the Anemiaceae and Lygodiaceae, as in several more advanced homosporous ferns. It remains to be demonstrated whether these are merely expressions of environmental influence or are, in part, genetic.

The archegonia are of a usual type. There is a single neck canal cell with two to four nuclei and a pad cell below the egg. The archegonia of *Anemia* point toward the apex, while those

of *Lygodium* and *Mohria* are straight or point away from the apex.

Antheridia of the two families are nearly identical to those of the Schizaeaceae, with a basal coin-shaped cell, a single ring cell, and a cap cell. The latter is divided in *Lygodium* (Fig. 15–17, *B*). The sperm are relatively large (Fig. 15–17, *D*) and are produced in numbers from approximately 25 to 156 per antheridium, depending on the species.

Very little information is available on the embryogeny of either the Anemiaceae or on the Lygodiaceae. Later stages in embryogeny and young sporeling form suggest that the

Filicales: Selected Significant Families **265**

embryonic organs, leaf, stem, root, and foot are all primary parts of the embryo and are in the same spatial relationships as in higher filicales. In *Lygodium* (Rogers, 1927) the first two divisions of the fertilized egg are longitudinal to the archegonial axis. The embryo, when it has become a spherical mass with a diameter of approximately six cells, shows indications that the four organs are established. The leaf is soon the dominant part of the embryo and the apical cell of the root is endogenous in origin.

General Comments on the Sporangium

The sporangia found in the extant Gleicheniaceae, Stromatopteridaceae, Schizaeaceae, Anemiaceae, and Lygodiaceae form a structural continuum so finely gradate that none of these families may be characterized on the basis of this organ. Attempts to so characterize them in the past are based on characteristics that, it is becoming increasingly clear, are particularly unconservative. It seems probable now that "gleichenaceous" and "schizaeaceous" sporangia evolved independently in coenopterid derivatives that are quite unrelated to the Gleicheniaceae (sens. lat.) and Schizaeaceae (sens. lat.) (see Eggert and Delevoryas, 1967).

An elongate sporangium with longitudinal dehiscence, devoid of an annulus and terminally situated on an axial entity, is interpreted as the ancestral form of filicalean sporangia. This is essentially what is found in the Trimerophytaceae, which in our present state of knowledge may be ancestral to most or all of the groups of ferns and fernlike plants (i.e., the Cladoxylales, the Aneurophytopsida, the coenopterid complex, the Ophioglossales, and the Marattiales). It is further interpreted that the most primitive sporangium in this line had an ontogenetic history much like filicalean sporangia. That is, a single apical cell, which was also the apical cell of the axial entity upon which the sporangium was borne, ceased to produce lateral segments and divided periclinally. The outer cell produced the outer wall layer and possibly also some cells of the inner wall layers. The inner cell produced sporogenous tissue, tapetum, and some or all of the cells of the inner wall. This would suggest that the tissue of the stalk, even if contracted and distinct, was, in part, of the same origin and continuous with the outer tissues of the axis below. This is in contradiction to some previously published interpretations but seems to fit well all the old and recently acquired evidence.

Classically sporangia have been categorized as either "eusporangiate" or "leptosporangiate." According to D. H. Campbell (1928), in the eusporangium "the spores arise from a group of hypodermal cells, generally traceable to a single primary cell [primary archesporial cell]. The cell outside these divides to form a several-layered wall, but the limits of the sporangium are not definite. . . ." The leptosporangium is "where the whole sporangium is directly traceable to a single epidermal cell, and where a very regular series of divisions takes place before the archesporium is finally formed." Bower (1923) states that the "customary distinction" is that the leptosporangium is derived from one cell while the eusporangium arises from a group of cells, and that the former is relatively delicate in construction at first while the latter is relatively massive. This is the original concept of Goebel. Both Campbell and Bower mention transitional types and the dilution of the distinction between the two. Eames (1936), who probably has had a greater influence on current sporangial concepts because so many extant students, the present author included, diligently studied Eames' volume, more clearly sets forth the definitions. He states that the "eusporangiate method of sporangium formation" is "where a group of cells, superficial in position, by periclinal division forms inner and outer cells, the inner forming sporogenous cells, the outer sterile cells only." Regarding the "leptosporangiate method": "Following the first division of the initial, the outer cell becomes a pyramidal apical cell which cuts off basal cells to form a stalk until a distal, arched, periclinal division limits growth in length. There is thus formed a central cell, usually tetrahedral in form, surrounded by a one-layered wall. Anticlinal divisions in the wall divide this layer into many cells. The central cell represents the primary sporogenous tissue.

From it are cut off by periclinal divisions one or two layers of thin cells which become tapetum." Included among the leptosporangiate taxa were only the families of the Filicales; all other vascular plants were considered eusporangiate. The Osmundaceae was considered leptosporangiate, but in regard to sporangial stalk and in part wall formation somewhat intermediate. The microsporangia of most seed plants fit Campbell's concept of eusporangia, since in these the archesporium is not related to the surface layer by periclinal divisions. Eames (1961) has considered the microsporangia of seed plants as completely wall-less. Fossil sporangia have frequently been classified as eusporangia if they are relatively large and if their wall is multiseriate (see D. H. Scott, 1920–1923).

It should be apparent at this point that none of the criteria used to distinguish the "leptosporangium" from the "eusporangium" is consistent. The concept of the latter fits only the lycopods, which historically were the center of its focus. The sporangia of this taxon were the first of the "eusporangiate" types to be completely described (Bower, 1894). Subsequently others were in general described as to how they differed. It is now known that the sporangia of the Marattiaceae do not have ontogenetic individuality, that those of the Ophioglossaceae arise from one to several cells with wall layers of diverse origin as in the Psilotaceae, that those of typical filicaleans may have multilayered walls that are traceable to the inner cell, and that sporangial size is no criterion, as is indicated by the massive ones of *Tmesipteris* and the smaller ones of the diploid race of *Psilotum nudum*, which overlap those of many more typical filicalean ferns.

In addition to most Filicales, *Equisetum* may be the only other extant genus that retains what is considered the primitive sporangial ontogeny. It may very well originate from a single cell which divides like an apical cell as Fagerlind (1961) suggests, but the size and form of the cell relative to neighboring cells has not allowed definite identification or clear-cut description of its segmentation.

In summary, the terms "leptosporangium" and "eusporangium" should be completely discarded as vague and presenting false impressions. To use one of these terms for the last time, a sporangium ontogenetically much more like the "leptosporangium" is considered the primitive type among most vascular plants.

The presumed ancestral filicalean sporangium had surface cells that were mostly thickened, primarily on their radial and inner tangential walls. Their greater shrinkage over the entire surface facilitated dehiscence. The position of dehiscence was probably predetermined by the shape of the cells at the apex, as it is in most of the extant schizaeaceous species. In these the cap cell or group of cells together form a triangle (Fig. 15–34, *G*) with an insignificant point of weakness at one apex. The action is equivalent to tearing a piece of cloth that has been notched. The notch and the weave of the cloth (as the general cellular orientation) determine the entire line along which tearing will occur. There is no specialization of cells along the line of dehiscence in *Stromatopteris* (Fig. 15–35, *A*, *B*), and in some species of *Gleichenia* (Fig. 15–34, *C*; Fig. 15–35, *G*) and *Actinostachys*, and these are considered primitive in this regard.

The annulus is assumed to have originated by gradual differentiation within the surface layer until complete dimorphism of cell types was attained, with the annulus probably in a subapical position. Known sporangia that show intergradations between annular cells and other surface cells [e.g., *Psilotum*, *Actinostachys*, *Schizaea*, *Stromatopteris*, *Osmunda* (Fig. 15–34, *F*), and the upper carboniferous *Seftenbergia* (Fig. 15–35, *I*)] are, it follows, considered primitive in this characteristic. The latter bore very anemioid sporangia (compare *I* with *E* and *F* in Fig. 15–35) in two rows along the vein on the lower surface of simple pinnules, and so the genus seems logically placed in the Anemiaceae. The annulus of *Seftenbergia* is not as clearly defined as others in the family to which it is assigned, and all other surface cells of its sporangium were somewhat thickened.

In the sporangia of many extant ferns, the annular cells become thickened early enough to restrict growth locally, and therefore constricted nipples surrounded by the annulus are seen in the mature organ (Fig. 15–34, *D*, *G*; Fig. 15–35, *E*). If the annular restriction is initially asymmetrically disposed and if surface cells tend to divide in the anticlinal plane more in regions where surface tension is greatest (a reasonable conclusion in the growth in circumference of the cambium, phellogen, and epidermis of many plants), then the asymmetry should become exaggerated by growth below the annulus. This is what is observed in *Osmunda* (Fig. 15–34, *F*), *Lygodium* (Fig. 15–35, *C*, *D*), and *Gleichenia* (Fig. 15–35, *G*, *H*, *M* to *O*).

The selective significance of the defined annulus seems to lie primarily in the post-dehiscence snapping mechanism and not in dehiscence itself. The very thick, flexible, and resilient walls, as seen in Fig. 15–16, *B*, allow for this mechanism but do not seem to improve dehiscence as such over the type seen in non-filicalean vascular plants.

The sporangial cap (i.e., those relatively thin-walled cells distal to the annulus) is assumed to have experienced both reduction and elaboration in its phylogeny. The primitive cap may have been composed of a very few to approximately 10 cells. Some species of *Schizaea* and *Actinostachys* (Fig. 15–34, *D*) show only a single cell, probably by reduction. In other species of *Schizaea* there are as many as six cells in the cap (Fig. 15–34, *G*) and the sporangial apex then is much like that found in *Anemia* (Fig. 15–35, *E*, *F*), *Lygodium* (Fig. 15–35, *C*, *D*), *Mohria* (Fig. 15–34, *B*, *E*), and occasionally *Gleichenia* (Fig. 15–35, *M*).

As the cap became more extensive and asymmetrical growth more pronounced, the annulus came to lie in a near-vertical position and the line of dehiscence became essentially transverse. This entire sequence of events probably occurred within the Gleicheniaceae.

Other changes that occurred in the phylogeny of the filicalean sporangium are changes in the position of annular differentiation irrespective of asymmetric growth, the initiation of asymmetric growth irrespective of annular restriction, and the differentiation of the annulus along a line that is interrupted by the sporangial stalk. These changes seem to have occurred independently in several familial lines traceable to the Schizaeaceae and Gleicheniaceae.

The psilotaceous sporangium is considered a specialized derivative of a primitive type. The annulus seems abortive and functionless. Its early ontogeny is likely to be a derived sequence of events, while its late ontogeny and final wall structure seem primitive. The fusion of sporangia and the increase in sporangial size probably occurred after the family became well differentiated.

Hymenophyllaceae

The family Hymenophyllaceae, the filmy ferns, is presented as two genera, *Trichomanes* and *Hymenophyllum*. Some recent authors (Copeland, 1947; Pichi-Sermolli, 1959) have recognized many more. The family includes about 650 mostly tropical species, nearly equally divided between the two genera. The large genera are cumbersome and possibly unnatural in part, but there are several reasons why the 34 genera of Copeland should not be recognized. First, in modern systematics the size of a taxon should in no way influence a decision to elevate the rank of its subtaxa (i.e., the convenience factor is not accepted as legitimate). Second, various subtaxa, no matter how homogeneous and natural they may be, do not justify elevation to the higher rank unless they differ in morphological magnitude in characteristics of a degree of conservativeness commensurate with the higher level. Third, in many fundamental features, the Hymenophyllaceae are poorly known. Very little is known of its leaf ontogeny, phyllotaxy, embryogeny, and soral ontogeny. Copeland distinguished his 34 genera primarily on the basis of external, mature morphology. If one lesson is to be learned from the knowledge accumulated about ferns in the last 50 years, it is that many features, such as leaf form, leaf venation, leaf branching pattern, soral form, soral position, sporangial structure, spore shape, gametophyte form, antheridial ontogeny, sporangial size, and plant habit, are to some extent polyphyletic and some may well have evolved in jumps rather than gradually. Any system of fern classification must de-emphasize to some extent external form and appearance, to a much greater extent than when dealing with such groups as angiosperms.

The members of the Hymenophyllaceae have mostly creeping stems with spaced leaf attachments. Some *Trichomanes* species grow upright with a crown of leaves (e.g., *T.*

FIGURE 15–18.   *A*. Portion of a fertile frond of *Trichomanes australicum*; *B*. of *Trichomanes* sp.; *C*. of *Hymenophyllum* sp.; *D*. of *Trichomanes membranaceum*.

australicum, which looks like a miniature tree fern with a trunk of perhaps 10 cm tall and a crown of pinnatifid leaves). The leaves range downward in size to only a few millimeters and in general are quite delicate, often one cell thick except at veins. They are pinnate to dichotomous and are simple, unlobed to highly dissected. Many species are epiphytes and some form creeping mats on rocks and bark and are easily mistaken for thallose hepatics without close examination.

Filmy ferns, although they expose very delicate photosynthetic tissue, often have extremely tough and wiry stems, roots, and leaf veins. They almost invariably grow in extremely damp places but on occasion are subjected to drying and can usually survive. This ability is in some instances attributable to the sclerenchymatous framework which inhibits mechanical damage to delicate parts when turgor is low.

Leaf venation is uniformly open dichotomous in the filmy ferns (Fig. 15–18, *A* to *D*). In the leaves of many species there are sclerenchymatous strands that extend from the margins of the laminae backward and may or may not connect with the true veins. The leaves of *Trichomanes proliferum* become compounded in a peculiar manner, as residual meristematic areas are left behind on the major axes of the frond during early development and at some later time grow out to form complete new fronds. According to Bell (1960) the process may go on indefinitely. This sheds doubt on classical concepts of what are the determining factors in leaf form (see the discussion of Kuehnert's work under Osmundaceae).

In those species in which the apex of the leaf is known, it has a lens-shaped apical cell and pinnae originate within the marginal series of cells. This is usual for ferns. The marginal meristem of the lamina is, however, peculiar to the family. In what Bower (1923) considers the ordinary fern type of marginal meristem (Fig. 15–20, *F*) a line of marginal initials is present and each of its cells divides anticlinally and obliquely with respect to a vertical tangent to the leaf margin, producing ultimately all internal and external tissue, as the cell lineages in the figure indicate. In what he terms the hymenophyllaceous type, each marginal initial divides transverse to the entire blade and

parallel to a vertical tangent at the margin (Fig. 15–20, *E*, *G*).

The rhizomes of the Hymenophyllaceae bear leaves that are spirally or distichously arranged. The branching is either axillary or nonaxillary. Adventitious roots are produced, but in some species the entire plant is rootless. Bell (1960) reports that in *Trichomanes proliferum* branches of the rhizome occur at, as well as between, leaf insertions. Those in the latter position are more limited in growth, are directed downward, and are, as are the others, devoid of a calyptra. The possibility of root reduction must be considered. In rootless species, absorbing hairs occur along the rhizome as well as on leaf axes.

Hymenophyllaceous stems are all protostelic (Fig. 15–19, *B*, *D*) and the leaf trace (Fig. 15–19, *C*; Fig. 15–20, *D*, left side) is simple without an associated stelar gap. If an axillary bud is present, its trace is united at the base with that of the leaf. Primary xylem maturation is exarch (e.g., *Trichomanes scandens* and *T. australicum*), mesarch, or centrarch [e.g., *Hymenophyllum scabrum*, *H. dialatum* (Fig. 15–20, *D*), and *Trichomanes latealatum*]. In *Hymenophyllum dialatum* the centrally located protoxylem is surrounded by stelar parenchyma (Fig. 15–20, *D* right-hand stele) and this in turn by an upper and a lower band of metaxylem. To the outside of this there is a complete ring of phloem. According to Bower (1923) certain other species are similar but without the lower plate of xylem, and in still others the lower part of the phloem ring is absent. In the most minute rhizomes of the family there may be only one central tracheid, as in *Trichomanes latealatum* (Sharma, 1960) and *T. proliferum* (Bell, 1960). The ultimate in stelar reduction appears in *T. motleyi*, where there is no xylem and the stele consists of only a few parenchyma cells. Bell suggests that each frond of *T. proliferum* is physiologically independent and that the entire plant may be regarded as a colony of leaves.

In *Trichomanes* the soral receptacle is a hair-like, terete axis with symmetrically disposed sporangia surrounded by a campanulate to slightly two-lipped indusium (Fig. 15–18, *A*, *B*, *D*; Fig. 15–19, *A*). In *Hymenophyllum* the receptacle is much shorter and the indisium is definitely two-parted with only basal fusion

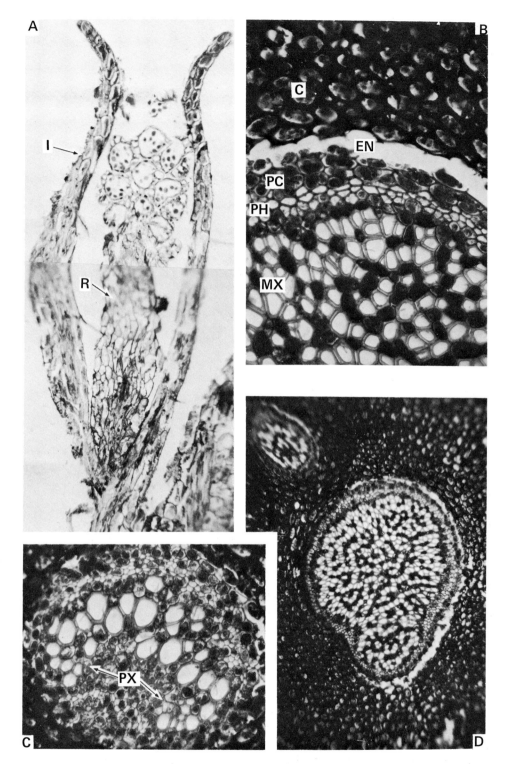

FIGURE 15–19. *A*. Longitudinal section of the sorus of *Trichomanes* sp. I = indusium; R = receptacle. *B*. Portion of a cross section of a stem of *T. australicum*. C = cortex; EN = endodermis; PC = pericycle; PH = phloem; MX = metaxylem. *C*. Cross section of the leaf trace in *T. australicum*. PX = protoxylem. *D*. Entire stem stele in a cross section of *T. australicum*.

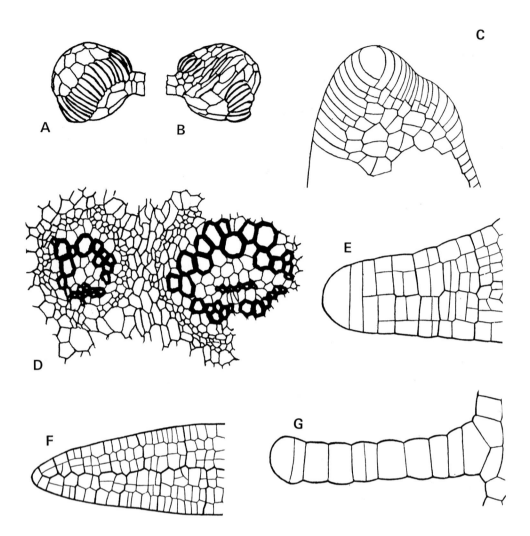

FIGURE 15–20. *A, B*. Sporangia of *Hymenophyllum dilatatum*, redrawn from Bower (1926). *C*. Frond apex of *Trichomanes pinnatum*, after Kupper (1906). *D*. Stem stele (right) and leaf trace (left) in *Hymenophyllum dilatatum*, after Boodle (1900). *E* to *G*. Leaf marginal meristems and patterns of cell lineages in *Trichomanes reneforme* (*E*), *Scolopendrium vulgare* (*F*), and *Trichomanes radicans* (*G*), after Bower (1926).

(Fig. 15–18, *C*). The sorus is usually marginal on vegetative leaves, but occasionally (e.g., *Trichomanes spicatum*) an entire leaf will be fertile and without lamina. The indusium may be free (Fig. 15–18, *A*) or fused laterally to the lamina (Fig. 15–18, *C*, *D*). Occasionally the sorus appears as a submarginal branch of the leaf with the plane of branching at right angles to that of the blade (Fig. 15–18, *B*). This condition should be studied developmentally.

The receptacle grows by means of an intercalary meristem at the base and new sporangia

arise just above the meristem. The order of initiation and maturation of sporangia in a given sorus is therefore basipetally gradate, as opposed to the acropetally gradate condition on the schizaeaceous fertile digit.

Hymenophyllaceous sporangia are much like those of the Gleicheniaceae but in general with greater development of the distal plate (Fig. 15–20, *A*). In ontogeny, the apical cell that produces the stalk is formed by a transverse division, as in the Anemiaceae and Lygodiaceae. The inner wall layer is uniformly

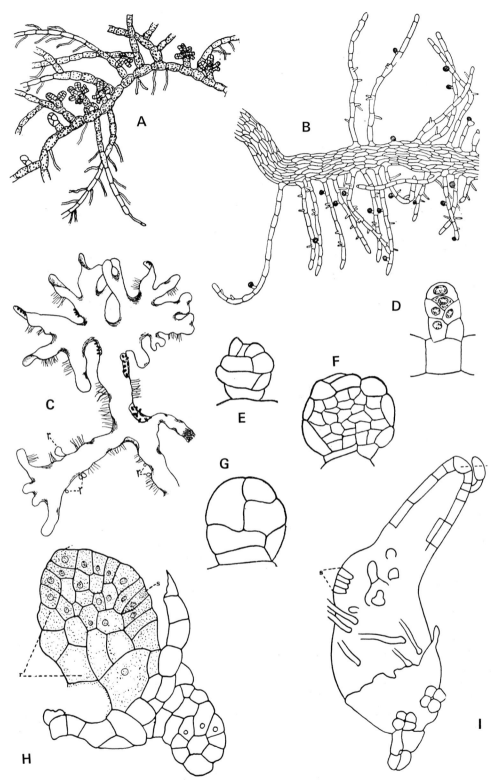

FIGURE 15–21. *A*. Gametophyte of *Trichomanes auriculatum*, after Stokey (1948). *B*. Gametophyte of *T. kraussii*, after Goebel (1930), by permission of Gustav Fischer Verlag, Jena. *C*. Gametophyte of *Hymenophyllum blumeanum*, after Stokey (1948). *D*. Young antheridium of *H. kurzii*,
after Stokey (1948). *E* to *G*. Antheridia of *Hymenophyllum* sp., after D. H. Campbell (1928). *H, I*.
Younger and older embryo of *Trichomanes venosum*, after Stone (1958).

one cell thick and it breaks down completely as the sporangium matures. Spores are relatively few in number per sporangium and are all trilete.

The gametophytes of the filmy ferns are surface living, green, and often perennial. Stokey (1948) reported keeping them in culture for 10 years. Those of *Hymenophyllum* are thin thalli and often highly branched (Fig. 15–21, *C*). Those of *Trichomanes* range from filamentous (Fig. 15–21, *A*) to narrow and delicate thalli that often have filamentous branches (Fig. 15–21, *B*). Bulbils or gemmae occur on the tips of rhizoidlike outgrowths in some species and marginal tissue proliferation accomplishes vegetative reproduction in others. Gametangia in the thallose *Hymenophyllum* gametophytes are mostly on the lower surface and occasionally in groups with the rhizoids. In the thallose *Trichomanes* gametophytes, antheridia are sometimes borne mostly on filamentous branches. Specialized archegoniophores, several cells in thickness, occur on the filamentous gametophytes (Fig. 15–21, *A*), each bearing a cluster of archegonia. Some species may be monoecious. The archegonia have a neck that is four cells long in *Trichomanes* and six to nine cells long in *Hymenophyllum*. In each there is an axial row composed of a pad cell, an egg, a ventral canal cell, and one binucleate neck canal cell.

The antheridia of the Hymenophyllaceae are relatively complex and rather variable. Within the family there seems to be a reduction series from antheridia of the gleicheniaceous type with the turbanate arrangement of jacket cells and a lateral operculum to types with considerably simpler construction (Fig. 15–21, *E, F, G*). Several species have been described in which the antheridial initial is formed by oblique divisions in a surface cell, but in *Hymenophyllum kurzii* the oblique divisions are continued until a stalk is formed (Fig. 15–21, *D*), in just the way in which the sporangial stalk and then the sporangial initial is formed in most ferns.

Stages in the germination of spores are known for about 30 species of *Hymenophyllum* and possibly 15 of *Trichomanes*, and they are all strikingly peculiar. In *Hymenophyllum* the spore divides transversely, sometimes before it is shed from the sporangium. It enlarges, sheds its spore coat, and then one of the two cells divides at right angles to the first division. The three cells then enlarge and the angles of internal wall contact shift to approach 120 degrees, so that now the structure appears as three radiating cells. In *Trichomanes* the more or less triangular or three-lobed spore cuts off a small cell at the tip of each lobe and leaves a large central cell. Gametophytic apices may be formed at one, or occasionally more than one, of the poles.

The embryos of only two hymenophyllaceous species are known, and these are considered particularly significant. In *Trichomanes reniforme* (Holloway, 1944) the first division of the zygote is transverse to the long axis of the archegonium, a feature known elsewhere among ferns only in *Psilotum, Tmesipteris, Actinostachys,* and *Schizaea* and thought to occur in *Stromatopteris.* The embryonic hemisphere away from the archegonial neck seems to give rise to the foot only, although Holloway did not express this fact with absolute certainty. This feature is also known only in the abovementioned genera among the ferns. The other hemisphere gives rise to the leaf, stem apex, and an endogenous root.

In *Trichomanes venosum* the first division is probably either transverse or longitudinal (Stone, 1958). In the four-celled stage, upper and lower hemispheres may be considered. The upper one (i.e., that toward the archegonial neck) produces leaf and stem, while the lower one produces foot only. Of particular interest is the absence of a root in the embryo, especially since this species does produce roots later. Stone considered this the result of reduction, but in view of the new information on rootless embryos of *Actinostachys* and *Stromatopteris* it may very well be a primitive absence.

Matoniaceae

The Matoniaceae seems a most natural and distinct family, represented by two extant genera: *Matonia,* with two species ranging from Indonesia to the Malay Peninsula, and *Phanerosorus,* also with two species in Borneo and New Guinea. Fossil forms were apparently geographically more widespread and quite similar to the living *Matonia.* The genus

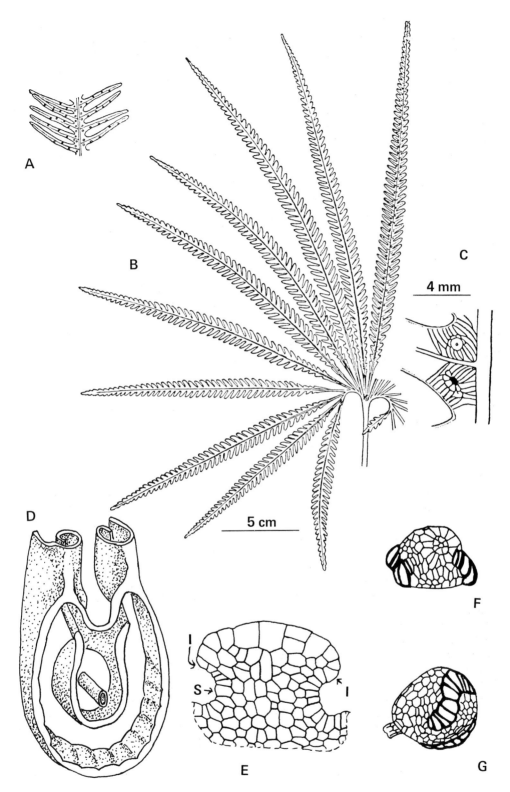

FIGURE 15–22. *Matonia pectinata.* *A.* Portion of frond showing soral distribution. *B.* Frond. *C.* Venation in part of the frond. *A* to *C* after Holttum (1954). *D.* Three-dimensional reconstruction of a part of the stem stele, after Tansley and Lulham (1905). *E.* Young sorus. I = indusium; S = position of sporangial origin. *F, G.* Mature sporangia. *E* to *G* after Bower (1926).

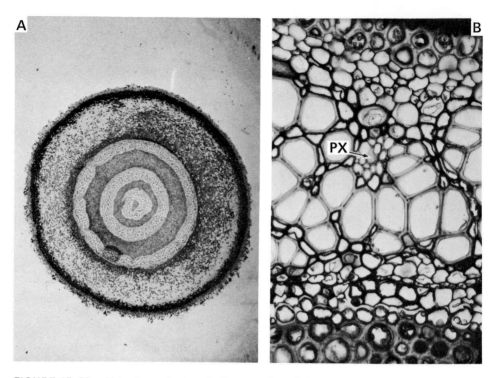

FIGURE 15–23. *Matonia pectinata.* *A.* Cross section of the stem. *B.* Portion of *A* enlarged. PX = protoxylem.

Phlebopteris (*Laccopteris*) is reported from Triassic to Lower Cretaceous rocks; *Matonidium*, whose generic separation from *Matonia* has been questioned, from Jurassic to Cretaceous, and *Matonia* itself from Cretaceous to present.

Matonia has a dichotomously branched horizontal rhizome with spaced leaves. Above the petiole the frond is divided into two major trusses, each of which is scirpoid (Fig. 15–22, *B*) and has elongate, pinnatifid segments. In the ultimate segments, the veins are free toward the margin but anastomosed near the base. The circular sori occur on either side of the midvein of the ultimate segment (Fig. 15–22, *A*) and numerous veins converge on them (Fig. 15–22, *C*).

Phanerosorus has a similar rhizome, bearing pendant, monopodial fronds in which there are some supressed branches and often pseudodichotomies. The veins are all free. The sori are terminal on veinlets in a row on each side of the midvein of the ultimate leaf segments.

Rhizome anatomy in the family is elaborate.

Large rhizomes of *Matonia* show three concentric amphiphloic siphonosteles (Fig. 15–23, *A*) with protoxylem poles embedded in the metaxylem (Fig. 15–23, *B*). The outer two steles are involved with leaf-trace separation (Fig. 15–22, *D*), the trace being large, simple, and with three protoxylem points. In smaller stems, one or two of the steles drop out; the central one is often solid. In *Phanerosorus* only two steles occur in the larger rhizomes.

The sorus of the Matoniaceae shows a ring of a few sporangia up through the center of which the receptacle is extended and grows out as an umbrellalike indusium over the spore-producing organs. A young stage in development is shown in Fig. 15–22, *E*, where S indicates the position of sporangial initials and I, the young indusial flap.

The sporangia are gleicheniaceous in general appearance but with an interrupted annulus (Fig. 15–22, *G*, *F*) that often has distinct crooks, as shown in *G*. The spores are all trilete.

The sporangia within a sorus all mature

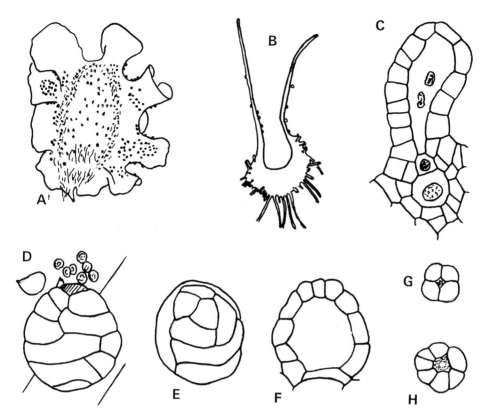

FIGURE 15–24. *Matonia pectinata*, after Stokey and Atkinson (1952). *A*. The gametophyte from below. *B*. Cross section of the gametophyte. *C*. Archegonium in longitudinal section. *D, E, F*. Antheridia. *G, H*. Cross section near the apex and near the base of the archegonium.

simultaneously, and it is thus the *simple type.* The character is shared by the Gleicheniaceae, the Stromatopteridaceae, the Psilotaceae, and the Platyzomaceae. The Osmundaceae and Schizaeaceae have been so categorized, but they do not have what may be called sori and thus are not comparable. Their sporangia are initiated in an *acropetally gradate* manner but generally all mature more or less simultaneously on a given frond. In the families Loxsomaceae, Hymenophyllaceae, and in part in the Cyatheaceae the pattern of sporangial maturation is *basipetally gradate,* owing to meristametic activity at the base of the receptacle which is pronounced only in the first two of these families. Other families of the Filicales show *mixed* development within a given sorus. It seems likely that the simple type is most primitive within the order and from it the basipetally gradate type arose at least twice.

The most advanced type, the *mixed,* seems to have arisen two or more times from both the simple and from the gradate types. The families that are not consistent in the sporangial developmental patterns are the Cyatheaceae and the Davalliaceae.

The gametophyte of *Matonia* is especially gleicheniaceous in character. It is thallose, green, and has a ruffled margin and a thick central cushion. Archegonia occur on the cushion and antheridia on the lower and some on the upper side of the wings (Fig. 15–24, *A, B*). The archegonium is of an ordinary type (Fig. 15–24, *C, G*). The neck canal cell contains up to four nuclei. Additional longitudinal divisions occur near the base in the neck cells (Fig. 15–24, *H*). The antheridium is complex and especially suggestive of gleicheniaceous types (Fig. 15–24, *D* to *F*). Early stages in the development of the gametophyte may appear

Filicales: Selected Significant Families **277**

FIGURE 15–25. *A*. Part of the fertile frond of *Loxsoma cunninghami*. *B*. Single sorus with the tubular indusium around its base in *Loxsomopsis costaricensis*. *C*. Sorus from *B* with indusium removed showing the stalk (sporangiophore) of the sorus.

as plates, masses, or filaments of cells. Stokey and Atkinson (1952) single out this range in form as being particularly suggestive of the Gleicheniaceae.

The embryo of one species of *Matonia* is partly known. In it, the first division of the zygote is longitudinal to the archegonial axis. The next division is transverse to this. The stage described next is of an embryo just before calyptral rupture. Here all four customary embryonic organs are well formed and appear to be primary parts of the embryo. There is little in organ orientation to indicate origins from certain quadrant zones. The foot appears relatively large and has a slightly irregular outline. There is a conspicuously precocious maturation of xylem elements in the embryo before the leaf tears out. The drawing by Stokey and Atkinson (1952) shows the vascular system with ends toward the stem, root, and leaf apices, and a bulge of it into the foot.

The Matoniaceae strongly suggests itself to be of close gleicheniaceous affinity. Possibly its greatest significance in the understanding of fern morphology and interrelationships is that it also suggests affinity with the Dipteridaceae and thus with the Polypodiaceae (sens. strict.).

Loxsomaceae

The Loxsomaceae, formerly included in the Hymenophyllaceae, includes the genera *Loxsoma*, with one New Zealand species, and *Loxsomopsis*, with three South and Central American species. *Loxsoma* has a thick rhizome with adventitious roots and spaced leaves that are 1 or 2 ft tall, two or three times pinnate, and have open venation. *Loxsomopsis* has a thinner rhizome and leaves to 8 ft tall.

Both bear marginal sori that are terminal on veins (Fig. 15–25, *A*). The receptacle is a terete structure with an intercalary meristem at its

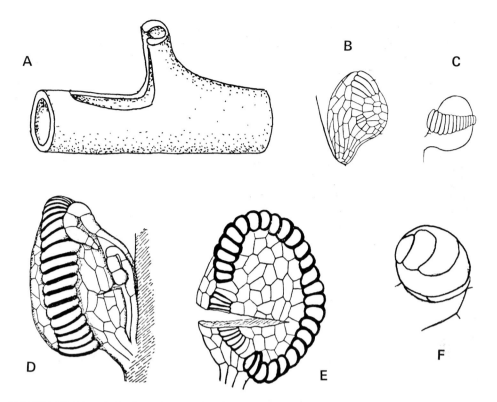

FIGURE 15–26. *A*. Portion of the stele of *Loxsoma cunninghami* reconstructed, after Gwynne-Vaughan (1901). *B, C*. Sporangia of *L. cunninghami*, after Goebel (1930), by permission of Gustav Fischer Verlag, Jena. *D, E*. Sporangia of *Loxsomopsis notabilis*, after Bower (1926). *F*. Antheridium of *Loxsoma cunninghami*, after Stokey and Atkinson (1956a).

base when young and surrounded at the base by a cuplike indusium (Fig. 15–25, *B*). After all sporangia are produced, the basal meristem produces the sporangiophore (Fig. 15–25, *C*).

The rhizomes contain amphiphloic siphonosteles with simple leaf gaps associated with the departure of the single, adaxially curved leaf traces. Sclerenchymatous masses with islands of included parenchyma occur in the stems, a feature also occurring in some species of *Dicksonia*. Epidermal appendages are simple, but some occur with a multicellular, conical base highly suggestive of Gleicheniaceae and Cyatheaceae.

The sporangia of the two genera are distinct. In *Loxsoma* the annulus is incomplete, subapical, and longitudinal as the sporangium is oriented (but it is asymmetrically pear-shaped), and it is composed of large to smaller cells (Fig. 15–26, *B, C*). Dehiscence is longitudinal. *Lox-*somopsis has a complete annulus that is more median on the sporangium and shows transverse to irregular dehiscence. In *Loxsomopsis* (Fig. 15–26, *D, E*), there are also specialized cells within the circle of the annulus adjacent to the line of dehiscence. These are the stomial cells, which mark the stomium or the predetermined line of separation across this layer. Specialized stomial cells are common among higher ferns and they are generally separated by thin-walled cells from the typical annular cells within the ring. Spores of the family are trilete.

The spores of *Loxsoma* and *Loxsomopsis* germinate readily and form a plate of cells or a filament that soon becomes a plate. Eventually a cordate thallus is produced that has a heavy midrib of up to 10 cells thick and a thin wing. Sex organs occur on the central cushion with some antheridia on the wings. Archegonia

FIGURE 15–27. *Plagiogyria semicordata.* *A.* Two fertile and a sterile pinna. *B.* Portion of a younger fertile pinna. *C.* Part of a fertile pinna from *A* enlarged. *D.* Sporangia. *E.* Sporangium with two annuli. *F.* Sporangium, showing the line of dehiscence at *D.*

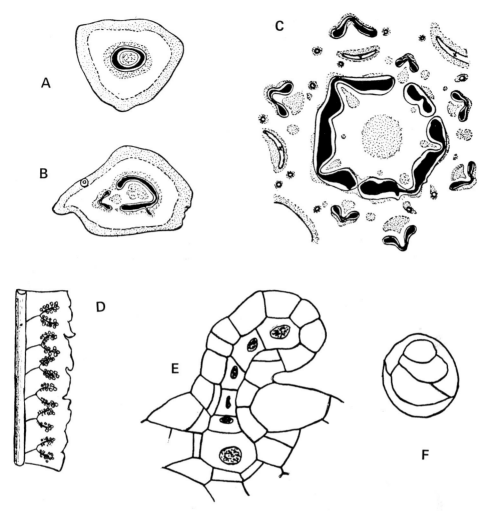

FIGURE 15–28. *A* to *C*. Cross sections of stems of *Plagiogyria pycnophylla*, after Bower (1923). *A, B*. From a small plant. *C*. From an older plant. *D*. Part of a fertile frond of *P. semicordata*, redrawn from Mettenius (1857). *E*. Archegonium of *P. semicordata*. *F*. Antheridium of *P. semicordata*. *E, F* after Stokey and Atkinson (1956b).

are restricted to the later-produced portions. Long, multicellular, and some multiseriate green hairs appear on the lower surface in the region of the notch. These compare favorably with similar hairs that occur on gametophytes of *Cyathea*. The archegonia are ordinary with a pad cell and a binucleate neck canal cell. Antheridia are intermediate in complexity (Fig. 15–26, *F*). The embryo is unknown.

The family Loxsomaceae is considered a specialized end of a line but combining features of the Schizaeaceae, Hymenophyllaceae, and Cyatheaceae.

Plagiogyriaceae

The family Plagiogyriaceae includes a single genus, *Plagiogyria*, with 36 species in eastern Asia and the Americas from Mexico to Brazil. The plants have thin runners or stolons that bear scale leaves and upright, occasionally dichotomous, stout stems that bear a crown of pinnate or bipinnate leaves with laterally enlarged bases. On either side of the petiole is a row of glandlike protuberances ("pneumatophores"). The ultimate leaf segments (Fig. 15–27, *A*, *B*) show open dichotomous venation.

The fertile pinna has a slightly reduced lamina (*A*) that recurves and partly protects the masses of sporangia (*B*). The sporangia are actually attached along ultimate veins in distinct elongate sori (Fig. 15–28, *D*). Bower (1923) describes simple hairs occurring on young leaves. Copeland (1947) describes the plants as devoid of dermal appendages and states that a gelatinous secretion dries and becomes flaky.

The stout, upright stem bears an amphiphloic siphonostele with mesarch primary xylem. The stele is only slightly dissected by narrow leaf gaps (Fig. 15–28, *C*). The leaf traces with their four protoxylem points tend to be V-shaped, with the opening of the V toward the stem stele. Within the petiole, the arms of the trace straighten out more laterally, and the central protrusion becomes more squared-off. Patches of sclerenchyma occur here and there in the stem (stippled areas in Fig. 15–28, *C*). The stolons possess simple, undissected amphiphloic siphonosteles, similar to those in upright stems of the young plants (Fig. 15–28, *A*, *B*).

A stolon arises on the upright stem in an apparent leaf position, but often near its base, almost at its point of attachment, there is an aborted leaf, suggesting that the stolon is actually epipetiolar in origin.

The sporangia are long-stalked with an oblique, uninterrupted annulus (Fig. 15–27, *D*). The line of dehiscence (*D* in Fig. 15–27, *F*) is lateral and nearly transverse. The stomium is well defined and there are nearly 10 stomial cells. The spores are trilete and are produced 48 to a sporangium.

A very anomalous sporangium is shown in Fig. 15–27, *E*, in which the annulus is divided into two rows that join below. Such a condition is very rare in ferns but is common in cycads.

The sporangia originate within a single sorus in a mixed fashion, but they all mature at about the same time.

The gametophyte is well known for two species (Stokey and Atkinson, 1956b). The spores are slow to germinate but eventually produce a filament and then a plate of cells with an apical meristem. The latter comes to be situated in the notch of the cordate-elongate thallus. The mature gametophytic body has large wings and a thick cushion. The game-

tangia occur on both surfaces. The antheridia are relatively large and somewhat complex (Fig. 15–28, *F*). The archegonia produce four neck canal cells (Fig. 15–28, *E*), and an incomplete jacket occurs around the venter. Some small cells are cut off on the inside of the neck cells and appear very similar to those in this position in the Schizaeaceae.

The embryo is undescribed.

The Plagiogyriaceae was considered by Bower to partly bridge the morphological gap between the Osmundaceae and certain less primitive ferns. His views were influenced by the structure of the stem, which is similar to that of certain Osmundaceae that have internal phloem; the open dichotomous venation; sporangia occurring along veins; the small-tree-like habit; the expanded petiole bases; and the oblique annulus. The family in many more features, including some of the same ones suggesting linkage to the Osmundaceae, suggests a relationship to the base of the pteridaceous-cyatheaceous line and to the Schizaeaceae. Although the opinion is expressed here and also by others [e.g., Pichi-Sermolli (1958)] that the Osmundaceae is the specialized end of a line, the interpretation, as most interpretations expressed in this text, is subject to modification and must accommodate new information and new arguments that are put forth.

Cyatheaceae

The Cyatheaceae as considered here includes the following genera, with species numbers indicated parenthetically: *Lophosoria* (1), *Metaxya* (1), *Thyrsopteris* (1), *Dicksonia* (about 25), *Cystodium* (1), *Cibotium* (about 10), *Culcita* (9), *Cyathea* (about 800), *Cnemidaria* 24), *Saccoloma* (1), *Orthiopteris* (about 9), *Dennstaedtia* (about 70), and *Hypolepis* (about 45). This familial composition is in close agreement with the interpretations expressed by Holttum and Sen (1961) except that the dennstaedtioids (the last four genera mentioned) were excluded by these authors. They admitted evidence of a relationship between the dennstaedtioids and the other genera (the tree ferns), and therefore their inclusion here is considered only a relative deviation in interpretation and not an absolute one. Bower

FIGURE 15–29. *Cyathea* growing in Fiji.

(1923) included the dennstaedtioids in the Dicksoniaceae. His Cyatheaceae included the equivalent of the *Cyathea* and *Cnemidaria*.

Within the assemblage of genera, *Cyathea* (Fig. 15–29), *Dicksonia*, and *Thyrsopteris* are distinctly arborescent, with the first attaining a maximum height of possibly 25 m. The genera *Cystodium* and *Cnemidaria* are similar to the above ones but so short that the term "tree" is hardly applicable. *Cibotium*, *Culcita*, and *Lophosoria* bear massive stems that are in part prostrate and in part upright. *Metaxya* is essentially prostrate, but its stem is similarly massive. The four dennstaedtioid genera all have creeping rhizomes, most with a diameter of 0.5 to 2 cm. The entire Cyatheaceae is characterized by relatively large bi- to quadripinnate leaves. Rarely the leaf is simple. Throughout, the family branching is rarely dichotomous and frequently lateral. Epipetiolar branches (Troop and Mickel, 1968) are produced in *Dennstaedtia*, *Hypolepis* (see Fig. 16–11, *C*), *Lophosoria*, *Cyathea* (*C. mexicana*), and occasionally in *Dicksonia* and *Metaxya*.

Throughout the Cyatheaceae, stem steles range from simple solenosteles (undissected, amphiphloic siphonosteles) with nonoverlapping leaf gaps, to dictyosteles with overlapping leaf gaps, to more complex polycyclic types. Most of the dennstaedtioids show the simple solenostele with simple, short leaf gaps (often somewhat lateral to leaf-trace attachment). Within the genus *Dennstaedtia* there are occasionally two concentric steles and an occasional stelar perforation (a gap not associated with leaf-trace departure). *Saccoloma* illustrates greater complexity, with as many as three concentric steles. Among these genera, the branch trace is occasionally attached to the leaf trace.

Among the dicksoniads both runners and upright stems occur on the same plant. The runners are uniformly solenostelic or show slight dissection. *Thyrsopteris* occasionally shows an additional pith strand. The upright stems show dissected, amphiphloic siphonosteles with *Thyrsopteris* again showing additional medulary strands, but here in a ring.

The upright stem of *Dicksonia* has a dictyostele with relatively short leaf gaps. Its stelar outline is highly irregular, both on the inside and outside, and is described as corrugated. Massive sclerenchymatous sheaths appear internal and external to the vascular tissues. There are no medullary bundles. Leaf traces in dicksoniads are simple but large and often have infolded margins. The trace breaks up soon after leaving the cauline stele.

The cyatheoids, *Cyathea* (including *Alsophila* and *Hemitelia* following Copeland, 1947) and *Cnemidaria*, show dictyostely in their trunks with a number of additional vascular bundles in the pith and in the cortex (Fig. 15–31, *B*). The cortical bundles are absent in some species. The vascular system of the leaf is multiple at its origin on the stele and individual traces arise at different vertical levels. usually many associated with a major gap (Fig, 15–31, *B*). Masses of sclerenchyma delimit the major cauline strands.

The genera *Lophosoria* and *Metaxya* have often been separated at the family level as the Lophosoriaceae or the Protocyatheaceae, and it is possible that plants similar to them gave

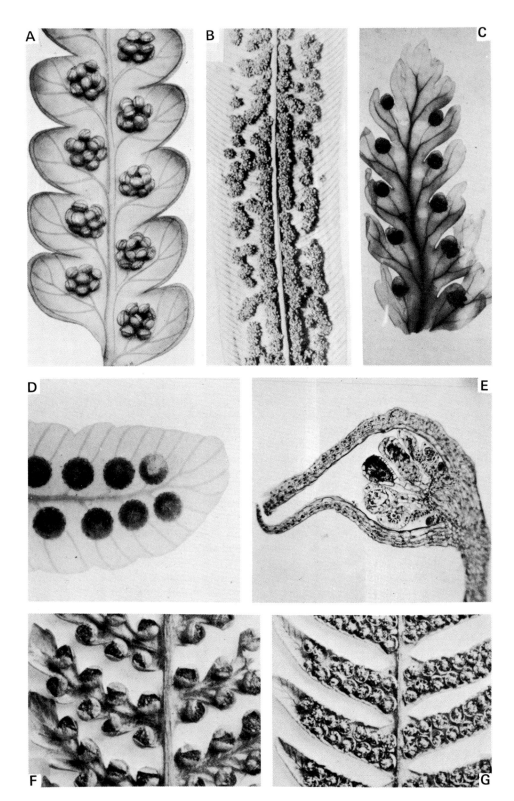

FIGURE 15–30. *A.* Portion of a fertile frond of *Lophosoria druinata*, after Bower (1912). *B.* Portion of a fertile frond of *Metaxya*, after Bower (1912). *C.* Portion of a fertile frond of *Dennstaedtia adiantoides*. *D.* Portion of a fertile frond of *Cyathea* sp. *E.* Longitudinal section through the sorus of *Dennstaedtia adiantoides*. *F.* Portion of the fertile frond of *Dicksonia navarrensis*, after Maxon (1911). *G.* Portion of the fertile frond of *Cyathea arborea*, after Maxon (1911).

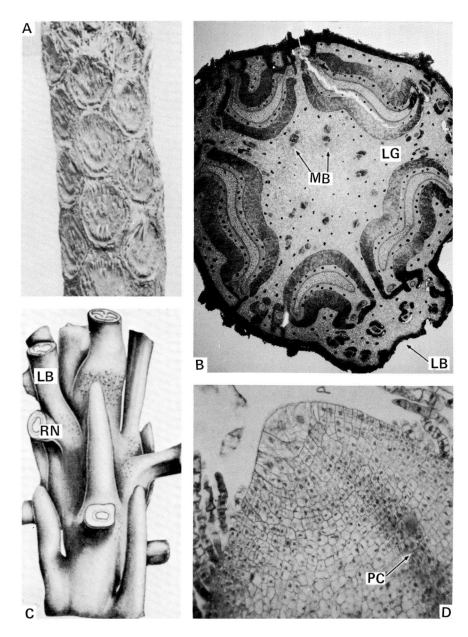

FIGURE 15–31. *A.* Surface view of the trunk of *Cyathea arborea*, after Maxon (1911). *B.* Cross section of the stem of *Cyathea* (*Alsophila*) sp.   *C.* Portion of the stem with the bases of its appendages in *Lophosoria pruinata*, after Bower (1912). LB = leaf base; RN = runner. *D.* Apex of a young leaf in *Cibotium*. PC = procambium.

rise to the dicksoniads, the cyatheoids, and the dennstaedioids. *Lophosoria* has a runner of simple solenostelic construction (RN in Fig. 15–31, *C*) that originates on the upright stem in connection with a leaf base (LB). The up-right stem varies from simple solenostelic to near dictyostelic. The leaf trace is simple. *Metaxya*, which has a creeping stem, also shows solenostely and no medulary strands and a simple leaf trace. Petiolar anatomy and

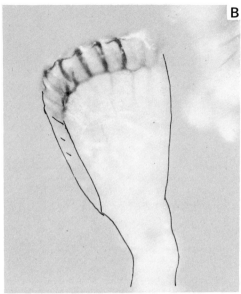

FIGURE 15–32. Sporangia of *Cyathea* sp.

pinna-trace origin in *Lophosoria* and *Metaxya* are particularly gleichenioid according to Bower.

The trunks of *Cyathea* appear columnar and have a thick buttress or gradual thickening toward the base. In cross sections, however, it is seen that the stem proper is very small at the base and increases toward the apex. The difference in trunk diameter is made up by a massive mantle of adventitious roots, which to a large extent supports the body. At the base of the trunk the stem is protostelic, then solenostelic; higher up the characteristic complexities appear. The vascular supplies to the first leaves are simple and become progressively more complex in successive leaves.

Many of the Cyatheaceae show epidermal appendages as simple hairs, with scales appearing in some dennstaedtioids and all cyatheoids. Venation is predominantly open dichotomous, with an occasional one showing some anastomoses.

The sporangia of the Cyatheaceae are generally grouped upon a circular, flattish, or slightly elevated receptacle (Fig. 15–30, *E*). Greatest receptacular elevation occurs in some species of *Cyathea*, where a short column may develop. Sori are rarely elongate and in part confluent (Fig. 15–30, *B*). Soral position is

marginal or submarginal in dennstaedtioids (Fig. 15–30, *C*); on the abaxial surface (the condition interpreted as primitive within the family) in cyatheoids (Fig. 15–30, *D*, *G*), in *Metaxya* (Fig. 15–30, *B*), and in *Lophosoria* (Fig. 15–30, *A*); and marginal in dicksonioids (Fig. 15–30, *F*). In the dicksonioid genus *Thyrsopteris* the sori appear on unlaminated parts of the frond and thus appear terminal on the axislike entities. In all cases in the family, the sori are either on or at the ends of veins. Sporangial maturation within individual sori is more or less simultaneous in *Lophosoria* and *Metaxya*, basipetally gradate to a greater or lesser degree throughout the dicksonioids, and mixed in the dennstaedtioids.

Bower (1913) reported that in *Thyrsopteris*, *Dicksonia*, *Saccoloma*, and *Odontosoria* the receptacle of the sorus was directly derived from the marginal initials of the pinnule and that both valves of the indusium were submarginal in origin. Holttum and Sen (1961) reported near-marginal origin of the sorus in *Dicksonia*, *Cyathea*, and *Cibotium*, with early stages of one strongly suggesting the others. They described and more completely and accurately illustrated the receptacle proper as submarginal in origin. The true indusial flap appears on the lower surface on the side of

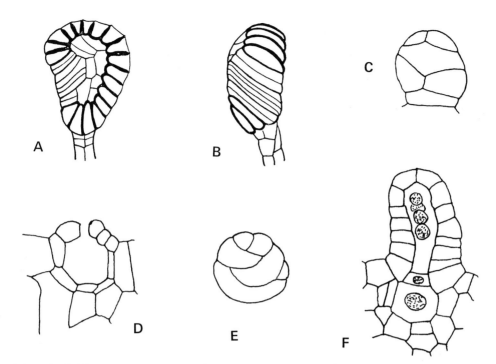

FIGURE 15–33. *A, B*. Sporangia of *Cyathea capensis*, after Bower (1926). *C*. Antheridium of *Lophosoria quadripinnata*. *D, E*. Antheridia of *Lophosoria quadripinnata*. *F*. Archegonium of *Cyathea dealbata*. *C* to *F* after Stokey (1930).

the receptacle away from the leaf margin proper. The latter, which is more massive than the indusium from the beginning, continues as leaf margin in *Cyathea* but develops as the outer flap of the sorus in *Dicksonia* and in *Cibotium*.

The indusium is absent in *Metaxya* and *Lophosoria*, presumably primitively so, and in some species of *Cyathea*, presumably by derivation. In the cyatheoids, the basic condition seems to be a single flap grown up from the base and on one side of the sorus. Holttum and Sen (1961) have described a complete reduction series from this *Hemitelia* type to the exindusiate condition in *Cyathea*. They describe another specialization series that involves a circumferential extension of the line of attachment of the indusium leading to the *Cyathea javanica* type of indusium, which is cup-shaped. In some *Cyathea* species the cup is open at the top only by a small pore and it tears and shrinks at maturity. The two-lipped indusium is common in the family (Fig. 15–30, *F*), occurring through the dicksonioids and denn-

staedtioids. The inner lip is generally interpreted as the true indusium, while the outer one is clearly a part of the leaf margin in many species and interpreted as such in others (see Holttum and Sen, 1961). In some species the two lips or valves are united to a degree. *Thyrsopteris* shows the two free of each other only in early stages of ontogeny; later there is a symmetrical cup. The cup-shaped indusium seems, therefore, to have been independently derived, and by different morphological pathways, in the cyatheoids and in the dicksonioids.

The sporangia throughout the Cyatheaceae all seem to be relatively minor variations of a simple type, one which is moderately large, has an oblique and uninterrupted (by the stalk) annulus, and some degree of stomial-cell differentiation (Fig. 15–32, *A, B*; Fig. 15–33, *A, B*). All the dennstaedtioids show an interrupted annulus, a condition also appearing to a variable degree in the dicksonioid *Cibotium*. Spores throughout the family are trilete.

The gametophytes of the Cyatheaceae are all green, surface living, and cordate. Those of

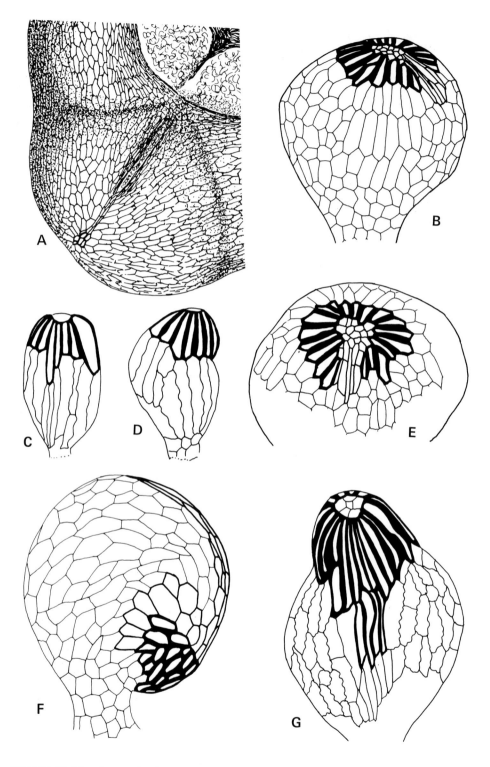

FIGURE 15–34. Sporangia of various ferns. *A. Psilotum nudum. B, E. Mohria caffrorum. C, D. Actinostachys oligostachys. F. Osmunda cinnamomea. G. Schizaea dichotoma.*

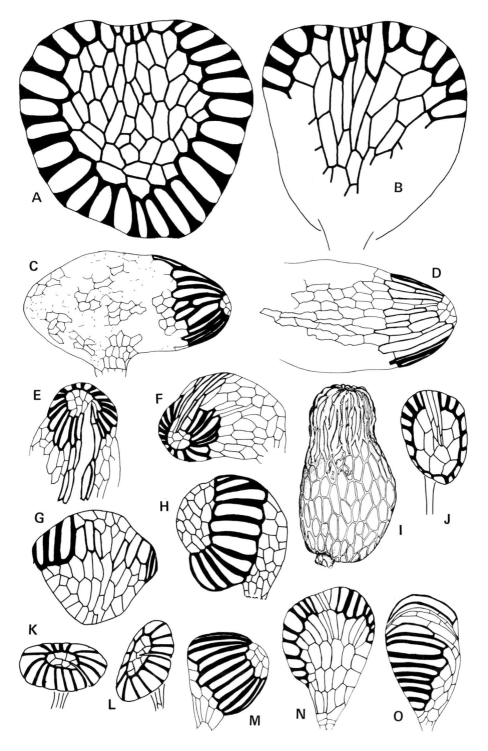

FIGURE 15–35. Sporangia of various ferns. *A, B. Stromatopteris moniliformis. C, D. Lygodium reticulatum. E, F. Anemia phyllitidis. G, H. Gleichenia caudata. I. Seftenbergia ophiodermatica,* after Radforth (1937). *J. Actinostachys oligostachys,* sporangium borne on gametophyte. *K, L. Stromatopteris moniliformis,* sporangia borne on underground axis. *M. Gleichenia brackenridgi. N, O. G. linearis.*

the cyatheoids and *Lophosoria* are somewhat massive, with thicker cushions than those of more advanced ferns but comparable to the Gleicheniaceae. The comparison extends also to the relatively complex antheridia (Fig. 15–33, *C*, *E*). A rare sunken antheridium has been described (Fig. 15–33, *D*). Within the cyatheoids there is a conspicuous range in variation in antheridia (see Stokey, 1930), often in the same species, with some nearly as simple as the "higher fern type." In the latter, characteristically the spermatogenous tissue is delimited by three cells: a basal, funnel-shaped cell; a ring cell; and a cap cell. Several species of cyatheoids and *Lophosoria* are known in which the gametophytic apex develops initially sub-

apically. Archegonia frequently have a neck canal cell with as many as four nuclei (Fig. 15–33, *F*).

The gametophytes of the dennstaedtioids, not many of which are known, are more delicate, with thinner cushions. Antheridia are mostly of the simpler type. Archegonia rarely show more than two nuclei in the neck canal cell (see Chapter 16).

The points of comparison having been made, it seems most reasonable to interpret the Cyatheaceae as a derivative from primitive gleicheniaceous stock or from a line in the vague area of convergence of the Stromatopteridace, Gleichenicacae, and the Schizaeaceae, as indicated in Fig. 16–24.

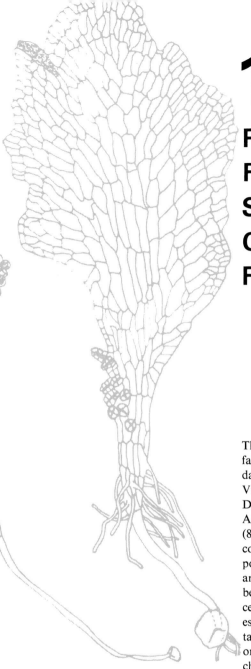

16

Relatively Advanced Filicales; Some General Considerations of Filicalean Ferns

The filicaleans so far not considered (see Table 16–1) fall into the families Platyzomaceae (1 gen.), Dipteridaceae (1 gen.), Polypodiaceae (about 55 gen.), Vittariaceae (9 gen.), Pteridaceae (about 55 gen.), Davalliaceae (12 gen.), Aspidiaceae (about 66 gen.), Aspleniaceae (9 gen.), Parkeriaceae (1 gen.), Blechnaceae (8 gen.), and Hymenophyllopsidaceae (1 gen.). These constitute a very heterogeneous and, most probably, polyphyletic assemblage of possibly 6,500 species and are considered here in a rather broad sense. These might be referred to as the "higher homosporous ferns," but certainly it should be pointed out that certain of these, especially the Platyzomaceae, Dipteridaceae, and certain Pteridaceae, are in many respects more primitive or generalized than genera considered in the previous chapter. Although the dennstaedtioids were included and briefly described under the Cyatheaceae, vegetatively and reproductively they are quite advanced and are used in the present chapter to illustrate certain points. In actuality, the separation at the family level of the dennstaedtioids, as well as the rest of the Cyatheaceae from the Pteridaceae, is difficult to defend.

In habit and habitat the higher Filicales are quite varied. Although most grow in habitats that are somewhat more humid than common mesic sites, a few are xerophytic (e.g., *Woodsia*) and *Ceratopteris* is a hydro-

TABLE 16—1. Systems of fern classification. The order of listing of orders and families in Pichi-Sermolli's system has been changed to facilitate diagrammatic comparison with the system followed in this text.

Copeland (1947)		Engler and Diels (1936)			Pichi-Sermolli (1958 and more recent modifications)			Bierhorst (present text)	
Order	Family	Subclass	Order	Family	Subclass	Order	Family	Order	Family
Filicales	Osmundaceae	Osmundidae	Osmundales	Osmundaceae	Osmundidae	Osmundales	Osmundaceae	Filicales	Psilotaceae
	Schizaeaceae	Leptosporangiatae	Filicales	Schizaeaceae	Filicidae	Gleicheniales	Gleicheniaceae		Stromatopteridaceae
	Gleicheniaceae			Gleicheniaceae		Schizaeales	Schizaeaceae		Gleicheniaceae
	Loxsomaceae			Matoniaceae		Hymenophyllales	Hymenophyllaceae		Schizaeaceae
	Hymenophyllaceae			Dipteridaceae		Matoniales	Matoniaceae		Anemiaceae
	Pteridaceae			Hymenophyllaceae		Platyzomales	Platyzomaceae		Lygodiaceae
	Parkeriaceae			Hymenophyllopsidaceae		Polypodiales	Dipteridaceae		Osmundaceae
	Hymenophyllopsidaceae			Loxsomaceae			Cheiropleuriaceae		Hymenophyllaceae
	Davalliaceae			Protocyatheaceae			Grammitidaceae		Matoniaceae
	Plagiogyriaceae			Dicksoniaceae			Polypodiaceae		Platyzomaceae
	Cyatheaceae			Cyatheaceae		Cyatheales	Cyatheaceae		Dipteridaceae
	Aspidiaceae			Polypodiaceae			Lophosoriaceae		Cheiropleuriaceae
	Blechnaceae			Subfamily:		Dicksoniales	Dicksoniaceae		Polypodiaceae
	Aspleniaceae			Dennstaedtioideae			Dennstaedtiaceae		Vittariaceae
	Matoniaceae			Lindsayoideae			Lindsaeaceae		Cyatheaceae
	Polypodiaceae			Davallioideae		Pteridales	Pteridaceae		Pteridaceae
	Vittariaceae			Oleandroideae			Negripteridaceae		Parkeriaceae
	Marsileaceae			Pteroideae			Sinopteridaceae		Davalliaceae
	Salviniaceae			Gymnogrammoideae			Cryptogrammaceae		Aspleniaceae
				Onocleoideae			Gymnogrammaceae		Aspidiaceae
				Blechnoideae			Actinopteridaceae		Blechnaceae
				Asplenioideae			Adiantaceae		Hymenophyllopsidaceae
				Dryopteroideae			Parkeriaceae		Loxsomaceae
				Polypodioideae			Vittariaceae		Plagiogyriaceae
				Elaphoglossoideae		Davalliales	Davalliaceae		
				Parkeraceae			Oleandraceae		
				Marsileaceae		Aspidiales	Aspleniaceae		
				Salviniaceae			Thelypteridaceae		
							Athyriaceae		
							Aspidiaceae		
							Lomariopsidaceae		
						Blechnales	Blechnaceae		
						Loxsomales	Loxsomaceae		
						Plagiogyriales	Plagiogyriaceae		
						Hymenophyllopsidales	Hymenophyllopsidaceae		
		Marsileales	Marsileaceae		Marsileidae	Marsileales	Marsileaceae	Marsileales	Marsileaceae
		Salviniales	Salviniaceae		Salviniidae	Salviniales	Salviniaceae	Salviniales	Salviniaceae
							Azollaceae		Azollaceae

phyte. The great majority grow in tropical and temperate regions, but a few extend to subarctic regions. Many, possibly the majority, of the higher ferns are low-growing terrestrial forms with creeping to upright stems. Epiphytism is illustrated by hundreds of species (e.g., most Polypodiaceae, some Davalliaceae, and some Aspleniaceae). In addition to the ferns that are commonly called the "tree ferns" covered in Chapter 15 and some Osmundaceae, a few trees are known in other families (e.g., some species of *Blechnum* and *Diplazium*). Many others, however, bear short, upright stems with a crown of leaves (e.g., species of *Dryopteris*, which differ from "trees" in ways not morphologically significant). Many of the epiphytes appear lianalike, with long creeping stems attached usually by adventitious roots (e.g., species of *Stenochlaena*). Epiphytes occasionally bear specialized, shield leaves that may only be parts of ordinary leaves and form a nest capable of accumulating masses of organic matter. They thus grow in a perched flowerpot of their own making.

Dichotomous branching of stems has been reported to occur among higher ferns rarely or commonly in *Lindsaea*, *Pellaea*, *Davallia*, *Dryopteris*, *Polypodium*, and *Pteridium*. Most others show lateral branching in no definite relation to leaf insertion or from superaxillary positions that may be shifted slightly to one side of a line extended apically from a leaf insertion. This is an area in which many more accurate descriptions are needed.

Branches from epipetiolar buds, in addition to occurring in several dennstaedtioids and tree ferns previously mentioned, are present in *Pteridium*, *Pteris*, *Histiopteris*, and, subject to interpretation, in the Psilotaceae and Stromatopteridaceae. Buds of a somewhat different nature occur on blades, leaf axes, or leaf tips of species of *Asplenium*, *Diplazium* (Fig. 16–1, *C*), *Woodwardia*, *Camptosorus*, *Adiantum*, and many others (McVeigh, 1937). In these the buds are more of the nature of vegetative reproductive bodies. In some they actually fall to the ground and grow (e.g., *Asplenium bulbiferum*), in others they produce a new plant only when they and their parental organ touch the substratum, as those at the tips of leaves in *Camptosorus*.

Leaf form among higher ferns is highly varied (see Tryon, 1964). The range is from simple and entire (Fig. 16–1, *A*) or variously lobed (Fig. 16–1, *B*) to highly compound in many common ferns. Certain individual genera such as *Polypodium* and *Adiantum* show much of the entire range in leaf forms. Dichotomous branching is very common on small leaves produced by young plants and occasionally on ones formed later. The bifurcate patterns are occasionally quite clearly defined, but in many leaf forms they grade imperceptibly into or are not clearly defined from pinnate patterns (Fig. 16–1, *B*; Fig. 16–2, *A*). Figure 16–1, *D* shows part of a leaf from a cultivated mutant form of *Nephrolepis*, the Boston fern, with a regular pattern of bifurcations in the pinnae. In the common form of the species, the pinnae are unbranched. In view of information available on frond development in *Psilotum nudum* and *Schizaea dichotoma*, it can be suggested that pinnate and dichotomous branching differ from each other only in a relative way, and, in heterogeneous taxa of ferns where one pattern occurs, the other may be expected now and again. Despite the inference that the branching character is of lesser morphological importance than previously assumed, it seems that among filicalean ferns in general, the pinnate pattern is the primitive one, being predominant in all presumed primitive families (i.e., Psilotaceae, Stromatopteridaceae, Gleicheniaceae, Schizaeaceae, and Osmundaceae). This conclusion has also been reached by Wagner (1952) and by R. Tryon (1964) in consideration of rather broad samples of ferns. It must be emphasized that the conclusion applies only within the Filicales, for if attention is extended back to possible ancestral groups such as the Trimerophytaceae, it might well be reversed.

Leaf dimorphism (i.e., gross differences between purely vegetative and sporangium-bearing leaves or parts is highly polyphyletic. Both complete and partial dimorphism occur in most of the families. Series leading to complete dimorphism may be recognized within the Polypodiaceae, Blechnaceae, Vittariaceae, and Aspidiaceae, for example. In the last family, one can recognize all degrees of lamina supression on fertile leaves and in the genus *Onoclea*, the remainder of the lamina becomes wrapped around the sori such that the entire fertile frond appears as a bunch of grapes.

FIGURE 16–1. *A. Polypodium piloselloides*, creeping stem with simple leaves borne on short lateral branches. *B.* Frond of *Doryopteris pedata*. *C.* Part of a frond of *Diplasium prolifera* with adventitious plantlets arising on the rachis. *D.* Mutant form of *Nephrolepis exaltata*, showing dichotomously branched pinnae.

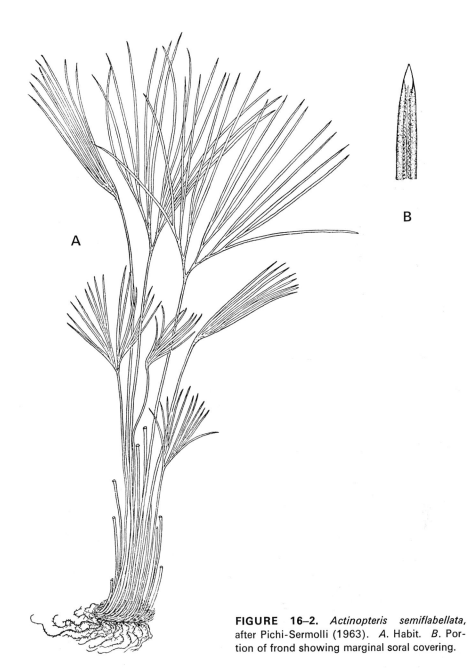

A

B

FIGURE 16–2. *Actinopteris semiflabellata,* after Pichi-Sermolli (1963). *A.* Habit. *B.* Portion of frond showing marginal soral covering.

In essentially all primitive Filicales, as well as in nearly all other nonflowering plants, if veins branch, they do so dichotomously. Although one can argue that in certain instances (e.g., petals and leaves of certain angiosperms) dichotomous venation is derived by reduction, in most cases it is truly primitive. In higher ferns a variety of reticulate vein patterns has arisen (Fig. 16–12, *C*; Fig. 16–13, *A*) and the types are often characteristic of generic groupings. A wide range of venation patterns is illustrated and discussed by Dickason (1946). Dichotomous venation in ferns is often associated with definite centers of meristematic activity within a marginal meristem (Hagemann, 1965), while in other ferns it is apparently not (Hara, 1962). Some reticulate patterns seem the result of fusions within a dichotomous system [e.g., *Onoclea* (Hara, 1964)]. This is not so, or doubtfully so, in others.

Well-defined roots are present in essentially all Filicales, the only exceptions being the Psilotaceae and certain Hymenophyllaceae. *Salvinia*, a presumed filicalean derivative and here ordinally separated, is also rootless. All filicalean roots are calyptrate and grow by means of a single apical cell (Fig. 16–3, *A*). They bear hairs that, with rare exceptions, are nonseptate, develop dark resistant walls, and persist on older parts of the organ. In some of the nest-building epiphytes, it is the persistent root hairs that make up a large part of the enclosed "substratum." Fern roots are all exarch and bear two to four protoxylem points. The cortex is commonly in part sclerenchymatous (Fig. 16–3, *B*) but not always (Fig. 16–3, *C*). Endodermal cells are frequently very narrow (Fig. 16–3, *D*; this is not a thickened cell wall; the entire endodermal cell is darkly stained). Pericyclic cells are characteristically enlarged. Much of the cortex in older fern roots is often composed of pseudoperiderm (i.e., the cells of this primary tissue develop suberized walls and then loose their contents and thus assume the characteristics of true cork; Fig. 16–3, *B*, outer cortex). Branch roots are typically of pericyclic origin. The adventitious roots that grow from other organs are in general deep-seated in origin, often arising in the pericycle or in this general region before differentiation. The origin is occasionally cortical and may even be in the outermost layer of the cortex [e.g., *Ceratopteris* (Lachmann, 1906)]. In this genus the epidermis expands mitotically and contributes to root-cap tissue. McVeigh (1937) lists seven genera and 16 species of higher Filicales reported to produce stems from roots.

Vascular systems in stems of higher ferns range from protosteles (e.g., *Lindsaea*; Fig. 16–7, *A*) and some of its close allies to simple amphiphloic siphonosteles [i.e., solenosteles, e.g., some dennstaedtioids (Fig. 16–7, *C*; Fig. 16–11, *E*), *Adiantum* (Fig, 16–10, *A*), and some others of the Pteridaceae] to dictyosteles with amphicribral bundles in the majority of higher ferns (Fig. 16–9, *A*, *C*, *D*; Fig. 16–10, *C*). Protosteles occasionally occur in thin runners

in species that have more complex steles in larger stems (Fig. 16–7, *B*). Some authors have elected to refer to dictyostelic types as polystelic and each bundle as a meristele because of the histological completeness and essential radial symmetry of the bundles. The entire stelar organization is occasionally bilateral [e.g., *Pteridium* (Fig. 16–8, *A*) and some other Pteridaceae, some Aspidiaceae, and some Polypodiaceae]. The maturation pattern of the primary xylem is mesarch in many genera (Fig. 16–8, *B*; Fig. 16–7, *D*). In the runner of *Nephrolepsis* (Fig. 16–7, *B*) it is exarch, but it is mesarch in larger stems of the species. The initial pole of primary xylem maturation in many genera is on the margins of the ribbon-form xylem mass of a given bundle, such that maturation proceeds in one direction from each pole and parallel to the circumference of the stele (Fig. 16–8, *E*; Fig. 16–9, *B*). This is neither exarchy, endarchy, nor mesarchy in the usual sense but seems to be derived from the latter by some modification. Pericycle is generally conspicuous (PC in Fig. 16–8, *E*) and the endodermal cells are narrow (EN) as in the roots. In several families, the inner tangential walls of the cells of the ground tissue adjacent to the endodermis are conspicuously thickened (W in Fig. 16–8, *E*; Fig. 16–9, *B*) Tyloses in the protoxylem occur in probably all higher fern families (Fig. 16–8, *D*; Fig. 27–8, *Y*), where they often form a pseudoparenchymatous mass.

A relatively simple protostele with or without a degree of medullation is assumed to be ancestral to the more elaborate steles of the Filicales. The most primitive type is closely approximated in the Psilotaceae, Stromatopteridaceae, Gleicheniaceae, some Osmundaceae, Schizaeaceae, Hymenophyllaceae, Lygodiaceae, and some Pteridaceae (e.g., *Lindsaea*). The *first stage* in specialization might be assumed to involve a sharper differentiation of the pith (i.e., a loss of medulary tracheids), as observed in some Osmundaceae, to some extent in the Psilotaceae, and in the Schizaeaceae. The *second stage* in specialization may be the differentiation of a small and variable amount of internal phloem with or without an internal endodermis. This stage can be observed in some Schizaeaceae and in some Osmundaceae, although the living representatives of the latter may have steles reduced from

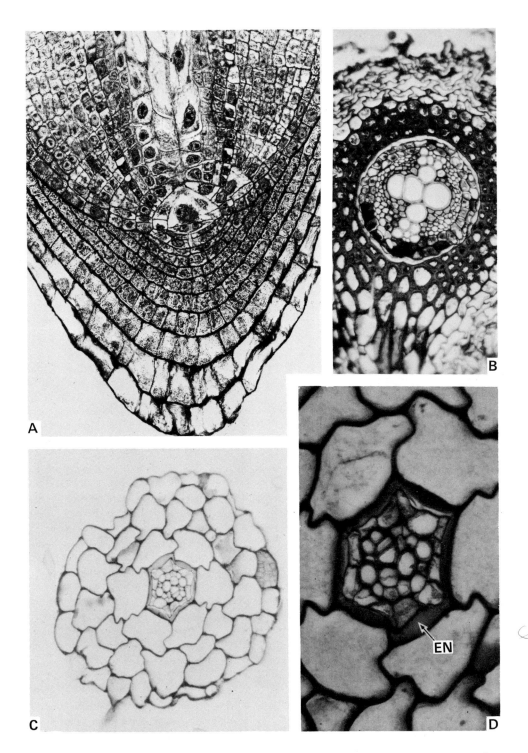

FIGURE16–3. *A*. Longitudinal section of the root tip of *Dennstaedtia adiantoides*. *B*. Cross section of a root of *Blechnum* sp. *C*. Cross section of a root of *Cryptogramma stelleri*. *D*. Portion of *C* enlarged. EN = endodermis.

Relatively Advanced Filicales **297**

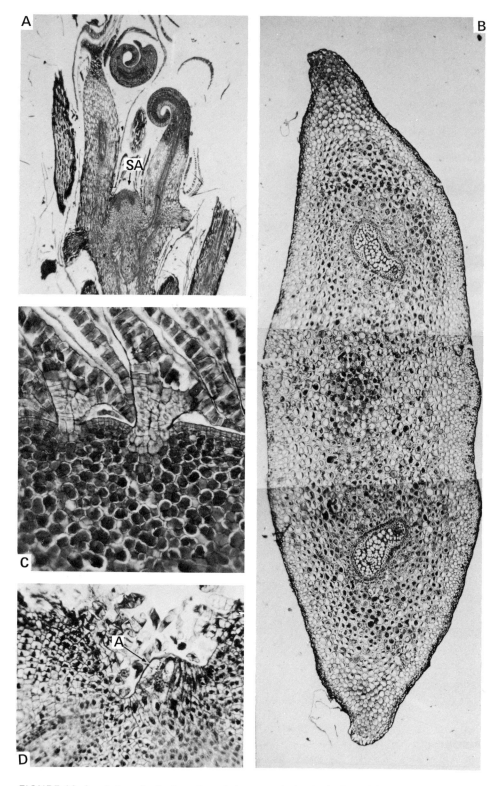

FIGURE 16–4. *A*. Longitudinal section of the stem tip in *Asplenium viride*. SA = shoot apex.
B. Cross section of the petiole of *Onoclea sensibilis*. *C*. Scales on the surface of the rhizome of
Davallia fijiensis. *D*. Sunken stem apex of *Pteridium aquilinum* in longitudinal section.

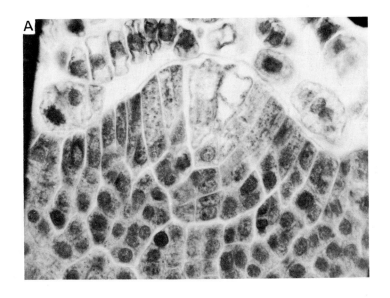

A

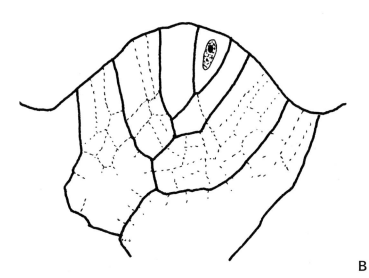

B

FIGURE 16–5. Stem apex of *Polypodium peroussum* in longitudinal section. *B* is an outline drawing of part of *A*.

well-defined solenosteles. The two stages are modified to various degrees by the basipetal encroachment of parenchyma enclosed within the leaf trace, as we observe in the fossil Osmundaceae, in the Gleicheniaceae, or in *Lindsaea* (Pteridaceae). Somewhere in the transition from the first stage to the second stage or in some lines well into the second stage is the modification of the procambium such that the pith becomes ontogenetically derived from isodiametric meristematic cells. In the Osmundaceae the procambium may have been so modified at a stage in specialization even below the second stage. At the *third stage* in specialization we observe a solenostele with a complete layer of internal and external phloem and endodermis and with well-defined leaf gaps (Fig. 16–10, *A*; Fig. 16–11, *D*, *E*). If the gaps

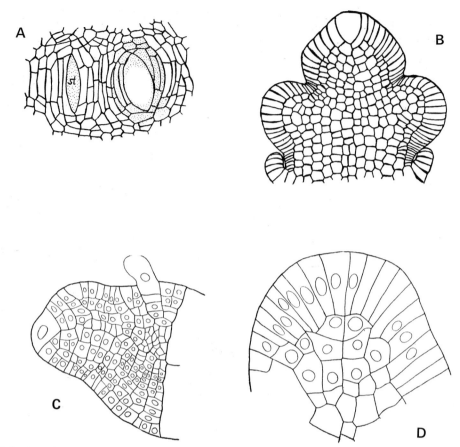

FIGURE 16–6. *A.* Apical cell of the stem, st, and that of a young leaf to its left as seen from the surface of *Pteridium aquilinum,* after Klein (1884). *B.* Tip of a growing frond of *Ceratopteris,* after Bower (1923). *C, D.* Two longitudinal views of the frond apex of *Dennstaedtia punctilobula,* after Conrad (1908).

overlap, the stele is a dictyostele. The third stage appears in varying expression in the Cyatheaceae, Pteridaceae, Anemiaceae, Platyzomaceae, Loxsomaceae, Plagiogyriaceae, Dipteridaceae, Davalliaceae, Aspleniaceae (Fig. 16–10, *B, D*), and Blechnaceae (Fig. 16–10, *C*). At the *fourth stage* in specialization a much finer and more obvious network of stelar strands is observed (Fig. 16–11, *F*), which is usually accompanied by the multiplication of leaf traces at their origin on the stele (Fig. 16–11, *B*), as seen in most Polypodiaceae. The traces are double in some Blechnaceae (Fig. 16–10, *C*) and Aspidiaceae (Fig. 16–4, *B,* seen in the petiole). Stelar perforations may appear at any stage from the second to the fourth. Polycyclic steles appear independently in

several filicalean lines and might be considered additional specializations at the third stage (e.g., *Matonia, Pteris,* and some dennstaedtioids) or the fourth [e.g., *Platycerium* (Polypodiaceae)]. Bilateral symmetry in the stele (Fig. 16–8, *A;* Fig. 16–11, *A, D*) is treated also as polyphyletic at different levels of stelar specialization.

The small stems of sporelings of most advanced ferns show protosteles (Fig. 16–23, *G*), and the progressively larger stems produced as the plant matures show progressive stelar elaboration until the limit in size and complexity for the species is attained. For a particular stelar form to differentiate, the maximum stem diameter and the particular upper size limit of a stem would be expected to vary, and with

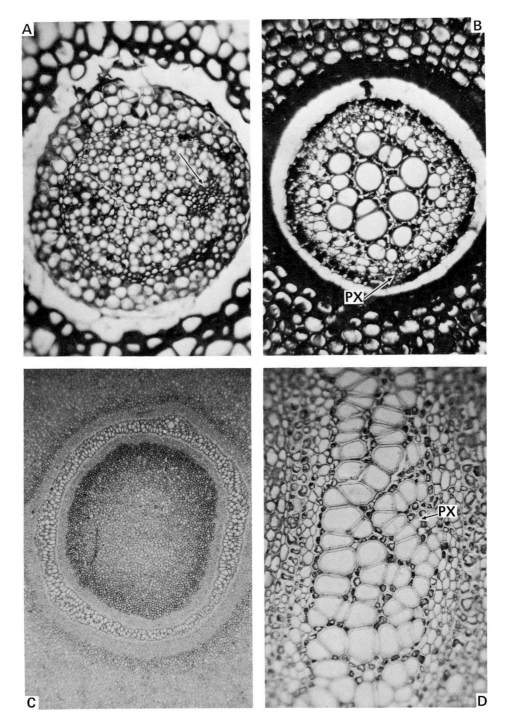

FIGURE 16–7. *A*. Cross section of the stem of *Lindsaya linnearis*. The arrow indicates the parenchymatous area, which extends into the petiole and some distance into the cauline stele. *B*. Cross section of the runner of *Nephrolepis exaltata*. One of the four protoxylem points is indicated. *C*. Cross section of the cauline stele of *Dennstaedtia adiantoides*. *D*. Portion of *C* enlarged. PX = protoxylem.

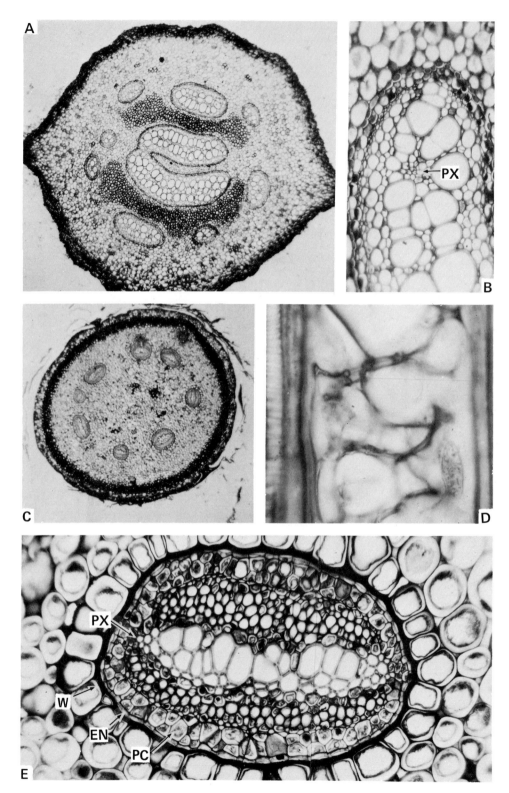

FIGURE 16–8. *A.* Cross section of the stem of *Pteridium aquilinum.* *B.* Portion of *A* enlarged.
C. Cross section of the stem of *Cyclophorus.* *D.* Longitudinal section through the protoxylem of
the stem of *Pteridium aquilinum* showing a mass of pseudoparenchyma. *E.* One bundle from *C*
enlarged. PX = protoxylem; W = thickened inner cell wall of ground parenchyma cells; EN =
endodermis; PC = pericycle.

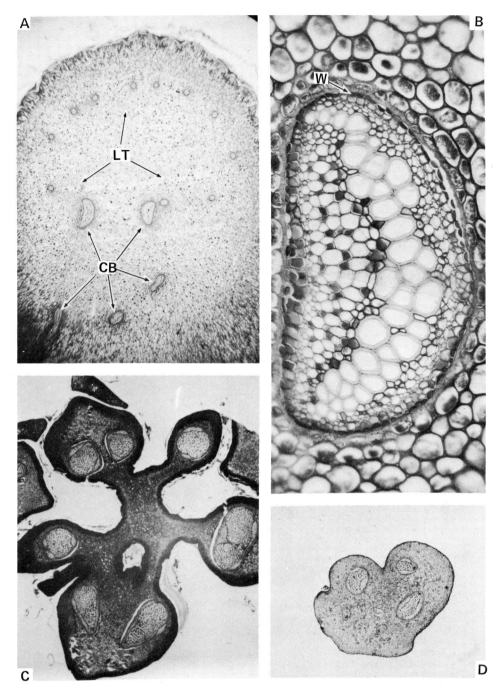

FIGURE 16–9. *A.* Cross section of the stem and leaf base in *Davallia fijiensis*. Eleven leaf traces, LT, are shown in a semicircle outside the ring of cauline bundles, CB. *B.* Single cauline bundle from *A* enlarged. W = the line of thickened cell walls on the inner sides of the limiting ground parenchyma cell layer. *C.* Cross section of the upright stem of *Matteuccia struthiopteris*. *D.* Cross section of the runner of *M. struthiopteris*.

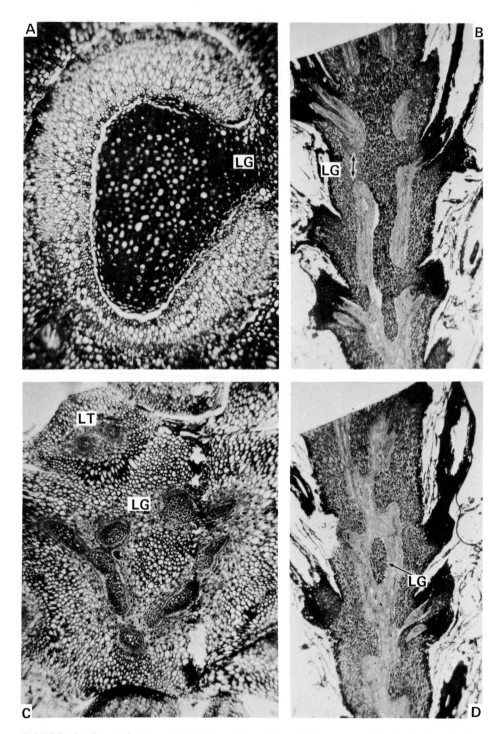

FIGURE 16–10. *A*. Cross section of the cauline stele of *Adiantum* sp. *B*. Radial longitudinal section of the stem of *Asplenium trichomanes*. *C*. Cross section of the stem of *Doodia maxima*. *D*. Longitudinal section of the stem of *Asplenium trichomanes*, showing the stele in tangential section. LG = leaf gap; LT = leaf trace.

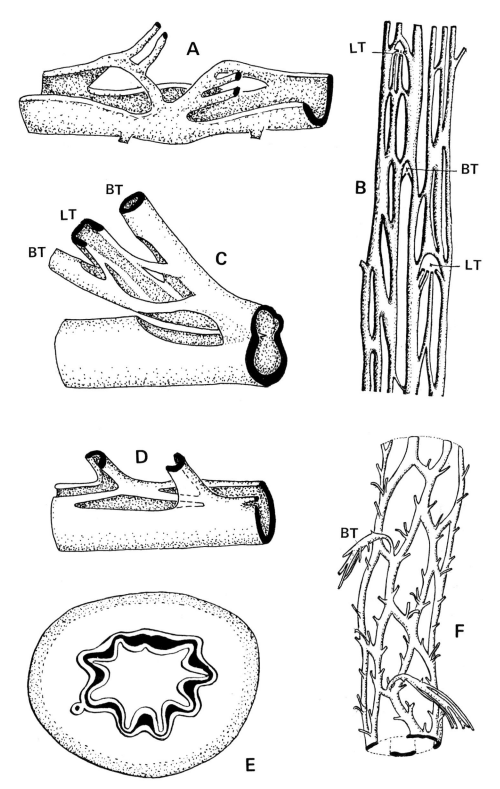

FIGURE 16–11. *A.* Stelar reconstruction of *Antrophyum lineatum*, redrawn from Williams (1927). *B.* Stele opened out and flattened in *Stenochlaena tenuifolia*, after Mettenius (1857). *C.* Reconstructed stele of *Hypolepis repens*, redrawn from Gwynne-Vaughan (1901). *D.* Reconstructed stele of *Pellaea rotundifolia*, redrawn from Gwynne-Vaughan (1901). *E.* Cross section of the stem of *Histiopteris incisa*, after Bower (1923). *F.* Reconstructed stele of *Aspidium cristatum*, after Sadebeck (1902). LT = leaf trace; BT = branch trace.

relatively little genetic change. If this is true, occasional reversions to more primitive types by mere reduction is expected.

Metaxylem elements of filicalean ferns (Bierhorst, 1960) show predominantly scalariform pitting. The pits are superimposed upon an overall cell pattern that is helical to slightly reticulate. The basic organization may be visualized by following pit rows around the cell or by overmacerating in a strong alkaline solution such that the wall breaks between adjacent pits of a row. In the early metaxylem elements, the pattern is generally easily observed, as the secondary wall between rows of pits is thicker than that between adjacent pits of a given row. The reticulate nature is expressed in varying degrees and is the result of forkings and anastomoses in the helical framework. The anastomoses are readily detected in elements formed later, since the rows of pits at these loci are disrupted (Fig. 27–9, S, center). The points of anastomosing within the helical framework are arranged with little regard for cell edges and faces, and therefore the pit rows are generally continued across the cell edges (i.e., they are predominantly *trans-edge opposite*). The individual pits commonly extend the entire width of a given face, which gives them their scalariform character on broad faces that are generally the tracheid to tracheid interfaces. Narrow faces are generally tracheid to parenchyma interfaces, and on them the pitting often approaches circular bordered (Fig. 27–9, S). Transverse rows of short pits on a single face occur sporadically and not constantly in species or even single cells. In early stages of ontogeny of the pitted elements a thin helical band appears (Fig. 27–9, Q). This is followed by deposition of second-order wall material between the gyres, which eventually comes to define bordered pits and obscure the initial helical organization of the element (Fig. 27–9, R, S). In occasional genera elongate pits assume varous orientations, even longitudinal on the cell (Fig. 27–8, Z).

Trans-edge opposite scalariform pitting seems the fundamental type within vascular plants and, in addition to occurring in filicalean ferns, occurs in the two orders of water ferns, in most lycopods and sphenopsids, and in many angiosperms. In *Lycopodium*, the Marattiales, to some extent in the Cycadales, and in a number of angiosperms the forkings within the basic cell framework tend to be in longitudinal rows along the cell edges, and therefore the pitting tends to be *trans-edge alternate*.

The first protoxylem elements to mature in filicalean organs that illustrate a degree of elongation proximal to the meristematic zone are generally annular-helical in organization (Fig. 27–8, U, V); those that mature later are helical-reticulate, then simple reticulate (Fig. 27–8, W, X). In organs showing little elongation (e.g., stems of *Osmunda*, *Schizaea*, and *Stromatopteris*, and some stems in the Psilotaceae) the first elements are often quite reticulate and the later ones scalariformly pitted.

True vessels occur in vegetative organs of *Pteridium*, where the perforation plates are scalariform. Secondary wall patterns on distinct end plates described in *Woodsia* and *Notholaena* (White, 1963) suggest that they also produce true vessels. In many other genera in several families there is some differentiation of pit groups at tracheid ends such that an end plate may be designated. True and well-defined vessels occur elsewhere in non-seed-bearing vascular plants in the genera *Marsilea, Equisetum*, and *Selaginella*.

Stem apices of all filicalean ferns grow by means of a single apical cell that varies as to its size and ratio of width to depth. It is often situated on an apical dome, much as are the apices of many flowering plants (Fig. 16–4, A), or it may be on a nipple at the bottom of an apical depression (Fig. 16–4, D). Segmentation patterns in apical cell derivatives are, in general, easily followed in section. Figure 16–5, B is a tracing of part of A, and the outlines of the cell packets traceable to lateral cell derivatives of the apical cell are heavily outlined. From the upper surface this apical cell appears triangular and is seen to produce segments on the three faces. In a few higher ferns the apical cell of the stem has only two cutting faces and is thus similar to that of the leaf (Fig. 16–6, A). The bilateral symmetry expressed in the apical cell is correlated with bilateral histology of the stem axis (Fig. 16–8, A).

Leaf apices of all higher ferns thus far described, even those with indeterminate leaves, have apical cells with two cutting faces, such as the right-hand apical cell in Fig. 16–6, A in

Pteridium. The apical cell of a leaf of *Ceratopteris* is shown in Fig. 16–6, *B*, which also shows the characteristic manner of origin of fern pinnae from the marginal series of cells proximal to the apical cell. Leaf marginal meristems show a line of cells (Fig. 16–6, *D*), a single one of which appears similar to an apical cell when cut in a section transverse to the plane of the blade (Fig. 16–6, *C*). Each cell of the marginal meristem thus has two cutting faces corresponding to its two narrow sides.

The first major line of filicalean ferns, consisting of the families Matoniaceae, Platyzomaceae, Cheiropleuriaceae, Dipteridaceae, and Polypodiaceae (Fig. 16–24), is considered here of monophyletic origin from early gleicheniaceous forms and to have given rise to no other known ferns. The sori throughout the group of families are mostly relatively small, on the abaxial surface, exindusiate, and circular in outline (Fig. 16–13, *A*; Fig. 16–12, *C*). Only in the Matoniaceae is an indusium developed. In some Polypodiaceae sunken sori, elongate sori, cenosori (large, compound sori), and even the acrosticoid condition exist. The latter condition is where sporangia, usually in great numbers, are scattered more or less uniformly on a surface and not in recognizable sori. Within the genus *Platycerium* there exists a series from the ordinary polypodiaceous sorus to the acrosticoid condition. The sorus in this line may be fundamentally marginal and through phylogenetic change shifted to the superficial position on the abaxial side. In the Gleicheniaceae, although the sori are superficial, they may be initiated marginally. There is contradictory information on this point in the literature (see Holttum and Sen, 1961) and it should be reinvestigated and photographically documented.

The families Matoniaceae, Platyzomaceae, Cheiropleuriaceae, and Dipteridaceae, although the known members of each are best considered isolated relicts, in many features seem to bridge the morphological gap between the advanced Polypodiaceae and the primitive Gleicheniaceae. Simultaneous maturation of sporangia in sori occurs in the Platyzomaceae and Matoniaceae, while mixed maturation occurs in the Polypodiaceae, Dipteridaceae, and Cheiropleuriaceae. Solenosteles occur in the Platyzomaceae, Dipteridaceae, and Cheiropleuriaceae; the protostele also is found in the latter. A polycyclic solenostele occurs in the Matoniaceae and a complex dictyostele in the Polypodiaceae. The annulus is interrupted in the Polypodiaceae and also, although in an unusual manner, in the Matoniaceae, while it is oblique and interrupted in the Platyzomaceae and the Cheiropleuriaceae. In the Dipteridaceae, it is either interrupted or uninterrupted (Fig. 16–15, *C*, *D*; Fig. 16–16, *A*, *B*). The spores are trilete in the Platyzomaceae, trilete to occasionally monolete in the Cheiropleuriaceae, and monolete in the Dipteridaceae and Polypodiaceae. The antheridium suggests gleichenioid complexity in the Matoniaceae, Dipteridaceae (Fig. 16–19, *A*, *B*), and Cheiropleuriaceae (Fig. 16–19, *C*, *D*), and to a lesser extent in *Grammitis* (Polypodiaceae) (Fig. 16–19, *E*, *G*). Most Polypodiaceae described show the spermatogenous tissue limited by a cap cell, a ring cell, and a proximal funnel-shaped cell. In addition to the characteristics mentioned, within this series of families there is a more or less definite progression from forms with hairs to forms with scales, from forms with dichotomous venation to forms with reticulative venation, and from terrestrial plants to epiphytes. It should be reasonably clear that this all points to the interpretation that the advanced Polypodiaceae carry a very primitive sorus which never in its phylogenetic history had an indusium.

The second major group of filicalean families consisting of the Pteridaceae, Cyatheaceae, Davalliaceae, Vittariaceae, Plagiogyriaceae, Hymenophyllopsidaceae, Blechnaceae, Aspidiaceae, Aspleniaceae, and Parkeriaceae (Fig. 16–24), suggests itself to represent a major monophyletic assemblage derived from primitive forms separate from the series discussed above. Within this assemblage, there is a broad range in morphology, but, with a minimum of unsupported speculation, the relatively advanced families may all be derived from primitive pteridaceous forms or from hypothetical forms combining features of primitive cyatheaceous and pteridaceous ones. The assemblage as a whole seems to go back to ancestral types combining features of the Gleicheniaceae and, to a lesser extent, the Schizaeaceae.

The sorus in the second assemblage seems

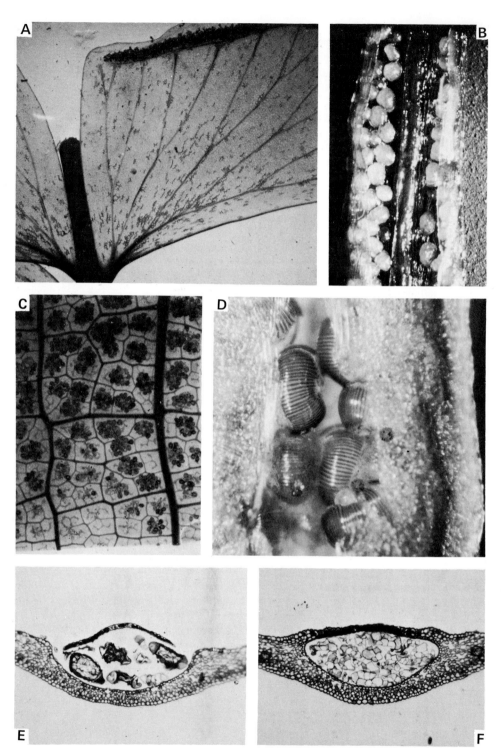

FIGURE 16-12. *A.* Portions of two fertile pinnae and a piece of the rachis of *Lindsaya lancea*. *B, D.* Fertile part of the frond in *Ceratopteris thalictroides*. *C.* Part of the lamina of *Dipteris conjugata*, showing sori and venation. *E, F.* Cross sections at two different levels of the same sorus in *Davallia bullata*.

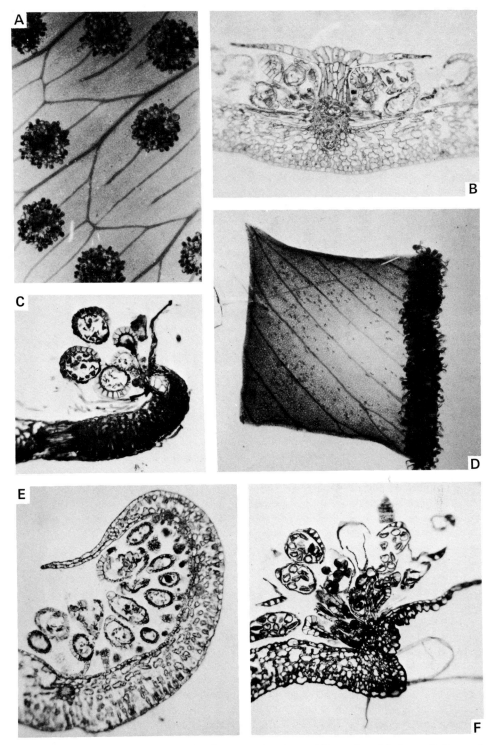

FIGURE 16–13. *A.* Sori and venation in a part of a pinna of *Cyrtomium falcatum.* *B.* Sorus of *C. falcatum* in cross section. *C.* Cross section through the margin of a fertile pinna of *Pteris* sp. *D.* Portion of a fertile pinna of *Pellaea viridis.* The piece is torn away from the midvein of the pinna along the right side. *E.* Cross section through the fertile pinna margin of *P. rotundifolia.* *F.* Cross section through the fertile pinna margin of *P. viridis.*

in all cases ultimately phylogenetically traceable to one that was exindusiate, marginal or nearly so, round to slightly elongate, and which was at or along the terminal part of a vein. In its fundamental features this exists in the Gleicheniaceae, Stromatopteridaceae, Plagiogyriaceae, *Lophosoria* in the Cyatheaceae, and in several pteridaceous genera such as *Cryptogramma* and *Monachosorium*. From this fundamental soral type, the discrete, marginal type of the dicksoniads and dennstaedtioids has evolved, enclosed by two lips, one an extension of the leaf margin (usually a tooth of a small lobe) and one a new structure, the indusium. The Davalliaceae, the near-marginal sorus of which is shown at two cross-sectional levels in Fig. 16–12, *E* and *F*, have essentially the same type of sorus and may be interpreted as possibly of dennstaedtioid derivation. In another direction in soral specialization within the Pteridaceae, the sorus more or less retained its primitive form but became linearly extended along the veins and confluent with other sori, as in *Ceratopteris* or *Jamesonia*. In both these genera, the sporangia are sparsely distributed. In *Ceratopteris* the fertile leaf segments are contracted and the margins are inrolled (Fig. 16–12, *B*, *D*). In *Jamesonia* a few sporangia also occur between the veins on the lower surface of the lamina; an exaggeration of this condition is seen in *Acrosticum*, where the sporangia are completely scattered and occur in large numbers. Elongate, superficial, and more or less confluent sori along veins seems to be the most probable basic condition within the Vittariaceae (Fig. 16–14, *E*), which are considered of pteridaceous origin. An advanced condition exists in *Vittaria*, where the sorus is sunken in a submarginal groove (Fig. 16–14, *F*). Intermediate conditions are also found in this family.

In many Pteridaceae the sori have retained a primitive form but have become clustered in a marginal or submarginal series with individual sori oriented transverse to the conspicuous band. This occurs in *Adiantum* and *Lindsaea* (Fig. 16–12, *A*), each of which has an indusial flap covering groups of sori and in *Cheilanthes* and *Pellaea* (Fig. 16–13, D to F), which are exindusiate but in which the margin of the lamina is somewhat recurved. In each of the genera *Adiantum*, *Lindsaea*, and *Cheilanthes*

there is a transition from distinct sori to elongate coenosori parallel to the margin, the only condition found in the genera *Pteridium*, *Pteris* (Fig. 16–13, *C*), and *Actinopteris* (Fig. 16–2, *B*). There is frequently a near-marginal vein running just under the coenosorus which otherwise disrupts the dichotomous venation (seen in cross section in Fig. 16–13, *C*).

The terms "marginal sorus" and "submarginal sorus," as well as what is called indusium as opposed to leaf margin, are not always objective designations. The margin of the lamina in *Pellaea rotundifolia* (Fig. 16–13, *E*) seems relatively distinct, although at the very outside there is no mesophyll. The counterpart in *Pellaea viridis* is less clear and might conceivably suggest another interpretation. Figure 16–13, *C* (Pteris) is particularly similar to *F*, but developmental information presented by Bower (1918) (Fig. 16–16, *N* to *Q*) indicates that the receptacular line is marginal and the extended flap is a superficial outgrowth. Compare these figures with those of Palser and Barrick (1941), which show submarginal origin of the sorus in *Cystopteris* (Aspidiaceae) (Fig. 16–16, *K* to *M*).

The Aspleniaceae exhibit long or short sori, each with a single indusial flap along veins of the lamina (Fig. 16–14, *A*, *B*). The primitive Blechnaceae show sori much like those of asplenoids and also transitional forms leading to elongate coenosori along small veins parallel to the midvein of the leaf segment. The indusial flap is often thick and leathery (Fig. 16–14, *D*). In some species of *Blechnum*, the lamina is reduced nearly to extinction (Fig. 16–14, *C*).

The Aspidiaceae probably show greater variation in soral morphology than any other fern family. The sori are most often small, superficial, or submarginal (Fig. 16–16, *K* to *M*) and round or crescent-shaped. Occasionally they are elevated (Fig. 16–16, *D*). The indusium is often a single flap of delicate tissue arising from the base of the receptacle and varying in the extent of its attachment (e.g., *Dryopteris*, *Ctenitis*, and *Cystopteris*). The attachment is completely circular in *Paranema* (Fig. 16–16, *D*) and in some *Woodsia* species. The indusium is occasionally attached above the level of the sporangia and forms an umbrella-shaped covering [e.g., *Cyrtomium* (Fig. 16–13, *B*) and *Polystichum*]. In occasional

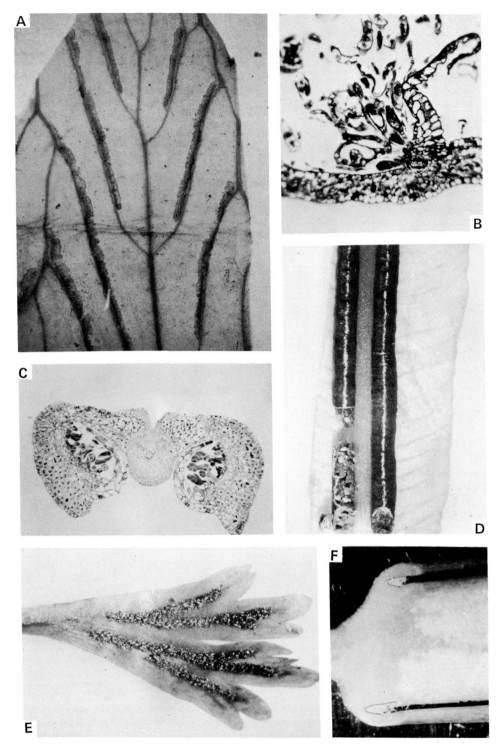

FIGURE 16–14. *A.* Part of a fertile pinna of *Asplenium* sp. *B.* Cross section through the sorus of *A. bulbiferum.* *C.* Cross section through the fertile pinna of *Blechnum* sp. *D.* Part of a fertile pinna of another *Blechnum* sp. *E.* Fertile leaf of *Hecistopteris pumila.* *F.* Part of the fertile leaf in *Vittaria elongata* cut obliquely on the left.

311

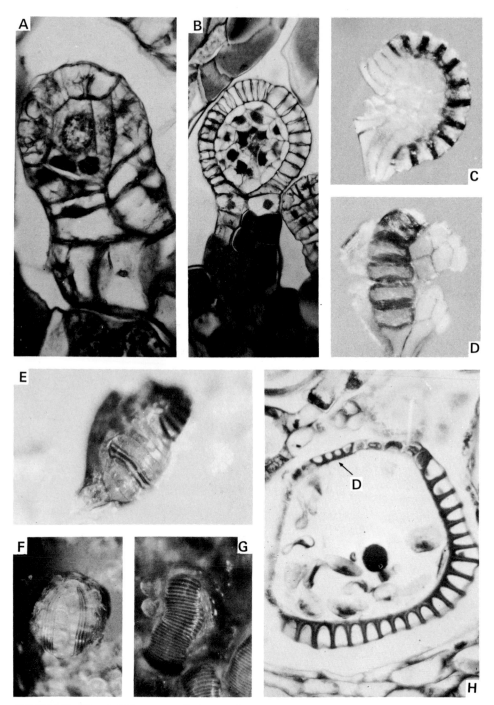

FIGURE 16–15. *A, B.* Two stages in the development of the sporangium of *Blechnum* sp. *C, D.* Sporangia of *Dipteris conjugata.* *E.* Sporangium of *Blechnum orientale.* *F, G.* Sporangia of *Ceratopteris thalictroides.* *H.* Longitudinal section through the sporangium of *Onoclea sensibilis* through the entire annulus. Dehiscence occurs at D by separation of the thick-walled cells.

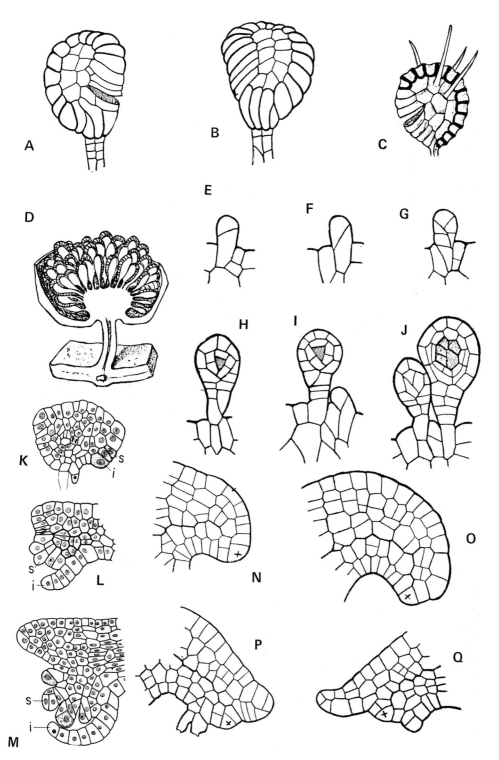

FIGURE 16–16. *A, B.* Sporangia of *Dipteris lobiana*, after Bower (1926). *C.* Sporangium of *Dictyocline griffithii*, after Ren-Chang (1935). *D.* Sorus of *Peranema cyatheoides*, after Diels (1902). *E* to *J.* Sporangial development in *Phlebodium aureum*, after Bower (1923). *K* to *M.* Soral origin in *Cystopteris bulbifera*, after Palser and Barrick (1941). *N* to *Q.* Soral origin in *Pteridium aquilinum*, after Bower (1918).

species of *Polystichum* or *Ctenitis* the indusium is absent. The complete acrosticoid condition has developed in *Elapholossum* and nearly so in *Quercifelix*, in which the sporangia occur on veins and spread between them here and there.

The sporangia of the higher Filicales are all fundamentally alike. The annulus is typically vertically oriented and interrupted by the stalk (Fig. 16–15, *E*; Fig. 16–16, *C*). Stomial cells are generally distinct and number two (Fig. 16–15, *E*) to several (Fig. 16–15, *F, H*). Stalks are generally thin. The sporangia vary somewhat in shape (compare Fig. 16–15, *E* with *F, G*), but they are mostly somewhat vertically flattened. Variation in size and number of annular and stomial cells, length and thickness of the stalk, and presence (Fig. 16–16, *C*) or absence of episporangial paraphyses are of some systematic significance. Developmental patterns of sporangia (Fig. 16–15, *A, B*; Fig. 16–16, *E* to *J*) are relatively uniform. The stalk initial divides obliquely (Fig. 16–16, E, F), and after several such divisions the terminal sporangial initial is established (*G*). The latter divides periclinally, establishing the outer wall initial and an inner cell. The sporogenous tissue, the tapetum, and the inner wall layer, which also acts as tapetum, are derived from the inner cell. Possibly the most complete descriptions of sporangial development in higher ferns, especially those cell lineages within the surface layer, are presented in several publications by K. A. Wilson (1958a, 1958b, 1959, 1960). Complete discussions of paraphyses, both episporangial and intersporangial (receptacular), are given by R. Tryon (1965) and Wagner (1964b).

The gametophytes of all higher filicalean ferns are surface living, thallose, and green. In shape they vary from strap-shaped to cordate (Fig. 16–17, *B*) and in size they are mostly less than 0.5 cm across. They are either branched or unbranched. The margins are frequently irregularly folded and frequently bud to reproduce vegetatively. Rhizoids occur on the central cushion (Fig. 16–17, *A*), and hairs of various sorts occur either on one or both surfaces or on the margins. For a systematic treatment of such features see Stokey (1951). An apical meristem is present in the notch (Fig. 16–17, *C*) and this is continuous with the marginal meristem of the wings. Archegonia are usually borne on the lower surface of the cushion and have antheridia either lateral to them or, occasionally, marginal (e.g., *Ceratopteris*). With few exceptions, antheridia develop before archegonia. Degrees of expression of the dioecious condition have been described in several genera (e.g., *Ceratopteris*), but this may or may not be genetic. In *Woodsia* (Fig. 16–18, *H*) filamentous branches of a thallose gametophyte bear antheridia. The spores germinate to produce filaments (Fig. 16–18, *A*; and irrespective of cell shape, *E*), then plates (Fig. 16–18, *A* to *D*), and in some genera the apex arises subapically (Fig. 16–18, *I* to *K*).

In *Platyzoma* (Bower, 1923) there are large and small spores as well as some of intermediate sizes. The size of the sporangium is correlated with spore size. The smaller spores produce filamentous to narrow strap-shaped antheridium-bearing gametophytes (Fig. 16–18 *F*), while the larger ones produce more thallose gametophytes (Fig. 16–18, *G*) which when young produce antheridia and when older only archegonia (A. Tryon, 1964). Spores of intermediate sizes have not been grown. This is the closest approach to heterospory and heterothallism known among the Filicales. The families Salviniaceae, Azollaceae, and Marsileaceae, considered filicalean derivatives and ordinally separated, have developed complete heterospory and heterothallism.

With few and relatively minor variations (see Stokey, 1951) most advanced filicalean ferns produce antheridia in which the spermatogenous tissue is delimited by only three cells: a cap cell (C in Fig. 16–21, *E*), a distal ring cell (R_D), and a basal or proximal cell (R_P), which may approach ring form, be funnel shaped as in Fig. 16–21, *E*, or rarely be flat as in Fig. 16–20, *E* (the basal cell, BC). During development the antheridial initial may be produced by a transverse division (Fig. 16–20, *A*) or by one or more oblique divisions (Fig. 16–21, *C, D*). It is suspected that the basal cell in some cases is derived from the antheridial initial and in others from the cell below. The antheridial initial divides more or less transversely (Fig. 16–20, *B, C*), but the resultant wall is curved upward such that the inner cell cut off is lens-shaped with a flat lower (proximal) face and a concave upper face that does not intersect the outer wall of what is now its sister cell. The

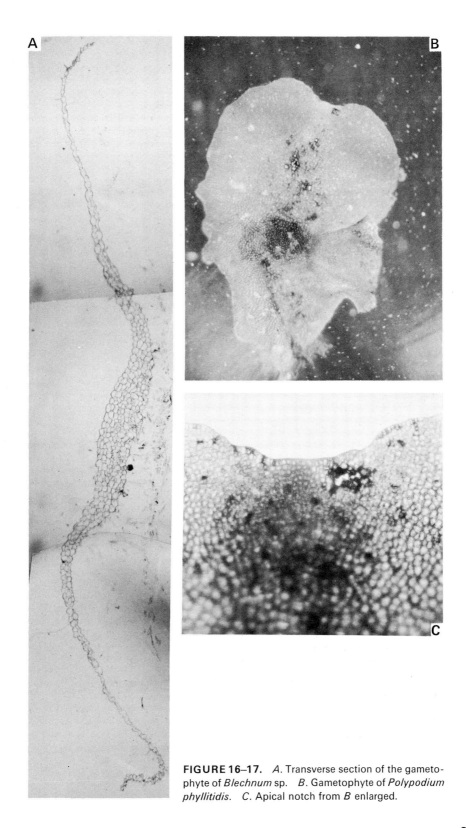

FIGURE 16–17. *A*. Transverse section of the gametophyte of *Blechnum* sp. *B*. Gametophyte of *Polypodium
phyllitidis*. *C*. Apical notch from *B* enlarged.

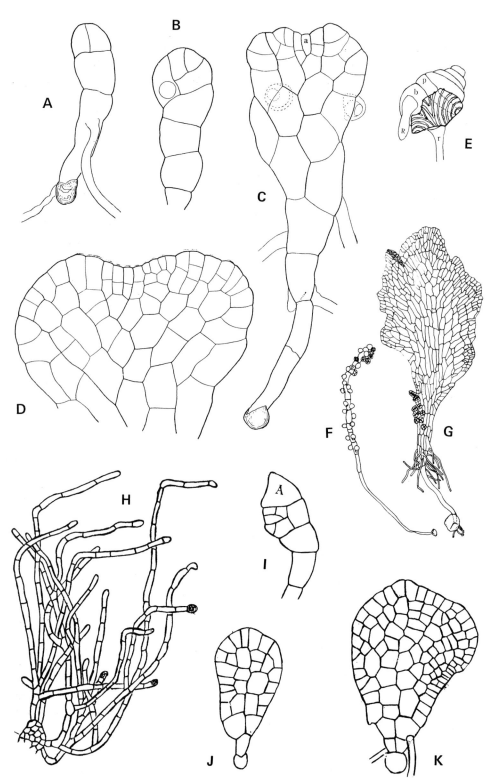

FIGURE 16–18. *A* to *D*. Stages in the development of the gametophyte of *Dennstaedtia punctilobula*, after Conrad (1908). *E.* Young gametophyte of *Ceratopteris thalictroides*, after Nishida (1962). *F, G.* Male and female gametophytes of *Platyzoma microphyllum*, after A. Tryon (1964). *H.* Portion of a gametophyte of *Woodsia*. *I.* Expanding tip of a young gametophyte of *Asplenium nidus*. *J, K.* Two stages in the development of the gametophyte of *Pteris longifolia*. *H* to *K* after Goebel (1930), by permission of Gustav Fischer Verlag, Jena.

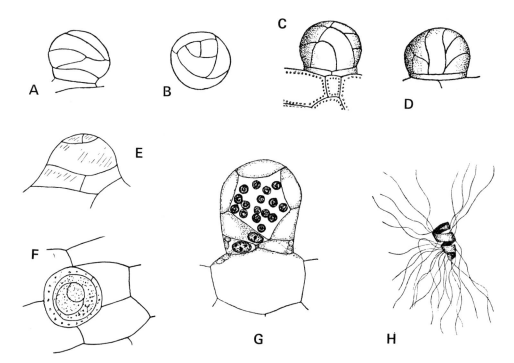

FIGURE 16–19. *A, B.* Antheridia of *Dipteris conjugata*, after Stokey (1945). *C, D.* Antheridia of *Cheiropleuria biscuspis*, after Nakai (1933). *E* to *G.* Antheridia of *Grammitis billardieri*, after Stone (1960). *H.* Sperm of *Pteridium aquilinum*, after Lagerberg (1906).

outer, bell-shaped cell then divides to produce the apical cap cell (C in Fig. 16–20, *E*) and the distal ring cell. The inner cell (primary spermatogenous cell, PA) may now bulge down into the basal cell, if it did not do so even before it was cut off, or it may remain flat-bottomed (Fig. 16–20, *E*; Fig. 16–21, *B*). Divisions in the spermatogenous tissue are always simultaneous (Fig. 16–20, *F*). A blepharoplast in the form of a chain of beads (B in Fig. 16–21, *A*) develops in each spermatid, and ultimately a multiflagellate, coiled sperm is produced (Fig. 16–19, *H*; Fig. 16–21, *B*).

Archegonia of higher ferns vary slightly and *Dennstaedtia* is selected to illustrate their ontogeny (Fig. 16–22, *A* to *H*). A superficial initial divides transversely to produce the neck mother cell and the inner cell (NMC and IC in *A*). The former divides twice anticlinally to establish the four mother cells of the vertical rows of neck cells (one such division is indicated in *B* to *D*). The inner cell generally produces a pad cell (PC in *B* to *D*) and its sister cell divides to produce the rest of the axial row:

one neck canal cell, one ventral cell (VCC in *H*), and the egg (E in *H*). As in other archegonia, the egg and ventral canal cell are sister cells. There are generally only two nuclei in the neck canal cell, but in the figure three are shown (NCN in *G*). The jacket (J in *H*) varies in its distinctiveness.

Root, stem, leaf, and foot are primary parts of the embryos of all higher Filicales (Fig. 16–23, *F*, H). The first division of the zygote is longitudinal (Fig. 16–23, *A*) and the second pair of divisions transverse to this. The four primary embryonic components seem traceable to the four-celled or quadrant stage or to the eight-celled stage (Fig. 16–23, *B* to *E*). There are several excellent and relatively complete descriptions of higher filicalean embryogeny in the literature [e.g., D. H. Campbell (1928) as well as a number based on relatively few early stages]. It appears likely that some of the incomplete studies were overinfluenced by older descriptions of other species. Not a single study, to the author's knowledge, is sufficiently documented.

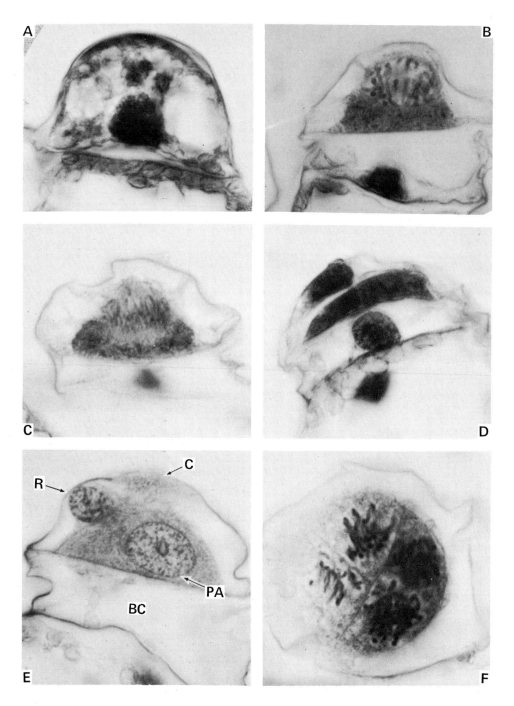

FIGURE 16–20. Antheridial development in *Blechnum* sp. C = cap cell; R = ring cell; BC = basal cell; PA = primary spermatogenous cell.

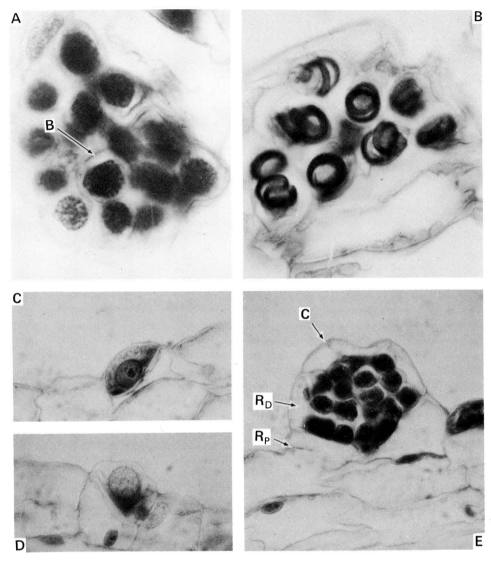

FIGURE 16–21. *A, B.* Later stages in the development of the antheridium of *Blechnum* sp. *C* to *E*. Three stages in the development of the antheridium of *Dennstaedtia adiantoides*. C = cap cell; R_D = distal ring cell; R_P = proximal ring cell.

The fern life cycle is in general quite "normal" and complete in its morphological and cytological alternation of generations. Greatest incompleteness is expressed in one *Vittaria* species (Wagner, 1963) in which the gametophyte is purely vegetative and apparently its sporophyte is completely lost. Unusual alternations of generations, both naturally occurring and artificially induced, are reported in a number of genera (Steil, 1939). These fall into the categories apogamy, apospory, and parthenogenesis. Apogamy (literally without gametes) is defined as the vegetative production of sporophyte from gametophyte. It is expressed in various degrees from the production of a complete sporophyte to possibly only a single tracheid in the gametophytic tissue. Apospory (without spores) is the vegetative production of a gametophyte from a sporophyte and also shows various degrees of

Relatively Advanced Filicales **319**

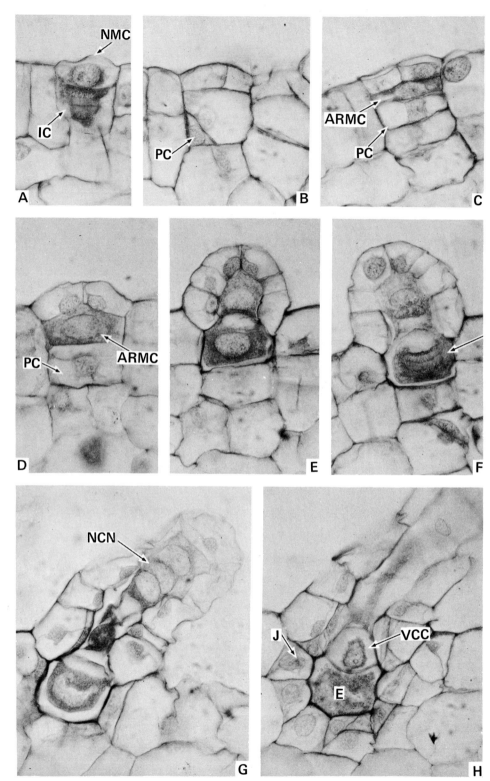

FIGURE 16–22. Development of the archegonium in *Dennstaedtia adiantoides.* NMC = neck mother cell; IC = inner cell; PC = pad cell; ARMC = axial row mother cell; NCN = neck canal nuclei; J = jacket; VCC = ventral canal cell; E = egg.

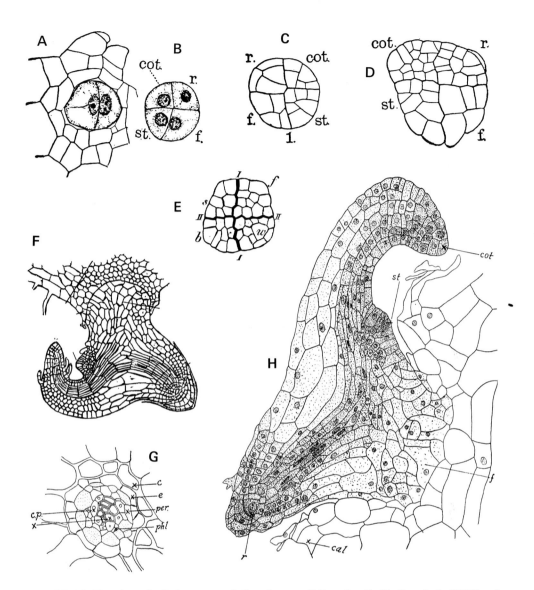

FIGURE 16–23. *A* to *D*. Embryogeny of *Onoclea sensibilis*, after D. H. Campbell (1928). *E.* Embryo of *Pteridium aquilinum*, after Hofmeister (1862). *F.* Older embryo of *Pteris serrulata*, after Goebel (1930), by permission of Gustav Fischer Verlag, Jena. *G.* Cross section of the stele in a young sporophyte of *Histiopteris incisa*, after E. O. Campbell (1936). *H.* Older embryo of *H. incisa*, after E. O. Campbell (1936).

expression. For the most part these anomalies have no real part in the overall course of fern phylogeny, but from other considerations they are important.

No one knows why a particular cell or group of cells develops into a gametophyte while others form sporophytes. The abnormalities referred to above, as well as normal morphological and cytological alternation of generations in many polyploids, indicate that haploidy and diploidy alone do not determine the characteristics of a generation. Theories that have been presented to explain why an object, single cell or propagule, develops into a sporophyte or a gametophyte due to nutritional status or due in some way to the

Relatively Advanced Filicales   **321**

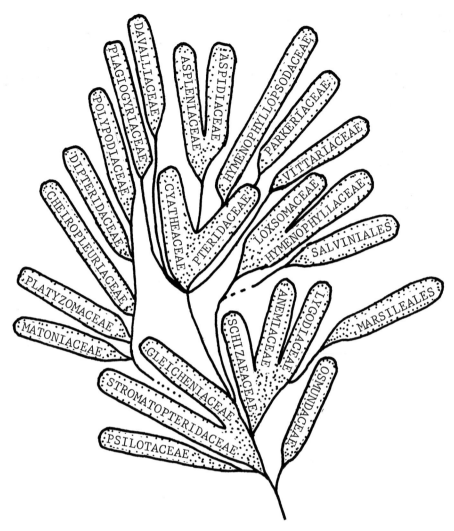

FIGURE 16–24. Summary diagram indicating suggested lines of derivation of the families of the Filicales, Salviniales, and Marsileales.

difference in the structure to which it is attached or in which it is contained break down completely in certain taxa. The subterranean axes of *Psilotum* and *Stromatopteris* produce superficial buds or gemmae that develop into subterranean axes of the same generation as the one that produced them, even if they become detached. The bud-producing axes of *Psilotum*, both sporophyte and gametophyte, may be vascularized or not, and the sporophytic ones may be entire subterranean plants not attached to aerial green parts. The same is true of *Stromatopteris* except that the gameto-

phyte is never vascularized, but the sporophytic axes still are occasionally unvascularized. These subterranean bodies are saprophytes containing the same fungus (within each genus,) and their nutritional status is apparently identical. No theory attempting to explain generation differences can overlook these two genera.

It is assumed that it is the same genome being expressed in both gametophyte and sporophyte and not two separate sets being turned on and off at the appropriate time, although both concepts may in part be true.

It is certainly true that two relatively closely related forms may be extremely similar in their sporophytes and drastically different in their gametophytes and embryos (e.g., *Actinostachys* and *Schizaea*), and conversely in many higher ferns. A certain set of expressions has evolved in the sporophyte and another in the gametophyte, with considerable overlap. The degree of overlap or the degree of differential expression of certain genomic segments, it is suggested, has occasionally changed and is of some morphological significance. A particular feature expressed in both generations, either in an identical or in a differential form, may have selective significance in only one. The ontogenetic similarities in later stages of development between the antheridium of *Equisetum* and its sporangium provoke such ideas, as well as similarities between trichomes of gametophytes of certain ferns and those on their sporophytes. There is an irregular taxonomic pattern of distribution of antheridia and archegonia, the initials of which are established by a series of divisions similar to those which set off the sporangial initial. In the opinion expressed here, these are all subtle expressions of apogamy and differ only in degree from those which drastically upset the life cycle but which have some considerable significance in overall fern phylogeny.

In summary, of those features that have been brought out in this and in the preceding chapters on filicalean ferns, the following list of presumed primitive and presumed specialized features is presented. It should be noted that these interpretations are presented for the Filicales as circumscribed here only and not for ferns or fern-like plants in general. The interpretations conform to a large extent with those of previous publications. The differences are primarily related to the new information available on the Psilotaceae, Stromatopteridaceae, and Schizaeaceae.

Primitive	Advanced
1. Plants terrestrial, relatively small; stem upright to horizontal but not long and creeping.	1. Long-stem creepers; tree-form types; epiphytes.
2. Leaves in their totality poorly differentiated from stems, but pinnae well defined.	2. Leaves very distinct from stems.
3. Leaves, determinate, pinnate.	3. Simple leaves; some dichotomous ones; indeterminate ones.
4. Venation dichotomous.	4. Venation reticulate.
5. Apical cell of leaf with three cutting faces.	5. Apical cell of leaf with two cutting faces.
6. Leaves retaining vestiges of apical growth within marginal meristem of simple units (corresponding to ends of vein systems).	6. Marginal meristem more or less uniform.
7. Leaves irregularly arranged.	7. Leaves with fixed phyllotaxy.
8. Leaves monomorphic.	8. Leaves dimorphic.
9. Branching dichotomous in stem; possibly with some epipetiolar buds.	9. Other types of branching.
10. Simple trichomes only.	10. Complex hairs and scales.
11. Roots absent or poorly differentiated from stem.	11. Roots fixed in organography.

Primitive	Advanced
12. Medullated or unmedullated protostele in stem.	12. Stems with solenosteles then dictyosteles (some protosteles likely by reduction).
13. Primary xylem in stem mesarch to irregular.	13. Xylem exarch or lateral in bundles with unidirectional, circumferential maturation.
14. Leaf trace simple, relatively large, somewhat adaxially curved, with (?) three protoxylem points.	14. Double and multiple leaf traces.
15. Sori present and distinct; terminal or marginal; probably slightly elongate.	15. Sori superficial; sori extended along veins, in various kinds of coenosori, or acrosticoid.
16. Sporangia in single sorus maturing simultaneously and on entire leaf, or portion of, in acropetally gradate fashion.	16. Basipetally gradate maturation in single sori; mixed maturation in a single sorus (not necessarily derived from above); sori of mixed ages on entire frond.
17. Sori exindusiate.	17. Indusiate.
18. Sporangia relatively large, high spore number.	18. Sporangia smaller with fixed and smaller number of spore mother cells (specialized sporangial enlargement likely occurred within Psilotaceae).
19. Spores monolete (not in vascular plants as a whole).	19. Spores trilete (reversal likely in some generic lines).
20. Sporangium wall of several layers with more than one persisting at maturity.	20. Wall of two layers only; inner one acting as second tapetal layer.
21. Sporangial stalk relatively massive.	21. Stalk thin.
22. Annulus apical or subapical.	22. Annulus oblique, then longitudinal and interrupted by stalk.
23. Dehiscence longitudinal.	23. Dehiscence oblique, then transverse.
24. Line of dehiscence not anatomically specialized.	24. Well marked, then with stomium.
25. Gametophyte axial.	25. Gametophyte filamentous or thallose; each probably at times gave rise to the other.
26. Gametophytic rhizoids septate.	26. Nonseptate.
27. Antheridia relatively large with a number of cells to the one-cell-thick wall. Opercular cell lateral.	27. Antheridia relatively small; few cells in wall; opercular cell apical.

Primitive	Advanced
28. Archegonia relatively large, straight necked, more than two nuclei in neck canal cell.	28. Archegonia smaller, curved neck, only two neck canal nuclei.
29. Embryo rootless and leafless, large foot.	29. Embryo with four organs, small foot.
30. Embryo exoscopic.	30. Embryo endoscopic.
31. Zygote divides transversely.	31. Zygote divides longitudinally.
32. Spore germule a three-dimensional cell mass.	32. Spore germule a filament or plate.

17

Marsileales

The Marsileales is an order of superficially rather unfernlike, mostly aquatic to subaquatic plants. The one family, Marsileaceae, includes three rather closely related genera: *Marsilea*, containing possibly 60 species of wide distribution; *Pilularia*, with six species similarly distributed; and *Regnellidium*, with a single species of Brazil. The order is known from a number of spore form genera of Cretaceous rocks. Its earliest record may be in the Triassic.

The three genera have creeping, branched, and matted rhizomes that bear roots and upright leaves. The mats are often rooted on wet soil and extend out over deeper water. In one species of *Marsilea*, the near-xerophytic *M. hirsuta*, underground tubers are formed on the rhizomes. The leaves of *Pilularia* are filiform and devoid of lamina (Fig. 17–1, *C*). Those of *Regnellidium* bear two opposite pinnae (Fig. 17–1, *B*). Those of *Marsilea* bear two or rarely three pairs of pinnae (Fig. 17–1, *A*). The rachis between pinna-pair attachment is generally very short, suggesting near-common attachment of the four pinnae. Lamina venation is dichotomous with marginal anastomoses (Fig. 17–2, *B*) or reticulate (Fig. 17–2, *A*). Rhizome branches occur either lateral and adjacent to leaf insertions or above them.

A solenostele occurs in the rhizomes (Fig. 17–2, *C*), with usually complete symmetry of tissues from internal to external endodermis (Fig. 17–2, *D*). The internal endodermis is occasionally absent in *Pilularia*. The xylem maturation pattern is mesarch. The rhizome shown in Fig. 17–2 has a sclerotic pith and inner cortex, zones that are uniformly parenchymatous in submerged stems. At the apex of the rhizome there is an apical cell with three cutting faces. There are simple stelar gaps associated with the departure of the simple leaf traces.

327

A

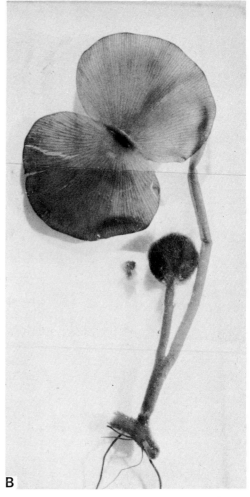

B

FIGURE 17–1. *A. Marsilea polycarpa. B. Regnellidium diphyllum. C. Pilularia americana.*

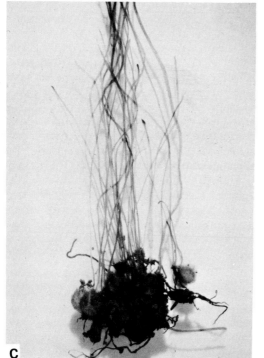

C

FIGURE 17–2.   *A, B*. Cleared leaf tip of *Marsilea vestida, A*, after Gaudet (1964), and *Regnellidium diphyllum, B*.   *C*. Cross section of the stem of *Marsilea quadrifolia*.   *D*. Portion of *C* enlarged.   C = cortex; E = endodermis; PC = pericycle; P = pith; PH = phloem; MX = metaxylem; PX = protoxylem.

Roots arise at leaf bases. They are diarch and contain true vessels. The perforation plates (White, 1961) suggest those of some angiosperms with disrupted scalariform bars. Root apices are as in other ferns.

Leaf apices bear an apical cell with two cutting faces and the pinnae arise from a group of cells in the submarginal series. The marginal meristem of the lamina is particularly uniform. Hagemann's (1967) description of pinna ontogeny in *Regnellidium* is one of the best descriptions ever presented.

Regnellidium is the only nonflowering plant that produces latex (Labouriau, 1952). It is formed in unbranched, occasionally septate tubes that are found throughout the body.

The reproductive structures of the Marsileaceae are nutlike, epipetiolar bodies called sporocarps (Fig. 17–1, *A* to *C*; Fig. 17–3, *A* to *C*). They tend to be spherical in *Pilularia* and *Regnellidium* but somewhat flattened in *Marsilea*. They are near-sessile to occasionally long-stalked. The stalk in some *Marsilea* species occasionally branches (Fig. 17–3, *A*). Some species of *Marsilea* produce a high number of sporocarps in a single vertical line on one side of the petiole (Fig. 17–1, *A*; Fig. 17–3, *C*). Two bumps occur on the sporocarp near the stalk attachment in some species of *Marsilea* (Fig. 17–3, *B*; Fig. 17–4, *C*).

The sporocarp of *Marsilea* and *Regnellidium* has a vascular supply that branches from the margin of the petiolar trace. The trace extends through the stalk and into the sporocarp, where it follows a longitudinal course beneath the stony layer along the upper edge of the sporocarp. In *Marsilea*, this is the edge where the two bumps are present and where there is frequently a distinct external ridge ("raphe"). From the main trace (midvein) of the sporocarp a pinnate series of traces extends downward in the soft hyposclerotic layer in each face of the structure (Fig. 17–5, *A*, *B*). The specimens shown in Fig. 17–4, *B*, *C* are halves of sporocarps of two species of *Marsilea* viewed from the inside after some internal tissue has been excavated. In each the midvein of the sporocarp is not visible and runs across the upper edge of the structure and parallel to the plane of the paper. One of the two lateral vein systems is shown in each. Some of the lateral veins anastomose farther down (Fig.

17–5, *A*, *B*). Figure 17–4, *D* shows the midvein of a sporocarp as viewed from the inside of a scooped-out sporocarp. The most distal pair of pinnately arranged veins may be greater developed than the more proximal ones, and, in fact, several of the more proximal ones may be attached to the distal lateral veins rather than to the midvein itself. This gives the impression of a dichotomy of the midvein, which may or may not be actual, and which sometimes extend back nearly halfway through the sporocarp.

On the inside of the sporocarp of *Marsilea* and *Regnellidium* there are elongate sori oriented parallel to the lateral vein system (Fig. 17–4, *C*). Several sori are shown in isolation in Fig. 17–4, *E* to *G*. Each sorus is represented by a ridge of tissue (receptacle) (R in Fig. 17–4, *A*) to which are attached a number of megasporangia (MGS) along its crest and microsporangia (MCS) along its flanks. The larger sporangia in Fig. 17–4, *E* to *G* are megasporangia, while the smaller ones are microsporangia. Each sorus receives a vascular trace (blackened in Fig. 17–5, *A*, *B*) that arises at or very near a forking in the vein system (arrow in Fig. 17–4, *B*, *C*). The trace extends directly into the ridge, then a branch of it extends in either direction within the ridge and parallel to the lateral veins of the sporocarp (Fig. 17–5, *A*, *B*). The sori, when viewed in a longitudinal section of the sporocarp cut transverse to its two flat sides, are seen surrounded by delicate diaphragms (Fig. 17–3, *D*, *E*; Fig. 17–4, *A*) usually referred to as indusia. These are ontogenetically superficial outgrowths of the inner surface and may be designated as indusia if it is kept in mind that the indusium is a polyphyletic structure, not necessarily homologous from one fern family to another.

The sporocarp of *Pilularia* appears quite different from those of the other two genera, but the differences are in reality rather superficial. In early ontogeny, the orientation of parts in the sporocarps is essentially the same throughout the family, but in *Pilularia* differential growth results in its four elongate sori being oriented longitudinally within its sporocarp. The midvein of the sporocarp is diminutive, and its laterals are elongate and now run lengthwise within the sporocarp (Fig. 17–5, *C*).

FIGURE 17–3. *A.* Base of the fertile leaf in *Marsilea quadrifolia* showing three sporocarps. *B.* One sporocarp from *A*. The arrows indicate the bumps or horns. *C.* Sporocarps at the base of the leaf in *M. polycarpa*. *D, E.* Sporocarps of *M. polycarpa*, *D*, and *M. quadrifolia*, *E*, cut longitudinally but transverse to the flat sides.

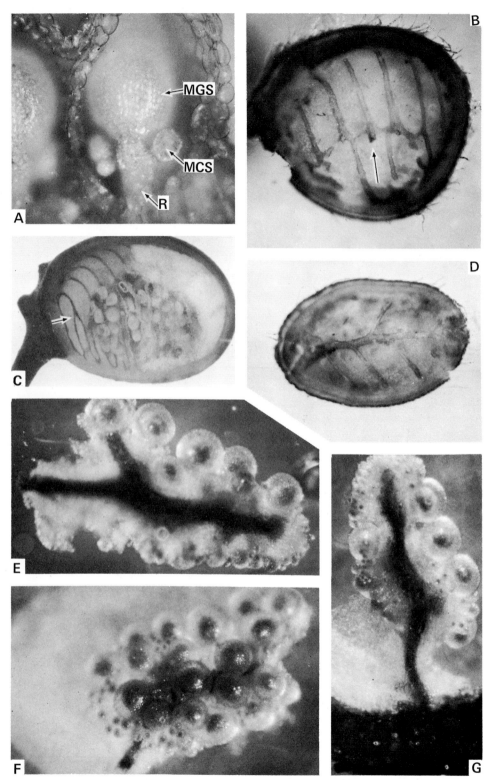

FIGURE 17–4. *A.* Portion of Fig. 17–3, *D* enlarged. MGS = megasporangium; MCS = micro-sporangium; R = receptacle. *B, D.* The sporocarp of *Marsilea polycarpa* as viewed from the inside after the sori and other soft tissue is removed. *B* shows the venation of the side wall with the arrow indicating one of the soral attachments. *D* shows the venation across the top of the sporocarp: a midvein with pinnately arranged branches. *C.* Inside of the sporocarp of *M. quadrifolia*, a view comparable to *B*, but not all soft tissue has been removed. Arrow indicates the attachment of the soral trace. *E* to *G. Regnellidium* sori removed from the sporocarp.

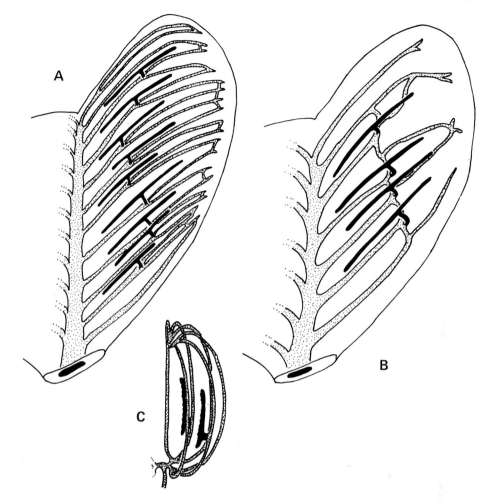

FIGURE 17–5. Sporocarp venation. *A. Marsilea quadrifolia.* *B. Pilularia globulifera,* redrawn from Meunier (1887). *C. Marsilea polycarpa.*

Megasporangia tend to occur at the end of the elongate sorus toward the base of the sporocarp and microsporangia at the other end.

Marsilea polycarpa (Fig. 17–1, *A*; Fig. 17–7, *A* to *F*) produces a row of a number of sporocarps on one side of the petiole, and at maturity they are distinctly interspaced. They originate, however, from single, adjacent, lateral cells along a flange at the base of the leaf primordium (Fig. 17–7, *A*). The flange (FL) is only relatively slight and arises sometime *after* the vegetative pinnae (STP) are formed. The initial cells on the flange *do not* arise in acropetal succession, and the flange itself does not arise in such a succession with the pinnae. Each

sporocarp initial divides as an apical cell with three cutting faces (Fig. 17–7, *B*). The initial of the singly occurring sporocarp of *Pilularia* is described also as a single cell with two or three cutting faces (Meunier, 1887; Johnson, 1898). Further growth of tissue associated with young sporocarps in *Marsilea polycarpa* results in their becoming less perfectly aligned and separated along the petiole (Fig. 17–7, *C* to *F*). At this stage there is a mixed series of sporocarps with smaller, less developed ones among larger ones (Fig. 17–7, *F*). Apical growth is soon replaced by marginal growth, and the young sporocarp becomes concave on its *adaxial* side. The abaxial side

Marsileales   **333**

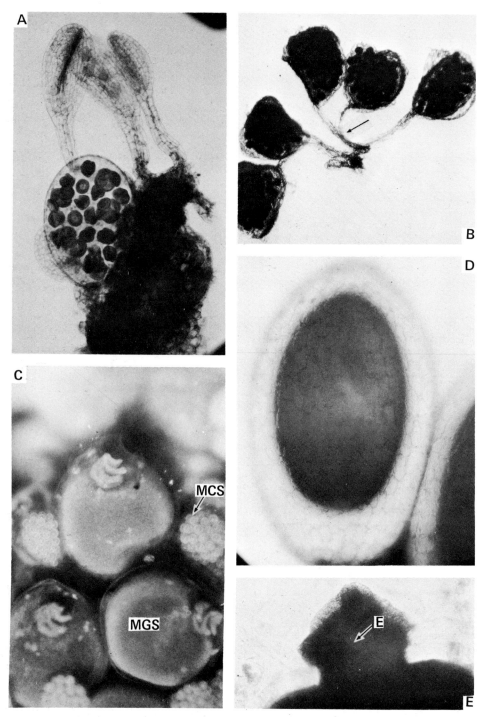

FIGURE 17–6. *A.* Part of a sorus of *Marsilea quadrifolia.* *B.* Group of microsporangia from a sorus of *Regnellidium.* *C.* Group of sporangia of *Regnellidium.* MCS = microsporangium; MGS = megasporangium. *D.* Single megasporangium of *Marsilea quadrifolia.* *E.* Apex of the megaspore of *Regnellidium.*

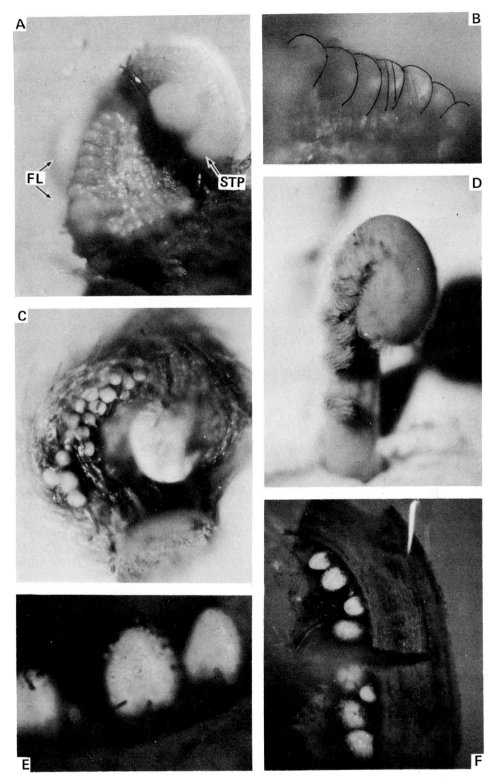

FIGURE 17–7. *Marsilea polycarpa.* *A*. Entire young leaf showing the lateral flange, FL, and a line of adjacent sporocarp initials, some of which have already divided, as shown in the part enlarged in *B*. STP = sterile pinnae. *C*, *D*. Later stages in sporocarp development and scattering. *E*, *F*. Line of sporocarps from *D* viewed from the other side. Three are enlarged in *E*.

335

of each sporocarp becomes very hairy at an early stage in development (Fig. 17–7, *D*). The same sporocarps in *D* are seen from their adaxial sides in *E* and *F* with the petiole cut lengthwise. In *E* it is seen that the margin is now entirely on the adaxial side and surrounds the concavity. Later stages in sporocarp ontogeny are well known for *Pilularia* and *Marsilea* (Johnson, 1898; Eames, 1936). Two rows of soral initials, each originating along one sporocarp margin, are forced into an internal position by differential growth (i.e., inrolling; Fig. 17–8, *A*, *B*), and the indusia are formed as outgrowths on the concave face. The fruitlike body is thus produced with sori in an apparent internal position. Note in particular that the sporocarp has grown toward its adaxial side to effect closure and the sori are therefore borne on the equivalent of the upperside of ordinary fern leaves.

The sporocarp of the Marsileaceae has in general been interpreted as a modified pinna (Bower, 1923). Its later ontogeny, its position, the nature of its vascular supply from the petiolar trace, its overall vascular system, and the fact that it is a soral-bearing outgrowth of a leaf all support this contention. Eames (1936) considered the sporocarp of *Marsilea* as the equivalent of the entire leaf tip with its four pinnae. He considered the bumps that occur at the proximal end of the sporocarp and occasionally are slightly vascularized as representing a vestigal pair of pinnae. His interpretation may be considered as differing only in degree from others, since in many ferns some pinnae, especially near the proximal end of a series, are often more highly compound than others.

Early ontogeny of sporocarps in *Marsilea polycarpa* contradicts the pinna interpretation. The series originates more or less synchronously and the entire group originates after the vegetative pinnae are well formed. The series of sporocarp initials could not with certainty be traced through the marginal meristems of the vegetative pinnae and may not therefore be ultimately traceable to the marginal series of the leaf apical cell. The sporocarp initials are single cells with three cutting faces, a condition unknown for any fern pinna. Their early stages in development are very comparable to those of single filicalean sporangial stalk initials. The

new interpretation presented here is that these are organs which truly changed their morphological nature in midontogeny. That segment of the genome governing sporangial ontogeny is expressed in early stages and that concerned with pinna ontogeny in later stages. The Marsileaceae, therefore, phylogenetically synthesized a new organ, the sporocarp, by modifying the primordium of one by superimposing the later stages of ontogeny of another. It is particularly interesting to note that the marginal series of sporocarp initials in the Marsileaceae strongly suggests marginal series of sporangial stalk initials in the Schizaeaceae and Lygodiaceae (ignore the indusium in the latter). The structure and development of the functional sorus of the Marsileaceae also shows closest similarity to that of the Schizaeaceae. If the interpretation that the sporangial stalk is the homolog of an ancestral axial entity (see Chapter 15), part of a leaf or otherwise, is valid, then the growing point of the sporangium might be expected to occasionally express a slightly greater developmental potential. This is what is considered to have occurred in the Marsileaceae. Organ metamorphosis occurs elsewhere, especially in flowering plants, and the final products are usually outstanding anomalies not morphologically intergrading with the normal organs. If such a change took place in the history of the Marsileaceae, it is guessed that it was by way of major genetic changes and that intermediate forms are not to be expected.

In *Marsilea* the megasporangial stalk initials are recognizable as conspicuously large cells on the crest of the receptacular ridge, shown in cross section in Fig. 17–8, *C* to *I*. A few cells are cut off before the sporangial initial is established (F), which then divides periclinally (G). From then on ontogeny follows the usual filicalean pattern, leading to a central mass of megaspore mother cells surrounded by three layers (Fig. 17–8, *J*), the inner two of which soon decompose. After meiosis a number of tetrads are formed (Fig. 17–6, *A*, the large sessile sporangium), but from them all only a single megaspore matures (Fig. 17–6-*D*). The thick-walled megaspore has no trilete marking, but at its tip there is a conspicuous beak (Fig. 17–6, *C*, *E*).

The microsporangial stalk initials originate

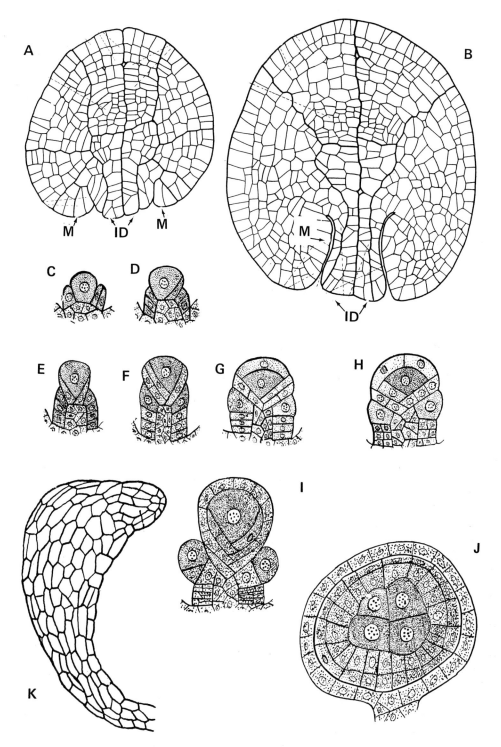

FIGURE 17–8. *A, B.* Two stages in the development of the sporocarp of *Pilularia*, after Johnson (1898). M = margin; ID = indusium. *C* to *J*. Developmental series of cross sections of the sorus in *Marsilea hirsuta*, after Tournay (1951). The megasporangium is shown at the top and microsporangial initials developing below (bulging conspicuously in *I*). *K*. Sporangium of *Pilularia*, after D. H. Campbell (1904).

337

on the receptacular ridge (Fig. 17–8, *I*). These divide to produce long stalks that occasionally branch (Fig. 17–6, *A*, *B*). The terminal sporangial initial is eventually formed and the microsporangium is then formed in the same fashion as the megasporangium.

The sporangia have no dehiscence mechanism. *Pilularia*, however, seems to produce a vestigial, subapical annulus (Fig. 17–8, *K*), and thus its sporangium has been described as schizaeaceous in form. Some tendency exists toward mixed development of sporangia in at least *Marsilea polycarpa* and in *Pilularia*, but maturation is more or less synchronous.

When the sporocarps are ripe, they resemble dried nuts and in this form may remain alive and viable for many years, at least 35 to the author's knowledge. They must be soaked in water and ordinarily scarified in order to "germinate." Most of the internal tissue of the ripe sporocarp is gelatinous and can absorb water readily. When the sporocarp of *Marsilea* germinates, it splits open along its upper edge and the tissue mass extends out, appearing as a worm, and carries with it the elongate sori (Fig. 17–10, *A*). The germination is similar but possibly less regular in *Regnellidium*. In *Pilularia*, the sporocarp breaks up into four parts.

Following germination, the spores are released by tissue decomposition and the subsequent stages in the life cycle are extremely rapid. If open, dried sporocarps are placed in water at room temperature, sperm of *Marsilea crenata* are observed swimming about in 5 hours, of *M. quardifolia* in 8 to 9 hours, and of *Pilularia* in 18 hours. The archegonia mature in 15 hours in the two *Marsilea* species and in 28 to 30 hours in *Pilularia* (Buchholz and Selett, 1941). After this rapid gametophyte development, it is only a matter of several days until advanced embryos are seen. The family is thus adapted to wet conditions, can survive over long periods of drought, and is capable of becoming reestablished in a very short time.

The microspores germinate immediately on shedding. An unequal division first produces a large cell and a small one (Fig. 17–9, *A*). The small one has been interpreted as a remnant of the vegetative body and thus called a "prothallial cell," or it has been considered the homolog of similar cells in filicalean ferns which produce the first rhizoid and thus called the "rhizoid cell." Neither interpretation can be defended (see comments under *Selaginella*). In certain species the small cell may divide once. The larger cell divides equally (Fig. 17–9, *B*), and each of the two resultant cells, which have been called antheridial initials, goes through a series of divisions (Fig. 17–9, *C* to *F*) so as to produce an isolating jacket around the two primary spermatogenous cells (in *F*). The latter each go on (*G* and *H*) to produce a packet of 16 sperm which are corkscrew in shape, multiflagellate, and bear a terminal vesicle (Fig. 17–10, *B*).

The megaspore is large enough to be clearly seen with the naked eye, and on shedding it contains a single nucleus and a quantity of stored food material. The nucleus takes up a position at the apex where the cytoplasm extends into the protrusion. The first division is either transverse, cutting off a cell the shape of the apical nipple, or this is preceded by a lateral division (Fig. 17–9, *I*, *J*). Subsequent divisions (*K*) isolate the single archegonial initial (AI in *K*). No further divisions occur in the inner cell, which occupies essentially all the volume of the megaspore. The archegonial initial divides transversely (Fig. 17–9, *L*) to establish the neck initial and the axial row initial. Subsequent divisions are as in other archegonia. The neck at maturity is only two cells long (Fig. 17–9, *N*, *O*). There is a single, uninucleate neck canal cell (NCC in *N*).

The female gametophyte secretes a gelatinous sheath that completely surrounds the megaspore wall and extends out at the spore apex as a thin, cone-shaped mass. The sperm are attracted to the mass and slowly swim through the cone. At one stage the cone may be seen containing a number of sperm all oriented toward the archegonium. The sperm of *Marsilea* are among the best known structurally because of their large size, the facility with which they may be obtained, and the particular ease with which they may be observed swimming slowly through the viscous gelatinous sheath of the female gametophyte.

The embryo is composed of relatively few cells and grows entirely within the apical nipple of the female gametophyte. Its segmentation patterns are relatively diagrammatic. The first division of the zygote is longi-

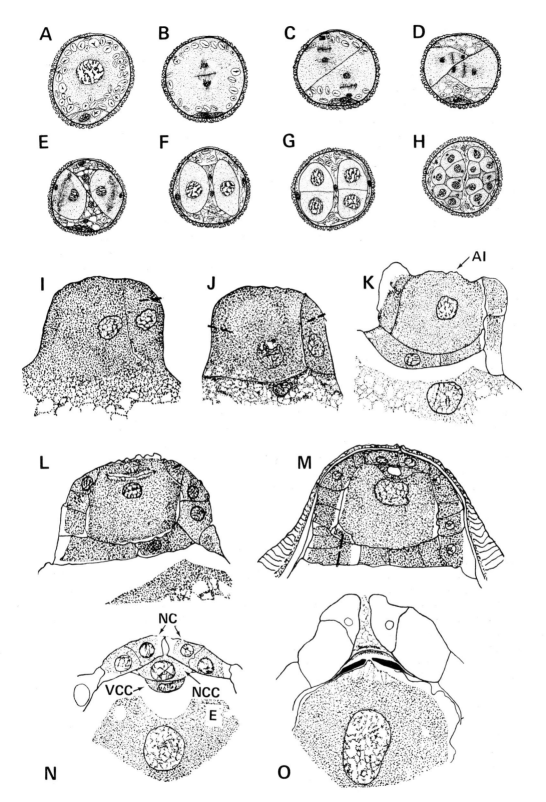

FIGURE 17–9. *A* to *H*. Development of the male gametophyte in *Marsilea quadrifolia*, after Sharp (1914). *I* to *O*. Development of the archegonium in *Marsilea diffusa*, after Demalsy-Fellar (1957). The archegonial initial is established in *K* after the two divisions shown in *I* and *J*. NC = neck cells; VCC = ventral canal cell; E = egg.

339

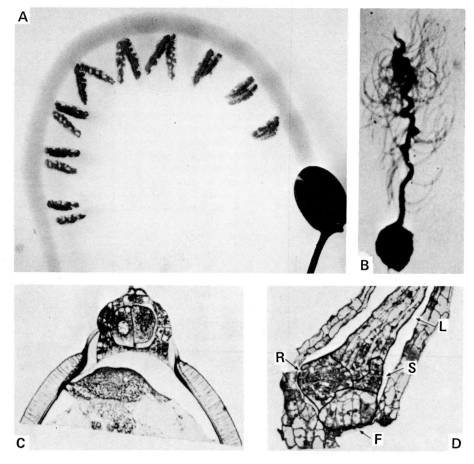

FIGURE 17–10. *A*. Germinated sporocarp of *Marsilea quadrifolia*. *B*. Sperm of *M. quadrifolia*, after Lang (1936). *C*. Gametophyte of *M. narda* containing a two-celled embryo, after Thompson (1934). *D*. Older embryo of *M. narda*, after Thompson (1934). L = leaf; R = root; F = foot; S = stem.

tudinal (Fig. 17–10, *C*). The organs, root, stem, leaf, and foot are traceable to quadrant cells (Fig. 17–10, *D*, in which the primary organs have been outlined).

The Marsileaceae is clearly a family of ferns of filicalean affinity. The vegetative structure of its sporophyte, its sporangia (although reduced and of two kinds), its sorus, and even its peculiar sporocarp do not alone justify ordinal separation, although some will disagree. However, the gametophytes have advanced far beyond their homosporous ancestors, producing a distinct morphological hiatus. Therefore, it seems consistent with a reasonably conservative approach

to taxonomy to recognize the order Marsileales.

Anatomically, the stems, roots, and leaves of the Marsileaceae are relatively generalized in terms of ferns, even though the plants may have a gross unfernlike appearance. These features, as well as others of the sporangium and sorus, indicate origin from a form combining features of the Schizaeaceae, Anemiaceae, and Lygodiaceae. There is in no way a conclusion. The elongate sorus, whose separate vascular supply parallels that of the sporocarp wall, is particularly suggestive of the Stromatopteridaceae. Stem anatomy and branching pattern suggests certain Pteridaceae.

18

Salviniales

The Salviniales include two genera, *Azolla*, with 6 worldwide species, and *Salvinia*, with 10 mostly tropical ones. There are many more fossil species described, some of *Azolla* as old as Cretaceous. Both genera were widespread during Tertiary times. These genera of small, floating, mat-forming aquatic ferns have many characteristics in common, but their differences as well as their distinctiveness throughout their known geologic history lead many authors to place each in its own family, the Azollaceae and the Salviniaceae.

Salvinia (Fig. 18–1, *A*) has a horizontal, branched rhizome that bears leaves in whorls of three. The leaves alternate from node to node such that there are six orthostichies. There are no roots, but one leaf of each whorl is submerged, highly branched (pinnate, obscurely pinnate, or possibly monopodial), hairy, and suggests root function (Fig. 18–1, *B*). The other two leaves of a whorl are laminate with reticulate venation (Fig. 18–1, *B*), usually less than 2 cm long, and may appear somewhat cup-shaped. Their upper surfaces bear a mass of egg-beater-like hairs (Fig. 18–1, *C*) that can trap considerable amounts of air if the plants are immersed and also have been reported to digest external protein (Andrews and Ellis, 1913). The hairs on the submerged leaves (Fig. 18–1, *D* to *F*) are composed of three cells each, a foot cell and one long and one short horizontally oriented cell. Reproductive structures ("sporocarps") are borne on submerged leaves (Fig. 18–1, *B*; Fig. 18–3, *A*). In the rhizome there is a poorly developed vascular cylinder with a small pith surrounded by a few tracheids. The leaf trace is simple. Branching is nodal but not axillary.

Azolla (Fig. 18–2, *A*, *B*) has a thin, branching, horizontal rhizome bearing leaves and roots. The leaves are minute, often in the range 0.5 mm or less, and are

FIGURE 18–1. *Salvinia natans.* *A.* Plant as viewed from above. *B.* Two floating leaves and a submerged one, the latter bearing two sporocarpiferous trusses. *C.* Egg-beater trichomes from the upper surface of the floating leaf. *D.* Two-armed trichomes from the submerged leaf. *E.* One trichome from *D* enlarged and seen from the side. *F.* Large circular basal cell of the trichome in *E* as seen from above.

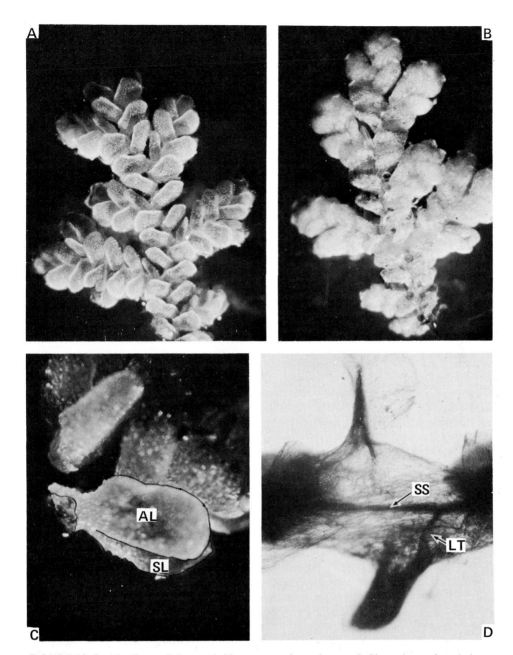

FIGURE 18–2. *Azolla caroliniana.* *A.* Plant as seen from above. *B.* Plant as seen from below. *C.* Two lobes of a leaf. AL = aerial lobe; SL = submerged lobe. *D.* Part of a plant cleared to show the stem stele, SS, and the leaf trace, LT.

arranged in alternate rows (Fig. 18–2, *D*). Each leaf is bilobed. The submerged lobe (SL in Fig. 18–2, *C*) is more delicate and less extended than the aerial lobe (AL). Figure 18–2, *A* is of the upper side of the plant and

shows all aerial lobes, while *B* is of the lower side and shows all submerged lobes. At the base of each leaf there is a small cavity opening by a small pore that contains the nitrogen-fixing, blue-green alga *Anabaena*. At the rhizome apex there is an apical cell with two cutting faces The leaves are traceable to segments produced on the upper side, while branches and the endogenous roots arise from tissues derived from lower segments. Branches occur at nodes. The small stem stele (SS in Fig. 18–2, *D*) is essentially protostelic. The protoxylem is on the upper side and metaxylem occurs as an arc across the lower side with parenchyma in between. The leaf trace is simple and diminutive (LT in Fig. 18–2, *D*). The apical cell of the root is relatively much larger than that of other ferns. The root cap is only two cells thick, tenuously attached, and occasionally slips away, leaving the root apex to appear stemlike. Reproductive bodies ("sporocarps") are borne in pairs (in fours in one species) on the lower leaf lobes.

Sporocarps of *Salvinia*, considered single sori, are borne terminally on each of the branches of the sporocarpiferous branch of the submerged leaf (Fig. 18–3, *A*). The proximal one (shown enlarged in *B*) contains only megasporangia, while others contain only microsporangia. The hairy sporocarp wall, generally interpreted as indusium, is only two cells thick, except at the apex. Within a young sporocarp there is an elevated sporangiferous receptacle (SR in Fig. 18–3, *F*) which becomes highly branched in microsporocarps (Fig. 18–3, *E*) and in megasporocarps of some species. In species such as *S. natans*, there are approximately 20 short-stalked megasporangia symmetrically disposed around the receptacle. The microsporangia are produced in greater numbers. The microsporangiate sorus shown in Fig. 18–3, *C* was smashed out, then stained, and appears as such in *E*. Stalks of microsporangia are longer, thinner, and occasionally branched (Fig. 18–3, *D*). Sporangial walls show no sign of cellular differentiation or of a dehiscence mechanism (Fig. 18–3, *D*). The sporogenous tissue in the young sporangium of *Salvinia* is surrounded by only two cell layers, rarely three. Thus the cell layer, which is the mother layer of the tapetum and the inner wall layer in other ferns, here acts directly as tapetum. In the megasporangium 32 spores are formed, but only one matures. In the microsporangia 64 trilete spores are produced, which are shed as a unit in a hardened, rounded, and internally alveolar mass, the massula. There is a tendency for mixed development of sporangia in *Salvinia* (note the several large ones in Fig. 18–3, *C*, one at the arrow).

Morphologically the sporocarps of *Azolla* are much like those of *Salvinia*. The large ones in Fig. 18–4, *A* are microsporangiate, while the one in *B* is megasporangiate. The sporocarp wall is delicate and two cells thick except at the apex. Both kinds of sporocarps begin their development in the same way. An apical megasporangial initial appears at the apex (Fig. 18–5, *A*), and below it the sporocarp wall (SW) appears as a superficial outgrowth. Further development of the megasporangium takes place, and eventually microsporangial initials appear on the stalk below (MI in Fig. 18–5, *C*). From this point onward, in any one sporocarp if the megasporangium develops the microsporangia abort (Fig. 18–5, *D*), and if the megasporangium aborts the microsporangia mature. The two kinds of sporocarps thus diverge rather late in ontogeny. Note in particular that the first sporangium is apical in origin and subsequent ones arise below on a stalk that grows in length from beneath. The microsporangia come later to be situated on a distinct column (SR in Fig. 18–4, *C*). It is these soral features and the aquatic habitat of the Salviniales that have caused many to suggest that among other ferns, the order is most nearly related to the Hymenophyllaceae.

The megasporangium in some species shows the three cell layers partly developed surrounding the sporogenous tissue (Fig. 18–5, *C*). Each megasporangium produces 32 spores, but only one matures. As it does, it comes to nearly fill the sporangium, and the latter fills the sporocarp. A mound or cushion is developed on the top of the spore and on it are three "floats" (FL in Fig. 18–4, *F*). These bodies contain the aborted spores and, in origin and structure, are as the massulae in microsporangia. Part of the sporangium wall remains attached (SW in Fig. 18–4, *F*).

The microsporangia develop in the same way as the megasporangia (Fig. 18–5, *E* to *H*). They become long stalked, globose, and generally show no differentiation of cells in the wall layer (Fig. 18–4, *C* to *E*). A vestigial, oblique, and uninterrupted annulus is reported on microsporangia of some species. The 64

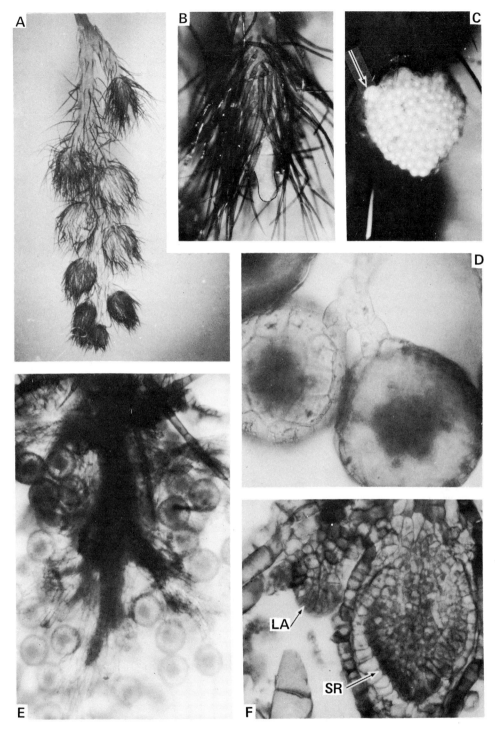

FIGURE 18–3. *Salvinia natans.* *A.* Sporocarpiferous truss from a submerged leaf. *B.* Mega-sporocarp from the upper end of *A* (i.e., proximal end). *C.* Microsporocarp from *A* with wall removed. *D.* Pair of microsporangia from *C.* *E.* Highly branched sporangiferous truss from within the mass shown in *C.* *F.* Longitudinal section through the tip of a sporocarpiferous branch of a submerged leaf. LA = apex of that branch of the leaf; SR = sporangiferous receptacle before branching.

345

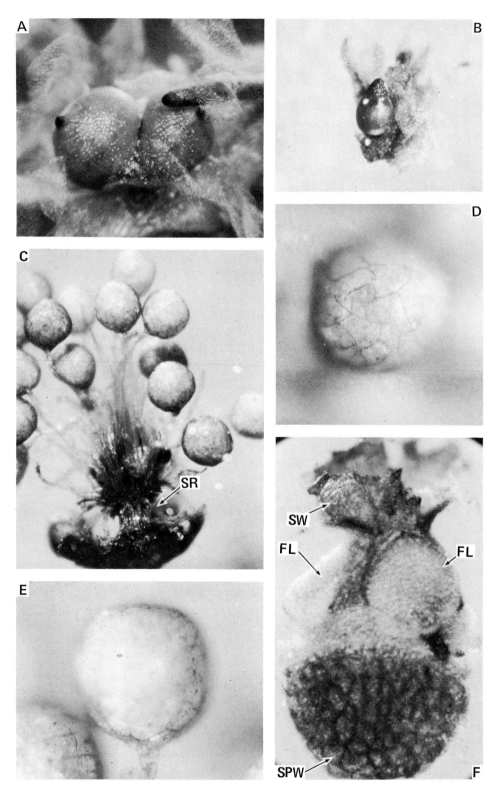

FIGURE 18–4. *Azolla caroliniana. A.* Two microsporocarps. *B.* Megasporocarp. *C.* Microsporocarp with wall removed. SR = short stalked sporangiferous receptacle. *D.* Surface view of a microsporangium. *E.* Microsporangium showing stalk. *F.* Megaspore with its accessories. SW = sporangium wall; FL = floats of the apical cushion; SPW = outer spore wall (perispore) around base.

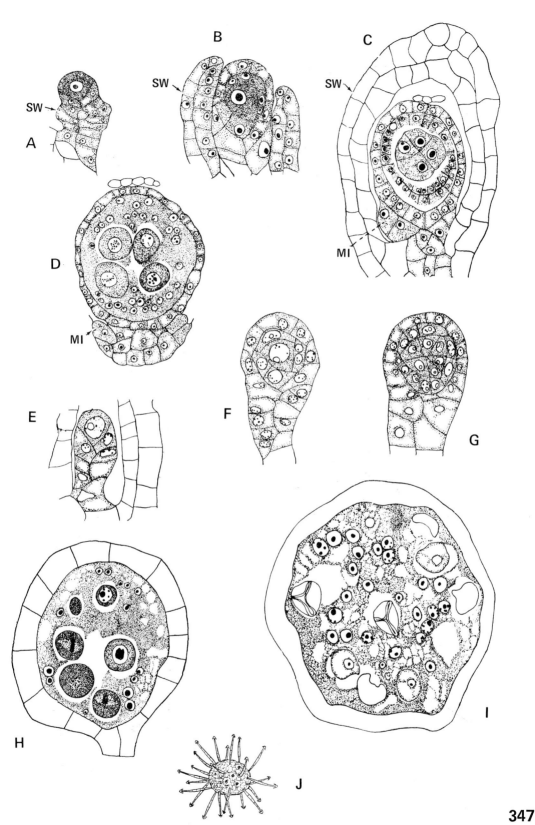

FIGURE 18–5. *A* to *D*. Development of the megasporangium and its covering in *Azolla nilotica*, after Demalsy (1953). SW = sporocarp wall; MI = microsporangial initials. *E* to *I*. Development of the microsporangium in *A. nilotica*, after Demalsy (1953). *J*. Free massula containing microspores and with projecting glochidia of *A. filiculoides*, after Svenson (1944).

microspores are at first distributed uniformly within the liquid, multinucleate contents (periplasmodium) of the sporangium (Fig. 18–5, *I*). The spores become peripherally situated and the mass develops numerous internal vacuoles and external projections (glochidia), then hardens before it is shed as a unit (Fig. 18–5, *J*). The presence, absence, and form of the glochidia are important specific characters of the massula.

The fossil *Azolla primaeva* from Eocene rocks bears two kinds of sporocarps, one of which contains three megasporangia and the other microsporangia and megasporangia (Hills, 1967).

In both *Salvinia* and *Azolla* ripe sporocarps sink to the bottom of the water. They are released in the former by tissue decomposition and in the latter by what appears to be circumscissile dehiscence of the sporocarp. In *Salvinia* the spores rise to the surface, where the rest of the life cycle is completed, but in *Azolla* the female gametophyte remains below until it contains a well-developed embryo.

The megaspore of *Salvinia* has some bilateral symmetry and it floats in a definite orientation. The spore divides to produce a small apical cell and a large central cell. From the former is built up a bilateral, somewhat protruding cellular and photosynthetic mass that bears archegonia on its upper surface. The inner cell forms a free nucleate mass (seen as a space within the spore wall, SW in Fig. 18–6, *J*). The mature female gametophyte is shown from one side and contained within the sporangial wall in Fig. 18–6, *H*. In *I* the apical pad is shown alone. The archegonia are ordinary in ontogeny and complete in cellular makeup (Fig. 18–6, *G*; AR in *I*).

In *Azolla* the first division of the megaspore is unequal and similar to that in *Salvinia*. *Azolla*, however, forms a more rounded archegonium-bearing cushion above the central free nucleate mass. The cushion displaces, but does not dislodge, the spore accessories (i.e., the external, acellular pad upon which are situated the three "floats" and the remains of the sporangium wall). These structures remain until embryos are well formed. One to several archegonia similar to those of *Salvinia* are produced; subsequent ones are formed only if the first one goes unfertilized.

In *Salvinia* the male gametophyte develops as a protruding structure from the massula while still contained within the sporangium wall (Fig. 18–6, *E*). Each gametophyte (shown from two views in Fig. 18–6, *C*, *D*) contains two separated and asymmetrically disposed spermatogenous areas, interpreted as antheridia, of four sperm each. At the opposite end there is a "prothallial cell" (PC). Sperm are released apparently by wall decomposition.

The male gametophyte of *Azolla* (Fig. 18–6, *A*, *B*) contains a "prothallial cell" (PC in *B*) within the spore wall (SPW) and a single, protruding antheridium that is composed of eight sperm delimited by a five-celled jacket. The gametophyte does not protrude from within the massula, but the latter must in part decompose to allow the sperm to escape. Cell lineages within the antheridium are unlike those in antheridia of similar appearance in filicalean ferns. The bulging antheridial initial is cut off first. The inner cell then divides unequally to cut off the "prothallial cell." In the development of the antheridium the primary spermatogenous cell is not the sister cell of the jacket mother cell as is the case in filicalean ferns.

The embryology of *Azolla* is consistent with that of most higher Filicales. The first division of the zygote (heavy wall in Fig. 18–6, *K*) is oblique. The first stem and the first leaf (S and L in Fig. 18–6, *L*) seem related in origin to the two outer quadrants, while the foot and root (F and R) seem related to the inner ones.

The embryogeny of *Salvinia* is not at all clear. Asymmetry is evident from the first division, and the orientation of parts in the older embryo somewhat confuses the issue. The first leaf (L_1 in Fig. 18–6, *J*) appears terminal and the stem apex (ST) is inverted. The first division of the zygote is nearly longitudinal. An octant of cells is established after several more divisions. Four basal octant cells (i.e., those away from the archegonial neck) form foot. The leaf and stem arise from the outer octants. A functionless area, referred to as a "vestigial root," is present in the outer or in the inner group. Certain aspects of *Salvinia* embryogeny suggest that of the rootless *Trichomanes*. However, the embryogeny of neither one is known with any degree of certainty.

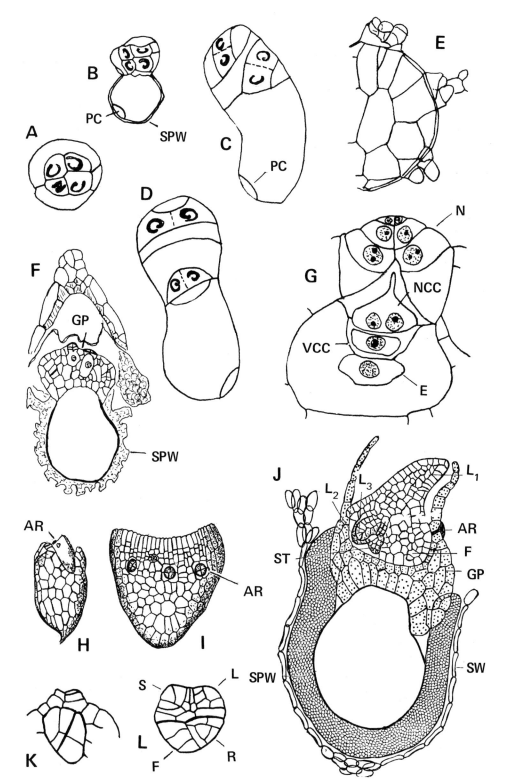

FIGURE 18–6. *A, B.* Cross and longitudinal sections of the male gametophyte of *Azolla filiculoides.*
C, D. Two longitudinal views of the male gametophyte of *Salvinia natans,* after Belajeff (1898).
E. Male gametophytes projecting from the surface of the massula in *S. natans.* *F.* Female gameto-
phyte and its accessories in *Azolla filiculoides.* *G.* Archegonium of *Salvinia natans,* after Yasui (1911).
H, I. Two views of the female gametophyte of *S. natans.* *J.* embryo of *Salvinia* contained within the
female gametophyte. *K, L.* Two early stages in embryology of *Azolla filiculoides.* *A, B, F, K, L* after
D. H. Campbell (1928). *E, H* to *J* after Pringsheim (1863). PC = "prothallial" cell; SPW = spore
wall; NCC = neck canal cell; VCC = ventral canal cell; E = egg; AR = archegonium; L = leaf;
S = stem; F = foot; GP = gametophytic pad; SW = sporocarp wall; ST = stem apex.

349

19

Marattiales

The Marattiales is a morphologically distinct order of obscure affinities. Most authors have recognized only a single family, the Marattiaceae, while others, to accommodate the living genera, have recognized as many as four. An intermediate position is taken here with the presentation of two families. The first, the Marattiaceae, includes *Marattia*, with about 60 species; *Angiopteris*, with possibly 100 species; *Macroglossum*, with 2 species; and *Archangiopteris*, with 1 to 4 species. The second, the Danaeaceae, includes *Christensenia*, with one or possibly more species, and *Danaea*, with about 30 species. The Marattiales are mostly plants of tropical rainforests. Four genera are essentially restricted to the western Pacific area. *Danaea* occurs only in the American tropics.

Angiopteris, *Macroglossum*, and *Marattia* have rather large, globose stems that are occasionally 2 ft or more in diameter. The stem is shielded by fleshy stipules, two of which are attached to each leaf base. The specimen in Fig. 19–1, *A*, side view, and *B*, top view, was only about 20 cm across. In *C* the specimen is shown after a transverse, tangential slice was made. The same structures, petiole (P), stipules (S), and young, still-coiled leaf (L) are indicated in *B* and *C*. *Archangiopteris*, *Christensenia*, and *Danaea* produce creeping rhizomes that are mostly dorsiventral. They bear similar stipules, but they and the petioles are spaced. The stems bear thick, fleshy roots (R in Fig. 19–1, *A*). Many species produce adventitious buds on stipules (SB in Fig. 19–5, *B*). The entire structure in Fig. 19–1, *A* to *C* was of such origin and it was still attached to its parental organ.

Leaves of the Marattiales are one to three times pinnate (Fig. 19–1, *D*) except in *Danaea*, where they are occasionally simple, and in *Christensenia* (Fig. 19–2,

351

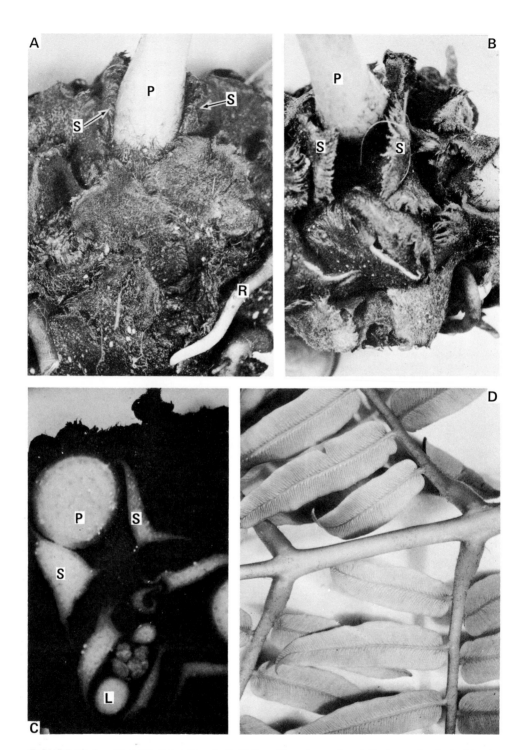

FIGURE 19–1. *Angiopteris evecta.* *A, B.* Side and top views of a relatively small spherical trunk. × 0.6. *C.* Same specimen as *A* and *B* with some parts sliced off. *D.* Portion of a frond. × 0.6. P = petiole; S = stipule; R = root; L = young leaf uncoiling.

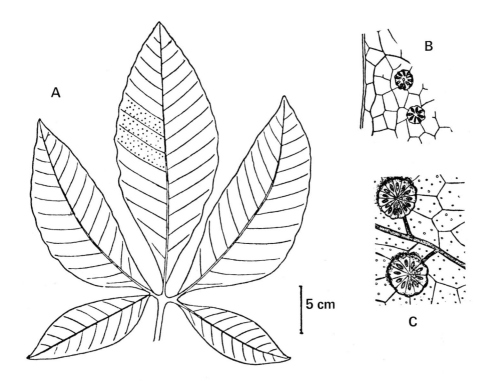

FIGURE 19–2. *Christensenia aesculifolia.* *A*. Leaf. Dots represent synangia. *B, C*. Portions of blade with synangia and showing venation. *A, B* after Holttum (1954); *C* redrawn from Diels (1902).

A), where they are palmate. Leaves of the Marattiaceae are occasionally extremely large, up to 14 ft. long with petioles as large as a man's arm. Conspicuous swellings (pulvini) occur at the bases of pinnae in several genera (Fig. 9–1, *D*) and at the base of the blade in the simple-leafed *Danaea*. Venation is open dichotomous (Fig. 19–1, *D*; Fig. 19–6, *A, B*) except in *Christensenia*, where it is reticulate (Fig. 19–2, *B, C*).

Marattialean roots have certain distinctive features. They are fleshy and nearly naked. The few hairs have been described as septate. The stele is polyarch (Fig. 19–3, *B*) with long, thin xylem arms. Parenchyma is occasionally present in the center. Phloem areas are small, alternating with xylem arms, and usually two to three cells to the inside of the endodermis. The pericycle is one or two cells thick and its cells are not enlarged as are those of filicalean ferns. Mucilage canals occur in the cortex and throughout the plant body. The outer epidermal cell walls are thickened when exposed.

Cross sections of many Carboniferous roots are readily recognized as marattialean.

Large marattialean stems have complex anatomy (Fig. 19–3, *A*; Fig. 19–4, *C*). The photograph in Fig. 19–3, *A* is of the same specimen as is shown in Fig. 19–1, *A* to *C* after it was cut transversely and painted with a solution of phloroglucinol–hydrochloric acid to stain lignified cell walls. The stele on first examination appears polystelic, but the large, curved sheets of vascular tissue are not distinct (Fig. 19–4, *C*). In small plants the stele (Fig. 19–4, *B, D*) is an amphiphloic siphonostele with distinct gaps from which arise the double leaf traces. The specimen in Fig. 19–4, *A* is slightly larger than the one in *B* and shows the beginnings of the adult complexity. In the older plant the traces to a single leaf often show considerably separated attachments to the cauline stele (Fig. 19–4, *C*). The traces of large leaves divide profusely before entering the petiole (Fig. 19–3, *A*). A part of the cauline vascular system (Fig. 19–3, *C*) shows xylem

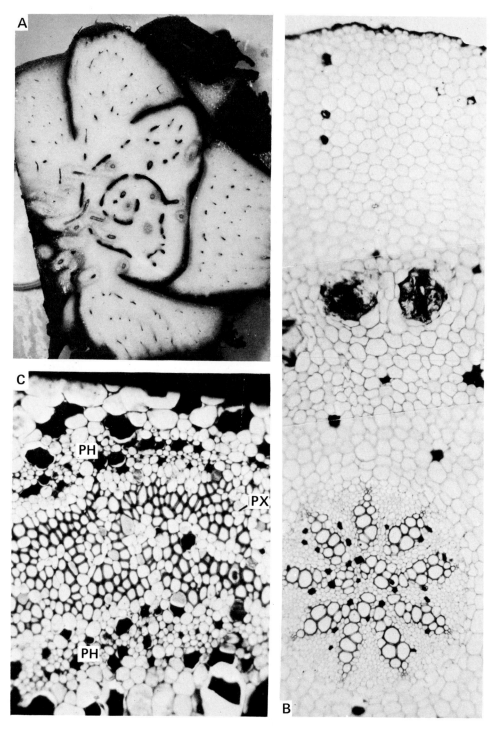

FIGURE 19–3. *A.* Cross section of the plant of *Angiopteris evecta* shown in Fig. 19–1, *A.* The surface was painted with hydrochloric acid–phloroglucinol solution to stain lignified tissue. *B.* Sector of a cross section of a root of *Marattia alata.* *C.* Portion of the vascular cylinder of the stem of *Danaea simplicifolia.* PH = phloem; PX = protoxylem pole.

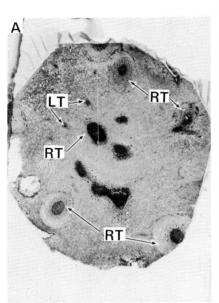

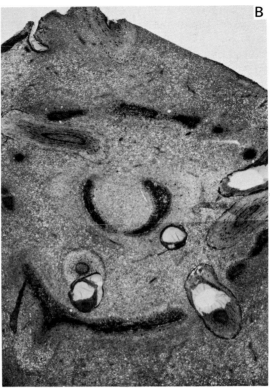

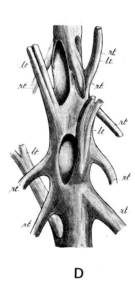

FIGURE 19–4. *Angiopteris evecta.* *A.* Cross section of the stem of a very small plant. LT = leaf trace; RT = root. *B.* As *A*, but of a slightly larger stem. *C, D.* Reconstructions of steles of an older, *C*, and a younger, *D*, plant, after Farmer and Hill (1902). lt = leaf trace; rt = root.

with a considerable amount of included parenchyma, embedded protoxylem points (PX), and phloem followed by pericycle and endodermis on both sides.

The form genus *Psaronius* includes trunks of Carboniferous and Permian marattialean ferns. These were large tree ferns with columnar trunks (Fig. 19–14, *A*) and pinnate leaves. They bore roots very similar in structure to those of the extant genera of the order. The stems also were similar to those of extant Marattiales but more complex. The trunks at their bases were composed of a small true stem and a massive root mantle. Farther up the mantle decreased and the stem increased, but the total diameter of the trunk decreased, just as in some Cyatheaceae. The smaller, basal part of the true stem showed an amphiphloic siphonostele or two concentric ones. At higher levels the complexity increased (Fig. 19–14, *D*) with as many as 12 stelar cycles present. Each cycle bore large gaps, as in modern forms. Leaves were spirally arranged at the base and whorled at the apex. Leaf traces were large and single.

Stem apices of all young marattialean plants described have a single narrow apical cell (Fig. 19–5, *A*). Older plants of some species may have several apical initials in a similar prismatic layer.

The stipules are outgrowths of the leaf bases and their vascular supply comes directly from the leaf traces (Fig. 19–5, *C*). Each pair of stipules encloses the next younger leaf (Fig. 19–5, *D*).

The sori of *Angiopteris* are oblong rings of free sporangia on the lower surfaces of leaves and each is over a vein (Fig. 19–6, *A*, *C*). Those of *Macroglossum* show many sporangia in a groove on each side of a vein. Sori of *Archangiopteris* show two elongate, occasionally forking, series of sporangia along the veins. *Christensenia* bears a ring of sporangia fused together to form a synangium (Fig. 19–2, *B*, *C*). Each sporangium of *Christensenia* dehisces by an apical slit rather than by a longitudinal one as in the three aforementioned genera. *Danaea* produces an elongate synangium (Fig. 19–6, *B*) and each sporangium forms a terminal pore when ripe. The entire synangium is often sunken in a groove. *Marattia* produces a rather complex bivalved sporocarp (Fig. 19–6,

D, *E*; Fig. 19–8, *F*, *G*) in which are contained two linear synangia. The sporocarp opens when ripe and each sporangium dehisces by means of a longitudinal slit toward the inside (Fig. 19–6, *D*).

The synangium of *Danaea* begins as an elongate receptacular meristem sunken in a groove over the vein (shown in cross section in Fig. 19–7, *A* and in longitudinal section in *B*). All the cells of the meristem divide parallel to its surface (Fig. 19–7, *C*, which is *A* enlarged, and *D*, which is a portion of *B* enlarged). The nuclei of isolated hypodermal areas, the future sporogenous areas, stain deeper than elsewhere (arrows in Fig. 19–7, *C*, *D*). Growth in the anticlinal direction of the intersporangial areas keeps pace with the growth of the sporangia. Few additional cell divisions take place in the median line of the synangium, and here the growth is primarily by cell elongation (Fig. 19–7, *E*; Fig. 19–8, *A*, *C*, *E*). Between the sporangia and within one of the lateral series, however, the cells divide and maintain their isodiametric form (Fig. 19–7, *F*; Fig. 19–8, *B*, *C*). The internal tissue of each sporangium, which begins as approximately 10 to 12 cells, multiplies to about 20 to 25 cells before any differentiation may be seen (Fig. 19–7, *E*, *F*). Peripheral cells of the inner mass at this point begin to stain differentially and then to enlarge (Fig. 19–8, *B*, *D*) and are recognizable as the tapetum. The covering cells of the sporogenous mass increase and ultimately form a wall about five cells thick. The tapetum breaks down ultimately and the inner wall cells shrink considerably and partly decompose. Note in particular that there is no ontogenetic individuality of the individual sporangia, but they remain indistinguishable until the inner cells assume different cytological characteristics. Recall that in the linear syngangium of *Ophioglossum* the sporangia at maturity appeared even less distinct than in *Danaea*, but they were distinct in origin from particular sporangial initials.

In *Danaea eliptica* (Bower, 1923) adjacent sporogenous areas are in part confluent, with little or no intersporangial tissue.

Although the Marattiales is a specialized and distinct taxon and does not suggest itself to be of angiospermous affinity, the manner of origin of the synangium may present clues

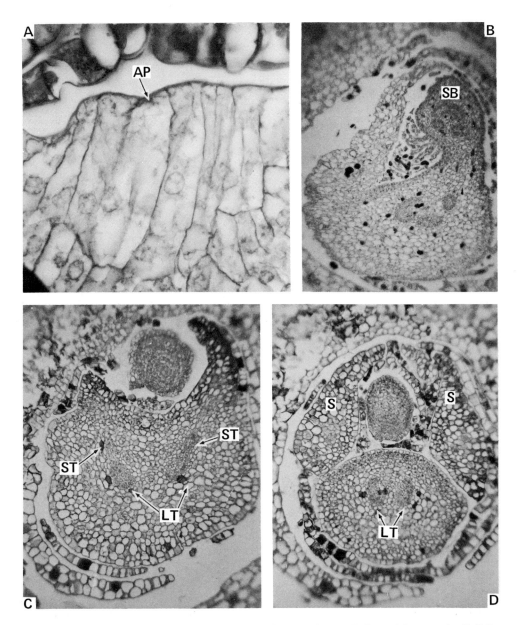

FIGURE 19–5. *A*. Longitudinal section of the stem apex of a small plant of *Danaea simplicifolia*. *B*. Cross section of a leaf of a young plant of *Angiopteris evecta* through the attachment of the stipules. *C*. Cross section through a leaf of a young plant of *Danaea simplicifolia* at the level where the stipular traces branch from the leaf traces. *D*. Cross section of the same leaf as in *C*, but at a slightly lower level, where the stipules are separated from the petiole. The stipules extend as flanges both above and below their attachment. The next younger leaf appears between the two stipules. AP = apical cell; SB = stipular bud; ST = stipular trace; LT = leaf trace; S = stipule.

FIGURE 19–6. *A, C. Angiopteris* sp., sori attached to a pinna. *B. Danaea simplicifolia,* portion of the blade with elongate synangia. *D. Marattia* sp., an open sporocarp in which can be seen the open sporangia of one of the two synangia. *E. Marattia* sp., unopened sporocarps.

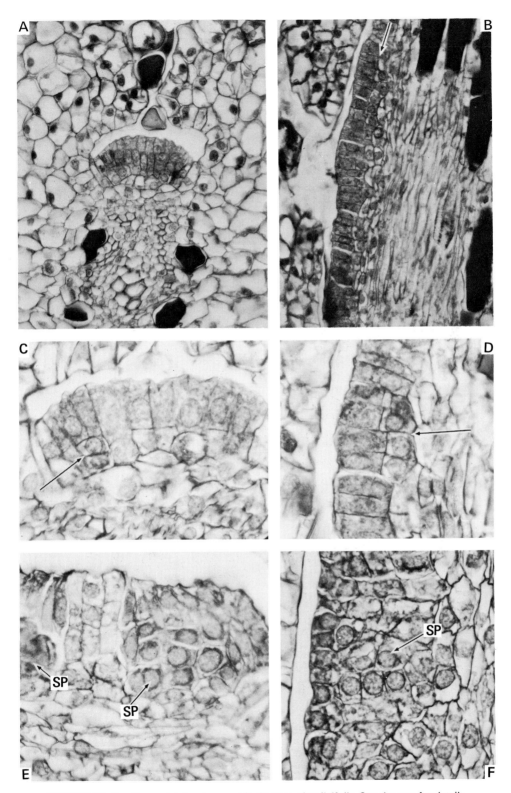

FIGURE 19–7. Synangial development in *Danaea simplicifolia*. See the text for details.

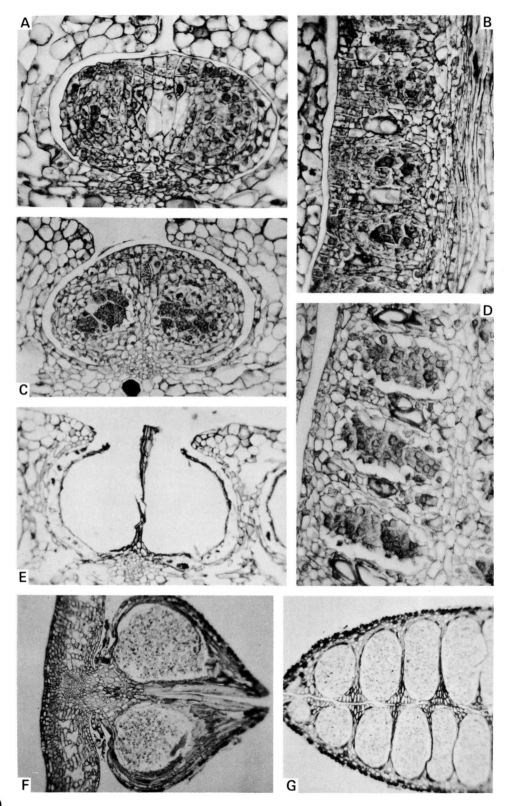

FIGURE 19–8. *A* to *E*. Synangial development in *Danaea simplicifolia* continued from Fig. 19–7. *F, G*. Transverse and longitudinal sections of the sporocarp of *Marattia* sp.

to the manner in which the elongate, laminar "microsporangium" of the Ranales originated. With a little further loss of sporangial integrity in a syngangium like that of *Danaea*, such that the entire hypodermal area would become one continuous sporogenous mass (a tendency seen in *D. eliptica*) and with dehiscence function shifted from individual sporangia to the elongate mass, a "microsporangium" of the angiosperm type would result. If such a sequence of events did take place in the history of angiosperms, it might be anticipated that occasionally the typical, elongate microsporangium would show a tendency to divide. This could conceivably be interpreted to occur in the peculiar stamens of such families as the Malvaceae, Bombacaceae, and Euphorbiaceae, but any assumption that these are primitive angiosperm families would be difficult to defend.

The sorus of *Angiopteris* also begins as a surface receptacular meristem (Fig. 19–9, *A*). As in *Danaea* the entire surface layer divides periclinally and the individual sporangia may be distinguished only after cytological differentiation of patches of hypodermal cells. In Fig. 19–9, *A*, the section is longitudinal to the sorus and SP indicates a future sporangium and ISP an intersporangial area. *Angiopteris* differs from *Danaea* after this stage in ontogeny primarily in the fact that the intersporangial areas do not keep pace with the sporangial ones (Fig. 19–9, *B*, *C*), and the sporangia at maturity appear separate (Fig. 19–9, *D*).

The sporocarp wall of *Marattia* is particularly massive, especially along the two distal edges (Fig. 19–8, *F*). The entire sporocarp wall arises from the receptacle in the manner in which a lateral series of sporangia arise in *Danaea*. Despite its massiveness, the wall seems to be composed of sporangial walls and the intersporangial tissue of each synangium. The receptacle of *Marattia* at maturity is larger than those of the other genera and its two synangia come to appear near laterally attached to a ridge (Fig. 19–8, *F*).

It is difficult to ascribe an annulus to the Marattiales. The exposed wall areas show external cells all of which have thickened and lignified walls (Fig. 19–9, *D*; all the specimens in Fig. 19–6 are stained with phloroglucinol-hydrochloric acid). In *Angiopteris* there is a band or crest of enlarged cells with thicker walls than elsewhere. The band is at the apical end of the longitudinal line of dehiscence and oriented more or less transverse to it. This has been called the annulus, and, even though it does not appear to function as such except in conjunction with all other exposed wall cells, it may be homologous to the annulus in some other ferns or fernlike plants. In form and position it is particularly suggestive of similar cell groupings among coenopterid ferns.

The sporangiate fructifications of the Carboniferous Marattiales are classified into the following seven genera (Mamay, 1950): *Cyathotrachus* (synangia pedicellate; sporangia enclosed in a continuous synangial sheath; basal portion of synangium with central column; apical portion hollow and cuplike); *Ptychocarpus* (synangia pedicellate; sporangia enclosed in a continuous synangial sheath and fused to a central column extending through the entire length of the synangium); *Scolecopteris* (synangia pedicellate; sporangia attached to a central receptacle but free distally); *Sturiella* (synangia pedicellate; sporangia basally fused but free above; annulus present); *Acitheca* (Fig. 19–14, *B*, *C*; synangia sessile; sporangia attached at their bases to a central column, with distal portions free; sporangial apices long and bristlelike); *Asterotheca* (synangia sessile; sporangia attached to a receptacle, but free distally, their long axes parallel to the plane of the pinnule); and *Eoangiopteris* (sori linear; sporangia in two rows along fleshy receptacle; sori situated along lateral veins; sporangia free).

Kidston (1925) was impressed by rather close similarity between individual sporangia of *Acitheca* and *Telangium* of the pteridosperms. He hinted that all evidence of the existence of Marattiales in the Carboniferous may be disputable. Recently attitudes of skepticism regarding conclusions based on association of parts without organic connection have been intensified following several rather remarkable and unexpected discoveries of organ attachments in the "psilophytes," sphenopsids, and aneurophytes. Despite this, the designation of the seven fructification genera as marattialean is almost beyond dispute. They all show a much closer similarity to the extant Marattiales than they do to any

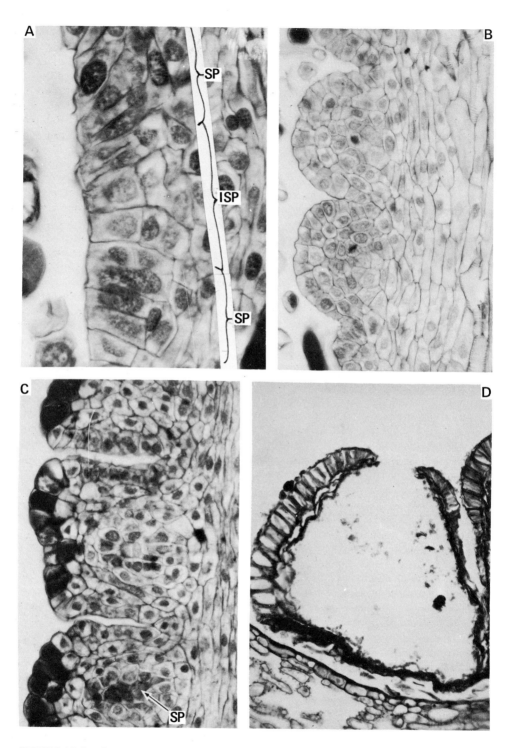

FIGURE 19–9. Sporangial development in *Angiopteris* sp. In *A*, SP = sporangial region of receptacle; ISP = intersporangial region. In *B*, SP = sporogenous tissue.

other taxa. They are borne on *Pecopteris* foliage.[1] The somewhat similar microsporangiate fructifications of pteridosperms are borne on *Neuropteris*, *Alethopteris*, or *Sphenopteris* foliage. *Pecopteris* foliage has not been found organically attached to *Psaronius* but has frequently been found in close association with it. The pinnule trace of *Pecopteris* closely approximates the petiole bundles of *Psaronius*. Finally, the structure of the *Psaronius* trunk is so different from that of other taxa and so very similar to extant marattialean stems that it must be placed in the order.

The gametophyte of *Marattia* (Fig. 19–10, *A* with two young sporophytes), *Angiopteris*, *Macroglossum*, *Christensenia*, and *Danaea* are known. They are all large and conspicuous, probably all perennial, and easy to locate in the field. They are thalloid, surface living, dark green, relatively thick, and often appear more like thallose liverworts than thallose gametophytes of the Filicales. The central cushion or midrib is many cells thick (Fig. 19–10, *B*), and even the margins of the wings are often two cells thick (Fig. 19–10, *D*). All are mycorrhizal with a restricted fungal zone near medianly situated in the thicker parts of the body. The central cushion continues to grow, at least in *Angiopteris*, *Marattia*, and *Danaea*, in thickness over its entire expanse, and it extends itself laterally as periclinal divisions begin in the wing lateral to it. This results in archegonia, which are initiated on the margins of the cushion, later assuming positions well within the cushion. Antheridia (Fig. 19–10, *C*) are produced on the thinner portions of the body below and more or less scattered above. The young gametophyte assumes a two-dimensional form when composed of very few cells and after a few more divisions apical meristematic activity is established (Fig. 19–12).

The antheridia of the Marattiales are massive and sunken, suggesting comparison with the Ophioglossales. A single antheridial initial divides periclinally and establishes the wall initial and the primary spermatogenous cell. The latter goes through a series of simultaneous

[1] This is a form genus of carboniferous fernlike foliage based on pinnule form and venation. See Fig. 3–14 in Andrews (1961) and Fig. 73 in Arnold (1947).

divisions (Fig. 19–10, *E*) until the large number of spermatids are formed. The sperm are large and coiled. A beaded blepharoplast (B in Fig. 19–10, *H*) is formed which is later associated with the flagella. The antheridial wall proper is one cell thick and covers a small area at the surface (Fig. 19–10, *F*). Within it a triangular opercular cell (Fig. 19–10, *G*) is differentiated. An internal jacket derived from cells adjacent to the antheridium surrounds the spermatogenous tissue (Fig. 19–10, *F*).

The archegonium develops according to the usual sequence of divisions. The axial row consists of a pad cell, the egg, a ventral canal cell, and a binucleate neck canal cell (Fig. 19–11, *B*). The stage shown in *A* precedes the final division, which forms the egg and the ventral canal cell. The neck is very short, only three to four cells long. Its cells do not elongate and they (at least in *Danaea simplicifolia* and probably in *Angiopteris* and *Marattia*) are entirely deciduous (Fig. 19–11, *D*). The venter and the neck canal are at first short (Fig. 19–11, *A*), but as the result of growth in thickness of the archegonial cushion, both by periclinal divisions and cell elongation, the archegonium becomes progressively more stretched (Fig. 19–11, *A* to *D*). These points are important, since in *Danaea*, *Macroglossum*, and *Angiopteris* the zygote has been reported to elongate before division and to cut off by a transverse wall a one- or two-celled suspensor. The suspensor in *Macroglossum* is larger and more definable, but the existence of an elongate cell in the suspensor could not be confirmed in the three genera available to the author for study (i.e., *Danaea*, *Angiopteris*, and *Marattia*).

The first division of the zygote is likely transverse throughout the order, and in some members at least the cell toward the archegonial neck forms or remains the unicellular suspensor. It is doubtful, however, that all the single-celled, elongate suspensors described are embryonic in origin, for reasons given above. The proembryo cell forms a small spherical mass of cells, and when it is from four to eight cells in diameter, the apical cells of embryonic organs may be detected. The organs are difficult to trace back with precision, but the most careful work of D. H. Campbell (1911) would indicate that the hemisphere toward the suspensor and archegonial neck

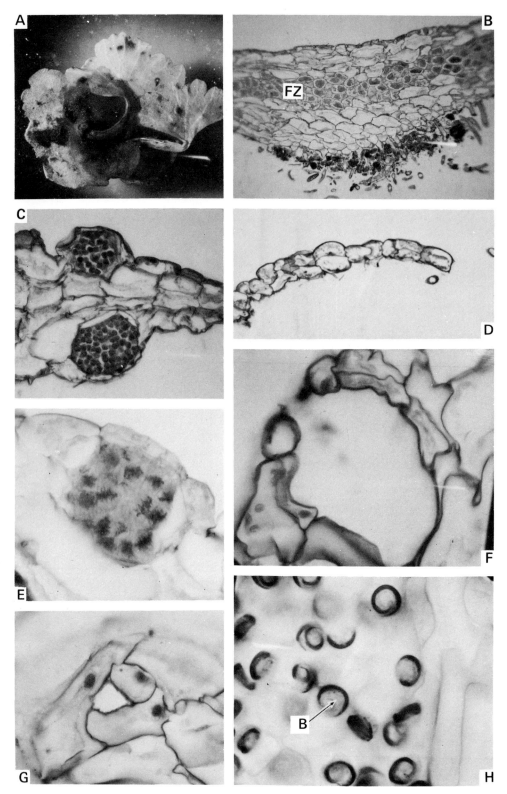

FIGURE 19–10. *A.* Gametophyte with attached young sporophyte of *Marattia* sp.   *B* to *H. Angiopteris.* *B.* Cross section through the midrib region of a gametophyte.   *C.* Cross section through the gametophyte lateral to midrib. Two antheridia are shown.   *D.* Cross section through the edge of the wing of a gametophyte.   *E.* Antheridium in longitudinal section, showing the spermatid mother cells in division.   *F.* Longitudinal section through an empty antheridium.   *G.* Surface view of an antheridium, showing operculum.   *H.* Immature sperm. The granules at B constitute the blepharoblast. FZ = fungal zone.

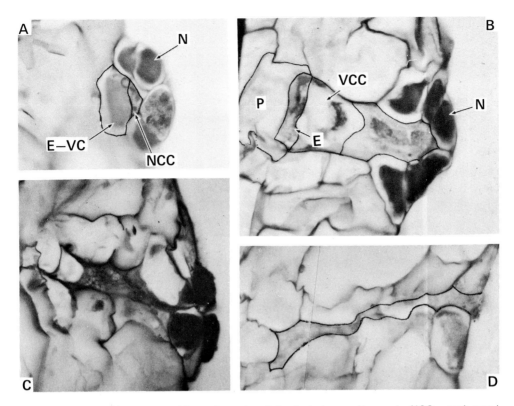

FIGURE 19–11. Younger to older archegonia of *Angiopteris* sp. N = neck; NCC = neck canal cell; E–VC = mother cell of egg and ventral canal cell; VCC = ventral canal cell; E = egg; P = pad cell.

gives rise to foot while the deeper hemisphere forms leaf, stem, and root. This is the interpretation placed on the young embryo in Fig. 19–13, *A*, where NC indicates the neck canal, S the suspensor, and LF the apical cell of the first leaf. The other embryonic organs do not appear in the section. The embryo grows upward into and eventually out of the upper side of the gametophyte (Fig. 19–13, *B* to *E*). The leaf is soon the dominant organ. The vascular system is primarily a leaf–root trace with only a slight extension of procambium toward the stem apex (Fig. 19–13, *C*). The major procambial strand to the leaf in *B* is out of the plane of section. The foot is small and is represented by a girdle of tissue attached to one half to two thirds of the circumference of the embryonic axis. The edge of the foot, F_e, is shown in Fig. 19–13, *D*. In another section of the same embryo in *E*, the foot is cut tangentially in its broadest aspect.

Insofar as vascular plants as a whole are concerned, free sporangia are primitive and synangia are derived. The application of this

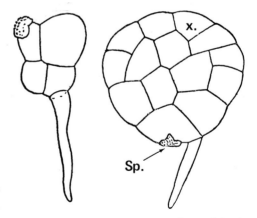

FIGURE 19–12. Young gametophytes of *Angiopteris evecta*, after D. H. Campbell (1928). Sp = spore wall.

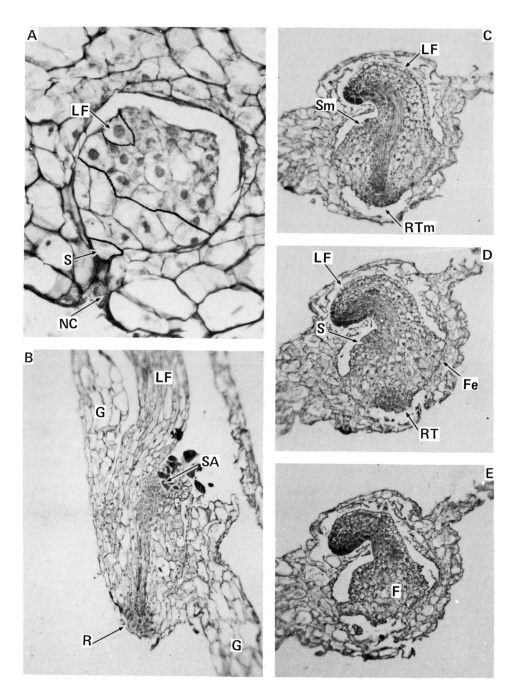

FIGURE 19–13. *A.* Young embryo of *Danaea simplicifolia*. S = suspensor. *B* to *E. Angiopteris* sp. *B.* Young sporophyte after the first leaf has expanded. *C* to *E.* Successive sections of an embryo. G = gametophytic tissue; LF = leaf; SA = stem apex; R = root; Sm = median section of stem apex; RTm = median section of root apex; S = stem apex; Fe = edge of foot; F = foot.

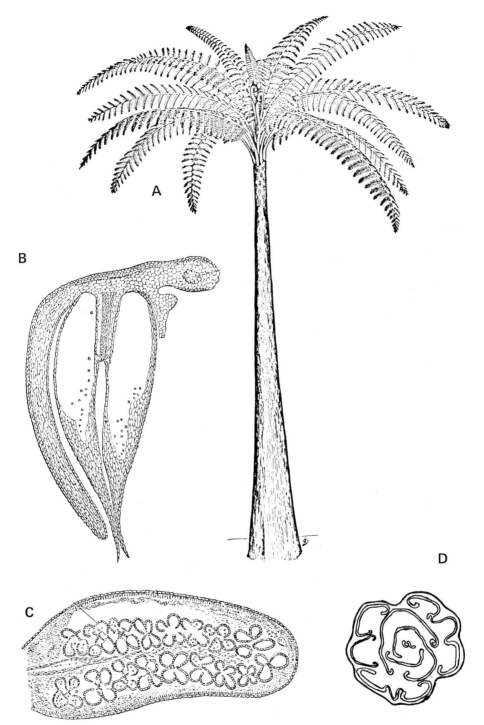

FIGURE 19–14. *A.* Reconstruction of *Psaronius*, after Morgan (1959). *B, C.* Fertile pinna of *Acitheca* (*Scolecopteris*) *polymorpha* in longitudinal and paradermal sections, after Renault (1881). *D.* Outline of the vascular tissue of the stem of *Psaronius punctatus*, after Sterzel (1887).

principle to the Marattiales (as well as to the Cycadales, see Chapter 20) needs re-examination. The similarity between *Marattia* and *Angiopteris* is striking, both in external morphology and in internal structure. If sori are not present, the genera may not be distinguished without resorting to morphologically insignificant specific characters. The sporangia of *Angiopteris*, although discrete at maturity, have no morphological integrity when initiated. On the contrary, a linear series of its sporangia originate, as does a synangium. In the Marattiales, the difference between free sporangia and synangia is directly attributable to differential growth of the intersporangial areas. As viewed here, this leads only to one interpretation: that *Angiopteris* is indeed very closely related to *Marattia*, much closer than their mature sporangiate fructifications would suggest, and that the free sporangiate condition expressed in *Angiopteris* is derived from a synangiate one.

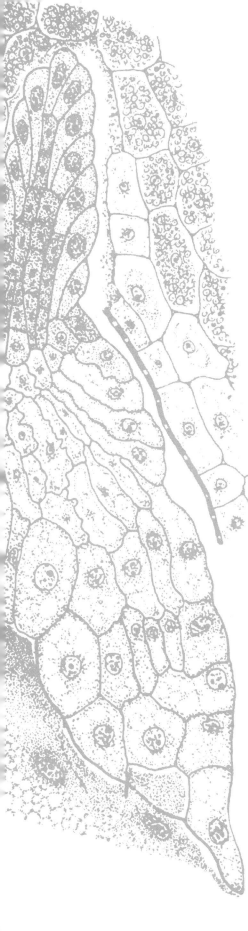

20

Cycadales

The Cycadales, representated today by 9 or 10 relict genera, reached their peak during mid-Mesozoic times and have been on the decline ever since. It is indeed fortunate that most of them are in cultivation or they would certainly be faced with the danger of extinction. Their antiquity is indicated today by the few species per genus and their disjunct distribution. The living genera are usually treated as belonging to either one, two, or three families. When treated as belonging to three families, the genera are classified as below, with the species numbers and distribution indicated.

Cycadaceae
  Cycas, 20 spp., Polynesia to Madagascar, north to
    Japan
Stangeriaceae
  Stangeria, 1 sp., S.E. Africa
Zamiaceae
  Lepidozamia, 2 spp., E. Australia
  Macrozamia, 14 spp., temp. Australia
  Encephalartos, 30 spp., trop. and S. Africa
  Dioön, 3 to 5 spp., Mexico and Central America
  Microcycas, 1 spp., Cuba
  Ceratozamia, 4 spp., Mexico
  Zamia, 30 to 40 spp., trop. America, W. Indies
  Bowenia, 2 spp., N. Australia

The Cycads mostly appear palmlike, with thick cylindrical trunks (*Cycas*, Fig. 20–1, *A*; *Dioön*; *Cerato-zamia*) to 50 ft tall in *Dioön* or with basal, tuberous, and often near-spherical stems (*Zamia*, Fig. 20–2, *B*; *Bowenia*; *Stangeria*, Fig. 20–2, *C*). The spirally arranged leaves of the usually conspicuous crown are tough and fibrous and pinnate (bipinnate in *Bowenia*). The plants are often called sago palms, as several species are used

FIGURE 20–1. *A* to *D. Cycas circinalis.* *A.* Large plant with a branched trunk growing in the park in Suva, Fiji. *B.* Crown of a plant with a nearly mature microsporangiate strobilus. *C.* Crown of a plant showing the following zones of appendages from the apex downward: a terminal cluster of megasporophylls, a zone of cataphylls, a zone of vegetative leaves (basal parts only shown), another zone of cataphylls, and then a zone of megasporophylls with the individual members extending outward. *D.* Large number of seeds developing on megasporophylls below a crown of vegetative leaves. *E* to *G. Encephalartos* sp. *E.* Young microsporangiate strobilus just protruding from within a crown of cataphylls. *F.* Nearly mature microsporangiate strobilus in the center of the crown and below it the cataphylls. *G.* Young megasporangiate strobilus.

FIGURE 20–2. *A. Dioön edule* with a megasporangiate strobilus. *B. Zamia* sp. with a megasporangiate strobilus. *C. Stangeria paradoxica.* *A* to *C.* Growing in the Fairchild Tropical Garden, Miami, Florida.

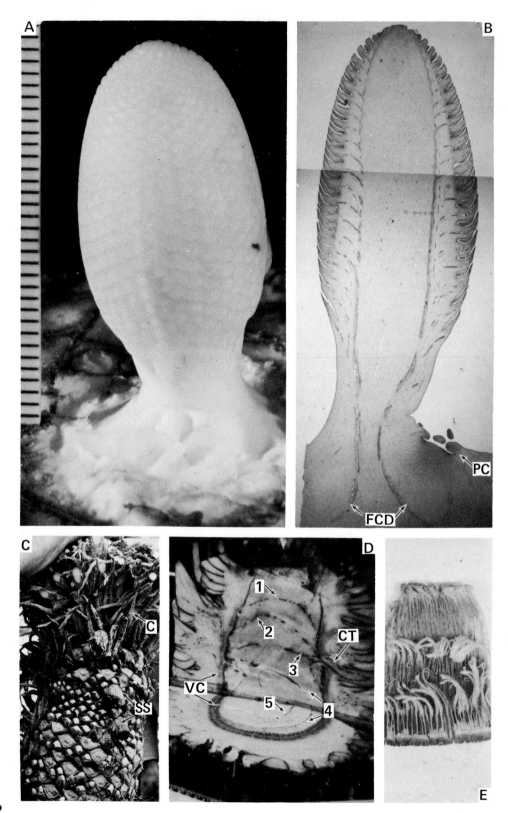

to prepare a starchy food from the pith or occasionally from the seeds. Some or all species are considered poisonous if consumed without special preparation.

Most species of cycads are native to exposed habitats where they are subjected to considerable drying and often grow in extremely well drained substrata. Under these conditions the growth rate may be extremely slow with a *Dioön* 6 to 7 ft. tall reported to be nearly 1,000 years old. However, in a conservatory the same species may grow perhaps 50 times as fast. Branching is usually the result of adventitious bud formation and enhanced by physical injury. This usually makes for more highly branched specimens in public parks and poorly branched or unbranched ones in undisturbed native habitats.

Cycad vegetative leaves persist for 3 to 10 years, and when they drop the bases often persist even longer. Abscission is sometimes smooth and level with the trunk surface, but more often abscission is in progressive stages as surface periderm is lost bit by bit until the surface no longer shows signs of leaf attachment. Entire leaves show circinate vernation in *Ceratozamia* but only pinnae do in *Cycas* (Fig. 20–4, *D*; this is a cross section of a young rachis, showing two still-coiled pinnae at top), Pinnae of *Cycas* have a single midvein and no lateral veins, but extending out into the lamina is a sheet of transfusion tissue (TT in Fig. 20–4, *G*). In *Stangeria* there is a midvein and dichotomously branched lateral ones. The other genera are devoid of midveins and show open dichotomous venation with most of the bifurcations near the base of the pinna (Fig. 20–4, *F* is a cross section through the lamina near its middle).

Leaves of some genera are dimorphic (e.g., *Cycas* and *Dioön*). Within the single phyllotactic series are zones of vegetative leaves and zones of cataphylls (C in Fig. 20–3, *C*). Above the letter C in the figure are the cutoff bases of several vegetative leaves and below it are persistent leaf bases after abscission of cataphylls (the white and rounded ones) and vegetative leaves (the larger, sigillarioid ones). The cataphylls are simple, about 5 to 10 cm long, very hairy, and sharp-pointed. They completely cover the apical dome during periods between the times when new crowns of vegetative leaves are produced.

All cycads produce terminal reproductive strobili except the megasporangiate *Cycas*, in which there are no strobili, and some species of *Macrozomia*, in which the strobili are axillary. Vegetative axes are, however, continued after cone production with no external manifestation of branching. There is an overtopping that, owing to the size and shape of the whole plant, is essentially entirely internal. The strobilus is produced directly from the stem apex, and at an early stage in development the entire cylinder of the stem is continued into the cone axis (FCD in Fig. 20–3, *B*; the same specimen before sectioning is shown in *A* with a millimeter scale). An adventitious apex originates at the base of the new cone (in face view at the base of the cone in *A* and in section to the right in *B*). A very short distance below, the pith is several inches in diameter, so that the new apex relatively speaking is still approximately medianly situated on the axis. That is, the massive size excludes appreciable disturbance in symmetry. Procambial strands (PC in *B*) originate in association with the leaves of the new apex and then extend themselves downward to connect with the vascular cylinder of the stem. New crowns of leaves later push the cone into a lateral position (old strobilar stalks, SS, appear in Fig. 20–3, *C*). The vascular supplies to old cones appear as

FIGURE 20–3. *Dioön spinulosum.* *A.* Young megasporangiate strobilus that was buried well within the crown of the plant. At the base and in front of the strobilar stalk several primordial appendages covering the newly developed lateral apex are seen. *B.* The same object as in *A* in longitudinal section cut in a plane transverse to that of the paper in *A.* PC = isolated procambium of new leaf on the new apex; FCD = future cone dome. *C.* Side view of the trunk. C = cataphyll; SS = strobilar stalks. *D.* Trunk in *C* cut transversely in half, then longitudinally. The surface was painted with phloroglucinol–hydrochloric acid solution to stain lignified material. VC = vascular cylinder of trunk; CT = traces to cone; 1 to 5 indicate younger to older cone domes. *E.* View from the pith side of a portion of the stele from the trunk in *C* after it had been retted in horse manure suspension. The two series of vascular bundles curving into the pith are parts of two cone domes.

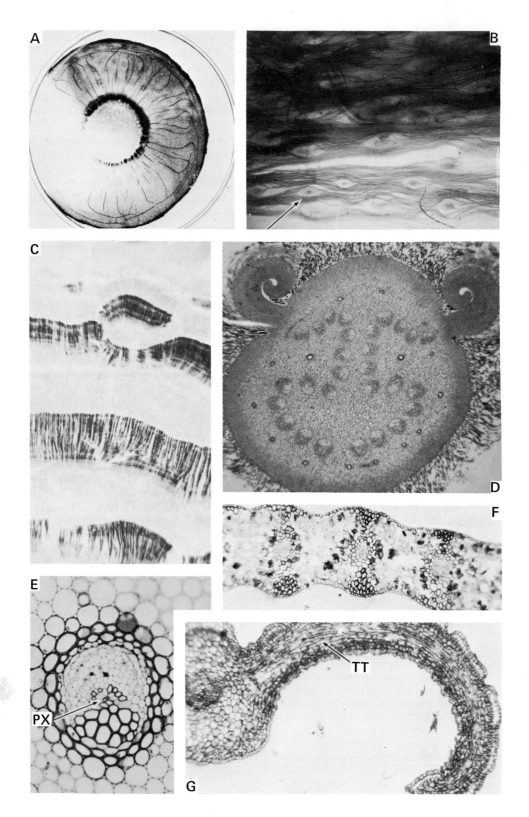

systems of medullary bundles (cone domes) in older stems. Five such cone domes are numbered in Fig. 20–3, D, where 1, 2, and 3 appear in longitudinal section, 4 in both longitudinal section and cross section, and 5 in cross section only. Some of the bundles of 3 are seen leaving the cylinder as cone traces (CT.) Portions of two cone domes are shown from the pith side of a retted vascular cylinder in Fig. 20–3, E.

The stem apex of cycads is the most massive among all vascular plants, often to several millimeters across. As Foster has described for several species, there are a few superficial initials at the surface on the crest of the dome. These give rise by anticlinal divisions to surface cells on the flanks and by periclinal divisions to the nearly spherical mass of vacuolated central mother cells below. Cells around the lower periphery of the central zone divide to produce subapical rib meristem. Small plants have stem apices that increase as the entire plant enlarges. The several large specimens of *Dioön* and *Cycas* available to this author for dissection over the years, however, showed conspicuous variation in stem-apex size. It is suggested that there are a series of short plastochrons when a crown of leaves is being initiated and when the stem apex is actually decreasing in size, and one long plastochron between periods of crown production when the apex is enlarging. This cannot at present be demonstrated since it would involve the slaughter of many old plants that are not available.

Cycad stems are conspicuous for their soft texture (external toughness is attributable to leaf bases only, Fig. 20–3, D), massive pith, and cortex. Resin[1] canals (Fig. 20–5, A, B)

occur throughout the parenchymatous tissue of stem and petiole (clear, circular areas in pith in Fig. 20–4, A and in D). The vascular cylinder is essentially complete. The primary xylem is endarch and there is no clear distinction between it and secondary xylem. A leaf receives a number of traces (shown in the rachis cross section in Fig. 20–4, D) that have separate cauline origins. Some traces to a given leaf originate close to a petiole attachment, while others originate at distant points and completely girdle the stem cortex, where they branch somewhat and eventually enter the petiole (Fig. 20–4, A). The xylem has many rays one or two cells wide and many cells high which are continuous to the pith as well as broader rays through which the leaf traces run (arrow in Fig. 20–4, B). Leaf gaps may be designated only when coupled with considerable interpretation. Accessory cambia (Fig. 20–4, C) appear in older stems of a number of genera and usually originate from secondary phloem of the youngest vascular cylinder (note a new arc at the top in C).

The transition of tracheary element types in cycads is ordinary in most respects. Within the metaxylem, however, the order of appearance of pit types is somewhat unusual and comparable to that in *Lycopodium*. The last reticulate elements show broad irregular openings with slight borders (Fig. 27–9, A) followed by similar elements but with extensive borders and with closer groupings (B). These are followed, at least in the three genera that are known, by elements with scalariformly bordered pits (C). The still-later-matured elements show circular bordered pits except in *Zamia*, in which they remain scalariform.

---

[1] In other reports this has been called mucilage. The substance is in part miscible with water, its

odor does not suggest high terpene content, but it dries into a hard, clear, somewhat crystalline mass.

FIGURE 20–4. *A.* Thick hand section through the stem of *Zamia* sp. boiled in alcoholic phloroglucinol, then placed in concentrated hydrochloric acid. Many leaf traces are seen in the cortex, some of which girdle the stem near the outside. Resin canals appear as holes in the pith. *B.* Slab of fresh wood peeled from a dissected trunk of *Cycas revoluta*. Broad rays in which leaf traces (one at arrow) are situated are seen. *C.* Cross section of part of the trunk of *C. revoluta*, showing portions of three concentric zones of secondary vascular tissue. The small arc of secondary tissue at the top was formed by a cambium that originated within the secondary phloem. *D.* Cross section of a young leaf of *C. revoluta*. Note circinate vernation of the pinnae at top. *E.* Vascular bundle within the rachis of *C. revoluta*. PX = protoxylem. *F.* Cross section through a pinna of *Dioön spinulosum*. *G.* Cross section through an immature pinna of *Cycas revoluta*, showing part of the midvein region (left) and half of the lamina (right). TT = transfusion tissue.

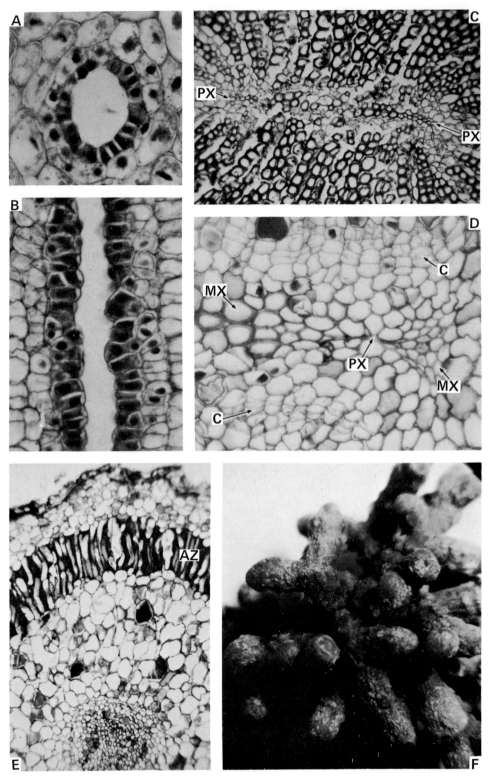

FIGURE 20–5. *A, B.* Cross and longitudinal section of a resin canal from an immature leaf of *Cycas revoluta*. *C.* Cross section of the center of a diarch root of *C. revoluta*. *D.* Cross section of a mesarch root of *Dioön edule* in the region of a primary xylem pole. *E.* Cross section through a coraloid root of *C. revoluta*. *F.* Mass of coraloid roots of *C. revoluta*. PX = protoxylem; MX = metaxylem; C = cambium; AZ = algal zone.

Leaf traces are endarch at their attachment in the pith region of the stem. They become mesarch in the cortex and during their course their centrifugal metaxylem becomes progressively reduced and their centripetal metaxylem progressively enlarged. The trace in Fig. 20–4, *E* is from the petiole, where it is weakly mesarch but near exarch (note that the phloem is on the side of the protoxylem with the least metaxylem). Farther out in the pinnae many traces are completely exarch.

Roots of cycads originate as thick (about 3 to 7 mm diameter) and fleshy axes from the bases of stems. At the point of attachment there are up to eight protoxylem points. The roots are progressively thinner away from the stem and the number of protoxylem points is progressively reduced as pairs of points come together until a diarch condition is reached. Branch roots are mostly diarch. Primary xylem maturation is for the most part exarch (Fig. 20–5, *C*), but at certain poles of larger roots weak mesarchy exists (Fig. 20–5, *D*). A typical periderm is produced and older roots exhibit accessory cambia. The first cambium (C in Fig. 20–5, *D*) appears several cells removed from the xylem such that in an old root the primary and secondary xylem are clearly separated (Fig. 20–5, *C*). The root apex has a common initial zone, and distal to it there is a massive root cap with a very conspicuous columella.

Some near-surface roots of possibly all genera of cycads if grown under nonxeric conditions turn upward and branch at the soil surface to form coraloid masses (Fig. 20–5, *F*). Such roots are always infected with the nitrogen-fixing, blue-green alga *Anabaena*, which occurs in a definite zone within the cortex (AZ in Fig. 20–5, *E*). Apices of coraloid roots have a root cap only about one to four cells thick and they apparently branch dichotomously. Branching has been described as exogenous in *Bowenia*, but this is doubtful.

All cycads are dioecious. The megasporangiate *Cycas* plants produce sporophylls on the stem within the overall phyllotactic system. A healthy individual will often produce successive zones of appendages in the following order: vegetative leaves, cataphylls, sporophylls, cataphylls, vegetative leaves, and so on (Fig. 20–1, *C*). Occasional intermediates between cataphylls and sporophylls are present (Fig. 20–6, *C*). Sporophylls within the family that are most leaflike are generally interpreted as most primitive. Such occur in *Cycas revoluta* (Fig. 20–6, *A*), where each sporophyll has a pinnate tip composed of two series of cataphyll-like pinnae and one to several pairs of sub-opposite ovules below. Other species of *Cycas* show a lesser degree of integrity of sterile pinnae on the sporophylls (Fig. 20–6, *B*, *C*). Those in *C* are from *Cycas rumphii*, which is often not recognized as distinct from *C. circinalis* (shown in *B*). In all other genera of cycads the sporophylls are in distinct cones (Fig. 20–1, *G*; Fig. 20–2, *A*, *B*; Fig. 20–6, *F*, *H*, *I*). Some of the megasporangiate cones are enormous. *Dioön spinulosum* is reported to bear a cone that when ripe with a full crop of seeds weighs up to 60 pounds and is nearly 2 ft long.

Megasporophylls of the strobiliferous genera bear two or rarely three ovules each with the micropyles directed toward the cone axis (Fig. 20–6, *D*). Distal portions of megasporophylls are often laminar but simple and not leaflike in appearance. These have been considered morphologically transitional between the *Cycas* type and the peltate types of some genera (Fig. 20–6, *D*, *F*). The two horns appearing on the peltate end in *D* are referred to in the generic name, *Ceratozamia*.

Microsporophylls of all genera are simple and in compact cones (Fig. 20–1, *B*, *E*, *F*; Fig. 20–6, *G*). In some genera there is a sterile extension beyond the sporangiferous zone on the microsporophyll (Fig. 20–7, *B*, *C*). Microsporangia occur on the lower surface of the sporophyll either completely covering it (Fig. 20–7, *A*) or in two separate zones (Fig. 20–7, *C*, *D*). When the former condition exists, less-developed sporophylls within the same cone show the latter condition. Microsporangia within the apparently continuous mass are actually attached in groups (sori), one of which appears in Fig. 20–7, *E*. The sporangia of a given sorus have a common vascular supply and when not crowded out of position appear to radiate from the common attachment. Microsporangial dehiscence is fundamentally longitudinal, but sporangia are often arched or bowed or otherwise ontogenetically distorted (Fig. 20–7, *E*, *H*). The wall is several cells thick (Fig. 20–8, *D*), and most cells of the

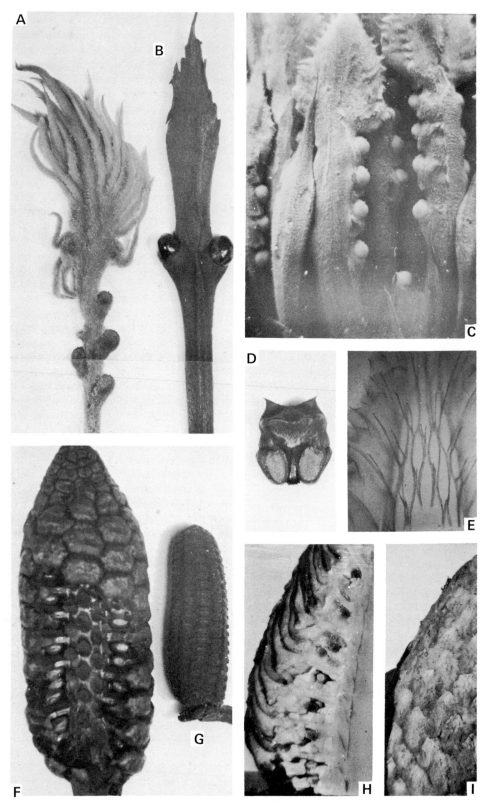

FIGURE 20–6. *A.* Megasporophyll of *Cycas revoluta.* *B.* Megasporophyll of *C. circinalis.* *C.* Part of a crown of megasporophylls of *C. circinalis* (*C. rumphii*). Note one on the outside left that is intermediate between a cataphyll and a megasporophyll and bears no ovules. *D.* Megasporophyll of *Ceratozamia.* *E.* Portion of a microsporangiate strobilar stalk of *Dioön spinulosum* cleared in lactic acid to show vascularization. *F, G.* Mega- and microsporangiate strobili of *Zamia* sp. Several sporophylls have been removed from the former to show attachments. *H, I.* Portions of megasporangiate strobilus of *Dioön spinulosum.* A radially cut surface appears in *H.*

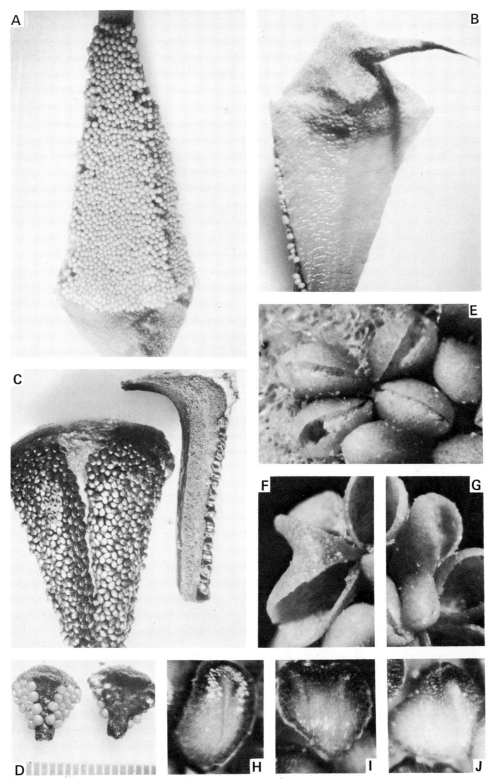

FIGURE 20–7. *A, B.* Microsporophylls of *Cycas circinalis* from the ab- (*A*) and adaxial (*B*) sides. *C.* Microsporophyll of *Dioön spinulosum* from the abaxial side and one cut vertically. *D.* Microsporophyll of *Zamia* sp. from the abaxial side (left) and from the adaxial side (right). *E.* Microsporangia of *Cycas revoluta.* The four open sporangia have a common attachment and constitute a sorus. *F, G.* Bisporangiate synangia of *C. revoluta.* *H.* Microsporangium of *C. circinalis,* showing its line of dehiscence. *I, J.* Bisporangiate synangia of *C. circinalis,* each showing two lines of dehiscence.

379

outer layer are involved in the dehiscence mechanism. At the distal end of the line of dehiscence there is a broad zone of cells that are more isodiametric and have thicker walls than elsewhere (Fig. 20–7, *H*) and do not function as an annulus.

During the preparation of this text many thousands of microsporangia of *Dioön* (2 spp.), *Zamia* (3 spp.), *Macrozamia* (1 sp.), and *Cycas* (2 spp.) were examined. In the first three genera every sporangium had essentially the same form and structure except for differences in shape referable to crowding. In *Cycas revoluta* and *C. circinalis*, however, approximately 2 per cent of all corresponding structures were bisporangiate synangia (Fig. 20–7, *F, G, I, J*). These varied somewhat in their external expression of doubleness and usually were uniloculate. In addition to these, nearly 10 per cent of the sporangia on some sporophylls showed slight indication of fusion in pairs at the very base. This is indeed interesting, since synangia are common among pteridosperms and cycadeoids, which are presumably phylogenetically related to the Cycadales. It is a distinct possibility that free sporangia are derived within the extant members of the order.

The vascular cylinder of a cycad stobilus is composed of distinct bundles (Fig. 20–6, *E*; Fig. 20–8, *F*), although at the base of a large cone they may be indistinct, especially in those which produce secondary xylem. The mesarch traces to sporophylls are either single or double at their points of departure from the axial ring, more often the former. In a single cone usually both conditions exist. On entry into the microsporophyll, the supply is generally double (Fig. 20–6, *E*, left side). This is true of megasporophylls of some genera, but in others the traces undergo further divisions while still in the cone-axis cortex (Fig. 20–8, *F*). The cone-axis bundle system of many species appears as a net with gaps (e.g., the megasporangiate cone of *Dioön* and *Cerato-zamia*), but in some others, especially the microsporangiate cones, the adjacent bundles at the base of a gap are not fused or only certain of these are (Fig. 20–6, *E*). The appendicular traces tend to be attached a slight distance from the base and on one side of the gap, whether or not it is closed and defined or open and ill-defined.

Insofar as is known, the cycadean ovule is composed of a nucellus that later comes to contain the female gametophyte and is surrounded by a single envelope, the integument. A major part of the nucellus is free of the integument at an early stage in development, but as a result of differential growth, at maturity the free portion represents only about one third of its longitudinal extent. This is seen by comparing Fig. 20–8, *A* with the slightly older stage in *B*. The point in the section in *C* where the nucellus becomes free does not show, but it is approximately at the letters IF. The integument, as the seed matures, comes to be composed of a thick, often brightly colored, fleshy outer layer (OF in Fig. 20–8, *C*); a stony layer (S); and a thin, inner fleshy layer (IF). At this stage the female gametophyte (FG) has come to occupy a large volume of the ovule and the nucellus is now a thin and papery layer on the inside of IF in Fig. 20–8, *C* and shown peeled back from the gametophyte in Fig. 20–9, *C*.

A vascular strand enters the base of the very short ovular stalk (funiculus) (Fig. 20–8, *F*) or it may fork before doing so. At the base of the ovule two concentric vascular systems are established. The bundles of the outer system, which number up to 12 but are constant for each species, are all established by branching at the ovular base (chalazal end) and remain unbranched in their longitudinal course nearly to the micropyle within the outer fleshy layer. The strands of the inner vascular system extend upward into that part of the ovule where the inner fleshy layer is not distinguished from the nucellus. They dichotomize along their acropetal pathway and end at about the line where the nucellus is free of the integument. A few tracheids may extend beyond this into the nucellus [e.g., *Zamia* (Shapiro, 1951) and *Bowenia* (Kershaw, 1912)] or possibly into the inner fleshy layer of the integument as reported in *Dioön* (Chamberlain, 1935). Various authors have attempted to interpret the inner vascular system as either nucellar or integumentary on the basis of subjective separation of zones below the line of "fusion," but this is not at all possible. In Fig. 20–8, *A* the outer vascular system is shown in part and indicated as the procambial strand at PC. Another procambial strand is shown extending

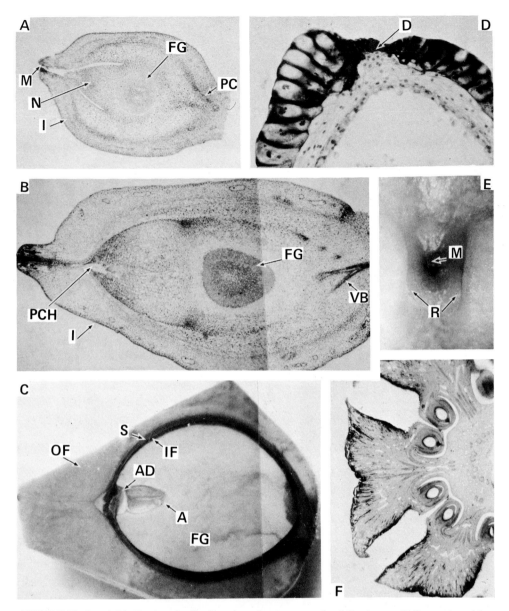

FIGURE 20–8. *A.* Median longitudinal section of a young ovule of *Zamia* sp. *B.* Somewhat older ovule of *Zamia* than the one in *A* and at the same magnification. *C.* Still older ovule of *Zamia*. *D.* Section through part of a microsporangium of *Cycas circinalis* at the line of dehiscence, D. *E.* View of the integument of *Cycas circinalis*. The brown, papery nucellus has been peeled off. The view is as seen looking up from an archegonium. *F.* Cross section of a relatively young megasporangiate strobilus of *Ceratozamia*. M = micropyle; N = nucellus; I = integument; PC = procambium; FG = female gametophyte; PCH = pollen chamber; VB = vascular bundle; OF = outer fleshy layer of integument; S = stony layer of integument; IF = inner fleshy layer of integument; AD = archegonial depression; A = archegonium; R = inner ridges of integument.

Cycadales **381**

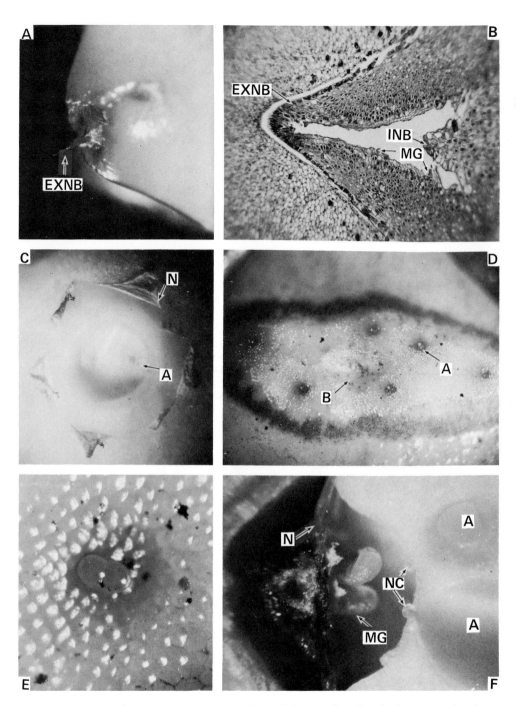

FIGURE 20–9. *A*. View of the outer apical surface of the nucellus after the integument has been removed from an ovule of *Zamia*. *B*. Longitudinal section through a part of an ovule of *Cycas revoluta* 18 days after pollination. *C*. View from the top of the female gametophyte of *Zamia* after the nucellus has been peeled back. *D*. Upper view of the female gametophyte of *Cycas circinalis*. One of the seven archegonia is indicated. *E*. Portion of *D* enlarged to show one archegonium with its two large neck cells. *F*. Longitudinally cut surface of part of an ovule of *Zamia*. The vertical axis as in *A* and *B* runs horizontally in the figure. *A*, *C* to *F* were taken while the material was still alive. EXNB = external nucellar beak; INB = internal nucellar beak; MG = male gametophyte; N = nucellus; A = archegonium; B = gametophytic mound or beak; NC = neck cells.

medianly to the base of the nucellus. At this point it branches to establish the inner vascular system. The bundle VB in Fig. 20–8, *B* is one of the outer system, whereas the outer one, which is attached to it, represents the trunk of the inner system. It is the double vascular system of the integument that sheds some doubt on the singleness of the integument. Unfortunately, the manner of initiation and the early ontogenetic stages of the integument are insufficiently known to further illuminate this point.

On the outer surface of the free portion of the nucellus of *Zamia floridana* (Shapiro, 1951) and *Z. intergrifolia* there are distinct stomata with well-formed guard cells and some with accessory cells but without substomatal chambers. In *Encephalartos*, *Cycas*, and *Cerato-zamia* there are occasional pairs of cells that might be interpreted as guard cells in the light of what is known of *Zamia*.

The distinction between integument and nucellus is not as true as it is arbitrary. The nucellus is recognized as the apex of a very young ovule. The integument arises subapically as a collar of tissue that grows up and eventually encloses the nucellus. We generally apply the terms integument and nucellus in regions below the level where they are free in the same sense as in the more distal portions. This is precisely the same as describing the leaf sheath of *Equisetum* as extending the full length of the internode below! In an ovule when the nucellus is described as not free of the integument below a particular level, it should be understood that within this region these entities were never free of each other and never in existence. The relative extent of that portion of the ovule in which the nucellus is free of the integument and that portion in which these tissue zones are "fused" is entirely a reflection of the relative growth rates of the portions of the ovule above and below the actual attachment of the integument. In seeds in which the free portion of the nucellus is very inextensive, the testa is not referrable in origin to integument but merely to a particular pattern of histological differentiation of surface layers. Another view (the more common one) would be to designate (interpret) the decurrent collar below the integumentary attachment as integument also, just as a decurrent ridge below a

leaf may be interpreted as part of the leaf. If this is done, it must be fully realized that it is done when using such designated zones for comparative purposes.

The nucellus when young has a rounded apex, and two to four cells within it a megaspore mother cell is differentiated. A linear tetrad is formed following meiosis and the most proximal cell is functional. These details are known for a very few species. The megaspore enlarges and its nucleus and subsequent derivative nuclei divide until a sac of possibly 1,000 free nuclei is formed. At this stage the gametophyte may be readily removed by dissection and looks like a small, white, peeled grape. Cytokinesis begins at the periphery and eventually the mass is entirely cellular. The female gametophytes (FG) in Fig. 20–8, *A*, *B* are cellular at their peripheries but still free nuclear in their centers. The megaspore wall is recognizable in suitable preparations, even in the mature gametophyte. De Sloover (1963) described the megaspore wall of *Encephalartos* as having developed centripetally, with a sporopollenin-containing intine that becomes covered by a cuticle.

As the female gametophyte grows from within, the nucellus extends itself apically, forming an initially solid beak (Fig. 20–8, *A*) extending into the micropyle. A canal is initiated lysiginously within the initial beak and the canal widens proximally into the pollen chamber (PCH in Fig. 20–8, *B*). Later the base of the chamber comes to be shaped like an inverted funnel with an internal nucellar beak in the center (INB in Fig. 20–9, *B*). In an older ovule, the apical part of the nucellus is readily pulled away from the integument, exposing the attenuated external nucellar beak (EXNB in Fig. 20–9, *A*). Both the internal and external nucellar beaks are variously expressed within the Cycadales, and the external one is frequently absent. The upper part of the integument from which the specimen in Fig. 20–9, *A* was removed appears in Fig. 20–8, *E*. The micropyle (M) is viewed from the inside. Shown also are two broad ridges (R) characteristic of *Cycas*, which are formed by a folding in of the stony and inner fleshy layers of the integument.

Archegonia are eventually formed at the apex of the female gametophyte in numbers of

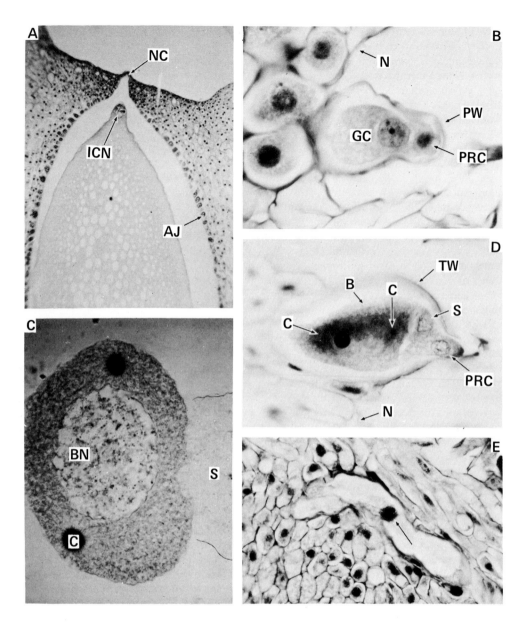

FIGURE 20–10. *A.* Longitudinal section through the upper part of an archegonium of *Ceratozamia*. *B.* Male gametophyte and part of the nucellus enlarged from Fig. 20–9, *B*. *C.* Part of the contents of a male gametophyte of *Ceratozamia*. *D.* Male gametophyte of *Cycas revoluta* 46 days after pollination. *E.* Part of a pollen tube of *C. revoluta* within the tissue of the nucellus, 18 days after pollination. The arrow indicates the tube nucleus. NC = neck cells; ICN = inner cell nucleus; AJ = archegonial jacket; N = nucellus; PW = pollen grain wall; PRC = prothallial cell; GC = generative cell; BN = body cell nucleus; C = centriole; S = stalk cell; TW = pollen tube wall; B = body cell.

usually two to ten among the various genera, except in *Microcycas*, where Caldwell (1907) reported hundreds, some of which were well on the flanks. Archegonia are frequently situated in an apical depression (AD in Fig. 20–8, *C*; Fig. 20–9, *C*, *D*, *F*). Within the depression some genera produce a sterile mound of tissue (B in Fig. 20–9, *D*). The archegonia arise from prominent superficial initials, not all of which produce mature archegonia. The first division is transverse and establishes a large inner cell and an outer neck initial. The latter divides only once, to produce the two neck cells, which later bulge conspicuously at the surface (Fig. 20–9, *E*; NC in *F*; Fig. 20–10, *A*). The inner cell enlarges occasionally to over 2 mm. Its nucleus (ICN in Fig. 20–10, *A*) remains apically situated until shortly before fertilization, when it divides to produce the small ventral canal cell and a massive egg. A conspicuous jacket lines the inner cell (AJ in Fig. 20–10, *A*).

The microspore (Fig. 20–12, *A*) divides first to cut off a small cell ("prothallial cell," p in Fig. 20–12, *B*, *D*) within its thick wall. The larger sister cell then divides to produce the generative cell (g) and the tube nucleus (t), which remains a free nucleus within the main body of the gametophyte. At this stage (Fig. 20–12, *B*) the male gametophyte is the mature pollen grain and is shed from the microsporangium.

The microsporangiate cone elongates to nearly twice its length the day most of the pollen is shed. The pollen is light, dry, and produced in large quantities per cone, but pollination is conspicuously inefficient. Chamberlain (1935) reported that seeds from a female cone 4 to 5 m from a male cone may show 15 to 20 pollen tubes and those 100 m away only 2 or 3. Cones 200 m from the pollen source show 0 to 3 seeds out of the entire cone, with evidence of having been pollinated. Reports of insect pollination are unsupported. The inefficiency of wind pollination is probably related to the fact that the pollen is all shed over a short period of time. If the wind is not from the proper direction, it is all wasted. This is related to the makeup of native cycad colonies that are generally isolated and composed of a very few to possibly 50 mature plants, not all of which are at the same reproductive stage. The present author's ob-

servations indicate, however, that the megasporangiate *Cycas revoluta* remains receptive for 3 to 4 weeks.

At the time of pollination the megasporophylls are loose enough that the pollen can sift down to the ovules, each of which excretes a pollination drop at the tip of the micropyle. On drying of the drop, whatever happened to land on it, size permitting, is pulled into the pollen chamber. Fungus spores are often pulled in and occasionally result in the destruction of the ovule. The proper pollen germinates on the nucellus (two male gametophytes, MG, are indicated in Fig. 20–9, *B*). A pollen tube extends from the grain (Fig. 20–12, *C*, *D*) and grows into the nucellus, where it generally branches. The main body of the male gametophyte enlarges and remains protruding into the pollen chamber (Fig. 20–10, *B*, 18 days after pollination; *D*, 46 days after pollination). Still later, the pollen tubes come to be directed toward the archegonium (Fig. 20–9, *F*; and in Fig. 20–11, *B* as they appear from the direction of the archegonia). The tube nucleus generally comes to be located within the tube deep in the nucellus (Fig. 20–10, *E*), but in one *Zamia* species the tube nucleus (TN in Fig. 20–11, *A*) in each mature male gametophyte was adjacent to the pair of sperm within the main body. (The position of the tube nucleus before displacement due to preparation is indicated by the arrow.)

The generative cell (GC in Fig. 20–10, *B*, 18 days after pollination) divides to form the stalk cell (S in Fig. 20–10, *D* at 46 days after pollination) and the body cell. The former is the smaller and usually cups over the persistent prothallial cell (PC in Fig. 20–11, *A*). The body cell produces two massive centrioles (C in Fig. 20–10, *D*), which are at first in a line with the entire cell group. Just before the division of the body cell to form two sperm (4 to 6 months after pollination) the centrioles assume positions in a line at right angles to that previously (Fig. 20–10, *C*). *Mycrocycas* is exceptional among cycads in having 8 to 11 body cells and twice that many sperm. The sperm are massive, 200 by 275 μ in *Dioön*, and of the same order of magnitude in others. Each sperm bears a ciliated band (CB in Fig. 20–11, *C*, *D*) traceable in origin to the centriole and bearing hundreds of cilia (C in Fig. 20–11, *D*).

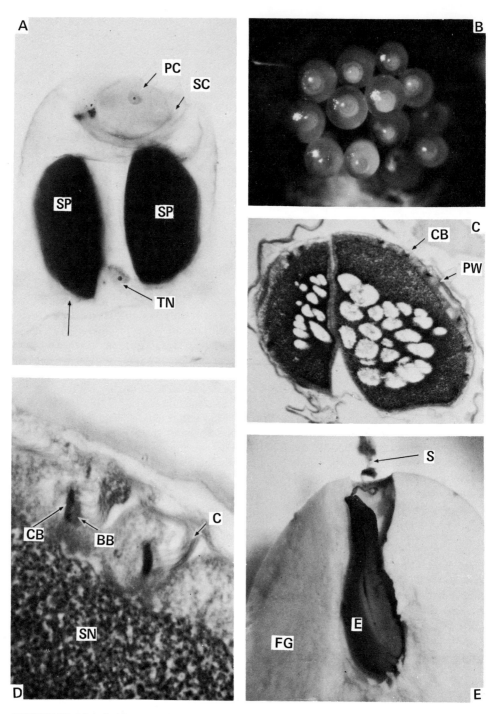

FIGURE 20–11. *A.* Mature male gametophyte of *Zamia*. The specimen was stained with osmic acid and flattened. The arrow indicates the position of the tube nucleus before it was dislodged. *B.* Group of mature male gametophytes of *Zamia* in the living state as viewed from the archegonia below. *C.* Cross section of a male gametophyte of *Zamia* showing two sperm. *D.* Portion of one sperm from *C* enlarged. *E.* Embryo and female gametophyte of *Cycas revoluta*. The remainder of the seed has been dissected away. SP = sperm; PC = prothallial cell; SC = stalk cell; TN = tube nucleus; CB = cross section of ciliated band; PW = pollen tube wall; SN = sperm nucleus; C = a mass of cilia; BB = group of basal bodies appearing as a band; E = embryo; FG = female gametophyte.

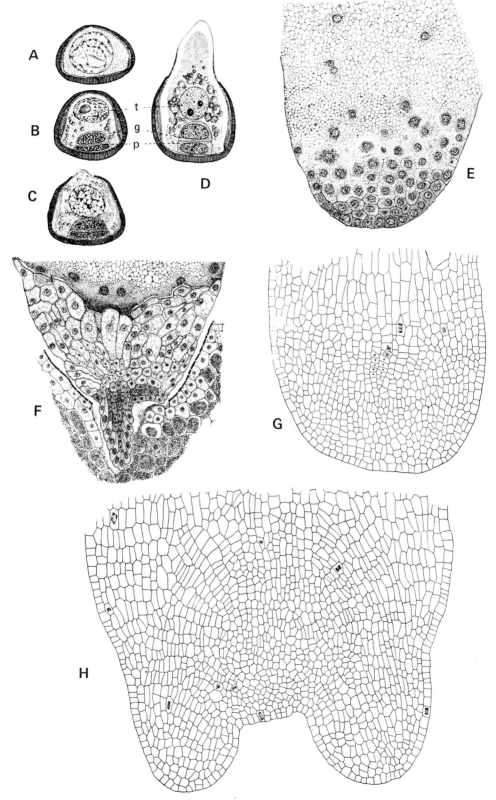

FIGURE 20–12. *A* to *D*. Stages in the development of the male gametophyte of *Dioön edule*, after Chamberlain (1909). *E, F*. Two stages in the development of the embryo of *Stangeria*, after Chamberlain (1916). *G, H*. Root and shoot ends of an older embryo of *Dioön edule*, after Chamberlain (1910). p = prothallial cell; g = generative cell; t = tube nucleus.

By the time the male gametophytes are mature, the tissue of the nucellus which separated the pollen chamber from the female gametophyte has broken down and disappeared (Fig. 20–9, F). According to Chamberlain, the two mature sperm actively break their way out of the body cell wall and then swim back and forth with a rolling movement within the pollen tube until the latter is ruptured. This takes more than $1\frac{1}{2}$ hours. In the material of Zamia sp. observed by the present author the process lasted only about 20 to 30 minutes and was not seen in as much detail. The drop of liquid containing the two sperm is spilled into the gaseous pollen chamber. The liquid as reported by Chamberlain has an osmotic strength at least equivalent to that of a 30 per cent sucrose solution, and when it contacts the two neck cells, the lowering of turgidity results in archegonial opening. A sperm is then violently pulled into the archegonium, with resultant mechanical disruption of the surface membrane and ciliated band.

Following fertilization in cycads the zygote nucleus and its derivatives divide without wall formation. The sac of free nuclei may reach a length of 5 mm with approximately 1,000 nuclei in Dioön or only 64 nuclei in Bowenia. Divisions up to the 256 nuclear stage are simultaneous and regular, but following this, irregularities set in and the exact theoretical numbers of nuclei (i.e., exact powers of 2) are not realized. During the early karyokineses, in addition to ordinary spindle fibers, there are numerous polar radiations, but centrioles have not been seen. Chamberlain has suggested that the free nuclear period arose as a consequence of enlarging eggs. He states that the mass of protoplasm became so large that the early mitotic figures could not segment it. The merit of this interpretation is diminished by the facts that free nuclear structures are known elsewhere among vascular plants where large size is not a factor and also that very long cells in essentially all vascular plants divide as the result of long-persisting phragmoplasts.

Wall formation eventually commences at the base, where more nuclei have formed (Fig. 20–12, E), and proceeds toward the neck of the archegonium. In some species wall formation is complete, and then a few large cells in the center of the mass break down. In other species the upper part of the sac remains free nuclear. Cells of the upper part of the cellular mass elongate (Fig. 20–12, F) and become the suspensor. The basal mass is pushed into the starchy gametophytic tissue below the lower limit of what was the archegonium. Eventually two pronounced tissue bulges are produced which form the two cotyledons and a stem apex becomes organized between them (Fig. 20–12, H). In some species there is an apical haustorium. The root apex becomes organized at the opposite end (Fig. 20–12, G) deep within the embryonic tissue and pointing toward the archegonial neck. Between the root apex and the suspensor a considerable amount of embryonic tissue remains as the coleorhiza. In Ceratozamia only one cotyledon develops, and this is on the side of the seed toward the ground after the precociously abscissed seed has fallen. The suspensor (S in Fig. 20–11, E) elongates to 7 to 8 mm, but most of the elongation is upon itself, so that it becomes tightly coiled.

Suspensors from several fertilized archegonia frequently come together to form compound structures, and it is not clear whether or not their terminal proembryos retain their integrities. If they do not, some embryos should be graft chimaeras. Cycads are ordinarily completely dioecious, but there are several instances reported by Chamberlain (as reported to him) of vegetatively reproduced plants of a different sporophytic sex than the parents. These may well have been chimaeras of compound embryonic origin. Our knowledge of the stem apex of cycads would seem to illuminate the possibility of a periclinal chimaera perpetuated at the apex such as occurs in angiosperms, in which more than one self-perpetuating initial zone occurs. A supposed sex chimaera in a cycad would likely show a crown of one sex and a small segment at the base of the plant of the other. It has not been demonstrated, but there are some indications at least that there is in cycads a heterogametic–homogametic sex differentiation (Marchant, 1968; Norstog, 1966). If such is the case, it is obvious that a graft-chimaera hermaphrodite of compound embryo origin would be possible only if the microsporangiate plants were heterogametic and the megasporangiate ones homogametic.

Taylor (1969) described a calcified cone of

Upper Pennsylvanian age that he referred to the Cycadales. The cone bore appendages in a spiral sequence and each bore on its lower surface eight to ten elongate microsporangia all arranged in a single row. Mamay (1969) described Lower Permian megasporophylls that were more convincingly cycadalean. Each organ bore two rows of ovules on its proximal end and a laminate structure distally. The megasporophylls were thus highly suggestive of those of *Cycas*, but were even more leaf-like.

For further discussion of the Cycadales see the end of Chapter 22.

21

Palaeozoic Pteridosperms

The Pteridospermales (=Cycadofilicales) were very common, mostly relatively large, and very fernlike seed plants. Indeed, they were originally thought to be ferns, and the name "age of ferns" given to the Carboniferous period was to a large extent a manifestation of this misconception. The better known Palaeozoic pteridosperms or seed ferns are found in Mississippian to Permian rocks and fall into two families, the Lyginopteridaceae and the Medullosaceae. Several less classifiable fossils are known from Devonian rocks and have been considered probable pteridosperms or some as prepteridosperms.

The best known lyginopterid is *Lyginopteris oldhamia* (*Calymmatotheca hoeninghausi*). The history of our knowledge of *Lyginopteris*, which is reviewed in part by Arnold (1947), illustrates a classic case of fossil plant reconstruction extending from 1828 to 1929.

Lyginopteris oldhamia had a stem up to 3 to 4 cm in diameter bearing adventitious, possibly prop, roots and spirally arranged leaves up to 0.5 m long. Each leaf (=*Sphenopteris hoeninghausi*) was once forked near its base and bipinnate (Fig. 21–1, *A*). The ultimate divisions were deeply lobed with free veins (inset in *A*). Relative sizes of parts and a somewhat soft-textured stem suggest that the plant required external physical support.

The stem of *Lyginopteris* had a pith composed of parenchyma with scattered islands of sclerotic cells (dark masses in the center in Fig. 21–2, *A*). Several mesarch, but near exarch, primary xylem strands formed a ring around the pith (the one indicated by the arrow in Fig. 21–2, *A* is shown enlarged in *B*). Secondary xylem formed a continuous ring external to the primary

391

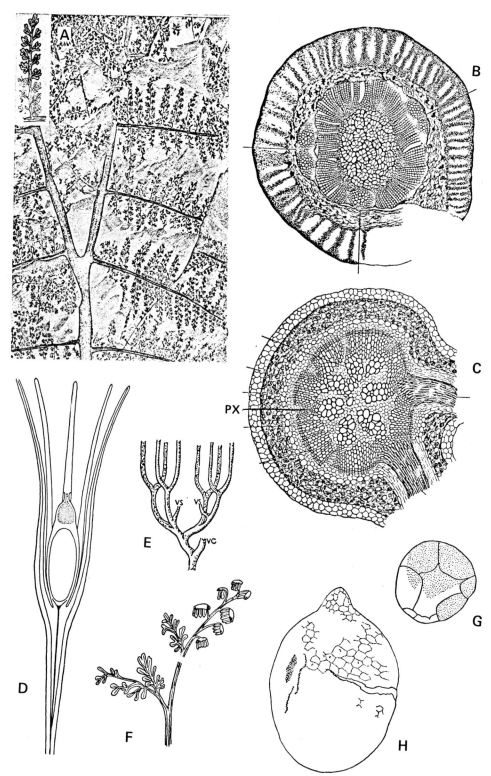

FIGURE 21–1. *A. Sphenopteris hoeninghausi,* after R. Potonié (1890). *B. Heterangium schusteri,* cross section of stem, from D. H. Scott (1920–1923). *C. Lyginopteris oldhamia,* cross section of root. PX = protoxylem, from D. H. Scott (1920–1923). *D. Genomosperma,* from Delevoryas (1962). *E. Geminitheca,* after Smith (1959). VS = ovule stalk; VC = base of another truss. *F. Crossotheca,* after Zimmerman (1930), by permission of Gustav Fischer Verlag, Jena. *G. Physostoma,* pollen grain with internal cells, after Oliver (1909). *H. Eosperma,* megaspore, after Barnard (1959).

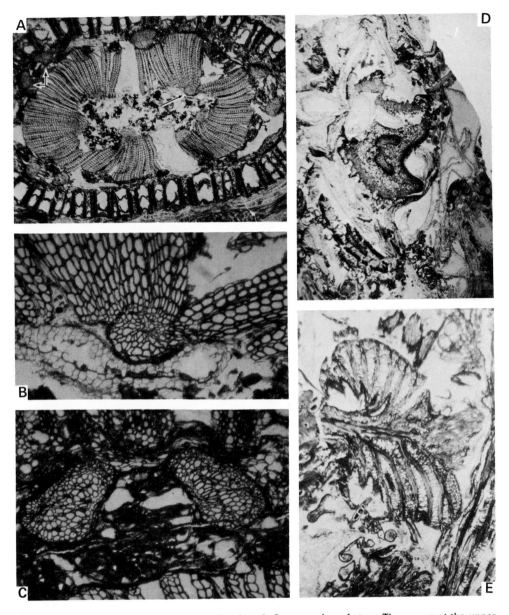

FIGURE 21–2. *A* to *C. Lyginopteris oldhamia.* *A.* Cross section of stem. The arrows at the upper left indicate a pair of leaf traces; another indicates a primary cauline bundle. *B.* Portion of *A* at arrow enlarged. *C.* Leaf traces indicated in *A* enlarged. *D. Lyginorachis,* cross section. *E.* Medullosan pinnule in paradermal section.

xylem. Secondary tracheids showed crowded pits with angular borders. Rays were 1 to 12 cells wide and a few to many cells high. Within the cortex was a conspicuous zone of fibers that appeared as radiating bands in cross section (Fig. 21–2, *A*) and as a single network in

tangential section. A leaf trace arose by a tangential division of a cauline strand and traveled out through the secondary xylem by way of a large ray. On the outer side of the appendicular trace was a strip of secondary xylem. The trace divided in the inner cortex of the stem (two arrows in Fig. 21–2, *A* and shown enlarged in *C*), and the two resultant traces extended into the petiole (= *Rachiopteris* or *Lyginorachis*, Fig. 21–2, *D*).

The root of *Lyginopteris* (= *Kaloxylon*) showed several exarch primary xylem poles (PX in Fig. 21–1, *C*), and opposite them in the secondary xylem were large rays and at some similar loci, lateral roots.

The lyginopteridaceous stem genus *Heterangium* (Fig. 21–1, *B*) had a structure very similar to that of *Lyginopteris* except that it was protostelic. The protoxylem poles were near the periphery of the primary xylem. The central mass was compsed of clusters of larger tracheids and a considerable amount of parenchyma. The phloem of *Heterangium* has been found particularly well preserved (Hall, 1952), showing many crowded and clearly discernible sieve areas.

Other known stems assigned to the Lyginopteridaceae include the *Lyginopteris*-like *Callistophyton* and the *Heterangium*-like *Schopfiastrum*. The apical region of *Callistophyton* has been described, and its very young fronds showed circinate vernation.

The Mississippian genus *Tetrastichia*, as pointed out by Delevoryas (1962), suggests ultimate phylogenetic continuity between the Lyginopteridaceae and fernlike aneurophytes. *Tetrastichia* had a thin stem with long internodes and decussately attached petioles that were forked at their base. The outer cortex had a network of fibers. The primary xylem was four-armed in cross section and suggests *Tetraxylopteris*. Some secondary xylem was present.

The seed *Lagenostoma lomaxi* is accepted by most botanists as belonging to *Lyginopteris oldhamia*. It has not been found in organic union with other parts of the plant, but it is frequently found in close association and its stalk and enclosing cupule bear very characteristic capitate glands (Fig. 21–3, *E*, *F*) known elsewhere only in *Lyginopteris*, The seed was probably leaf-borne as shown for *Pecopteris*, which is probably another lyginopterid, and *Neuropteris*, which is a medullosan (Fig. 21–3, *G*).

Lagenostoma lomaxi was a barrel-shaped seed (Fig. 21–3, *E*) with dimensions of about 5.5 by 4.2 to 4.5 mm. It was surrounded externally by a multipartite husk or cupule (CU

in Fig. 21–3, *F*; = *Calymmatotheca* when found detached). The single integument was free of the nucellus only at the apical end (Fig. 21–3, *F*). The nucellus was extended apically as a solid, inverted, bell-shaped beak (NB), and completely surrounding it was the pollen chamber (PC). The latter was delimited externally by another upward extension of the nucellus in the form of a hollow, inverted, bell-shaped mass. Surrounding the apical nucellar extensions were nine decomposition chambers in a ring, and one of the nine vascular bundles entering the base of the integument extended into each of them. A specimen of another species of *Lagenostoma* has been described (Long, 1944) in which the female gametophyte was preserved and showed several archegonia near its micropylar end.

The Mississippian seed *Eosperma* (Barnard, 1959) was similar in many respects to *Lagenostoma* but quite flattened. An interesting feature is the conspicuous megaspore wall with a reticulate surface pattern (Fig. 21–1, *H*), suggesting walls of spores that are shed externally. Pettitt (1966) described such surface patterns as representing the outlines and remains of adjacent nucellar cells and used the term "tapetal membrane." Lyginopterid megaspore walls have in general been described as thick. Spore tetrads were produced in some Lower Carboniferous seeds in which there was one elongate, massive magaspore and three aborted ones at its apex (Pettitt and Beck, 1968), and similar isolated ones have been recovered from Upper Devonian rock macerates (Chaloner and Pettitt, 1964). Pettitt and Beck removed one such megaspore from among the tentacles of a branched cupulelike structure also of Upper Devonian age.

The seed *Physostoma*, considered also to be lyginopteridaceous, was about 6 by 2.3 mm in size. The outer surface of the species illustrated was covered with unicellular hairs (Fig. 21–3, *B* to *D*). The integument was divided apically into about 10 free lobes (Fig. 21–3, *C*, which is a cross section at the level indicated in *B*). The pollen chamber was similar to that of *Lagenostoma* but extended more downward and laterally. The central column of the nucellus was short in *Physostoma calaratum*. In other species the column is undescribed but probably present (Leisman, 1964b). Some

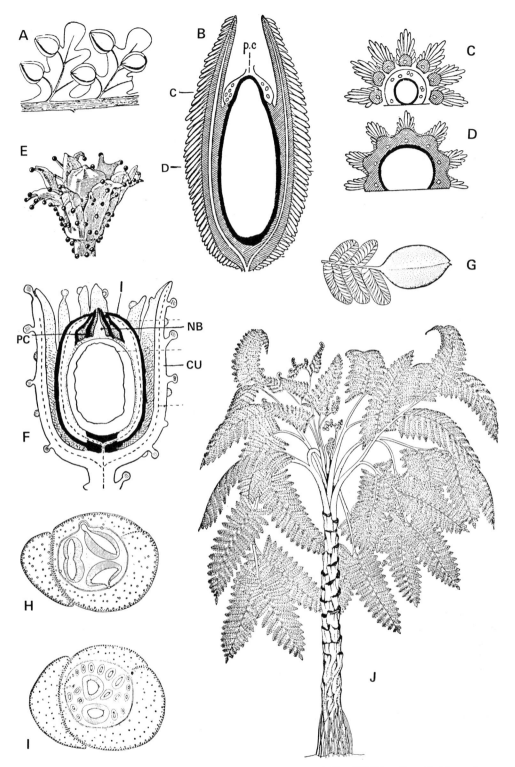

FIGURE 21–3. *A. Pecopteris* pinnules bearing seeds, after Zeiller (1900). *B* to *D. Physostoma elegans*, from D. H. Scott (1920–1923). The letters C and D in the longitudinal section in *B* indicate the levels that correspond to the cross sections in *C* and *D*. PC = pollen chamber. *E. Lagenostoma lomaxi* reconstruction, after Oliver and Scott (1904). *F.* Median longitudinal cut of *L. Lomaxi*, from Walton (1940). I = integument; PC = pollen chamber; NB = nucellar beak; CU = cupule. *G.* Portion of a *Neuropteris* leaf bearing a seed. *H. Medullosa noei*, cross section of stem. *I.* As *H*, but *M. primaeva*. *G* to *I* from Delevoryas (1962). *J. Medullosa* reconstruction, after Stewart and Delevoryas (1956).

pollen grains found in the pollen chamber showed some internal cells (Fig. 21–1, *G*).

The apical portion of the lyginopterid nucellus is characteristic and peculiar but still closely corresponds to that of the living cycads. In the extant forms there is an internal nucellar beak that is recognizable at or shortly after the time of pollination but is less extensive than in some lyginopterids. The sheath of nucellar tissue externally delimiting the pollen chamber is extended well into the micropyle in cycads as it is in some lyginopterids. No internal nucellar beak is present in the living cycads at an early stage in the development before the pollen chamber widens out at its base and also at a much later stage, after complete tissue breakdown all the way to the female gametophyte. This emphasizes particular difficulties in the interpretation of certain fossil seeds when only one or a very few specimens are available at an undetermined stage in development and in an overall developmental sequence that is unknown.

It is customary in a context such as the present one to attempt to define a "seed." Many definitions are too restrictive to include all structures that we recognize morphologically as seeds. In the view held here, there is only a single criterion sufficiently definitive and that is the retention of spores and their derivative gametophytes and subsequent embryos within them, all within the tissues of the parental sporophyte.

The sporangium as generally considered may be present or absent in a seed. One may interpret but not designate the nucellus as sporangial wall in some or all seed plants. The entire sporangium may be present as sporogenous tissue only; thus it may be truly naked, as cell lineages leading to the establishment of archesporia indicate. The sporogenous mass within an ovule or seed is not necessarily reduced to a single meiocyte or a single spore as shown by the multicellular archesporia of certain gnetophyte seeds.

Heterospory and heterothallism are considered mere correlatives of the seed habit. All known seed plants are heterosporous and heterothallic, or at least are thought to be so. The fact that this is not expressed as a difference in spore size in many angiosperms is not considered significant. If a new plant were to

be described in which the retained gametophyte produced male as well as female gametes, if other morphological conditions were met, there is no doubt that it would be called a seed plant. Such an occurrence is improbable but it may not be excluded as a possibility.

The time or stage in development at which the seed is shed from the parental sporophyte has little bearing on the morphological nature of the organ itself. Thus in *Ginkgo* the seed is shed even before fertilization occurs, at least in certain climates, but it is still a seed.

The number and specific morphological nature of the ovular envelopes are not necessarily the same from seed plant to seed plant, and any specific characterization of these in a "definition" of a seed is unwarranted.

At any rate, in attempting to define the "seed" we are attempting to fit a man-made term into a biological situation or vice versa. There is no doubt that we understand the structure and function of seeds, but we have not quite forced them to fit our terms!

The Lower Carboniferous genera *Genomosperma* and *Lyrasperma* have been referred to as seedlike. In *Genomosperma* the nucellus is free and quite exposed at its apex. The integument is composed of morphological units that are fused to each other only at their bases (Fig. 21–1, *D*). *Lyrasperma* is flattened on two sides and shows fusion of the integument to the nucellus except at the tip, where two halves of the integument extend outward. According to Delevoryas (1962): "A more nearly typical seed would have a nucellus even more completely covered by the integument, with only a small micropyle through which pollen might enter the ovule." It should be apparent that the morpological differences between *Genomosperma* and *Lyrasperma*, on the one hand, and *Conostoma*, on the other, are indeed slight.

The integument of pteridosperms may readily be interpreted as a series of morphological entities (ultimate units of a branching frond) that came to surround the megasporangium and eventually became fused together. The cupule represents a second envelope that has not evolved quite far enough to be called another integument. The cupulelike covering of seeds in the Lower Carboniferous *Geminotheca* (Smith, 1959) and *Stamnostoma* (Long, 1960) suggests how the foreshortening of interdichotomy units may result in a whorl of ultimate divisions around ovules (Fig. 21–1, *E*). In the figure VS is attached to an ovule (not shown) and VC is the trunk of another truss similar to its opposite member shown.

Crossotheca is likely the microsporangiate fructification of *Lyginopteris*. The fertile organs have been found attached to foliar parts (Fig. 21–1, *F*) classifiable as *Sphenopteris*, and one species was borne on foliage bearing all the specific characteristics of *S. hoeninghausi*, the leaf of *Lyginopteris oldhamia*. The ultimate branches of *Crossotheca* were flattened, with slight development of lamina, and bore peripheral, elongate, pendant, bilocular sporangia 3 by 1.5 mm in size (Fig. 21–1, *F*). The sporangia were apparently devoid of annuli and contained spores with triradiate markings. To supplement previously made comparisions, it should be pointed out that in the genus *Cycas* the sporangia are elongate, have no defined annulus, and are frequently fused together in pairs.

The pteridosperm family Medullosaceae occurs in Mississippian through Permian rocks. In some respects it seems more specialized than the Lyginopteridaceae, in others not. In all probability the Medullosaceae arose either from primitive lyginopterids or the two families had a common origin. Some of the organ genera assigned to the Medullosaceae are leaves: *Alethopteris, Neuropteris*: stems: *Medullosa, Sutcliffia*; seeds: *Pachytesta, Stephanospermum, Trigonocarpus*, (casts only), *Calathospermum*; Microsporangiate fructifications: *Paracalathiops, Lacoea, Potoniea, Dolerotheca, Goldenbergia, Aulacotheca, Whittleseya.*

Various instances of organic attachment have been reported between seeds and foliage and microsporangiate organs and foliage. The most significant of these is a specimen described by Jongmans (1954), which was a *Neuropteris* with *Whittleseya* and *Pachytesta*-like seeds attached. Some inclusions are based primarily on association and/or structural similarities.

Medullosa has been reconstructed as a small tree (Fig. 21–3, *J*) bearing a crown of large pinnately compound leaves. At the base were adventitious roots and below the crown the massive leaf bases, which gradually sloughed off in older portions.

The stem in cross section showed several complete steles (Fig. 21–3, *H, I*), commonly three. Each stele had a core of primary xylem, likened to the entire stele of *Heterangium*, with protoxylem in a subperipheral position toward the outside of the organ. Secondary xylem completely surrounded each stele as did phloem. There were many rays, giving the wood the soft texture characteristic of lyginopterids and cycads. In the large cortex were strands of fibers, secretory canals, and many leaf traces, the latter arising at various levels and entering the massive leaf bases. Periderm formed deep within the cortex.

Some species of *Medullosa* had many steles, usually of conspicuously different sizes. In *M. leukarti* the larger, outer ones approximated a ring, and in *M. stellata* the ring was often complete and enclosed several diminutive steles. Medullosan leaves were more highly laminated and less dissected than those of lyginopterids. Pinnule venation was commonly pinnate, with dichotomous lateral veins (Fig. 21–2, *E*; Fig. 21–3, *G*).

Microsporangiate organs of medullosans are diverse, but all indicate relatively close interrelationship. *Codonotheca* was a small cup with a peripherally attached ring of elongate sporangia. *Whittleseya* (Fig. 21–4, *E*) differed in having its sporangia fused laterally. *Aulacotheca* (Fig. 21–4, *A*) showed the same fusion but extending to the tip, completing the closure of the internal cavity. In *Goldenbergia*, a form apparently close to *Aulacotheca*, the stalked synangia occurred in a single row along an ultimate pinna axis. *Thuringia* had a similar synangial form, but the central portion was filled with soft tissue. In *Potoniea* (Fig. 21–4, *F*), *Paracalathiops*, and *Lacoea* a cupulelike structure enclosed many, free, elongate sporangia. *Dolerotheca* was a massive synangium to 4 cm in diameter with elongate sporangia (0.8 by 14 mm) embedded in a solid tissue but otherwise similar to *Potoniea*. Spores recovered from medulosan microsporangia are monolete. Trilete spores have been reported as occurring in the pollen chambers of certain seeds (e.g., several species of *Stephanospermum*).

Both the *Codonotheca* and the *Crossotheca* types of fructifications are readily interpretable in terms of a fertile pinnule of the aneurophyte type, especially as seen in *Archeopteris*. A shortening of the latter would produce a

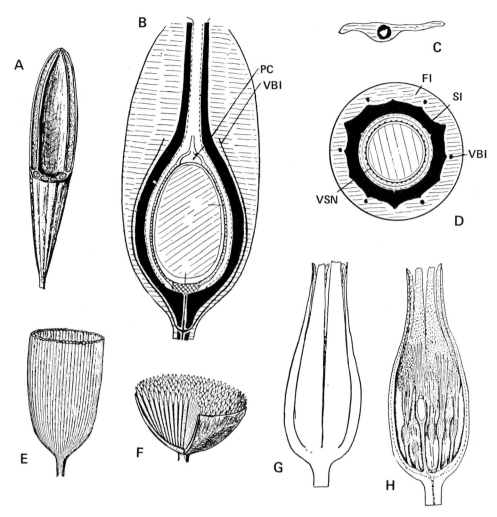

FIGURE 21–4. *A. Aulacotheca,* after Halle (1933), partly cut away. *B* to *D. Pachytesta olivaeformis* (same as *Trigonocarpus parkinsoni*). *B* shows a longitudinal sectional view, *C* a cross section in the micropylar region, and *D* across the center of the female gametophyte. PC = pollen chamber; VBI = vascular bundle of integument; Fl = fleshy layer of integument; SI = stony layer of integument; VSN = vascular system of nucellus. *E. Whittleseya,* after Halle (1933). *F. Potoniea,* after Halle (1933). *G, H. Calathospermum,* surface and internal views. *B, C, G, H* from Walton (1940).

fructification closely approximating that seen in pteridosperms.

Medullosan seeds have several features in common which suggest phylogenetic unity. They are large, mostly 2 to 5 cm long and up to 2 cm in diameter. The nucellus is free of the integument, except at the base. There is a double vascular system, in part integumentary and in part nucellar. The seed coat derived from the single integument is composed of an outer, fleshy layer (sarcotesta) and an inner, sclerotic layer (sclerotesta). The latter is fre-

quently ribbed or variously extended into the sarcotesta and is reflected in the external features of casts.

Pachytesta olivaeformis (= *Trigonocarpus parkinsoni*) is the most familiar of medullosan seeds (Fig. 21–4, *B* to *D*). In size it was approximately 2 by 5 cm with the micropyle about half of the total length. The nucellus was free except at the base, and its surface epidermis was relatively distinct. The seed coat (testa) showed the sarcotesta or outer fleshy layer (Fl in *D*) with distinct vascular bundles (VBI in *B*,

TABLE 21–1. Comparison of three cycadophyte groups.

Lyginopteridaceae	Medullosaceae	Cycadales
1. Ultimate leaf units dissected.	1. Ultimate leaf units mostly with pinnate venation, lateral veins dichotomous.	1. Leaves pinnate and more reduced; medullosan condition of pinnae in some species.
2. Stem stele of discrete bundles or protostelic; mesarch.	2. Stems polystelic; advanced types with a complete cylinder with smaller bundles near extinct, still however, mesarch, and with internal and external secondary xylem.	2. Stem essentially a complete ring, endarch.
3. Leaf traces mesarch.	3. Leaf traces mesarch.	3. Leaf traces mesarch.
4. Leaf traces arise by tangential division of cauline strand.	4. Not clearly comparable.	4. Leaf traces arise mostly by tangential divisions, especially in seedling; sporophyll traces by tangential division.
5. Leaf traces single, then becoming double.	5. Leaf traces multiple.	5. Leaf traces multiple, some girdle stem. Sporophyll traces single, then double or double at point of attachment.
6. Microspores trilete.	6. Microspores monolete or trilete.	6. Microspores monolete.
7. Bisporangiate microsporangia.	7. Microsporangia free, fused laterally in a ring or fused on all sides in a mass.	7. Microsporangia free, with indications of ancestral bisporangiate synangial structure.
8. Seeds cupulate.	8. Seeds not cupulate.	8. Seeds not cupulate.
9. Pollen chamber limited externally by an inverted bell-shaped sheath with a solid nucellar beak internally.	9. Pollen chamber with the external sheath but not the internal beak.	9. Pollen chamber with the external sheath, but the internal solid beak present in only some species.
10. No distinct sclerotesta.	10. Testa zonated into outer sarcotesta, then sclerotesta, then thin fleshy layer.	10. Testa as in Medullosaceae.
11. Single vascular system in seed.	11. Double vascular system in seed.	11. Double vascular system in seed.
12. Decomposition lacunae in seed coat.	12. Decomposition lacunae in seed coat.	12. In some species the fleshy layer gelatinizes between the tough epidermis and sclerotesta.
13. Circinate vernation.	13. Vernation not seen.	13. Circinate vernation in some species.
14. No defined annulus.	14. No defined annulus.	14. No defined annulus.
15. Very thick megaspore wall.	15. Thick megaspore wall.	15. Relatively thick megaspore wall.
16. Soft-textured secondary xylem with a high proportion of ray tissue, long tapering tracheids.	16. Xylem of similar nature.	16. Xylem of similar nature.
17. Mucilage canals absent.	17. Mucilage canals in stems, etc.	17. Resin (mucilage?) canals in stems, etc.

and *D*). The sclerotesta (blackened in *B* and *D*) was ribbed with three major ribs associated with three internal grooves (shown in *D*). Internal to the sclerotesta there was likely a thin, inner, fleshy layer, the limit of which is indicated by the dashed line extending up into the micropyle in *B*. The pollen chamber (PC in *B*) was dome-shaped and covered by a hollow, inverted, bell-shaped upgrowth of the nucellus, but without the internal nucellar beak extending into it such as occurred in lyginopterids and is present in living cycads. The tip of the seed was flattened, as seen in the distal cross section in *C*. The inner vascular system (VSN) entered the base of the nucellus and extended upward as a vascular sheath not clearly composed of discrete bundles.

Most other medullosan seeds show the triangular form as indicated by the three major ridges in the sclerotesta of *Pachytesta*, often without the minor ridges (e.g., *Stephanospermum*). In this genus there is also a distal six-toothed buttress that surrounds, but does not extend as far as, the micropyle. Most commonly in the Medullosaceae the inner (nucellar) vascular system is composed of discrete vascular bundles.

Presumed medullosan seeds have been found in different species directly attached to the rachis of the ultimate pinna, terminal on a pinna, or on long naked stalks.

In the Lower Carboniferous genus *Calatho-spermum* (Fig. 21–4, *G*, *H*) and in *Gnetopsis*, both rather unassignable pteridosperms, a number of ovules occurred within a single cupule, a structure that may or may not be the homolog of cupules surrounding single seeds of other genera. Andrews and Mamay (1955) suggest a possible homology between the cupulelike covering of the *Potoniea* type of microsporangiate fructification and the cupules of the abovementioned ovulate ones.

It is very difficult not to entertain the hypothesis of direct descent of the Cycadales from the Pteridospermales. One precedes the other in the fossil record with no intervening time gap. Structural parallels between the two orders are multiple and many are shared by no other taxa. Features that seem to be of significance in comparison are given in Table 21–1.

A presumed derivation of cycads from medullosans is particularly well supported and seems contradicted only by differences in stelar morphology. Concentric steles in some species of *Medullosa* have been likened to similar-appearing ones in living cycads, but in the latter the outer vascular zones are derived from accessory cambia and are in no way comparable to those of the former. A hollow cylindrical medullosan stele must loose its internal phloem and centripetally developed xylem to approach the cycadean type. Changes comparable to these are assumed to have occurred within the articulates.

22

Mesozoic Pteridosperms and Derivative Taxa

A variety of seed plant taxa known from Triassic and Jurassic rocks suggest themselves to be derivatives of Carboniferous pteridosperms. For the most part these are very fragmentarily known, with the exception of the cycadeoids, and to various degrees several suggest possible angiosperm affinity.

The family Peltaspermaceae of Upper Triassic age is considered pteridospermalean and may truly be a link between more primitive forms and angiosperms. The leaves (*Lepidopteris*, Fig. 22–1, *C*) were pinnately compound and up to about 30 cm long. Pinnate organs about half the size of leaves bore microsporangia that were on the lower sides of ultimate units in two short rows. Each microsporangium was approximately 1 by 2 mm in size and dehisced longitudinally (Fig. 22–1, *G*). The pollen grains were oval with a single longitudinal furrow. Seeds were borne on the underside of peltate, stalked structures that were arranged spirally on other axes measuring up to 27 cm long. The individual ovuliferous discs were about 1.5 cm in diameter and bore up to 20 seeds 4 by 7 mm in size. The nucellus was free of the integument nearly to the base of the ovule, formed a small projection into the micropyle, and surrounded a pollen chamber in which pollen grains have been found.

In any consideration of the origin(s) of the angiosperms, the ovulate disc of the peltasperms bearing a ring of ovules should not be overlooked. If the disc is folded medianly its resemblance to certain winteraceous carpels is apparent. In these, the ovules are inserted, not in two marginal or submarginal series, but in a

401

FIGURE 22–1. *A. Umkomasia*, ovulate fructification. *B. Dicrodium*, portion of leaf. *C. Lepidopteris*, portion of leaf. *D. Lepidopteris*, ovulate fructification. *E. Pteruchus*, microsporangiate fructification. *F. Pilophorosperma*, ovule and associated parts. *G. Lepidopteris*, microsporangiate organ. *H. Lepidopteris*, ovule-bearing disc and stalk. *I. Sagenopteris*, portion of a leaf. *J.* Part of one leaflet from *I* showing venation. *K. Caytonanthus*, pollen grain. *A* to *E*, *G* after H. H. Thomas (1955); *F, H* after Delevoryas (1962); *I, J, K* after Harris (1951).

complete ring, and the application of the descriptive term peltate can be defended.

The Corystospermaceae of Triassic age is also classified as pteridospermalean. Leaves (Fig. 22–1, *B*) were pinnate with open dichotomous venation. The microsporangiate fructifications (*Pteruchus*, Fig. 22–1, *E*) were dichotomously branched systems with terminal, flattened segments on the lower sides of which were borne microsporangia. The latter were 1 by 4 mm in size and contained winged pollen. *Umkomasia*, one of the ovuliferous form genera, was a structure up to 3.4 cm in length with lateral branches in one plane and each in the axil of a bract (Fig. 22–1, *A*). On each lateral was a pair of bractioles and several ovules, each covered with a helmet-shaped structure ("cupule"). The micropyle was upturned and in *Pilophorosperma* (Fig. 22–1, *F*) it was bifid at the tip.

For a more detailed account of the corystosperms and peltasperms, the student is referred to H. H. Thomas (1955).

Hydropteridangium (*Harrisiothecium*) (Harris, 1935) is a peculiar Triassic plant that may be related to others considered here. The plant was an axis 4 cm long and 2 to 3 mm thick that bore laterals in all planes. Each lateral branched three-dimensionally and irregularly, ultimately terminating in microsporangiate organs. The latter were capsuloid, 2 by 3 mm, and bivalved. Embedded, or probably so, in the inner face of each valve were up to seven elongate sporangia containing winged pollen. Associated leaves were forked twice and pinnate.

Another rather unassignable form is the Triassic *Zuberia* (Frenguelli, 1944). Its leaf was forked and pinnate. The ovule, although poorly preserved, seemed associated with a "cupule" similar to the helmet of the corystosperms. The microsporangiate fructification was forked, then bore pinnately arranged ultimate radial axes each of which had a basal, sterile portion, then was covered entirely to its tip with many sporangia.

The Caytoniaceae, often considered a distinct order, the Caytoniales, is known from Upper Triassic to Cretaceous rocks and seems to represent another specialized, pteridosperm-derived taxon. *Caytonia* was much discussed during the two decades following its description by H. H. Thomas in 1925 with prime interest focused on its near state of morphological angiospermy and its possible relationship to flowering plants.

Caytonaceous leaves (= *Sagenopteris*, Fig. 22–1, *I*) were palmately compound and the leaflets showed reticulate venation (Fig. 22–1, *J*). The microsporangiate fructification (= *Caytonanthus*) consisted of an axis with short lateral branches, some of which were again branched (Fig. 22–2, *B*). On the ultimate tips were elongate synangia containing winged pollen (Fig. 22–1, *K*). Each synangium had three or four locules (Fig. 22–2, *A*) that dehisced longitudinally. The ovuliferous fructification (= *Caytonia*) consisted of an axis perhaps 4 cm long with two rows of laterals, more or less suboppositely paired (Fig. 22–2, *C*). Each lateral or spermocap was a saclike, recurved body 4 to 5 mm in diameter with a projecting lip and internally a single row of ovules (Fig. 22–2, *D, E*). The ovules were in a single cavity (*D*) or in separate ones (*E*). Pollen grains have been found within the micropyles of the enclosed ovules and they may have sifted into the opening of the spermocarp. It is possible, on the other hand, that the spermocarp was much more of an open structure at pollination time and that its near closure was accomplished by differential surface growth immediately after. Each ovule had a single integument that was free of the nucellus to the base, as shown in Fig. 22–2, *E*.

The relationships of the Caytoniaceae are not at all clear, and at present the working hypotheses are mere reflections of blackboard geometrical exercises, but they are entertained as no others are available. The structure of the ovules is consistent with that of pteridosperms. There are suggestions of pinnate branching in the fructification axes. The microsporangiate organs could conceivably have been derived from types known in several pteridosperm families. The spermocarp is reasonably consistent in its morphology with ovuliferous organs of corystosperms and peltasperms. If the helmet of the corystosperms contained several ovules instead of one, the morphological condition found in *Caytonia* might be closely approached. Similarly, a reduction of ovule number and an overgrowth of the disc in the peltasperms would result in a similarity.

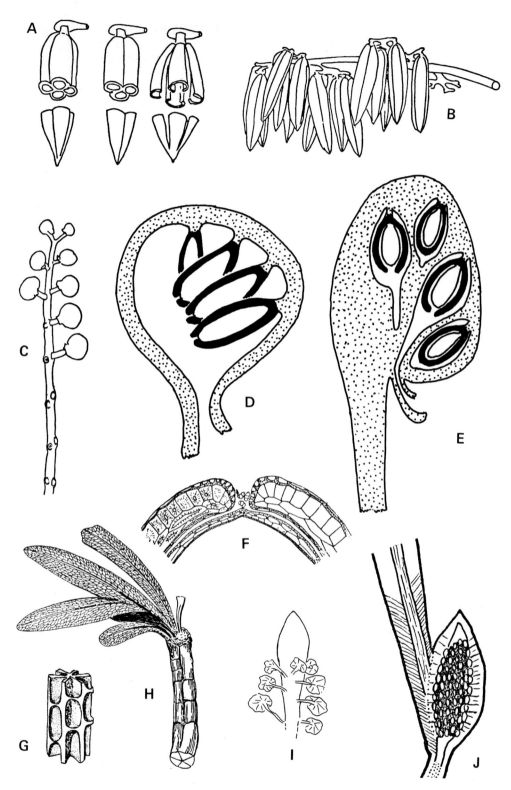

FIGURE 22–2. *A, B. Caytonanthus. C. Caytonia,* series of ovulate organs. *D. C. sewardi,* a single ovulate organ longitudinally cut. *E.* As *D,* but *C. thomasi. F. Caytonia,* tip of an ovule. *G. Verte-braria,* form of the xylem mass. *H. Glossopteris. I. Lidgettonia. J. Scutum. A* to *C, F* after Harris (1951); *D, E* based on Harris (1951); *G* after Walton and Wilson (1932); *H* after Edwards from Pant (1962); *I* based on H. H. Thomas (1958); *J* after Plumstead (1952).

The covering of the spermocarp of *Caytonia* has been called the homolog of the cupule of carboniferous pteridosperms, as has also the helmet of the corystosperms. There is no evidence to support this interpretation, and even the superficial similarity is elusive.

At the end of Pennsylvanian times the greatest ice age of all times set in upon the world. The major glaciated or very cold areas included what is now South America, much of the southern part of Africa, Australia, the Indian peninsula, Antarctica, New Zealand, and other smaller land masses. There is some evidence that these all formed part of a single land mass ("Gondwanaland") which later underwent physical dissection and drifted apart. Subsequent climatic moderation allowed revegetation of denuded areas by what is called the *Glossopteris* flora, which is recognized as distinct from northern floras from Permocarboniferous to mid-Cretaceous times.

Most peculiar of the isolated southern flora was the Permocarboniferous *Glossopteris* and the assemblage of forms assigned to the Glossopteridales. *Glossopteris* had a stem 1 cm more or less in diameter and a crown of linear to ovate leaves perhaps 10 to 15 cm long) Fig. 22–2, *H*). Attachments and arrangements are imperfectly known but they may have been opposite or whorled. A root *Vertebraria* (Schopf, 1965) showed a xylem mass that had radiating arms with transverse plates between the arms (Fig. 22–2, *G*) and tracheids with circular bordered pits. The leaf genus *Glossopteris* had a midvein and reticulate venation. Other leaf genera lacked the midvein and one showed open venation. Fructifications found attached to glossopterid leaves are single (Fig. 22–2, *J*) or in groups (Fig. 22–2, *I*) and were inserted in a manner similar to that of the fertile spike of *Ophioglossum*. The preservation in all cases was very poor and it is not known what was borne on them. Pant (1958) suggested that the leaf appendages of *Lidgettonia* (Fig. 22–2, *I*) were peltate organs that bore seeds which he found in association. Associated winged pollen also may be glossopterid. At least some of the Glossopteridales were probably gymnospermous plants, but others assigned to the order may be otherwise and unrelated.

An even more enigmatic group is the Pent-

oxylales of Jurassic age. The stem (=*Pentoxylon*) was several centimeters in diameter and contained five larger steles and five much smaller alternating ones, all in a single ring. The larger steles each had a tangentially elongate mesarch primary xylem mass and was surrounded by secondary xylem, mostly toward the inside of the stem. The smaller ones were almost entirely secondary. The wood was compact with uniseriate rays and had circular bordered pits on radial tracheidal walls. Short shoots 5 to 7 mm in diameter were spirally borne, covered with closely spaced leaf bases, and had a crown of leaves. The leaves (=*Nipaniophyllum*), of the *Taeniopteris* type,[1] were about 1 by 7 cm in size and had a multiple vascular supply and a midvein with sparsely dichotomized lateral veins. Ovuliferous branches (=*Carnoconites*) occurred at the crown of some short shoots. There was a peduncle axis divided into several branches, each of which terminated in a cone. The cone was composed of its axis and a series of sessile, fleshy seeds all closely associated, so as to simulate an anonaceous multiple fruit. The microsporangiate structure (=*Sahnia*), also at the end of a short shoot, was at its base a sheath of tissue that became divided farther up into a number of distinct branches which in turn bore unilocular sporangia terminal on short lateral branches.

Both the glossopterids and the pentoxylids could conceivably be derivatives of cordaites or have common ancestry with them. Similarities of pentoxylids to ginkgophytes have been pointed out by several authors in the past. To some the stem suggests the Medullosaceae and the leaf anatomy the cycadophytes. A reasonable interpretation of *Pentoxylon* must await new information or new convincing argument.

The Cycadeoidales (same as Bennettitales) of Triassic–Cretaceous occurrence were superficially much like the true cycads (Cycadales), but major differences in fundamental morphological features lead to the conclusion that the two orders represent parallel lines independently derived from Palaeozoic pteridosperms.

The cycadeoid family Williamsoniaceae includes forms that had columnar trunks approximately 2 m in height. Some were branched

---

[1] *Taeniopteris*, renamed *Rhabdotaenia* by Pant, seems glossopteridaceous in all detail.

(*Williamsonia sewardiana*, Fig. 22–3, *A*; *Wielandiella*), others not (*Williamsonia gigas*). Stems were covered with persistent, rhomboidal leaf bases. *Wielandiella* seemed to have produced terminal fructifications, below which a pair of lateral branches arose so as to give the plant a repetitive pattern of pseudodichotomies. Leaves of various species approximated 10 cm in length and were mostly pinnately compound (Fig. 22–3, *A*) or rarely simple (*Williamsoniella*). Stems in cross section showed a conspicuous pith and cortex with secretory sacs. There was a thin cylinder of xylem, the primary portion of which was endarch. Rays of the secondary xylem were mostly uniseriate, and tracheidal pitting was scalariformly bordered or multiseriated bordered. Leaf traces were multiple, but none girdled the stem.

Both megasporangiate and microsporangiate fructifications of the Williamsoniaceae are known, but in most cases it is not known whether or not they were within the same strobilus or even on the same plant. The megasporangiate strobilus of *Williamsonia gigas* was borne among the leaf bases. Its basal axis was covered with many small bracts, the more distal ones covering the functional reproductive parts. Terminal on its axis was a conical receptacle covered with distinctly stalked ovules among fleshy sterile scales. The pollen-bearing structure had a basal, urn-shaped portion with free microsporophylls attached to the upper edge. The comparable structure of *W. spectabilis* is illustrated in Fig. 22–3, *B*, which shows the pinnately divided appendages and pollen sacs, each of which had several internal cavities. In some other forms the pollen sacs were inserted on the inner face of the appendages. *Williamsoniella* is known to have produced bisporangiate strobili. Its terminal ovuliferous receptacle was similar to that of *Williamsonia*. At the base of the receptacle was a whorl of 12 or more microsporophylls on the adaxial face of which were several pollen-bearing capsules with several spore masses in each. Long, slender, hairy bracts occurred below the microsporophylls and the entire strobilus may have looked like a flower.

The Cycadeoidaceae (same as Bennettitaceae) is known primarily in terms of *Cyca-deoidea*. *Bennettites* is not strictly synonymous, as it applies only to certain European species not recognized as separate at the generic level. *Cycadeoidea* had a short, branched or unbranched, spherical to conical to irregular trunk up to 50 cm in diameter. Covering the surface were rhomboidal leaf bases with many multicellular hairs in between. At the apex was a crown of pinnately compound leaves that reached a length of 10 ft in some species.

The trunk in cross section showed a large pith surrounded by a thin zone of xylem, which was in turn surrounded by a large cortex. Primary xylem was endarch. The secondary wood showed scalariform and circular bordered tracheary pitting and uniseriate to biseriate rays (Fig. 22–3, *H*). There were also larger rays that formed a network and through which the leaf traces ran, as in the true cycads. There were no girdling traces.

The cones of *Cycadeoidea* were borne among the persistent leaf bases, axillary in some species. Their vascular supplies, however, were branches of leaf traces and not necessarily of those leaves with which they seemed to be associated. Cross sections of cone axes surrounded by sterile scales are shown in a tangential section to the trunk in Fig. 22–3, *G*. At least six species have been described in which all cones on a particular plant were in the same stage of development, suggesting monacarpy (i.e., once-in-a-lifetime reproduction). Terminal on the cone axis was the ovuliferous receptacle, which bore upright, sessile, or short-stalked ovules and scales with expanded tips. The tips fused together to form a surface with pores through which micropyles extended (Fig. 22–3, *E*). Each ovule had a pollen chamber, and external nucellar beak (PC and NB in Fig. 22–3, *E*), and a nucellus free to the base.

Covering the receptacle and attached around its base was a massive, compound, pollen-producing organ (Fig. 22–3, *C*), presumably a fused whorl of compound sporophylls. Wieland, in making his subsequently widely reproduced reconstruction, assumed this was an immature stage and that free microsporophylls unfolded later. Delevoryas (1963) recently showed this not to be the case. The distal part of the microsporangiate organ was parenchymatous, with no indications of fusion or canals. Within the fertile region trabeculae

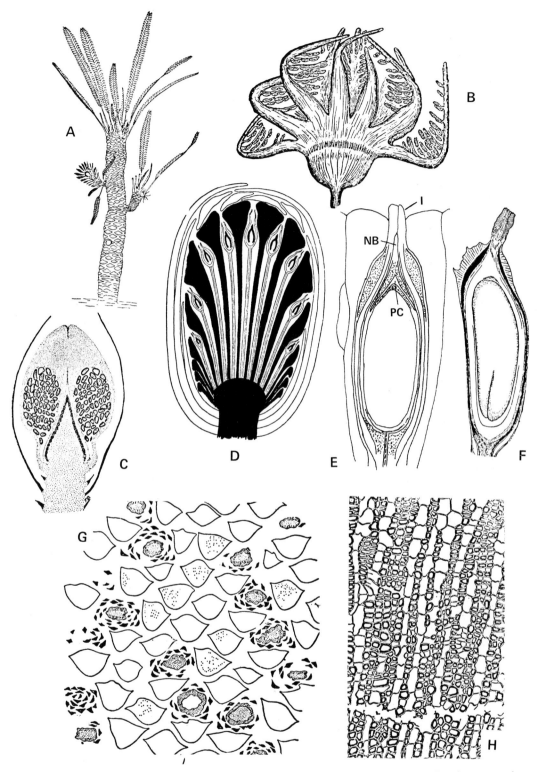

FIGURE 22–3. *A. Williamsonia sewardiana*, from Delevoryas (1962). *B. W. spectabilis*, microsporangiate fructification, after H. H. Thomas (1913). *C. Cycadeoidea* fructification, after Delevoryas (1963). *D. C. gibsoniana*, megasporangiate fructification, after Scott, redrawn from Chamberlain (1935). *E. C. morieri*, longitudinal section of ovule and adjacent scales, after Lignier, redrawn from Chamberlain (1939). *F. C. dartoni*, an ovule containing a mature embryo, after Wieland (1906). *G. C. jenneyana*, tangential section to the trunk showing cross sections of leaves and reproductive branches. *H. C. wielandii*, cross section of the wood, after Wieland (1906). PC = pollen chamber; NB = nucellar beak; I = projecting part of integument.

connected the outer wall with the inner wall, and along them were many synangia. Each synangium had a wall several cells in thickness. The outer cells were thick-walled and larger. The entire synangium, if this is what it was, had a wall structure peculiarly comparable to that of single sporangia among other vascular plants. Within the synangium were 20 to 30 presumed sporangia, separated by distinct walls. Sporangia dehisced into the synangial cavity and the entire synangium dehisced.

In later stages of development, the microsporangiate portions abcissed. The ovules and scales became elevated, presumably due to intercalary growth (Fig. 22–3, *D*). The entire mass thus matured into a fruitlike mass several centimeters in length. Many preserved dicotyledonous embryos have been found (Fig. 22–3, *F*) as well as pollen grains with indications of internal multicellular structure.

The stalk with its single terminal ovule of *Cycadeoidea* has been interpreted as representing a sporophyll. The work of Delevoryas on the microsporangiate organ leads one to suggest the possibility that the entire receptacle may also be an organ compounded of a whorl of appendicular structures. No structural evidence, however, is available for support, but such a morphological condition would bring the cycadeoid strobilus into closer conformance with those of pteridosperms and cycads.

Cycads and cycadeoids coexisted in Mesozoic times and their foliage showed amazing similarities in form, size, and venation. The two orders are readily separable if cuticular fragments are macerated out to show the cycadeoid stomatal apparatus, with a pair of subsidiary cells associated with the guard cells, or the cycad type, with a ring of subsidiary cells. Other cuticular details are also constant differences between the two orders.

23

Cordaitales and Calamopityaceae

The Cordaitales includes trees known to have existed in Carboniferous, Permian, and Triassic times. To the order have been assigned the well-known family Cordaitaceae and two very poorly known ones, the Pityaceae and the Poroxylaceae.

The Cordaitaceae includes trees to 100 ft tall of monopodial form, with spirally arranged leaves and axillary branching. The form genus *Cordaites*, originally applied to leaf impressions, has been applied to isolated stems as well as to the whole plant.

Cordaitean leaves were strap-shaped (Fig. 23–1, *A*, *C*) and commonly 15 to 20 cm long. An unusual species had a leaf 1 m long and 15 cm wide. The venation was parallel but traceable to a series of dichotomies. The leaves were tough and the longitudinally oriented fibrous strands varied in their relationship to veins and to variously extended hypodermal fiber systems. These structures form the basis for distinguishing the approximately 11 anatomical leaf species (Harms and Leisman, 1961). The leaves were thick at their regions of attachment and then tapered proximally. The leaf of *Cordaites crassus*, for example, was 4 mm thick at the base, 1.8 mm thick 5 mm out, 1.1 mm thick 15 mm out, and 0.8 mm thick 30 mm from the stem (Harms and Leisman, 1961).

The *Cordaites* stem had a large pith with conspicuous air chambers. The characteristic pith casts appear transversely septate at the margin, but petrified material shows the diaphragms to be incomplete, such that two or three large cavities also appear in a transverse section. The primary xylem was composed of small endarch bundles around the pith. The secondary xylem was compact, with narrow tracheids and mostly narrow

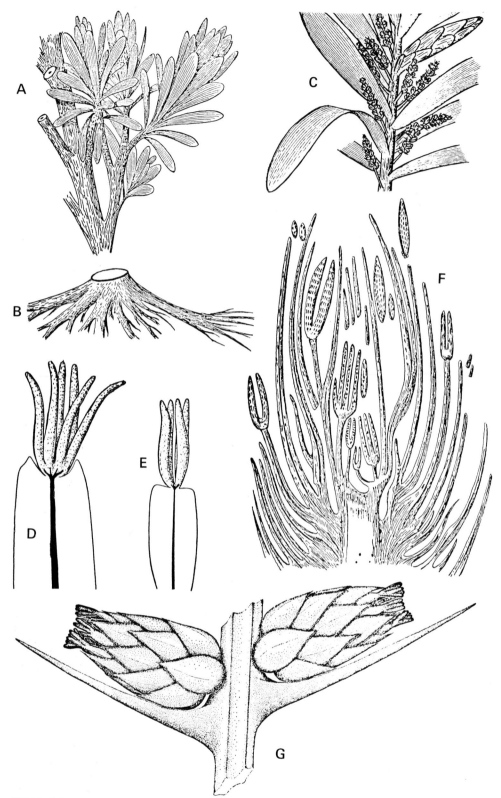

FIGURE 23–1. *A, B.* Reconstruction of part of the shoot and root systems of *Cordaites*, after Grand'Eury (1877). *C.* Part of a shoot of *Cordaites* bearing leaves, strobili, and one vegetative bud, after Grand'Eury (1877). *D, E.* Microsporangium-bearing organs ("sporophylls") of *Cordaianthus penjoni* and *C. saportanus*, after Florin (1951). *F.* Microsporangiate short shoot of *C. penjoni*, after Renault (1879). *G. C. concinnus*, a pair of microsporangiate short shoots on the strobilar axis with their subtending bracts, after Delevoryas (1962).

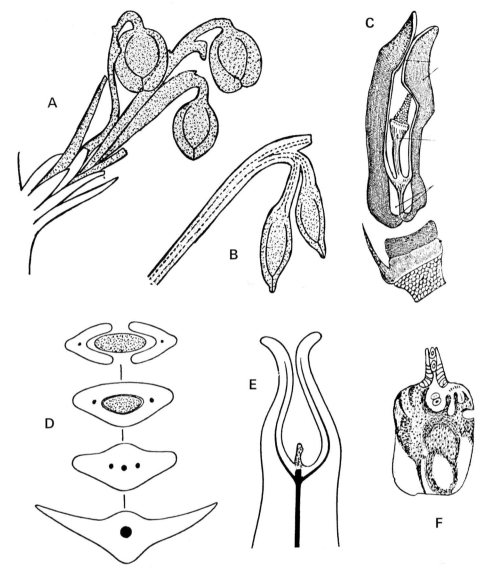

FIGURE 23–2. *A.* Megasporangiate short shoot of *Cordaianthus pseudofluitans.* *B.* Single ovuliferous structure ("sporophyll") from *C. pseudofluitans.* The ovules in *A* are viewed from their flat sides, while those in *B* from their narrow sides. *C.* Ovule of *C. williamsoni.* *D.* Four cross-sectional outline drawings in sequence through the upper part of an ovule, then deeper down to the stalk of *C. williamsoni.* The nucellus is stippled. *E.* Pair of terminal bracts and an aborted nucellus of *C. williamsoni.* *F.* Apex of an ovule of *C. williamsoni,* showing pollen chamber containing pollen grains. *A–E* after Florin (1951).

rays. Vascular pitting was primarily restricted to radial walls and was commonly uniseriate but occasionally bi- or triseriate to alternate-crowded (Fig. 27–13, *A*). Some scalariform pitting occurred in the metaxylem. The stem genus *Mesoxylon* (secondary wood shown in Fig. 23–3, *A*) was similar to *Cordaites* but had mesarch traces and endarch stem bundles or the mesarchy extended downward some distance into the cauline system. Cordaitean leaf traces were either single or double at their point of origin. Branch traces were double and

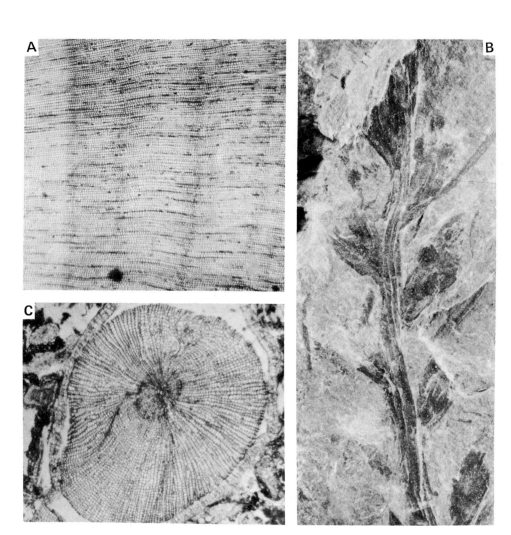

FIGURE 23–3. *A.* Cross section of the secondary xylem of *Mesoxylon.* *B.* Compression-carbonization of *Cordaianthus.* The main vertical axis is that of the strobilus. The stubby laterals are the fertile short shoots that are subtended by bracts, one of which is seen on the upper right. *C.* Cross section of *Amyelon radicans,* the root of *Cordaites.*

the two usually fused before entering the lateral branch. The cortex of young stems showed parenchyma with sclerotic nests and secretory canals.

The cordaitean root *Amyelon* (Fig. 23–1, *B*; Fig. 23–3, *C*) was exarch, protostelic, and mostly triarch. Periderm is seen surrounding the stele in most petrified specimens. The root genus *Premnoxylon* also was exarch, with two to seven or more primary xylem poles. It had a mixed pith and a distinct separation of primary xylem from secondary xylem.

Both mega- and microsporangiate fructifi-

cations of *Cordaites* are known under the form generic name *Cordaianthus.* These were slender branches (compound strobili) borne on vegetative shoots (Fig. 23–1, *C*), which in turn bore spirally arranged, reduced leaflike organs (bracts) with axillary reproductive shoots (reproductive short shoots or simple strobili, Fig. 23–1, *G*; Fig. 23–3, *B*). A compound strobilus was entirely megasporangiate or entirely microsporangiate.

The microsporangiate short shoot bore a spiral sequence of appendages (Fig. 23–1, *F*, *G*). The proximal ones were more leaflike and sterile, while the distal ones were more terete and bore one to several elongate sporangia (Fig. 23–1, *D* to *G*), each separately vascularized. Both fertile and sterile appendages of the short shoot fell within the same phyllotactic sequence and there were no axillary structures. The pollen grains had an equatorial bladder and, in some, the remains of a multicellular male gametophyte has been seen.

The megasporangiate short shoot had a very similar organization (Fig. 23–2, *A*). Within the spiral sequence were the proximally attached sterile organs and the distal fertile ones. From one to three ovules were borne on each fertile organ, and these probably became extended out of the short shoot late in development. Each ovule was composed of a nucellus (presumed megasporangium) enclosed by a pair of distinct lateral outgrowths with each of the three entities receiving its own vascular trace (Fig. 23–2, *D, E*). The megasporangium was occasionally incompletely developed (Fig. 23–2, *E*), and some forked tips of organs have been seen with no indication of a sporangium at all. The single, but two-parted, integument was completely free of the nucellus (Fig. 23–2, *C*), and a pollen chamber has been described containing pollen grains (Fig. 23–2, *F*). The entire ovule was distinctly bilateral and often appeared heart-shaped from the broad side. Note that Fig. 23–2, *A* and *B* are of the two different sides of ovules of the same species.

The Pityaceae and the Poroxylaceae are only tentatively retained in the Cordaitales. When they become better known, they may well be reassigned or taxonomically elevated. Already one genus of the Pityaceae, *Callixylon*, has been reassigned since Beck's discovery that it was in reality part of the same plant as *Archeopteris*.

In the Pityaceae, the Lower Carboniferous *Pitys* had a woody stem at least 1.5 ft in diameter. There was a large pith surrounded by mesarch primary xylem strands some of which were not in contact with secondary xylem. Within the pith were scattered tracheids or additional complete strands. A leaf trace was formed by a radial division of a bundle with no gap. The secondary xylem was compact. Leaf traces were single, then divided into three that entered the leaf. Young stems showed sclerotic nests in the cortex. The leaves were simple, fleshy, 4 to 6 mm by 50 mm, bore epi-dermal hairs and sunken stomata, and had a cross section suggestive of lyginopterid petioles. The Upper Devonian *Archaeopitys* had large mesarch strands scattered in the pith and a ring of strands at the pith periphery. The leaf trace was produced by a radial division of a peripheral bundle and the reparatory strand then turned inward into the pith. Secondary xylem showed uni- and multiseriate rays and multiseriate tracheary pitting.

The Poroxylaceae is represented by the Permocarboniferous *Poroxylon*. In its stem was a ring of exarch primary xylem strands surrounding a pith and in contact with the secondary xylem. The latter had large cells and broad rays suggestive of *Lyginopteris* and most especially of *Calistophyton*, both pteridosperms. The leaves of *Poroxylon* were simple, thick, laminate, petiolate, and had numerous parallel veins.

The Devonian and Lower Carboniferous family Calamopityaceae is a poorly known and probably somewhat unnatural one, placed in the pteridosperms. *Calamopitys* showed a mixed pith and an absence of leaf gaps, as did *Pitys* and *Archaeopitys*. Some species showed dense wood. Others produced paired leaf traces, each arising from separate cauline bundles. The outer cortex of young stems had an anastomosing network of fibrous cells.

The characteristics which the Pityaceae, Poroxylaceae, and Calamopityaceae have in common and those that selected representatives share with the Cordaitaceae, Aneurophytopsida, and pteridosperms are sufficient to lead one to suggest that the entire coniferophyte line and the entire cycadophyte line together constitute an assemblage phylogenetically traceable to a narrow segment of the aneurophytes. The vegetative and reproductive morphology of pteridosperms is interpretable in terms of aneurophytes without becoming excessively speculative. The gaps are not too great. Coniferophyte morphology, on the other hand, which is already established in the Cordaitaceae in terms of leaf form, branching pattern, strobilar organization, and ovule structure, is much more distinctive and less readily interpretable in terms of possibly ancestral taxa. Possibly answers to implied questions will be forthcoming when information accumulates on the Pityaceae, Poroxylaceae, and Calamopityaceae. At present it is difficult to interpret the two-parted integument characteristic of coniferophytes in terms of the multipartite one of cycadophytes unless the seed arose independently in each line. The kinds of seeds (if any) produced by members of the three above-mentioned families are not known, although *Rhabdocarpus* may possibly have been borne on *Poroxylon*.

24

Ginkgoales

Among the naked-seeded plants, there seems to be two major assemblages, the cycadophytes and the coniferophyte–gnetophyte line. A classification of these, acceptable at our present state of knowledge, is as follows:

Class   Cycadopsida
  Order   Pteridospermales
           Caytoniales
           Cycadeoidales
           Cycadales
           [Pentoxylales]
           [Glossopteridales]
Class   Coniferopsida
  Order   Cordaitales
           Protopityales
           Ginkgoales
           Coniferales
           Taxales
Class   Gnetopsida
  Order   Ephedrales
           Gnetales
           Welwitschiales

The mere temporal acceptability of this system is abundantly clear upon mention of our ignorance of the morphology of the Pityaceae, Poroxylaceae, Calamopityaceae, and certain presumed gymnospermous families of Mesozoic rocks (see Chapter 23).

The Ginkgoales has a special place in these considerations. The sole extant species of the order, *Ginkgo biloba*, vegetatively, down to many subtle histological details, is a clearly defined coniferophyte, but it shares many details of reproductive structures and processes with living cycads. Various authors have noted these and held views similar to those of Foster and Gifford (1959), who state: "... such similarities appear as the result of the retention, by both cycads and *Ginkgo*, of certain very ancient patterns of reproduction which probably were shared by many of the Paleozoic and Mesozoic gymnosperms." If this is so, it follows that the seed must have evolved in the ultimate common ancestor of the cycads and *Ginkgo*, for the common characteristics are those associated with the seed habit itself. A comparison of the seed of the Cordaitaceae, the presumably most primitive of clearly defined coniferophyte families, with that of a typical pteridosperm or cycad does not bear out the conclusion but suggests two completely separate origins of the integument and hence the seed itself.

Ginkgo biloba is now in wide cultivation throughout the world. It is an attractive tree of excurrent to irregular form to 100 ft tall with fan-shaped, deciduous leaves. It is hardy to about $-30°F$, but the reproductive cycle is rarely complete in areas where such temperatures are encountered. It may still persist as native stands in southeastern China, but these may represent re-establishments from cultivation. In China the species has been in cultivation for many centuries and we may be indebted to ancient horticulturists for its present-day existence. The starchy part of the seed, primarily the female gametophytic tissue, is widely used for food, either roasted or boiled. The canned product, which is available outside the Orient in stores with exotic stocks, is reasonably palatable if generously salted. Excessively large quantities of *Ginkgo* seeds have been reported to be lethal.

The genus *Ginkgo* is known in rocks as old as Triassic and the species *G. biloba* may go back nearly as far. As a species of vascular plant, therefore, it may be the oldest in existence, but as a genus, *Lycopodium* and *Selaginella* are far older; *Equisetum* is as old and *Ephedra* may be. *Ginkgo biloba* is not as genetically stagnated as its apparent antiquity might lead one to suspect. It shows variation from specimen to specimen in frequency of certain leaf forms and of anomolous reproductive structures and in hardiness of the entire plant, of reproductive structures that overwinter within the buds, and of incompletely developed seeds after they drop in the autumn. Such obvious points of variability are inconsistent with a species that has been in existence relatively unchanged for as long as *G. biloba* is reputed to have been.

Shoot dimorphism is conspicuous in *Ginkgo*. The spur shoots are produced in axils of leaves on long shoots and may persist as such for many years, producing each year a small crown of leaves and the reproductive structures. Spur shoots differ from long shoots primarily in internode length (Fig. 24–1, *A, B*), but there are also histological differences. The specimen in *A* shows one long shoot with its leaves attached. The axillary buds in *A* would probably have produced mostly spur shoots, as seen in the specimen in *B*. Spur shoots and long shoots are interconvertible. Certain spur shoots will grow into long shoots if the nearest long shoot tip is removed, indicating that apical dominance is in part responsible for some short shoots, but the same conversion occurs naturally and sporadically without apical injury. Long shoots frequently go into a short-shoot growth phase for one or more years, then revert (Fig. 24–1, *B*; note the short shoot segment along the main axis). The growth habit of the two shoot types seems related to quantities of auxin produced in the shoot apices. In the early spring spur and long shoot tips produce essentially the same quantity of auxin. As growth proceeds, auxin production increases gradually in each, and then at a particular stage, the long shoot tips experience a rapid increase, whereas short shoots continue a very slow increase. The growth pattern of the pith and the cortex is characteristically different in long and short shoots (Gunckel and Wetmore, 1946), and in the early spring all shoots show the same pattern. These authors describe all buds of *Ginkgo*, terminal and lateral, as producing short shoots each spring and a varying number of these changing to long shoots in the course of the season. This manner of description is, however, misleading, as there are comparable changes in growth patterns in stems of many angiosperms, relatively few of which produce definable spur shoots.

The shoot apex of *Ginkgo* (Foster, 1938) shows a small group of superficial, apical initials, a conspicuous subapical zone of central mother cells around which on its proximal

FIGURE 24–1. *Ginkgo biloba.* *A.* Long shoot. *B.* Long shoot bearing short shoots. *C.* Microsporangiate strobili and young leaves on a short shoot. *D.* Short shoot showing two ovuliferous stalks.

side is a zone of rib meristem. Except for quantitative features this is comparable to cycad apices as well as those of taxads and conifers (except the Araucariaceae).

Young stems of *Ginkgo* show an epidermis, a parenchymatous cortex, the vascular cylinder, and a parenchymatous pith. Pith and cortex are more extensive in spur shoots, which also contain more resin cavities. Epidermis is soon replaced by periderm, which originates in the outer cortex. Tannin cells similar to those of conifers are abundant in the cortex. The vascular cylinder in stems is complete (Fig. 24–2, *C*) even at levels in which growth in length has not ceased. At very young levels a very dissected vascular system exists and this is indicated by the inwardly projecting protoxylem areas of older regions. In a given section, such as the one in Fig. 24–2, *C*, the area that bulges most deeply into the pith is the downward continuation of the next higher leaf supply. The primary xylem is all endarch. The xylem between the bulges seems to be of cambial origin, but primary and secondary growth are highly telescoped in *Ginkgo* (as well as in most conifers) such that most of the primary xylem (including protoxylem) elements are in the same radial rows as later-formed xylem and radial rows in the apparent interfascicular areas begin with tracheids not typically secondary in structure. As soon as the cylinder is complete, distinct gaps are apparent (G in Fig. 24–2, *D*) and it appears as if two leaf traces arise from the base of each (or one that soon becomes double, as in Fig. 24–2, *A*, *B*). These are leaf gaps in the more classical sense. On the other hand, if only the course of the early protoxylem strands is considered, a very different stelar form is apparent and a different gap concept is applied.

The two traces that supply a leaf are most often continuous with two distinct protoxylem groups in the cauline cylinder, and they may arise as branches of two different vertical strands above the departure of a leaf supply 11 leaves below in the genetic spiral. When such a system is diagrammed, it appears as if there are no gaps and that leaf traces arise by tangential divisions of cauline bundles. If the two strands arising by tangential division in the cauline cylinder fuse, as they often do especially in the seedling (Fig. 24–2, *A*), and

separate only after curving outward to the leaf, and if this also happens in the system associated with the next leaf in the orthostichy (11 leaves up or down in the genetic spiral), then the leaf trace is designated as the single one above and not as the two strands arising by tangential divisions below. The stele then comes to be described as having gaps. In *Equisetum* (see Chapter 7), ignoring differences in phyllotaxy, the same kind of "protoxylem stele" appears as in *Ginkgo* and conifers, but with most pairs of "traces" fused and few unfused. In the opinion held here, the form exhibited by the early protoxylem strand network is phylogenetically much less conservative and of lesser comparative value than that of the entire stele.

Branches in *Ginkgo* are all axillary. On long shoots of older plants a bud occurs in the axil of every leaf, but many such sites are budless in seedlings. Short shoots bear no axillary vegetative buds but produce axillary reproductive structures in mature specimens. The branch supplies (BS in Fig. 24–2, *D*) are double and arise above the leaf trace on the flanks of the gap.

The secondary wood of *Ginkgo* has a uniform texture but otherwise poor physical properties. It is composed of tracheids of moderate wall thickness that are not long by conifer standards, and narrow rays that are one cell wide and one to five cells high in short shoots. Tracheidal overlap is inextensive and many tracheids end at the same level. This makes for very brittle wood of limited application. When a large tree is felled, the log is frequently shattered beyond use as it strikes the ground. Trees suffer greatly in high wind storms and a tree hit by lightning frequently presents a phenomenal sight of destruction long distances from the point of impact. The tracheary pits are circular bordered, in one or two rows, either opposite or alternate and restricted to radial walls except at the end of a growth ring, where they are on tangential walls. There is a distinct torus, and distinct bars of Sanio are present.

The primary xylem of *Ginkgo* is a very specialized type (here called the coniferophyte type) found also in the Coniferales, Taxales, Ephedrales, Gnetales, Welwitschiales, and Ophioglossales. These are also the orders in

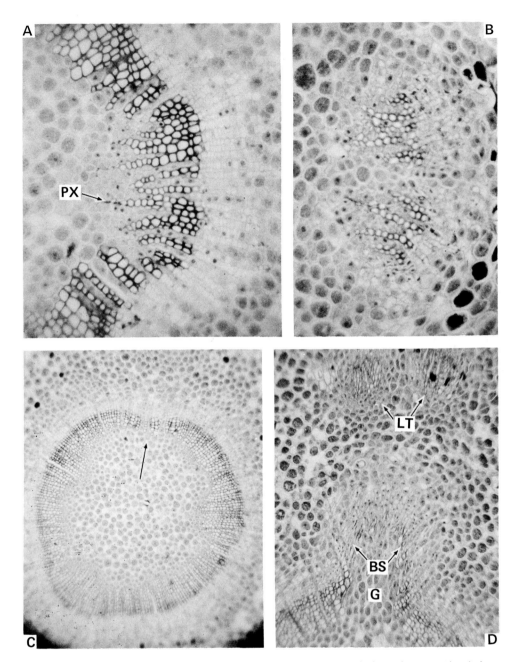

FIGURE 24-2. *Ginkgo biloba.* *A.* Portion of the vascular cylinder of a long shoot stem just below the point of departure of a leaf trace. PX = protoxylem of leaf trace. *B.* Cross section of the same leaf trace shown in *A* but at a higher level in the stem cortex after it has divided. *C.* Same vascular cylinder as in *A* just above the stelar gap. *D.* Cross section through a node of a long shoot. LT = leaf traces; BS = branch supply; G = gap.

which the torus is found, although its occurrence is inconsistent in the Ophioglossales.

In general, vascular plants present a sequence of tracheary elements from annular to helical to reticulate to pitted with variations in the completeness of the sequence, in the degree of intergradation of the morphological types and in a variety of minor structural characteristics of each type (Bierhorst, 1960; Bierhorst and Zamora, 1965). Variations in these regards are occasionally of diagnostic value but of little overall phylogenetic value. Greatest departures from the generalized sequence are to be found in the Equisetaceae (Bierhorst, 1958c) and in the Ophioglossaceae (Bierhorst, 1960), but not so great as to preclude the interpretation of the sequences in general terms.

Within the generalized sequence of primary xylem element types, there are two subsequences. One is the ordinary type and the other the coniferophyte type. The ordinary type shows a sequence of elements in which there is progressively greater coverage in area on the inner surface of the cell by secondary wall. Thus in the annular element a small part of the area is covered by the rings and between them the wall is primary only. The coverage is greater in the helical element (and from early-formed to later-formed helical elements) and still greater in the reticulate elements. In the transition from reticulate to pitted, the changes from early- to later-matured elements involves a progressively greater restriction of openings in the reticulum, usually with a progressively greater development of border around them. In the sequential sense, then, the wall is filled by secondary wall in a tangential manner.

In the coniferophyte sequence *centripetal wall filling* occurs along with *tangential wall filling*; that is, the "openings" in the secondary wall reticulum from early- to later-matured elements become progressively less evident not only by restriction in the area of the wall they occupy (compare Fig. 27–9, *H* with *I*, *L* with *M*) but also by progressively thicker deposits of secondary wall within them as compared to elsewhere on the cell. Near the end of the sequence, then, what appear to be openings in a secondary wall reticulum are in reality areas where the secondary wall is thinner and not absent (Fig. 27–9, *I*, *J*, which are face and sectional views of the same cell; Fig. 27–9, *G*,

J). At the end of the sequence the "openings" are no longer evident (cell to the right in *K*). The circular bordered pits in the coniferophyte sequence first appear as completely developed structures between and among secondary wall strands of the annular, helical, or early reticulate elements (Fig. 27–9, *D*, *E*, *H*, *L*, *M*). Where they first appear in the sequence they are completely distinct from all other openings in the secondary wall framework and are never seen as the end product of a progressively modified sequence of openings as in the ordinary transition. Although an occasional elongate pit has been seen in *Ginkgo* and a few conifers, the only genus exhibiting the coniferophyte transition that regularly shows scalariform pits is *Ophioglossum*, in which they appear last in the sequence of cells following elements with circular bordered pits.

Within the Cordaitales, insofar as is known (Bailey, 1925), the transition of primary xylem elements is of the ordinary type. There is thus a histological hiatus within the presumed coniferophyte–gnetophyte assemblage that may or may not reflect mere insufficient knowledge of the cordaites. The nearly idealistic series of intermediates between the Cordaites and the conifers in their megasporangiate fructifications, however, seems to outweigh evidence from primary xylem structure.

The similarities between the ophioglossaceae and the coniferophytes in primary xylem structure, secondary xylem, and periderm in *Botrychium* is anomalous in view of their divergent kinds of life cycles. It may be interpreted as evidence of an ultimate interrelationship going all the way back to a common non-seed-bearing ancestor such as an aneurophyte.

The leaves of *Ginkgo biloba* are fan-shaped and frequently bilobed (Fig. 24–1, *A*) but range from entire (Fig. 24–1, *B*) to deeply and highly dissected, as in the fossil ginkgophyte *Baiera* (Fig. 24–8, *D*). The degree of lobing or dissection is correlated with age of specimen, position on the plant, treatment it has received, and genetic differences. Two veins extend into the petiole and give rise to the finely dichotomous and rarely anastomosing vein system of the lamina (Fig. 24–1, *C*). Occasionally a leaf vein will show weak mesarchy, but most are endarch. Palisade mesophyll is well organized only in certain large leaves borne on long shoots. Vascular supplies to cotyledons differ from typical vegetative leaves in being mesarch at their base and exarch more distally.

The trees are dioecious. Sex chromosomes have been reported, but their existence has been denied by some workers. Early detection of the sex of an individual is of some importance, since the ovulate tree is undesirable as an ornamental because of the strong odor of lactic acid given off by the fleshy seeds.

The microsporangiate fructifications are catkinlike strobili (Fig. 24–1, C) borne singly in the leaf axils or on the upper sides of the bases of petioles. The strobilar axis is supplied by two traces that arise from the short shoot stele just as bud traces arise. Along the strobilar axis are stalked sporangiophores (Fig. 24–1, C; Fig. 24–3, A to C), each supplied by two traces and bearing two (rarely three to seven) pendant sporangia. The arrangement of sporangiophores is very irregular. Here and there it appears spiral, elsewhere patternless, or with attachments grouped in twos or threes (Fig. 24–3, A). In the region of attachment of sporangia to sporangiophores is a ridge of tissue with two variably developed horns (arrow in Fig. 24–3, C). Lines of dehiscence of adjacent sporangia oppose each other (Fig. 24–3, B, C), and as they dehisce by generalized surface cell shrinkage they are pulled apart by the shrinkage of two mucilage cavities located beneath each horn (Fig. 24–3, B). The sporangial wall is multilayered, but cellular breakdown beginning at the periphery of the sporogenous tissue ultimately involves all layers but the surface layer (Fig. 24–3, D). Conflicting literature reports indicate that sporangial initiation may or may not be the result of surface cells dividing periclinally. Microsporangia have been reported as occurring rarely on vegetative leaves. Both mega- and microsporangiate organs are initiated during the summer, and microsporangia are usually in premeiotic stages during the winter.

The megasporangiate organs of *Ginkgo* are borne on the short shoots of ovulate trees in the same relative positions as are the microsporangiate strobili on the male specimens (Fig. 24–1, D). Figure 24–4, E shows a top view of a leaf (LF) and an epipetiolar ovuliferous stalk (OS), both severed near their base. A pair of traces arising in a bud position supply the ovuliferous stalk (OSS in Fig. 24–4, D), and these each divide into two while still in the short shoot cortex. The resultant four bundles are outlined in Fig. 24–4, E. At the top of the stalk there are usually two ovules (Fig. 24–1, D; Fig. 24–4, A). More than two are rare (Fig. 24–4, C, center and right) and tend to be more frequent on certain specimens. Those illustrated in Fig. 24–4, C are from the well-known New Haven, Connecticut, tree. Other specimens rarely show a greater longitudinal distinctness of the stalks of individual ovules (Fig. 24–4, C, left). In specimens bearing more than two ovules on a common trunk, the number of vascular bundles still remains two times the number of ovules. Ovules are occasionally borne on vegetative leaves, and sometimes the normally ovule bearing organ is in part laminate (Fig. 24–8, E). The lamina in such cases is derived by tissue proliferation at or below the base of the ovule.

Each ovule (Fig. 24–4, F) is represented by a nucellus (N) and a single integument (I) that grows up around it and forms the micropyle (M). The single megaspore mother cell (NMC) originates a few cells from the exposed surface but comes to be deep-seated as the distal part of the nucellus expands. A pollen chamber (PC) is formed by breakdown of cells at the nucellar apex, and the contents of these cells form the pollination drop. Around the base of the ovule is a restricted aril or collar (C in Fig. 24–4, A, F). The apical part of the micropyle is occasionally two-lipped (Fig. 24–4, B), a feature rather general throughout the conifers.

The older ovule is spherical and drupelike. The outer fleshy layer is extensive and becomes very mushy just before the structures fall to the ground in the autumn, which may be before fertilization occurs. Growth of the embryo is an uninterrupted process but is often aborted by low temperatures in severe climates. The decomposing fleshy part of the seed coat with its quantity of lactic acid may represent a special protective mechanism by supplying substrate for microorganisms that in turn supply some heat to the seed. When the outer fleshy layer is removed, the distinctly bilateral stony layer is exposed. Beneath the latter is a thin inner fleshy layer that contains the entire vascular system of the ovule, made up of only two vascular strands. On occasion the stony

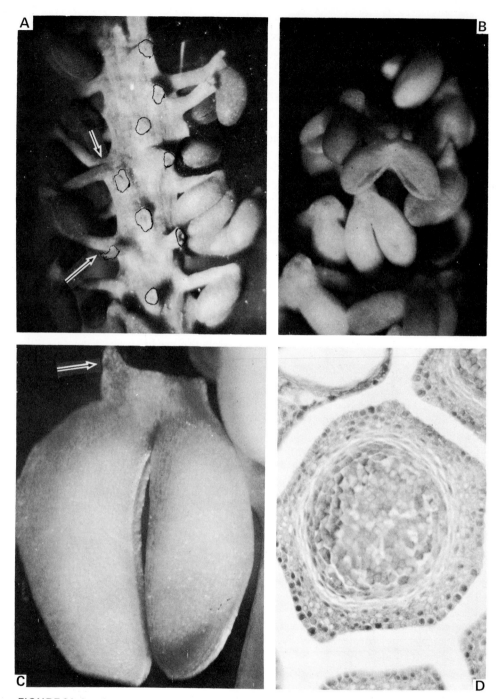

FIGURE 24–3. *Ginkgo biloba.* *A.* Microsporangiate strobilus with some of the sporangiophores removed. The arrows indicate loci where pairs of stalks are attached. *B.* Group of microsporangiophores on the strobilus. *C.* One sporangiophore enlarged. *D.* Cross section through a microsporangium.

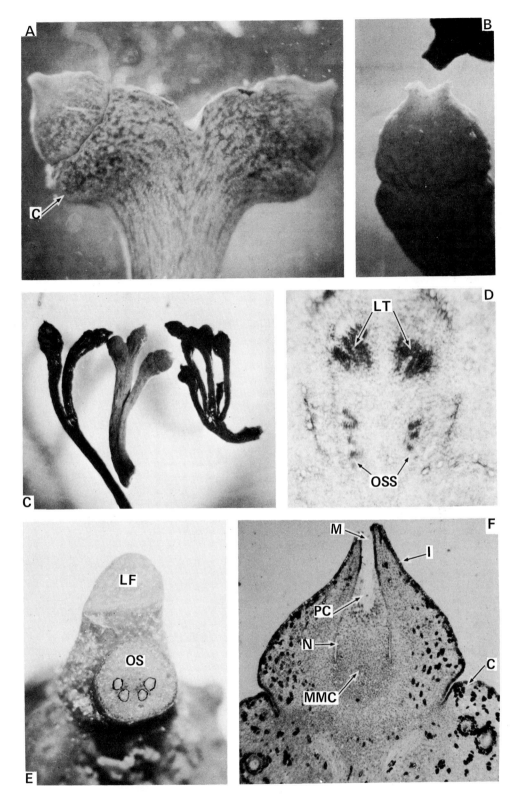

FIGURE 24–4. *Ginkgo biloba.* *A.* Tip of an ovuliferous stalk bearing two ovules. *B.* Tip of an ovule showing a two-lipped integument. *C.* Ovuliferous stalks with unusual branching and ovule numbers. *D.* Cross section through a node of the short shoot, showing the vascular supply to an ovuliferous stalk, OSS, and two traces to its subtending leaf, LT. *E.* The subtending leaf and its epipetiolar ovuliferous stalk both cut off near their bases. The veins of the fertile organ, OS, are outlined. *F.* Longitudinal section of a young ovule. M = micropyle; I = integument; PC = pollen chamber; N = nucellus; MMC = megaspore mother cell; C = collar.

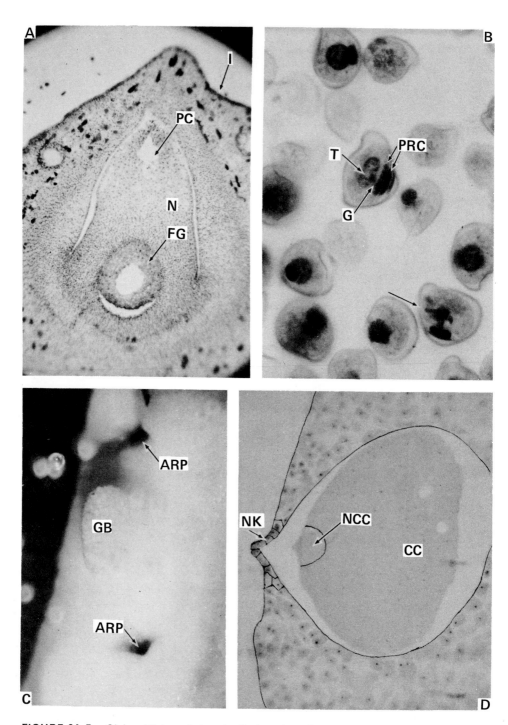

FIGURE 24–5. *Ginkgo biloba.* *A.* Longitudinal section of an ovule slightly older than the one in Fig. 24–4, *F.* *B.* Nearly mature pollen grains within the microsporangium. *C.* Upper part of the female gametophyte. *D.* Archegonium. I = integument; PC = pollen chamber; N = nucellus; FG = female gametophyte; T = tube nucleus; PRC = two prothallial cells; G = generative cell; GP = gametophytic beak; ARP = archegonial pits; NK = neck; CC = central cell; NCC = nucleus of central cell.

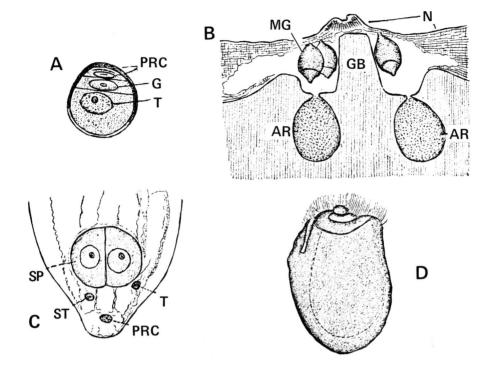

FIGURE 24–6. *Ginkgo biloba*, after Wettstein (1911). *A.* Mature pollen grain. *B.* Longitudinal section through a part of the ovule. *C.* Distal end of a male gametophyte. *D.* Mature sperm. PRC = prothallial cell; G = generative cell; T = tube nucleus; N = nucellus; MG = male gametophyte; GB = gametophytic beak; AR = archegonium; SP = sperm; ST = nucleus of stalk cell; PRC = nucleus of prothallial cell.

layer is three-sided, in which case the inner fleshy layer contains three strands.

In the temperate regions of the Northern Hemisphere pollen is shed in April or May. At this time the young leaves are partly expanded and the ovules and thin stalks are completely exposed. The specimens in Fig. 24–4, *A, F* are approximately at pollination stage. The pollen is shed in the four celled stage (Fig. 24–6, *A*) and carried by the wind. There are two prothallial cells (PRC), a generative cell (G) and the tube cell (T). In Fig. 24–5, *B* the nearly mature grains are seen within the microsporangium. The grain with parts labeled is essentially mature, while the one indicated by the arrow shows a mitotic figure in the formation of the tube and the generative cell.

The male gametophyte develops throughout the summer and early fall. It produces a short haustorial tube into the nucellus and its main body, which remains partly covered by the

pollen grain wall, extends into the pollen chamber (Fig. 24–6, *B*). The generative cell divides to produce a stalk cell and a body cell, and eventually the latter produces two large (about 70 by 90 μ) sperm each with a ciliated band (Fig. 24–6, *C, D*).

As the male gametophyte is developing the female gametophyte is doing the same more proximally and the nucellar tissue between them is diminishing. Within a linear tetrad the lowermost megaspore is functional. It first enlarges, then goes through a period of free nucleate divisions (FG in Fig. 24–5, *A*). Wall formation progresses from the periphery of the sac after several hundred free nuclei are formed, which is about 2 months after pollination. Usually only two, but occasionally three, archegonia are formed at the apex of the gametophyte and very rarely additional, quite lateral groups of archegonia are formed. Each archegonium is sunken in a pit (ARP in Fig.

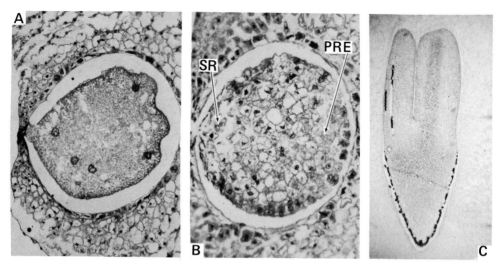

FIGURE 24–7. *Ginkgo biloba.* Three stages in embryo development. SR = suspensor region; PRE = proembryo region.

24–5, *C*) on either side of a gametophytic beak (GB in Fig. 24–5, *C*; Fig. 24–6, *B*). There are two neck cells, a small ventral canal cell, and a large egg. The central cell (CC) with its nucleus (NCC) is shown in Fig. 24–5, *D* before the final division to form egg and ventral canal cell.

Embryogeny begins with a series of free nuclear divisions until about 256 nuclei are formed (an eight-nucleate stage is shown in Fig. 24–7, *A*), at which time walls form simultaneously throughout the mass. Polarization is observable soon thereafter as the cells at the micropylar end of the embryo enlarge (SR, suspensor region in Fig. 24–7, *B*) much more than those at the chalazal end (PRE, proembryo region). The suspensor elongates to approximately 1 mm out of the neck of the archegonium and curves over and generally touches the gametophytic beak. Soon a distinctive apical meristem is organized over the proembryo region and from it two dominant centers form the two cotyledons (Fig. 24–7, *C*).

On germination of the seed the cotyledons remain within the tissue of the female gametophyte and continue to grow somewhat for nearly 2 years. On their surface are nonfunctional stomata.

The *Ginkgo* line seems traceable at least to the Lower Permian *Trichopitys*, which is often

placed in its own order, the *Trichopityales*. *Trichopitys* bore spirally arranged, dichotomously branched leaves without lamina (Fig. 24–8, *B*). In the axil of some leaves or on the upper surface of the leaf bases were small branched ovuliferous trusses (Fig. 24–8, *B*, *C*). Each ultimate branch bore a terminal, recurved ovule (Fig. 24–8, *A*).

A variety of Ginkgo-like genera and many species are known from rocks of Permian and Mesozoic age. Several of these are separated from the genus *Ginkgo* on the basis of differences of dubious intergeneric magnitude. The genus *Ginkgo* is recognized certainly in Jurassic rocks, which were laid down roughly at about the time the Ginkgoaceae reached its widest geographic distribution and was present in greatest numbers and diversity.

Sphenobaiera goes back to the Permian. The plant bore long and short shoots, and its slender dichotomous leaves (Fig. 24–8, *H*) intergrade with simpler ones of other ginkgoids (Fig. 24–8, *F*, *G*). *Sphenobaiera* bore on short shoots slender microsporangiate organs that were branched, and each ultimate unit bore three to five sporangia.

Baiera leaves (Fig. 24–8, *D*) intergrade with those of the living *Ginkgo* but with lesser development of petiole in the fossil. Associated with the Jurassic *Baiera muensteriana* are slender, catkinlike microsporangiate strobili. On

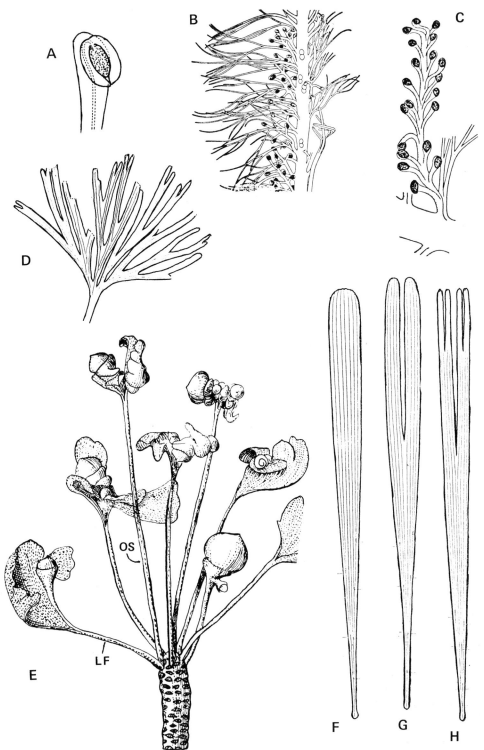

FIGURE 24–8. *A.* Ovule of *Trichopitys.* *B.* Axis bearing ovuliferous and sterile appendages in *Trichopitys.* *C.* Single ovuliferous appendage and the base of the associated sterile appendage of *Trichopitys.* *D.* Leaf of *Baiera münsteriana.* *E.* Short shoot of *Ginkgo* with ovules borne on modified vegetative leaves. *F, G.* Leaves of *Arctobaiera flettii.* *H.* Leaf of *Sphenobaiera horniana.* *A* to *C* after Florin (1951); *D* after Schenk (1867); *E* after Pilger (1926); *F* to *H* after Florin (1951).

427

the strobilar axes were sporangiophores each of which bore 10 to 12 sporangia and were quite similar to the occasional multisporangiate sporangiophores of *Ginkgo biloba*.

The known geographic and chronological distribution of *Ginkgo* (*Ginkgoites*) *adiantoides* probably gives a reasonable picture of what has happened to *G. biloba*, as the two are probably the same. During Eocene times the species was widespread. In North America it has been found in rocks of this age from Alaska to South Dakota. It has been reported from Oligocene and Miocene rocks at a few localities in the northwestern United States and southwestern Canada. By the Pleiocene it was restricted to Asia and western Europe and since then only to Eastern Asia. The still older *Ginkgo* (*Ginkgoites*) *digitata* of Jurassic rocks has been reported from North America, Europe, Asia, Japan, and Australia.

A discussion of coniferophyte phylogeny appears at the end of Chapter 25.

25

Conifers and Taxads

Most students of botany have a definite concept of what a conifer is like, even though their ideas are probably Pinaceae-centered. All conifers and taxads are woody perennial plants. Their growth habits range from excurrent trees to spreading trees to shrubs; at the extreme are the miniature forms of *Dacridium*, only a few inches tall, and the completely prostrate *Juniperus horizontalis*. Throughout the assemblage of genera there is a high degree of histological uniformity expressed in the xylem, the phloem, and the cortical tissues. Leaves vary from scale to needle to linear to broad types.

During the last two decades various authors have not differed greatly in the manner in which they classify these plants. The system in Table 25–1 reflects many generally accepted interpretations if one ignores the order of presentation of the families, which in this case is not to be considered linear.

Probably all extant conifer and taxad families were differentiated by Jurassic times. The incomplete fossil record suggests that possibly the Cephalotaxaceae and the Cupressaceae may not have been distinct until Upper Jurassic or Lower Cretaceous and that the Araucariaceae and the Pinaceae may be somewhat older than Jurassic. Comparative morphology of extinct and extant forms suggests that each of the still-existing families was separately derived from a complex of forms called transition conifers and included here within the broadly circumscribed Voltziaceae of Permian through Jurassic occurrence. Our knowledge of these fossils is extensive and somewhat detailed, to a large extent due to the classical studies of Rudolf Florin. Although the transition conifers are considered in terms of several families by some authors, the familial lines are not very distinct, and a large number of problematical form

TABLE 25-1. Some characteristics of extant taxad and conifer genera. (A. Leaf form: L = linear; B = broad; Sc = scalelike; N = needle. B. Leaf arrangement: Op = opposite; Sp = spiral; Wh = whorled. C. Sporangia per microsporangiophore. D. Ovules per cone scale. E. Number of cotyledons.)

Family	Genus	Species	Distribution	A	B	C	D	E
Taxaceae	*Amentotaxus*	1–4	Assam, W. China	L	Sp	3+		2
	Austrotaxus	1	N. Caledonia	B	Sp	3+		2
	Pseudotaxus	1	China	L	Sp	3+		2
	Taxus	10	North Temperate	L	Sp	3–9		2
	Torreya	6	E. Asia, California, Florida	L	Sp	3+		2
Cephalotaxaceae	*Cephalotaxus*	4–7	E. Asia	L	Op	3–8	2	2
Podocarpaceae	*Acmopyle*	3	N. Caledonia, Fiji	L	Sp	2	1	2
	Dacridium	20–25	N. Zealand to Indo-malaysia, Chile	L, Sc	Sp	2	1	2
	Microcachrys	1	Tasmania	Sc	Sp	2	1	2
	Microstrobus	2	Australia, Tasmania	Sc	Sp	2	1	2
	Phyllocladus	7	N. Zealand, Tasmania to Philippines	L, Sc	Sp	2	1	2
	Podocarpus	100	Tropics, north to Himalayas and Japan	Sc, L, B	Sp	2	1	2
Araucariaceae	*Saxegothaea*	1	Andes of Argentina	L	Sp	2	2	2
	Agathis	20	Indochina, W. Malaysia, to N. Zealand	B	Sp	5–15	1	2
	Araucaria	18	N. Zealand, Australia, N. Caledonia, S. Brazil, Chile	B	Sp	5–15	1–2	2 (4)
Cupressaceae	*Actinostrobus*	2	SW Australia	Sc	Sp		1–2	
	Austrocedrus	1	Temp. S. America	Sc	Op		1–2	
	Callitris	16	Australia, N. Caledonia	Sc	Op		∞	

Genus	N species	Distribution	Leaf	Habit			
Calocedrus	3	SE Asia, Formosa, Pacific N. America	Sc	Op	2–4	2	2
Chamaecyparus	7	N. America, Japan, Formosa	Sc	Op	2–5	2–5	2
Cupressus	16–20	Mediterranean, Sahara, Asia, N. America	Sc	Sp	2–6	6–20	2–5
Diselma	1	Tasmania	Sc	Op, Wh		2	
Fitzroya	1	Chile	Sc	Wh	2–5	1–6	2
Fokienia	1–3	China, Indochina	Sc	Wh	2–5	2	
Juniperus	60	N. Hemisphere	Sc, N	Sp	3–6	1–3	2–6
Libocedrus	5	N. Caledonia, N. Zealand	Sc	Op	3–5	1–2	
Neocallitropsis	1	N. Caledonia	Sc, L	Wh	∞	2–5	2
Papuacedrus	3	N. Guinea, Moluccas	Sc	Op	∞	2	
Pilgerodendron	1	S. Chile	Sc	Op	4–8	1–2	
Tetraclinis	1	Spain to Tunis, Malta	Sc	Op			
Thuja	5	China, Japan, N. America	Sc	Op	2–5	2–3	
Thujopsis	1	Japan	Sc	Op	2–5	3–5	
Widdringtonia	5	Tropics and S. Africa	Sc	Op	3–5	5+	2
Athrotaxis	3	Australia, Tasmania	Sc, B	Sp	2	3–6	
Cryptomeria	1	Japan	Sc	Sp	5–7	3–6	
Cunninghamia	3	China, Formosa	B	Sp	2–4	2–3	2
Glyptostrobus	1	China	L, B	Sp	4–7	2	
Metasequoia	1	China	L	Op		5–8	
Sciadopitys	1	Japan	Sc, L	Sp	2	5–9	
Sequoia	1	California	L	Sp	3–4	3–7	2
Sequoiadendron	1	California	Sc, N	Sp	3–6	5–8	3–5
Taiwania	3	China, Formosa	Sc	Sp		2	
Taxodium	3	SE U.S., Mexico	L	Sp	4–7	2	

Taxodiaceae

TABLE 25-1. *(Continued)*

Family	Genus	Species	Distribution	A	B	C	D	E
Pinaceae	*Abies*	50	North Temperate, Central America	N	Sp	2	2	5–7
	Cathaya	2	China	L	Sp	2	2	3–4
	Cedrus	4	Middle East, Algeria, Cyprus, Himalayas	N	Sp	2	2	9–10
	Keteleeria	4–8	E. Asia, Indochina	L, B	Sp	2	2	2
	Larix	10–12	Europe, N. Asia, N. America	N	Sp	2	2	6
	Picea	50	North Temperate	N	Sp	2		2	4–15
	Pinus	70–100	North Temperate, on mountains in tropics	Sc, N	Sp	2	2	4–15
	Pseudolarix	2	China	N	Sp	2	2	5–7
	Pseudotsuga	7	E. Asia, Western N. America	L	Sp	2	2	6–12
	Tsuga	15	E. Asia, N. America	L	Sp	2	2	3–6

genera and species are not readily assignable to families of more narrow circumscription.

Without reference to the fossil record, one may readily suggest on evidence from extant forms that conifers and taxads are an extremely ancient and relict group. Of the 53 genera listed in Table 25–1, 18 are represented by a single species, 15 by only 2 to 7 species each, 7 by 10 to 30, and 5 by 50 to 100. It will be noted also that each family is very widely distributed and yet the individual genera are often of extremely limited distribution. All these facts indicate great antiquity, which is completely borne out by the fossil record. Conifers probably reached their climax in mid-Mesozoic times and have been on the decline ever since. There is evidence that there were very extensive coniferous forests in northern Europe which were destroyed over a number of centuries by prehistoric man, and some think these forests were established and in continuous existence since Mesozoic times. Existing forests dominated by conifers are relatively inextensive and often are restricted to marginal habitats or are maintained as subclimaxes by occasional fires. The conditions necessary for the re-establishment of extensive coniferous forests in ordinary mesic areas probably no longer exist.

The Pinaceae (same as Abietaceae), primarily a North Temperate family (Table 25–1), includes among others the firs (*Abies*), spruces (*Picea*), pines[1] (*Pinus*), hemlocks (*Tsuga*), and larches (*Larix*). Most species are trees, although an occasional species of *Pinus* or *Tsuga* is somewhat shrubby, and all are monoecious. All genera in the family except *Cathaya* and *Keteleeria* are commercial sources of wood. Pinaceous leaves are linear to long-needle-form (Fig. 25–1, *A*, *B*, *D*). Three genera bear indeterminate spur shoots (*Cathaya*, *Larix*, and *Pseudolarix*), and the last two of these are deciduous. *Pinus* produces determinate short shoots in the axils of scale leaves. Each short shoot when mature has a short axis with an aborted apex and 10 to 15 leaves. Of these, from one to five of the distal ones develop into vegetative needles (the number varying according to the species), while the remainder envelop

[1] As a common name "pine" is also applied to other genera (such as *Araucaria*) and even to some angiosperms (such as *Casuarina*).

the short shoot axis as dried, resinous scales. The cross section of the nearly mature short shoot in Fig. 25–15, *D* shows two needles of *P. mugo* in the center and the series of scale leaves surrounding them. On the specimen in Fig. 25–1, *C* the vegetative short shoots are at the top and their needles have not yet grown out from the enveloping scale leaves as they have in the specimen in Fig. 25–1, *D*. The photosynthetic leaves have one or two veins (Fig. 25–15, *A* to *C*). When two, they are within the same endodermal sheath (E in Fig. 25–15, *C*). Protoxylem (PX) is on the adaxial side and maturation is endarch. There is often some indication of cambial activity, as indicated in *C*. In a number of species between the bundles and the endodermis there are isodiametric transfusion tracheids and often there are fibrous cells on the phloem side.

Both mega- and microsporangiate fructifications are clearly strobiloid in the Pinaceae, unlike members of certain other conifer families in which the conelike nature of the fructification may be obscured by reduction and modification. The megasporangiate cones are composed of a number of spirally arranged bracts (BR in Fig. 25–2, *A*, *C*) in the axils of which are produced undivided ovuliferous scales (also called cone scales; CS in Fig. 25–2, *A*, *C*), each bearing two inverted ovules on its adaxial (upper) surface (Fig. 25–3, *B* to *E*). There is a single integument that is two-lipped at the micropyle (Fig. 25–3, *C*) and generally fused to the nucellus for part of its length (Fig. 25–20, *B*). In the mature cones there are various degrees of fusion between, and hence distinctiveness of, bracts and cone scales. Bracts in some genera are trifurcate at their tips (Fig. 25–2, *B*, *D*). Although the bract is formed first and the cone scale in its axil (Fig. 25–19, *D*, right side), at pollination time either the bract or the cone scale may be extended farther (compare the two in Fig. 25–2, *A*, *C*; Fig. 25–3, *A*, *D*; Fig. 25–19, *A* to *C*). In *Pseudotsuga* and *Larix* (Fig. 25–2, *B*, *D*) the long bracts nearly completely hide the axillary cone scales at this stage. The microsporangiate cones (Fig. 25–1, *B*; Fig. 25–4, *A* to *D*; Fig. 25–17, *A*, *B*) bear a spiral sequence of sporangiophores, each with a variably developed sterile distal flap (according to genus) and a pair of elongate microsporangia

FIGURE 25–1. *A*. Shoot of *Tsuga canadensis* with megasporangiate cones. *B*. Shoot of *Pinus mugo* with a number of microsporangiate cones. *C*. Shoot of *P. mugo* with microsporangiate cones still enclosed within scale leaves. *D*. Shoot of *P. mugo* with two 1-year-old megasporangiate cones and a new one of the current season at the very top.

FIGURE 25–2. Young megasporangiate cones all at about the time of pollination. *A. Pinus mugo*. *B. Pseudotsuga*. *C. Picea abies*. *D. Larix*. CS = cone scale; BR = subtending bract.

435

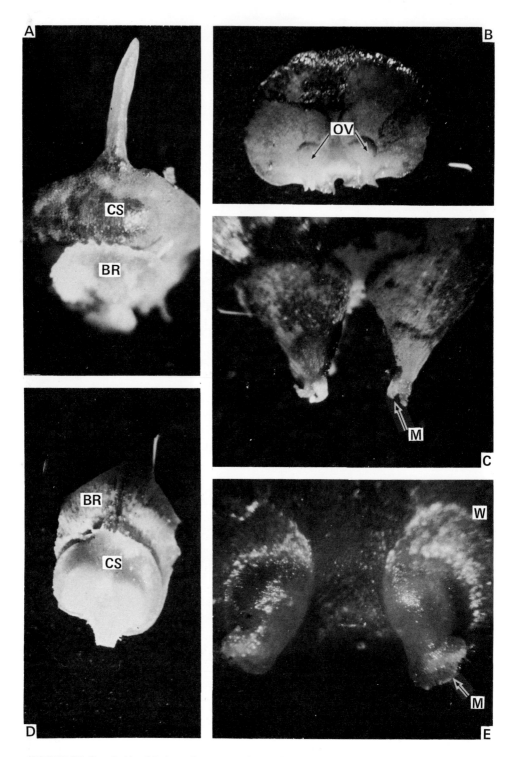

FIGURE 25–3. *A.* Abaxial view of a cone scale and its subtending bract of *Pinus mugo* at about pollination time. *B.* Adaxial view of a young cone scale of *Picea abies*. *C.* Two ovules from *B* enlarged. *D.* Abaxial view of a young cone scale and its subtending bract of *Larix*. *E.* Two ovules of a cone scale of *Pseudotsuga*. CS = cone scale; BR = bract; OV = ovules; M = micropyle; W = wing.

FIGURE 25–4. *A.* Microsporangiate shoot of *Pseudotsuga* and its subtending bract (extending to the right). At the base of the shoot is a series of sterile scale leaves and the strobilus is terminal. *B.* External view of the microsporangiate strobilus of *Pinus mugo*. *C.* Strobilar stalk and attached microsporangiophores of *Picea abies*. *D.* Microsporangiate strobilus of *Abies* with some sporangiophores removed.

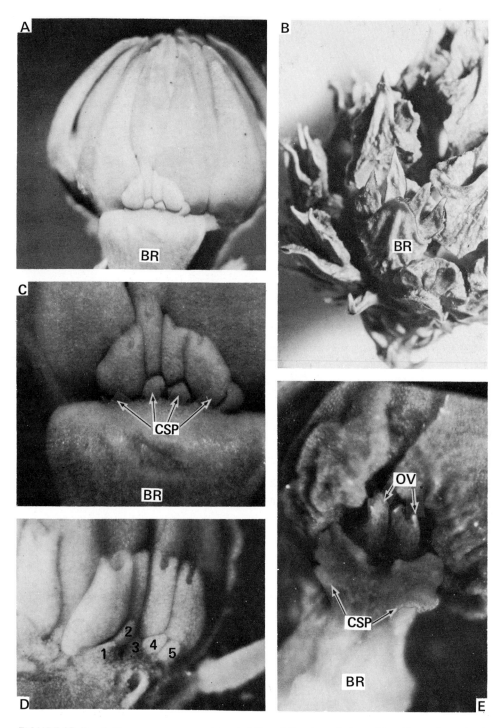

FIGURE 25–5. *A.* Young megasporangiate strobilus of *Cryptomeria japonica* with one bract bent back to expose the axillary complex. *B.* External view of an older megasporangiate cone of *Cryptomeria.* *C.* Portion of *A* enlarged. *D.* View of another axillary complex from *A.* The bract has been torn off. The five separate components of the cone scale are numbered and are just below the four ovules. *E.* View of a young megasporangiate cone of *Taxodium disticum.* A bract has been pulled back to expose an axillary complex. BR = bract; CSP = individual parts of a cone scale; OV = ovules.

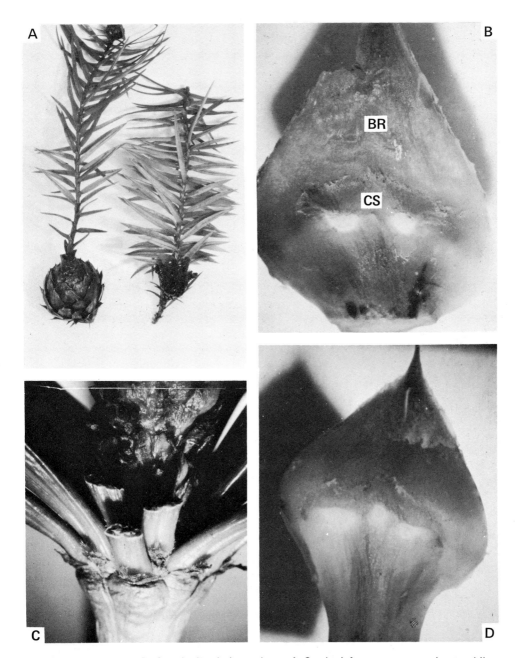

FIGURE 25–6. *A, B, D. Cunninghamia lanceolata.* *A.* On the left, a megasporangiate strobilus with its axis extended as a vegetative shoot. On the right, a cluster of microsporangiate strobili each in the axil of a bract upon an axis that is extended upward as a vegetative shoot. *B.* Cone scale and its subtending bract from a megasporangiate cone. The two white areas are ovule attachments. *D.* As *B*, but with three ovule attachments. *C.* Portion of a vegetative shoot of *Sciadopitys.* CS = cone scale; BR = bract.

(Fig. 25–4, *C*). Dehiscence is longitudinal, except rarely transverse or oblique. In other conifers it is uniformly longitudinal.

The Taxodiaceae includes small to gigantic monoecious trees with spirally arranged or rarely opposite leaves that range from scale-like to broad (Table 25–1). Three genera, *Glyptostrobus*, *Metasequoia*, and *Taxodium*, produce flattened, determinate, and deciduous branchlets. *Scidopitys* produces scale leaves in a spiral sequence on long shoots. The spiral is vertically contracted in zones along the shoot, where in the axil of each scale is a short shoot composed of two leaves fused together along opposing edges (Fig. 25–6, *C*; Fig. 25–15, *E*). Scale leaves within the extended portions of the spiral bear no axillary structures.

The strobili are generally small and retain their conelike appearance with a high number of parts. Microsporangiate strobili are frequently grouped on tasseloid branches as in *Taxodium*, but otherwise they resemble pinaceous ones. Certain genera bear only two microsporangia per sporangiophore, while others bear up to seven (Table 25–1). Megasporangiate strobili show a spiral sequence of bracts with axillary fertile complexes. In most genera the fertile complex is a single physical entity at maturity (the cone scale) bearing from two to seven ovules but variable in size in relation to the subtending bract and variably free of it. The specimen of *Cunninghamia* shown in Fig. 25–6, *B* shows from the upper surface a relatively large bract (BR) and a much smaller cone scale (CS), the distal edge of which appears as a fimbriate margin between the letters CS and BR. The two white areas are ovule scars (three in Fig. 25–6, *D*). In this genus the megasporangiate strobilar axis characteristically produces a distal vegetative extension (Fig. 25–6, *A*, left). Its microsporangiate strobili are axillary to grouped scale leaves, very similar to scales subtending ovulate cone scales (Fig. 25–6, *A*, right).

The ovuliferous cone scale of *Cryptomeria* holds a special place in any consideration of conifer morphology. At maturity it is fan-shaped and has four or five free tips. These are seen entending up on the adaxial side of the subtending bract, BR in Fig. 25–5, *B*. At an early stage in development (Fig. 25–5, *A*, *C*, *D*) the axillary complex is seen as a group of completely separate morphological entities. The bract (BR) has been pulled back from the young cone in *A* (enlarged in *C*) to reveal four sterile primordia or cone scale parts (CSP) and four ovules, all quite separate from each other. The two lateral cone-scale parts are inserted closer to the bract, and often when the bract is torn from the cone they go with it. Figure 25–5, *D* shows another complex from the same cone, composed of five (numbered) sterile entities and four ovules with gaping micropyles.

In *Taxodium* the cone scale shows little or no indication of multipartedness at maturity, but at an early stage (Fig. 25–5, *E*) the axillary complex is composed of two lobed and flattened entities (CSP) and two ovules (OV), all spatially separated.

The Araucariaceae are dioecious or rarely monoecious trees and generally important timber sources. The leaves are opposite or spirally arranged and narrow to broad (Fig. 25–7, *A*, *B*). All species are evergreen and none shows shoot dimorphism. Cones are characteristically quite large and composed of many units. The megasporangiate strobilus of *Agathis* (Fig. 25–7, *D*) is about the size of a small baseball, but that of *Araucaria*, which has deciduous cone scales, may approach 30 cm in diameter. The one in Fig. 25–7, *A* is shortly after pollination time. Microsporangiate cones are similarly relatively large. Those in Fig. 25–7, *C* approach the size of an adult index finger. The number of microsporangia per sporangiophore is from 5 to 15 throughout the family (cross section in Fig. 25–17, *F*). The cone scale bears one, or less commonly two ovules and at a relatively early stage in development comes to be fused to a large extent to the subtending bract (Fig. 25–8, *B*). The ovule is overgrown by a flap of cone-scale tissue and its micropyle is exposed only at a basal notch (arrow in Fig. 25–8, *B*, enlarged in *D*). The flap is free of the ovule and is easily peeled back, as was done to prepare Fig. 25–8, *C*. In some accounts the ovule is described as sunken into the cone scale, but obviously this is not the case. The integument is generally free of the nucellus to the base (Fig. 25–20, *E*).

The Cupressaceae is the largest of the conifer families in terms of numbers of genera. It

FIGURE 25–7. *A*. Shoot of *Araucaria cunninghamii* with a terminal megasporangiate cone. *B*. Vegetative shoot of *Agathis vitiensis*. *C*. Shoot with a number of microsporangiate cones of *Araucaria columnaris*. *D*. Megasporangiate cone of *Agathis vitiensis*.

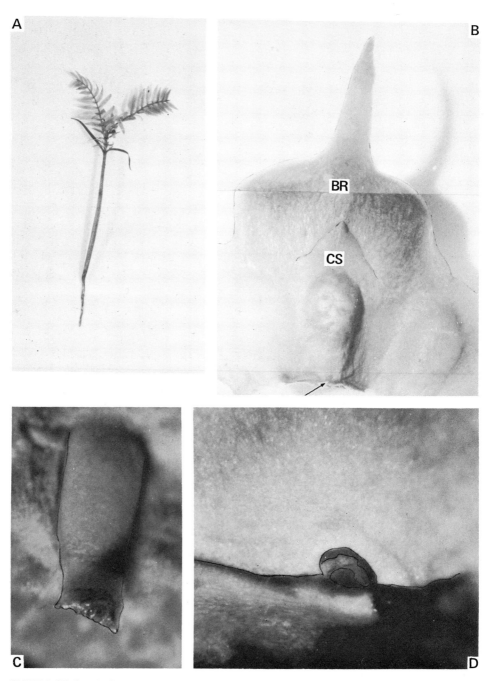

FIGURE 25–8. *A*. Seedling of *Araucaria* sp.   *B*. Adaxial view of the cone scale and bract of *Araucaria columnaris*. The arrow indicates the opening of the ovular pouch.   *C*. The ovule from *B* as seen after the cone scale flap is torn back.   *D*. Opening of the ovular pouch from *B* enlarged.

FIGURE 25–9. *A.* Shoot of *Thuja* with megasporangiate cones. *B.* Megasporangiate cone of *Neocaletropsis* from its distal end. *C.* Vegetative shoot (left) and megasporangiate cone (right) of *Neocalitropsis.* *D, E.* Two views of a young megasporangiate cone of *Chamaecyparis.* Exposed micropyles are visible in *D.* *F.* Young megasporangiate cone of *Juniperus communis.* *G.* Upper surface of a cone scale of *Cupressus sempervirens,* showing many seed scars.

443

includes many ornamentals and many commercial sources of wood. Leaves (Fig. 25–9, *A*, *C*) are all small, from scalelike to linear, and almost entirely opposite or whorled. All are evergreen and none shows shoot dimorphism. The species are dioecious or monoecious. Megasporangiate strobili (Fig. 25–9, *A* to *F*; right in *C*) are characteristically small, dry to fleshy at maturity, with the generally small number of bracts arranged as the leaves. There is a high degree of fusion between bract and cone scale (Fig. 25–20, *A*) and the former generally protrudes somewhat (Fig. 25–9, *F*). Ovules are upright (Fig. 25–9, *D*, *F*) and occur in variable numbers per cone scale (Table 25–1). Ovular scars appear as white areas in Fig. 25–9, *G*. Microsporangiate strobili are similarly small with short sporangiophores and a variable number of often near-spherical sporangia (Fig. 25–17, *G*). The microsporangiophores are generally whorled, unlike the other conifer families, in which they are spirally arranged.

The Podocarpaceae are also important in terms of wood and ornamentals. Leaves are spirally arranged and from scalelike to broad. Shoot dimorphism occurs in *Phyllocladus*, where the short shoot is a flattened photosynthetic fusion product, as its name implies. Microsporangiate strobili are short to long (Fig. 25–10, *A*, *E*), and each sporangiophore bears two microsporangia (Fig. 25–17, *D*, *E*). Additional strobili frequently arise from the bases of other strobili, which are axillary on the vegetative axis (Fig. 25–10, *D*). The species are dioecious or monoecious.

Megasporangiate strobili are in general unstrobiloid in appearance with from one to four (rarely to nine) bracts with their axillary complexes. In some species of *Podocarpus*, such as *P. macrophylla*, the uni- or biovulate strobilus is on a pedestal composed of a fattened segment of the axis with one or two very reduced leaves (or sterile strobilar scales). Three strobili are shown in Fig. 25–10, *B*; the center one is uniovulate and the other two are biovulate. Both the dark pedestals and the near-white cone units attached upon them become berrylike at a later stage in ontogeny.

A relatively generalized podocarpaceous strobilus is that of *Dacridium araucarioides*

shown in Fig. 25–13, *B* shortly after pollination time. Shown are three elongate bracts, each subtending a single cone scale that partly envelops an ovule (enlarged in *A*). As the cone matures the ovules enlarge, but the other components remain at about the size they were at pollination time (Fig. 25–13, *C*). The seed is dry and nutlike. The *Podocarpus* cone is similar but shows more fusion and different relative sizes of parts. In Fig. 25–12, *A*, *B*, which shows a strobilus at about pollination time, the bract (BR) is only slightly free of the cone scale. The ovule is exposed only by way of a small opening at the base (arrow in Fig. 25–12, *B*). The ovule with its enveloping cone scale develops into a drupelike structure (Fig. 25–10, *C*). *Dacridium taxoides* (Fig. 25–13, *D*, *E*) bears a cone scale (CS) and ovule quite similar to *Podocarpus* but with a distinct bract (BR). In various species there is a bump or vertical extension of the cone scale (the part above the letters CS in Fig. 25–13, *E*; the crest of the structure in Fig. 25–12, *B*).

The megasporangiate structure of *Podocarpus macrophylla* originates at the tip of a lateral shoot. Appendicular organs at a very early stage often appear opposite or subopposite and dicussate (Fig. 25–11, *A*). The bract (BR) is face to face with a member just like itself, and occasionally both of these are fertile. The apex of the shoot loses its identity and an outgrowth forms in the axil of the fertile bract. It grows flush against the organ in the opposite position and assumes a flat and uniform meristematic surface (side view in Fig. 25–11, *D*). In face view (Fig. 25–11, *C*) a very slight central mound (N, nucellus) is seen surrounded by a complete shallow ridge (I, integument) and this in turn by an outer ridge (cone scale, CS) that is interrupted at its base (left side in the figure). Soon the axillary complex points more downward and the axis below expands (side view in Fig. 25–11, *G*). Cone scale, integument, and nucellus grow independently in length, and therefore little fusion among them is observed later. At this stage the cone appears nearly identical to the older one of *Dacridium araucarioides* (compare Fig. 25–11, *F* with Fig. 25–13, *A*). Further growth of the cone scale results in the ovule being covered except at its microphyle (M in Fig. 25–11, *E*). As this growth takes place

FIGURE 25–10. *A.* Shoot of *Podocarpus macrophylla* with a number of microsporangiate strobili. *B.* As *A*, but with megasporangiate organs. *C.* Shoot of *P. minor* with a nearly mature seed. *D.* Attachment of three of the microsporangiate strobili from *A*. All three are attached to a common diminutive axis that is subtended by a leaf of the vegetative axis. *E.* Microsporangiate strobilus of *P. macrophylla*. *F.* Seedling of *P. macrophylla*. The two cotyledons are still contained within the remnant of the seed, which appears black among the leaves.

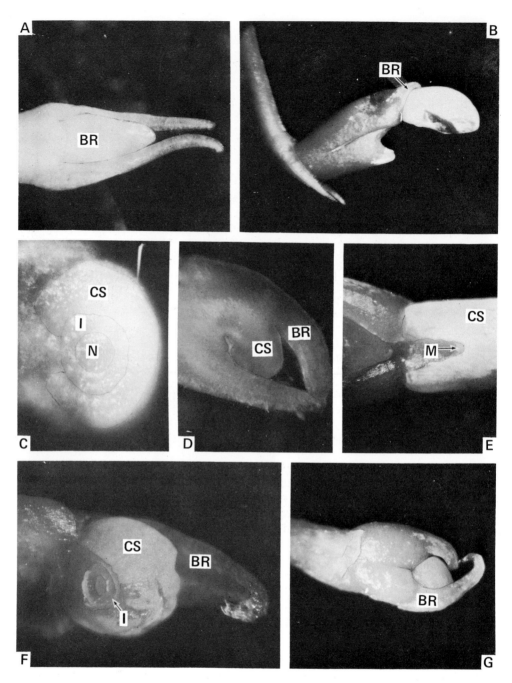

FIGURE 25–11. Megasporangiate organ of *Podocarpus macrophylla*. The entire complex is shown in *B* at about pollination time. The ovule completely enclosed by the cone scale is the white terminal structure distal to the subtending bract. *E* is a portion of *B* enlarged and is viewed from what is the lower side of *B*. *A*. Tip of the young ovuliferous shoot. The two extending structures are the reduced leaves, which appear at a later stage extending out at the 90-degree bend in *B*. The bract is viewed from the abaxial side and in this specimen is nearly opposite another reduced leaf, the one that appears slightly below and opposite the bract in *B*. *D*. Bract and cone scale from *A* viewed from the side after one of the two extended leaves is removed. *C*. Cone scale from *D* as viewed from the abaxial side. *G*. Stage in development slightly later than *D* and viewed from the same side. *F*. Adaxial view of the bract and cone scale from *G*. BR = bract; CS = cone scale; I = integument; N = nucellus; M = micropyle.

446

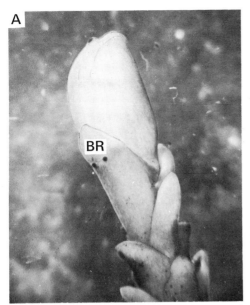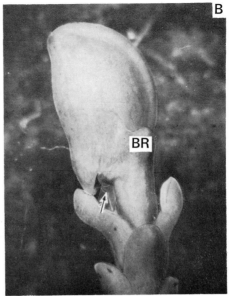

FIGURE 25–12. *Podocarpus minor,* the terminal megasporangiate complex. BR = bract; the arrow indicates the micropyle.

there is often a longitudinal separation of the bract and its opposite appendicular organ.

The monogeneric Cephalotaxaceae bear a close superficial similarity to *Taxus* in the Taxaceae but they have opposite leaves. Both are commonly referred to as yews, as are certain podocarps. The leaf traces are reported to be weakly mesarch. The microsporangiate cones of *Cephalotaxus* occur in cauliflowerlike groups (Fig. 25–14, *D*). Its microsporangiophores are much like those of the other conifers and bear three to eight microsporangia. Megasporangiate cones are borne on separate plants and are small, short-stalked, and bear five to seven pairs of opposite and decussate bracts. In the axil of each except the lowermost pair are two ovules with a small ridge of tissue between them. At maturity a cone contains one or two terete seeds with all other parts small and little in evidence. It thus may have the appearance of an ovule-bearing shoot of a taxad. The genus *Amentotaxus* has been included in the Cephalotaxaceae by some authors, but much evidence clearly points it out as a taxad quite different from *Cephalotaxus*, which is clearly a conifer (see Singh, 1961).

The development of the microsporangium of *Cephalotaxus* as described by Singh (1961)

illustrates to a large extent the ontogenetic pattern that is found throughout the coniferophytes, gnetophytes, and angiosperms (Fagerlind, 1961). The sporangium is first recognizable when a group of subepidermal cells are seen to be different from other cells of the region (Fig. 25–18, *A*). These give rise to the fertile tissue (SP), the tapetum (T) (Fig. 25–18, *A* to *E*), and the several hypodermal cell layers of the wall. Various authors have excluded the epidermis as a sporangial wall component because of its different origin. In angiosperms the inner wall layers (i.e., those related in origin to periclinal divisions in the inner tissue) are mostly absent, and Eames (1961) refers to such microsporangia as naked and sunken. The term "archesporium" has been applied to the mother tissue of the inner wall, tapetum, and sporogenous tissue (i.e., the original hypodermal layer) or to the inner tissue at a later stage in ontogeny after the wall is segregated from it.

It is of interest to note that the ontogeny of the "microsporangium" in seed plants parallels that of the "megasporangium." In both cases the total tissue included under the term is subject to interpretation. The megaarchesporium originates hypodermally and later often

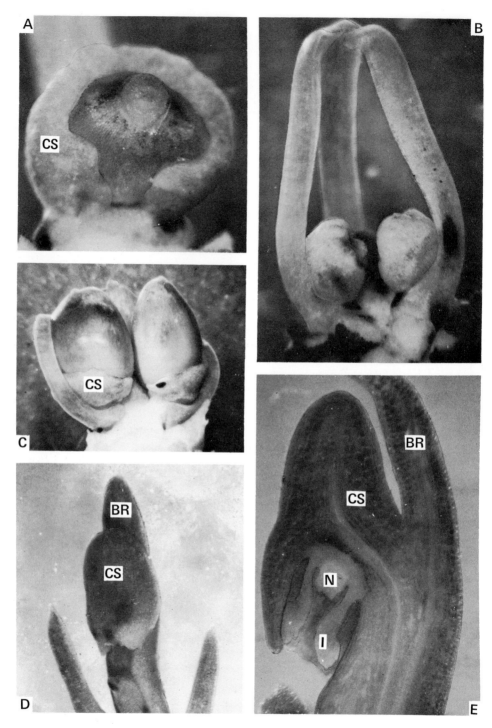

FIGURE 25–13. *A* to *C. Dacridium araucarioides.* *A.* Ovule enveloped by the cone scale. *B.* Terminal cone of three bracts and their axillary cone scales. *C.* As *B,* but at a stage when the seeds are mature and have grown completely out of the cone scales and above the distal ends of the bracts. *D, E. D. taxoides.* *D.* Terminal megasporangiate complex. *E.* Structure in *D* cut longitudinally in a plane at right angles to that of the paper. CS = cone scale; BR = bract; N = nucellus; I = integument.

FIGURE 25–14. *A*. Shoot of *Taxus baccata*. *B, C*. Ovules on the lower side of *A* enlarged. *D*. Clusters of microsporangiate strobili of *Cephalotaxus*. *E* to *H*. Part of the range in leaf form of *Taxus baccata*.

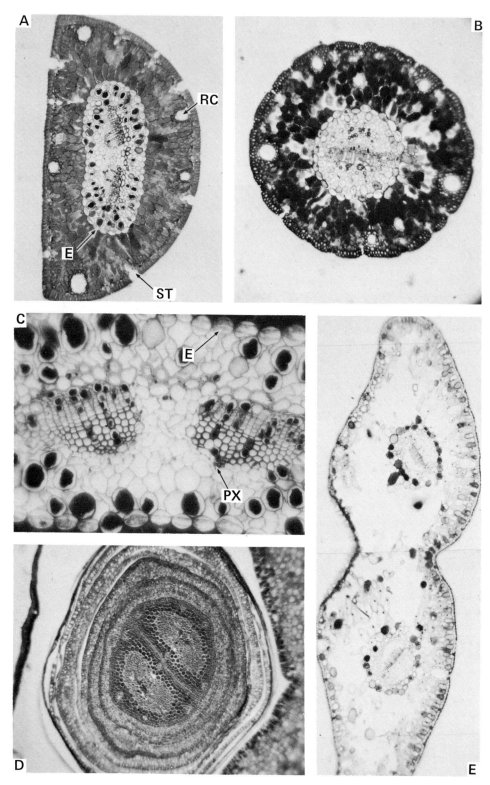

FIGURE 25–15. *A. Pinus mugo*, cross section of leaf. *B. P. monophylla*, cross section of leaf. *C.* Portion of *A* enlarged. *D. P. mugo*, cross section of short shoot. The two vegetative leaves are seen in the center surrounded by the series of scale leaves. *E. Sciadopitys*, cross section of a leaf pair.

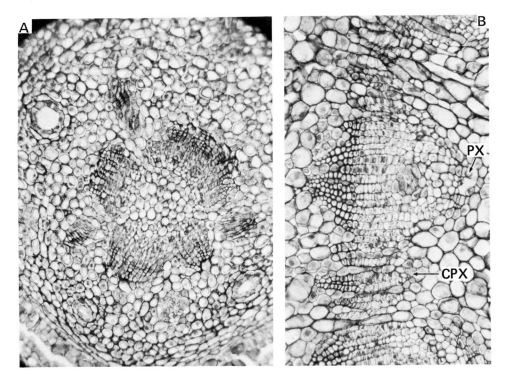

FIGURE 25–16. *Pinus mugo.* *A.* Cross section through the stem of a short shoot. *B.* Portion of another section of *A* enlarged. PX = protoxylem; CPX = cambial protoxylem.

comes to be deep-seated as cell layers are established between it and the apex of the nucellus. In gymnospermous plants in general a distinct tapetum is recognizable within the nucellus (Pettitt, 1966).

Again considering *Cephalotaxus*, Singh (1961), who considers the archesporium as the original hypodermal layer, states that separate microsporangia are established as a result of localized sterilization and hence dissection of the archesporial layer. As in conifers in general, the outer wall layer comes to be composed of larger cells (Fig. 25–18, *D*, *E*) on which develop differential wall thickenings (Fig. 25–18, *F*).

The Taxaceae are dioecious evergreen shrubs or small trees with spirally arranged linear to broad leaves. The most familiar genus is *Taxus* (Fig. 25–14, *A*), which has primarily linear leaves, but on certain specimens a range in leaf types may occasionally be found (Fig. 25–14, *E* to *H*). Microsporangiate strobili are small and the peltate sporangiophores bear three to nine microsporangia each. The ovule

is usually single and borne in a seemingly terminal position on a modified shoot (Fig. 25–14, *C*; Fig. 25–20, *C*) and below it are a series of bracts. Commonly and possibly in most or all ovuliferous shoots there is a hidden aborted terminal bud, and the ovule is in reality terminal on a branch of still a higher order. Two ovules per fertile shoot are relatively common (Fig. 25–14, *B*). There is no evidence for the presence of the equivalent of the axillary cone scale complex of conifer families unless the ovulate structures are compared in terms of common ancestors that had not yet evolved the bilateral axillary complex. At the base of the ovule in *Taxus* there is a plate meristem situated entirely across the axis (between the two arrows in Fig. 25–20, *D*). The periphery of the meristem grows up and around the ovule to produce a soft, red, and fleshy aril in the ripe seed.

The conifer cauline stele is fundamentally the same as that of *Ginkgo* (i.e., a series of collateral bundles appearing around a pith and showing degrees of independence in their verti-

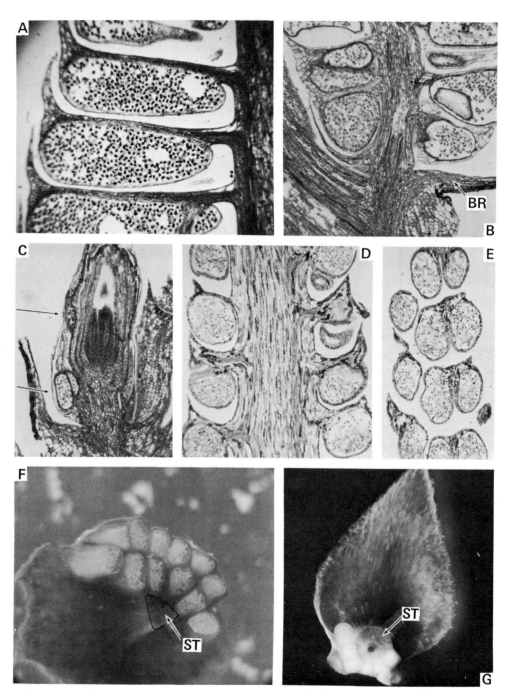

FIGURE 25–17. *A.* Radial section through a portion of the microsporangiate strobilus of *Picea abies.* *B.* Radial section through the base of the microsporangiate strobilus of *Pinus banksiana.* BR = bract subtending strobilus. *C.* Longitudinal section of a short shoot of *P. banksiana,* showing sporangia on several of the scale leaves (arrows). *D.* Radial longitudinal section of the microsporangiate strobilus of *Podocarpus macrophylla.* *E.* As *D,* but tangential section. *F.* Microsporangiophore of *Araucaria columnaris* cut transversely. *G.* Microsporangiophore of *Neocalitropsis* from its adaxial side. ST = stalk.

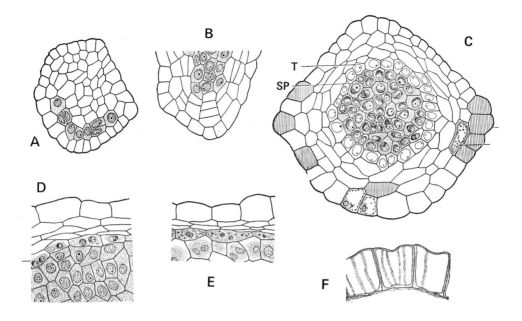

FIGURE 25–18. Development of the microsporangium of *Cephalotaxus drupacea*, after Singh (1961). Outer layers only appear in *D* to *F*. T = tapetum; SP = sporogenous tissue.

cal pathways). Leaf traces are single or double but generally single at their origin. Single traces supplying scale leaves are shown in the cross section of a short shoot axis of *Pinus mugo* in Fig. 25–16, *A* just outside the cauline ring. This species, as all other yellow pines, has double traces to its photosynthetic leaves. Among conifers in general, cambial activity appears very early in ontogeny, and frequently nearly all xylem elements are radially aligned from the pith outward. A few small bundles of the ring arise later, entirely from the cambium, but they still contain typical protoxylem elements (CPX in Fig. 25–16, *B*).

Namboordiri and Beck (1968) described the primary vascular system in stems of 30 species of conifers distributed among five families. Many of the species, especially those with spiral phyllotaxy, had a stele in which there were distinct vertical sinuous strands giving rise by tangential divisions to leaf traces all along one side and at points where two of the vertical strands closely approached each other (their type I) much as in the cones of cycads (Fig. 20–6, *E*). Their type II was similar but traces arose from both sides of each vertical strand. Their type III showed pairs of vertical

strands each giving off a strand by tangential division and the two then coming together between the vertical ones to constitute the leaf trace, which then diverges radially to the appendage. Gaps in the usual sense then may be designated only in the type III stele, which was found along with type II in the Cupressaceae, Podocarpaceae, and Taxodiaceae. Type I was found in the Pinaceae, Araucariaceae, Cephalotaxaceae, Podocarpaceae, and Taxodiaceae. Namboodiri and Beck interpreted type III as most advanced and derived from a type with more independent sympodial cauline strands as I or II. This in turn they related back to a system with independent vertical strands that produced leaf traces by radial divisions and then to the protostele. They further considered the single trace as primitive and their prime ancestral focus was on the aneurophytes. Within the Cordaitales leaf traces are single or double at their points of origin. In at least one species two traces to a given leaf have independent cauline attachments.

The structural similarities of the secondary xylem among all conifers and taxads are much more impressive than are the differences. The history of our knowledge of conifer wood (and

Conifers and Taxads **453**

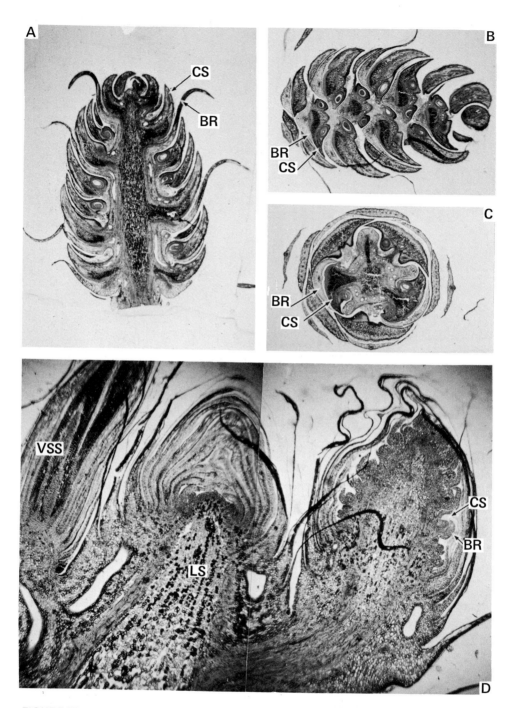

FIGURE 25–19. *A* to *C*. Radial, tangential, and transverse sections of the megasporangiate strobilus of *Larix* at about pollination time.   *D*. Longitudinal section through a shoot tip of *Pinus mugo* in the early spring. The branch on the right is terminated by a young megasporangiate strobilus.   BR = bract; CS = cone scale; LS = long shoot; VSS = vegetative short shoot.

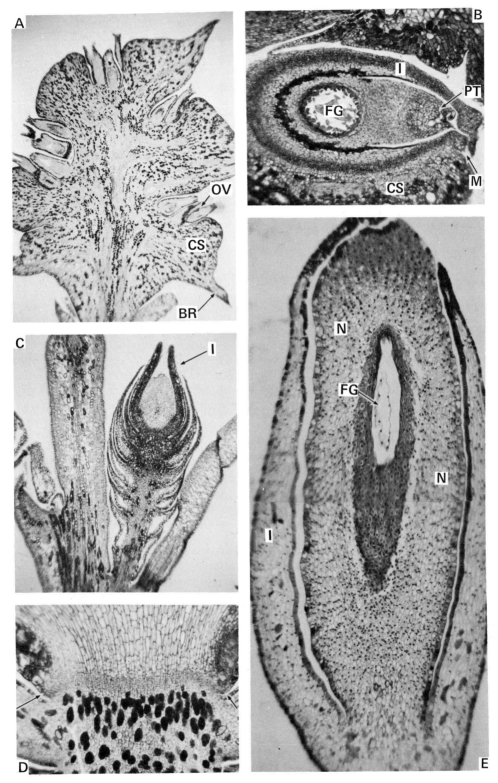

FIGURE 25–20. *A.* Longitudinal section of a young megasporangiate cone of *Cupressus semper-virens.* *B.* Median longitudinal section of an ovule on its cone scale of *Pinus mugo.* *C.* Longitudinal section of the ovuliferous short shoot of *Taxus baccata.* *D.* Base of the ovule in *C* enlarged, showing the transverse plate of intercalary meristem, the margin of which (arrows) later grows up to form the aril. *E.* Longitudinal section of an ovule of *Agathis.* OV = ovule; CS = cone scale; Br = bract; FG = female gametophyte; I = integument; PT = pollen tube; M = micropyle; N = nucellus.

the literature is voluminous) represents primarily an extensive search for characteristics that might be used to distinguish species, genera, and even families. The emphasis throughout has been, therefore, on differences and this point of view has been carried over to morphological discussions, with the unfortunate consequence of overemphasis of trivial structural differences.

Throughout the conifers and taxads the wood is relatively compact and of uniform texture (Fig. 27–11, C, F, G). Tracheids are long and relatively narrow and have circular bordered pits with tori. Pitting tends to be predominantly on radial walls except on the summer tracheids, which are frequently fiber-like. Pitting is predominantly uniseriate, but biseriate ("araucarioid") or grouped pitting has been described as occurring in *Agathis, Araucaria, Actinostrobus, Microbiota, Cedrus,* and *Keteleeria*. Rays are almost entirely one cell wide and relatively few cells high. Certain Pinaceae and Cupressaceae produce ray tracheids. These are cells within the rays that develop bordered pits and lose their contents at maturity. Occasionally they are vertically extended and seem to be part of the vertical system of elongate cells. Vertical parenchyma throughout conifers is scanty or absent. Resin canals occur in woods of many Pinaceae and rarely in the Taxodiaceae but are of more general occurrence in the nonwoody tissues of conifers. In older literature the "bars of Sanio" are inferred to be a particular conifer feature, but they occur in various forms in essentially all vascular plant taxa (Bierhorst, 1960).

Bannon (1958) described what he called perforations in tracheids of *Thuja*. These were lateral openings up to 180 μ high between adjacent "elements." From the information and illustrations that he presented it seems more likely that he was dealing with H-shaped tracheids in which the vertical arms were adjacent to each other. Such tracheids are unusual but not unknown elsewhere among vascular plants.

Coniferophyte (and gnetophyte) phloem tends also to be uniform in structure. The long sieve cells bear mostly small, rounded, and generally separated sieve areas, in contrast to most ferns, cycads, pteridosperms (where known), and primitive angiosperms, which show sieve areas with the groups presenting a reticulate pattern. Conifers do not produce companion cells in the angiosperm sense, but sieve cells are occasionally closely associated with certain ray cells, suggesting a similar physiological relationship.

Pollen of many conifers is winged, and when so there are generally two wings, although occasionally there are three or more. Within the wing or bladder there is a space between the exine and the intine. The pollen is generally shed in a multicellular condition, but occasionally (e.g., some Cupressaceae) it is in the microspore stage. In *Cedrus* (Fig. 25–21, *A* to *G*), which is similar in male-gametophyte development to many other Pinaceae, two prothallial cells (Pr_1 and PR_2 in *C*) are produced and then a generative and a tube nucleus (*C* to *E*). The generative cell divides to form the stalk cell (S) and a body cell (B) as the prothallial cells nearly completely disappear (*F, G*). At this stage (*G*) the pollen is shed and it is very similar to pollen of *Pinus, Abies* (Fig. 25–21, *H*), or other pinaceous genera. In other families, such as the Araucariaceae and some Podocarpaceae, the prothallial cells continue to divide, to form a more extensive tissue mass (Fig. 25–21, *I* to *K*), and in the latter all internal cell walls break down before the pollen is shed. In certain Cupressaceae several body cells are formed instead of the usual one.

The pollen germinates on the nucellus and sends down a tube (PT in Fig. 25–20, *B*; Fig. 25–22, *A, B*; Fig. 25–23, *B*), which is branched in some species. The tube, or a branch of it, acts as the sperm conveyer, unlike cycads and *Ginkgo*, in which the tube is a haustorial organ. The nonmotile sperm number two times the number of body cells. The degree to which a sperm is a completely organized cell varies within the order. Cupressaceous species with multiple sperm also show closely grouped archegonia, so that a single male gametophyte may be responsible for several fertilizations (Fig. 25–21, *M*).

The female gametophyte develops from the innermost megaspore of a linear tetrad. Early development is free-nucleate (FG in Fig. 25–20, *B, E*). When cell walls form, superficial archegonial initials differentiate in variable numbers at the apex or down on the

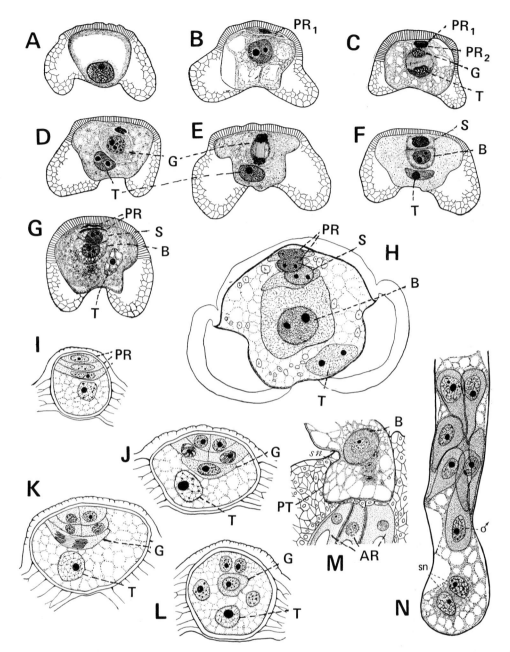

FIGURE 25–21. *A* to *G.* Development of the male gametophyte on *Cedrus deodara* to the stage at which pollen is shed, after Johri (1936). *H.* Male gametophyte at the time of shedding in *Abies balsamea*, after Hutchinson (1914). *I* to *L.* Stages in the development of the male gametophyte of *Podocarpus polystachya*, after Jeffrey and Chrysler (1907). *M, N. Cupressus arizonica*, after Doak (1932). In *M* the tip of the pollen tube is shown adjacent to three archegonia. *N* is a later stage, after the body cells have divided to produce a number of male cells. PR = prothallial cell; B = body cell; PT = pollen tube; AR = archegonia; sn = stalk nuclei.

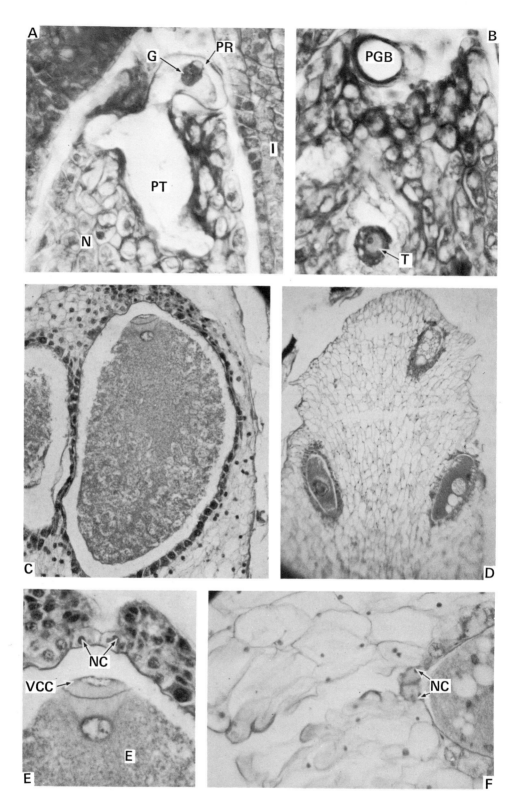

FIGURE 25–22. *A, B.* Longitudinal sections through tips of two ovules of *Pinus sylvestris*. In *A* a male gametophyte is shown having grown into the nucellus. In *B* a male gametophyte is encountered twice in the section. *C, E.* Longitudinal section of an archegonium of *Pinus.* *D.* Longitudinal section of the upper part of the female gametophyte of *Agathis*, showing three archegonia. *F.* Median longitudinal section of the upper part of the archegonium of *Agathis.* PR = prothallial cell; G = generative cell; PT = pollen tube; I = integument; N = nucellus; PGB = pollen grain body; T = tube nucleus; NC = neck cells; VCC = ventral canal cell; E = egg.

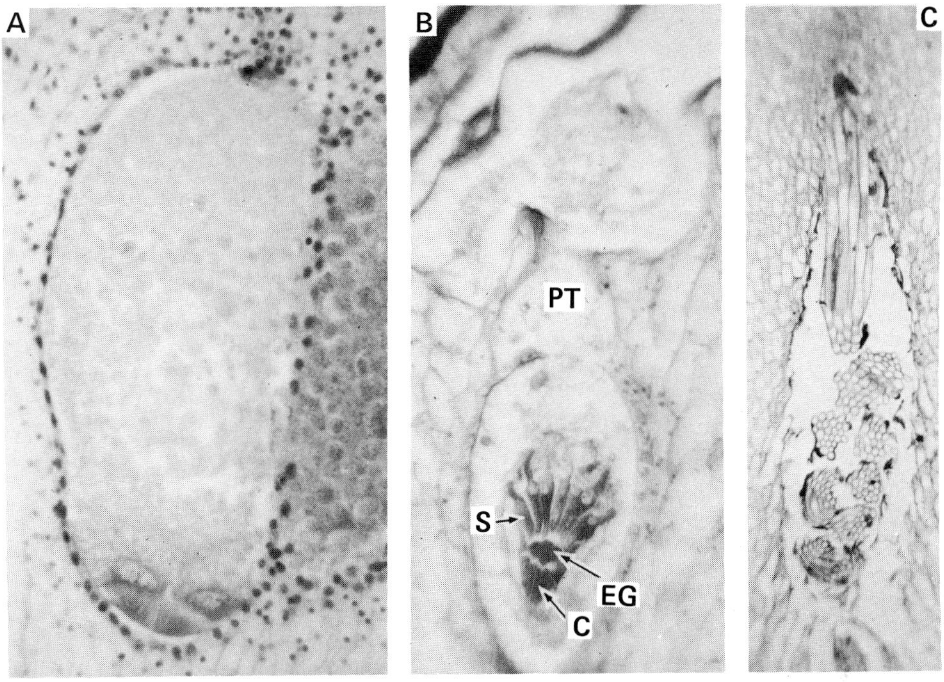

FIGURE 25–23. *A.* Archegonium of *Pinus* containing a proembryo at its base. *B.* Section through the female gametophyte of *Agathis* showing an embryo within an archegonium and an adjacent pollen tube. *C.* Longitudinal section of an archegonium of *Agathis* in which are sections of a coiled suspensor. *B, C* from slides prepared by A. J. Eames.

flanks of the gametophyte in the Araucariaceae. Some representative numbers of archegonia per female gametophyte are *Torreya*, 1; *Cephalotaxus*, 2 to 5; *Actinostrobus*, 25 to 30; *Widdrington*, 30 to 100; *Pinus*, 2 to 6. Three archegonia of the approximately 12 of one gametophyte of *Agathis* appear in Fig. 25–22, *D.* The archegonium has a usual pattern of cell lineages and is composed of a large egg cell (E), a ventral canal cell (VCC), and a pair of neck cells (NC), as shown in Fig. 25–22, *C, E.* The neck cells are commonly sunken in a cavity or even a deep channel (Fig. 25–22, *E, F*).

The embryogeny of conifers and taxads presents a degree of peculiarity unto these taxa themselves, shows a high degree of uniformity over and above generic differences, and shows significant similarities to other gymnospermous plants, especially *Welwitschia*.

Following fertilization the first several divisions are free-nucleate. At the first division in some Pinaceae the chromosomes of maternal and paternal origin remain distinctly grouped on a common metaphase plate and are mixed only after this karyokinesis. According to species, a variable but relatively small number of free nuclei are formed and these come to be located at the basal end of what was the large egg cell (Fig. 25–24, *A*). In *Pinus* the first four nuclei formed arrange themselves in a plane at the base and they each divide. A transverse wall separating the two groups of four nuclei is then formed. Vertical walls are then formed such that there are four completely bounded cells basally and four partially bounded cells above them (two of each group of four appear in Fig. 25–23, *A*; Fig. 25–24, *B*). Both tiers of four cells next divide transversely to result in the 16-celled stage (Fig. 25–24, *C*). The regularity of embryonic tiers varies among conifers. A less regular arrangement, characteristic of the Podocarpaceae, Taxodiaceae, Taxaceae, and Cephalotaxaceae, is shown for *Cephalotaxus* in Fig. 25–24, *F.* The cells of the second tier (suspensor tier, ST in Fig. 25–24,

Conifers and Taxads **459**

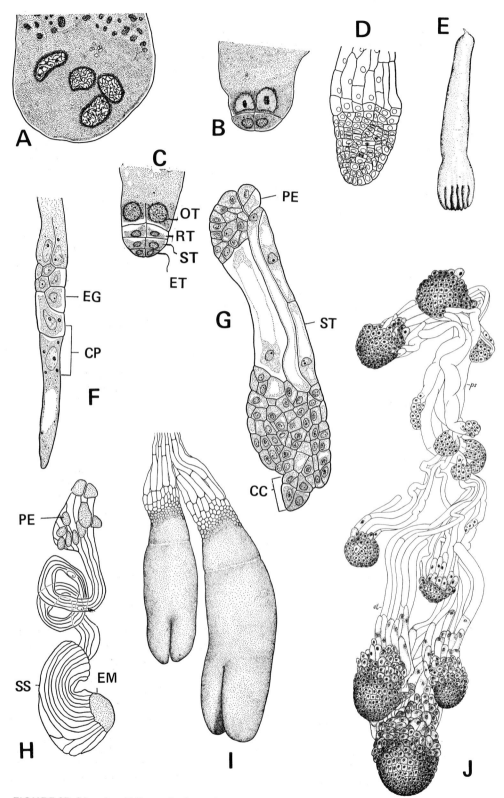

FIGURE 25–24. *A to E.* Stages in the embryogeny of *Pinus wallichiana*, after Konar and Ramchandani (1958). *F to H.* Stages in the embryogeny of *Cephalotaxus drupacea*, after Singh (1961). *I.* Embryos of *Sciadopitys*, after Buchholz (1931). *J.* Suspensor system with proembryos of *Torreya californica*, after Buchholz (1940). OT = open tier; RT = rosette tier; ST = suspensor tier; ET = embryonal tier; CP = cap cells; EG = embryonal group; PE = prosuspensor embryo; CC = cap cells; SS = secondary suspensor; EM = embryonal mass.

C) in *Pinus* elongate conspicuously as each of the four cells of the distal tier produces a mass of small cells or proembryo. The four pro-embryos separate and further elongation of the four suspensors exaggerates the separation both vertically and laterally. A few cells are added to each suspensor on the proximal side of each proembryo, and the elongation seems to be in acropetal waves. Each proembryo is a potential embryo, but some sort of competition generally results in the abortion of all but one. Apical organization follows within the pro-embryo and the inevitable centers of growth, the dominant cotyledons and the less dominant stem apex, appear (Fig. 25–24, *D*, *E*). In *Cephalotaxus* a calyptra or cap (CP) is present distal to the functional group of cells (EG in Fig. 25–24, *F*, *G*). In *Cephalotaxus* several abortive proembryos (PE in Fig. 25–24, *G*, *H*). are produced at the proximal end of its massive suspensor. In certain other conifers and taxads the suspensor systems become more highly dissected, with a subsequently higher number of proembryos (Fig. 25–24, *J*). The number of cotyledons per embryo throughout conifers and taxads varies, but the number two, which is characteristic of the Taxaceae (Fig. 25–24, *I*), Cephalotaxaceae, Podocarpaceae, some Cupressaceae, and some Taxodiaceae, pre-dominates. Higher numbers are found in the Pinaceae, especially in the genera *Pinus* (Fig. 25–24, *E*) and *Picea*, which bear from 4 to 15.

The total time between pollination and seed ripening is 1 year in most conifers. Minority genera in most families require 2 or rarely 3 years.

The transition conifers of Permian and Triassic age illustrate a complete gradate series of intermediate forms between the Cordaita-ceae and modern conifers in the structure of the megasporangiate fructifications. The earli-est (Lower Permian) of the transition conifers, however, already showed microsporangiate strobili, microsporangiophores (Fig. 25–25, *M*), and pollen (N) comparable to the modern types. This also holds for the wood, which suggests in some ways that of the Araucari-aceae (Lemoigne, 1967; Lemoigne and Scharr-schmidt, 1968), and the leaves, which were small, scalelike, and bifid. The evidence favoring phylogenetic relationship between conifers and the Cordaitaceae based on

ovulate fructifications is so convincing that it is tempting to suggest that apparent gaps with respect to other morphological features, which are now readily bridged at least by interpreta-tion, will eventually be filled as more becomes known of the trends of specialization within the Cordaitaceae.

If the compound strobilus of *Cordaianthus* (Fig. 23–1, *C*) is longitudinally condensed, a compact strobilus quite comparable to that of *Lebachia* results. *Lebachia* produced fertile short shoots in the axils of bifid-tipped bracts (Fig. 25–25, *A* to *C*) within compact cones. Each fertile short shoot had a short axis with spirally arranged scales and a stalk bearing a terminal ovule. The integument was two-parted and its tissue was continuous with that of the stalk below. The only indication of bilateral symmetry was the position of the ovule-bearing stalk. The fertile short shoot of *Lebachia* then compares grossly and in much detail with the fertile short shoot (simple strobilus) of *Cordaianthus* (Fig. 23–2, *A*). Other Permian transition conifers varied from the *Lebachia* type in the number of fertile and sterile parts comprising the fertile shoot. *Walchiostrobus* (*Ernestiodendron?*) sp. (Fig. 25–25, *D*) bore three to seven ovule-bearing stalks with inverted ovules and 20 or more sterile scales of different sizes all on a fan-shaped fertile short shoot. *Walchia* (*Ernestio-dendron?*) *germanica* (Fig. 25–25, *E*) bore on the short shoot axis three to seven ovule-bearing stalks with an occasional sterile scale below. Among these very closely related Lower Permian forms the fundamental characters of the ovuliferous complex or cone scale of the modern conifers is already suggested.

The Upper Permian *Pseudovoltzia* (Fig. 25–25, *F*, *G*) illustrates a still closer similarity to modern forms. Its axillary fertile complex was conspicuously flattened and subtended by an entire bract. On the rudimentary short shoot were three inverted ovules on separate stalks (the central one in *F* is removed from the stalk) and five distal sterile scales of different sizes, all with decurrent bases.

The fertile axillary complex of the Upper Permian and Triassic *Glyptolepis* (Fig. 25–25, *H*) was composed of two ovule-bearing stalks and a fan-shaped unit of five fused scales. A slight further loss of integrity of parts in a

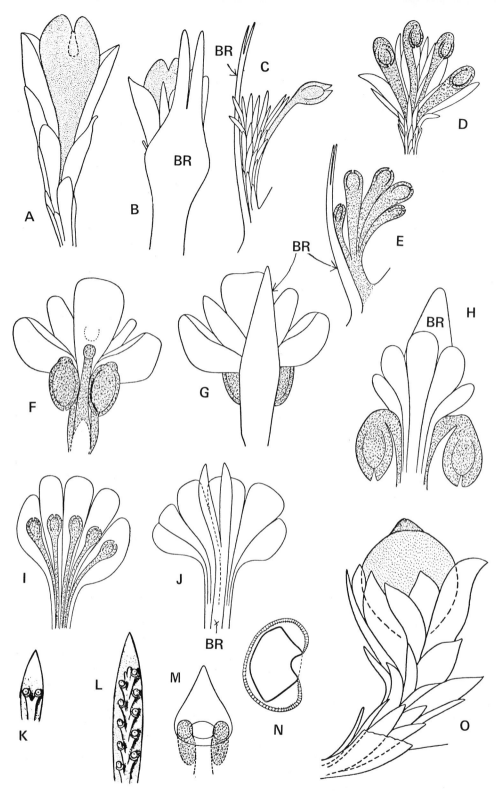

FIGURE 25–25. *A* to *J*. Megasporangiate axillary complexes and associated bracts in various fossil coniferophytes. *A, B. Lebachia piniformis* of the Lower Permian, adaxial and abaxial views. *C. Walchiostrobus elongatus* of the Lower Permian, side view. *D. Walchiostrobus* sp. of the Lower Permian, adaxial view. *E. Walchia germanica* of the Lower Permian, side view. *F, G. Pseudovoltzia liebeana* of the Upper Permian, ad- and abaxial views. *H. Glyptolepis longibracteata* of the Lower Triassic, adaxial view. *I, J. Voltziopsis africana* of the Triassic, ad- and abaxial views. *K, L.* Possible fossil ginkgophytes or possible taxads. *K.* Ovuliferous stalk and bract of *Stachyotaxus elegans*. *L.* As *K*, but of *Palissya sphenolepsis*. *M.* Microsporangiophore of *Lebachia piniformis*. *N.* Pollen grain of *L. piniformis*. *O.* Ovuliferous short shoot of *Palaeotaxus rediviva*. All after Florin (1951).

462

type such as this would produce a cone scale of the pinaceous type in which the ovules are lateral-adaxial and inverted, and evidence for the existence of sterile components in the cone scale still exists in its vasculature.

The Triassic genus *Voltziopsis* showed bifid bracts, as did the Lower Permian forms (Fig. 25–25, *I, J*). Its axillary fertile complex had a narrow base, five or six decurrent and partly fused sterile scales, and about five ovule-bearing stalks.

The transition conifers referred to above are just a few of many that have been described. The specialization trends of the axillary ovuliferous short shoot seem clear: (1) reduction and loss of its axis, (2) flattening in a plane tangential to the cone axis, (3) fusion of the sterile entities, (4) fusion of ovule-bearing stalks to the sterile parts in certain lines, and (5) reduction in number of sterile parts or ovule-bearing stalks or both in certain lines (probably a secondary increase in certain Cupressaceae). The individuality of the sterile components of the cone-scale complex is now best preserved in the Taxodiaceae. The student is strongly urged to read the 1951 classic publication by Florin in its entirety to more fully appreciate these remarks.

Palissya (Fig. 25–25, *L*) and *Stachytaxus* (Fig. 25–25, *M*) of Upper Triassic and Lower Jurassic rocks differed conspicuously from other coniferophytes. *Palissya* produced an axillary branched truss with an arilate ovule at each terminus. *Stachytaxus* was similar but bore two ovules per truss.

The microsporangiate strobilus in modern conifers seems to be the homolog of a single, simple strobilus of *Cordaianthus*. It would follow that the sterile scales on the basal part of the conifer microstrobilar axis are the counterparts of the sterile entities on the simple strobilus of *Cordaianthus* and the microsporangiophores the homologs of the distal fertile organs in the fossil form. The sterile flap of tissue at the tip of the coniferous microsporangiophore remains unsatisfactorily interpreted. It may be a flap of tissue with no homolog in its ancestral type or it may represent a sterilized sporangium. The very frequent occurrence in certain conifers as *Pinus* of vegetative leaves with one or two embedded sporangia at their base (arrows in Fig. 25–17, *C*) suggests

the homology between a sporangiophore and a single appendicular organ. Possibly looking only to *Cordaianthus* for counterparts is unjustified, but other forms suggesting close affinity with conifers in reproductive organs are unknown. If the suggested homology of the microsporangiate strobilus is correct, then it is asked whether the homolog of the entire compound microsporangiate strobilus of *Cordaianthus* exists among modern conifers. In many extant forms, especially in the Podocarpaceae and Taxodiaceae, the strobili are grouped on different-appearing axes that are entirely fertile. These may be favorably compared part-for-part with compound microsporangiate strobili of *Cordaianthus*, as Wilde (1944) did. The question, which still has several possible answers, is: Do all or certain of these strobilar groupings represent primitive conditions or secondary aggregations?

The oldest clearly defined taxad is the Triassic *Palaeotaxus* (Fig. 25–25, *O*), and this is followed in the rocks by Jurassic *Taxus* species. Ovulate fructifications of *Taxus* have never been satisfactorily interpreted in terms of conifers, as Florin has pointed out. Radial symmetry of the ovule-bearing branch seems to have existed throughout its recognizable history. The recent description of Loze (1965) that the ovule is in reality terminal on a branch of still another higher order does not change this very much, but it certainly suggests the need for further ontogenetic studies of a number of other taxaceous species. In view of the close histological and vegetative morphological correspondence between taxads and conifers, the two groups must certainly be interrelated and probably, as Florin suggests, by way of forms such as *Lebachia*.

The correspondence in the morphology of microsporangiate fructifications, vegetative organs, and many histological features between *Ginkgo*, on the one hand, and conifers and taxads, on the other, is again impressive. *Ginkgo* has been referred to as fernlike, because its fan-shaped leaf is so very similar in form and venation to *Adiantum*, et al. Other than overall shape, these similarities extend just as well to certain podocarps and araucarians. The seed of *Ginkgo* is said to be pteridospermlike in size, presence of a distinct pollen chamber, and in the nature of the massive fleshy layer. The same pattern of seed-coat zonation, however, occurs in several modern conifers and differs only in degree. The integument in *Gingko* is clearly two-parted, as it is in all coniferophytes where the feature can be described at all, and it differs markedly from the multiparted cycadophyte integument. The pollen chamber as seen in *Ginkgo* differs only relatively from the apical concavities, also formed by cell breakdown, which occur in many conifers and taxads. *Ginkgo* may be viewed as a well-defined coniferophyte that retains certain features of the male gametophyte and sperm which probably existed in ancestral forms common to conifers and taxads.

26

Gnetophytes

The gnetophytes are represented by three genera of extant plants, *Ephedra*, *Gnetum*, and *Welwitschia*. These are each highly peculiar and distinctive and therefore considered here, as well as in many other accounts, to represent separate orders, the Ephedrales, Gnetales, and Welwitschiales, within a single class, the Gnetopsida.

Ephedra

Ephedra includes about 35 widely distributed, xerophytic, dioecious species. Many are highly branched shrubs and one approaches tree form. A common form, as exhibited by the ornamental *E. girardiana*, shows one to several short thick stems above which there is profuse branching such that the entire plant appears as a hemispherical mass of thin green stems. Another cultivated ornamental, *E. campylopoda*, has pendulous branches and is commonly grown in hanging baskets. It is illustrated growing naturally between the stones of the Wailing Wall in Jerusalem (Fig. 26–1, *B*).

Leaves of *Ephedra* are highly reduced, opposite or whorled, fused into a basal sheath, and often nongreen at maturity (Fig. 26–1, *A*, *C*, *F*). Branching is axillary (Fig. 26–1, *C*), with additional accessory buds arising below and at the base of axillary ones (AB in Fig. 26–1, *E*). Sharply delimited intercalary meristems occurring above each node (IM and IMA in Fig. 26–1, *E*) produce most internodal tissue and later either form abscission layers or mature as transverse bands of sclerified parenchyma.

A cross section of an internode in some species of *Ephedra* shows a ring of 8 or 12 colateral bundles with alternate pairs of larger and smaller ones (Marsden and Steeves, 1955). Each pair of smaller bundles

465

FIGURE 26–1. *A*. Portion of a plant of *Ephedra girardiana*. *B*. *E. campylopoda* rooted between the stones of the Wailing Wall in Jerusalem. *C*. Portion of *A* enlarged. *D*. Sector from the cross section of a stem of *E. antisyphilitica*. *E*. Longitudinal section of a node of *E. antisyphilitica*. *F*. Portion of *A* enlarged. PX = protoxylem; L = leaf; AB = accessory bud; IM = intercalary meristem; IMA = intercalary meristem of axillary shoot.

supplies a leaf at the node above. Just above the node a large bundle produces a smaller one by tangential division toward the next larger one. Thus the paired alternation is re-established and the two leaf traces extend the entire length of the next internode. Just below the level of departure of the traces to leaves there is a complete doughnut-shaped girdle of primary vascular tissue that interconnects all bundles of the ring. Branch traces are two in number and arise from adjacent large bundles immediately above leaf-trace departure.

In other species the alternation of internodal bundles is three small and two large. In these the central bundle of each triad extends from nodal girdle to nodal girdle and is not otherwise connected to the rest of the vascular system.

Certain groups of pits on long sloping walls near the ends of cells are larger in diameter, lose their pit-closing membranes, and make up the foraminate perforation plates characteristic of the vessel members of *Ephedra* (Fig. 27–10, *A*). The plates show a uniseriate arrangement of pores in early-formed elements, but in later-formed ones most pores are two-ranked or irregularly grouped.

The similarities between *Ephedra* and *Equisetum* extend beyond the jointed stem with intercalary growth and reduced, whorled, and fused leaves. In each the leaf traces extend throughout an entire internode. In the *Equisetum* stem below those points where the leaf traces are double, the stele is essentially identical to that of *Ephedra*. The similarity extends also to the nodal metaxylem girdle and circular bordered pits in some protoxylem elements. These points are generally considered results of parallel development, as is done here, but Greguss (1955) was sufficiently impressed with similarities in external morphology to suggest phylogenetic relationship. It should also be pointed out that *Equisetum* sporangiophores are not so different from those of coniferophytes and gnetophytes that one could not readily be rationalized in terms of the other.

The stem apex of *Ephedra* has been interpreted as an advanced gymnosperm type (Gifford, 1943). A corpus and a tunica are clearly definable in most of the apices, but in an occasional one, as both Gifford (1943) and Seeliger (1954) illustrated, cells at the crest of the tunica divide periclinally. In addition to *Ephedra* and *Gnetum*, a tunica layer is known only in the Araucariaceae and in angiosperms.

The microsporangiate fructification of *Ephedra* is seen as a compound strobilus (Fig. 26–2, *A*) bearing a series of decussately arranged, broad, and cupped bracts (BR). In the axil of each bract is the simple strobilus (Fig. 26–2, *B*) consisting of a pair of basally attached and fused bracts or "perianth parts" enclosing the one compounded sporangiophore (Fig. 26–2, *B*, *D* to *F*) or in some species two or occasionally more separate sporangiophores with or without a protruding axial remnant between them. Eames (1952) interprets the latter condition, such as occurs in *E. distachya* and *E. intermedia*, as primitive and the condition in which the sporangiophores are completely compounded, such as occurs in *E.* sp. (Fig. 26–2, *B*, *E*) and *E. antisyphilitica* (Fig. 26–2, *D*, *F*), as derived. An intermediate condition appears in *E. foliata* (Fig. 26–3, *A* to *C*). The individuality of the two sporangiophores is only slightly expressed externally. There are two pairs of sporangia with broad vascularized septal zones in *B*. A section farther down (*A*) shows the common stalk of the two sporangiophores and significantly *three* vascular bundles, one of which remains median while each of the other two enter a sporangiophore septum. An early stage in the development of the strobilus of *E. foliata* appears in Fig. 26–2, *C*, from which the bracts subtending simple strobili have been removed. The two "perianth parts" (PP) are growing up from below and above and will soon enclose the apex of the simple strobilus.

At the tip of the sporangiophore, each sporangium is supplied by its own vein ending, which is a terminus of a dichotomous truss.

The megasporangiate fructification of *Ephedra* seems to retain the same compound strobilar organization as the microsporangiate one; however, its major axis is not differentiated from the vegetative stem in size, internodal length, or indeterminate growth pattern. The simple megasporangiate or ovulate strobilus, which is axillary to a bract, bears a short axis to which are attached usually three or four pairs of decussate bracts and one or two terminal ovules (Fig. 26–4, *A*, *B*). The ovule

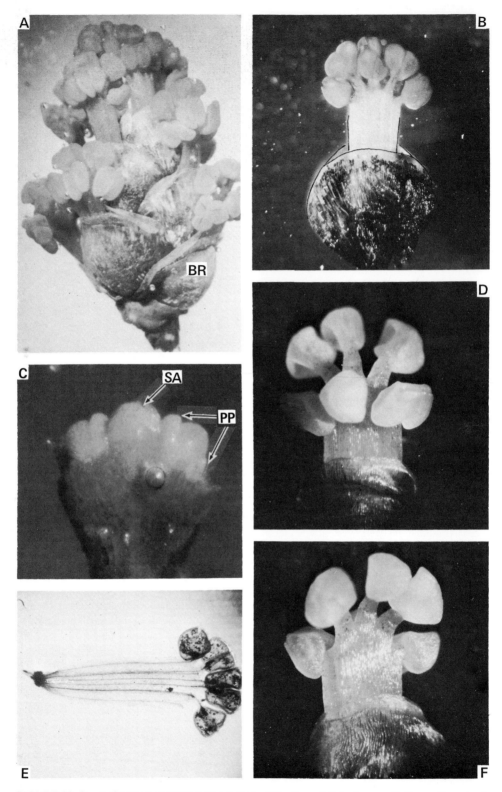

FIGURE 26–2. *A.* Compound microsporangiate fructification of *Ephedra* sp. *B.* One unit or simple strobilus from *A*, removed from its subtending bract. *C.* Tip of the still-growing compound microsporangiate fructification of *E. foliata*. *D, F.* Simple microsporangiate strobilus of *E. antisyphilitica* viewed from its abaxial, *D*, and adaxial, *F*, sides. *E.* Microsporangiophore from *B* cleared and stained. SA = shoot apex; PP = primordia of the two components of the sterile envelope ("perianth") of the simple microsporangiate strobilus; BR = bract.

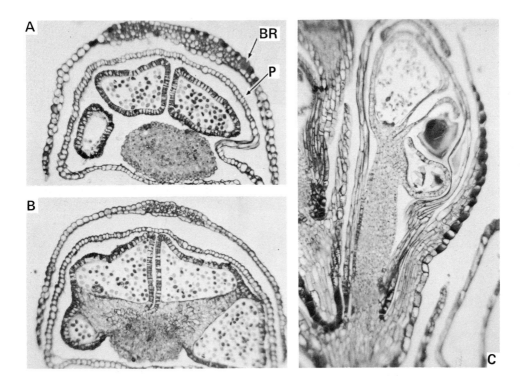

FIGURE 26–3. *A, B.* Cross sections at two levels of the simple microsporangiate strobilus of *Ephedra foliata.* *C.* Longitudinal section of the same structure. BR = bract; P = sterile envelope or "perianth."

has two integuments (outer, OI, and inner, II, in Fig. 26–4, *E*). The bracts have been removed from the specimen in Fig. 26–4, *C* and it shows the tip of the inner integument projecting as a small cylindrical tube (micropyle) through the apical opening of the outer integument.

The ovules vary in shape and vascularization (Eames, 1952), which is apparently due to degrees of doubleness. The outer integument is supplied by an anterior and a posterior vascular system, indicating that it represents another pair of fused bracts. Some authors have elected to apply the term integument only to the inner one, but the term as it is generally applied throughout all seed plants is not one that carries with it interpretive commitment and may certainly be applied to any complete ovular envelope, such as the outer one in *Ephedra*. The inner integument in *Ephedra* is partly fused to the nucellus (Fig. 26–4, *E*), is supplied by two bundles that end at the base or extend up to the level of separation from nucellus, and has been described as arising from two separate primordia.

The female gametophyte forms from the lowermost megaspore of a linear tetrad. Wall formation is delayed between the four megaspores, so a tetrasporic sac may be falsely indicated (Lehmann-Baerts, 1967). Divisions are then free nucleate until about the 256-nuclei stage. The cellular gametophyte shows a basal zone of small cells with larger ones above. Usually two elongate archegonia appear at the apex (Fig. 26–4, *E*; the second archegonium was in other sections). There are up to eight tiers of cells in the neck, but during ontogeny irregular divisions disturb the alignment (Fig. 26–5, *A, B*). As in other archegonium-bearing seed plants, there are no neck canal cells.

At the time the pollen is shed, each grain contains one complete prothallial cell, one free prothallial nucleus, a stalk cell, a body cell, and a tube nucleus. The pollen lands on a pollination drop (Fig. 26–4, *D*) and is pulled through the micropyle and into the lysiginous pollen chamber (PC in Fig. 26–4, *E*) and directly onto the female gametophyte. Soon

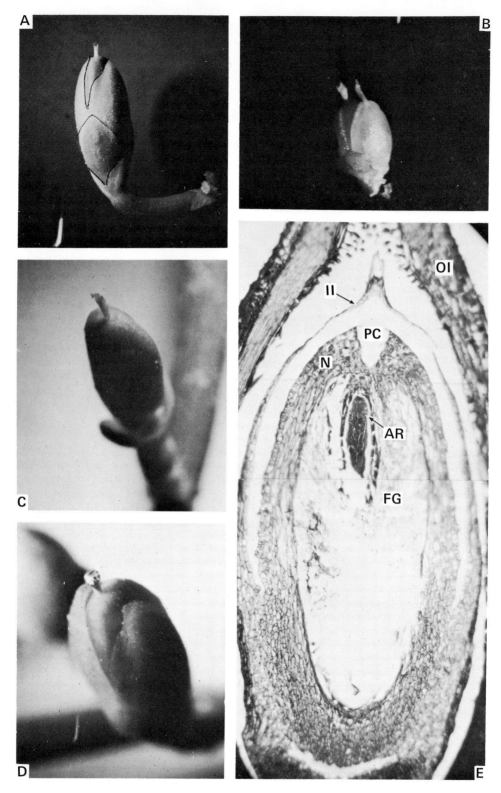

FIGURE 26–4. *A, B.* Uni- and biovulate megasporangiate simple strobilus of *Ephedra girardiana*. *C.* Structure in *A* with two pairs of bracts removed. *D.* As *A*, but showing the pollination drop at the tip of the micropyle. *E.* Longitudinal section of an ovule of *E. antisyphilitica*. OI = outer integument; II = inner integument; PC = pollen chamber; N = nucellus; AR = archegonium; FG = female gametophyte.

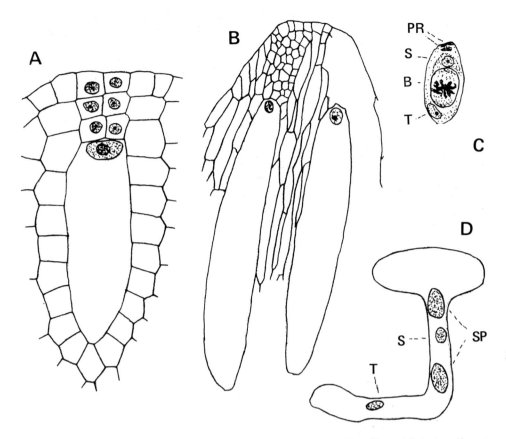

FIGURE 26–5. *A, B.* Two later stages in the development of the archegonium of *Ephedra trifurcata.* *C.* Pollen grain of *E. trifurcata.* *D.* Mature male gametophyte of *E. trifurcata.* All after Land (1904). PR = prothallial cell; S = stalk cell; B = body cell; T = tube nucleus; SP = sperm.

after pollination the body cell (B in Fig. 26–5, *C*) divides to produce two nonmotile sperm and the prothallial cells decompose. After the short pollen tube (Fig. 26–5, *D*) grows down through the archegonial neck, the male gametophyte discharges its four nuclei into the archegonium. Land (1907) described a number of small cells within the archegonium of nonzygote origin that were absorbed by growing embryos and suggested that this may have been the manner in which the endosperm of angiosperms originated. Land did not observe a second fertilization in *Ephedra trifurca,* but it has been reported by Khan (1940, 1943) and Mulay (1941) in *E. foliata,* in which the ventral canal nucleus was the second sperm receptor.

The fertilized egg divides to produce usually eight free nuclei (Fig. 26–6, *A* to *C* in sequence), all of which are potential embryos. The egg sac may also contain free nuclei derived from disrupted archegonial jacket cells. Several proembryos degenerate while others begin to elongate to form the suspensor tube (Fig. 26–6, *D*). A small cell is cut off distally and the remaining cell (primary suspensor cell) enlarges greatly (Fig. 26–6, *E* to *G*). The small terminal cell multiplies and its proximal derivatives act as a secondary suspensor (Fig. 26–6, *H*), while the more distal cells produce the embryo proper. Only one dicotyledonous embryo matures per seed.

In the young seedlings (Voth, 1934) one of the two exarch poles of xylem of the root enters each cotyledon after bifurcating. The two exarch traces of each cotyledon twist around nearly 180 degrees in their longitudinal course, to become endarch. Such twisting, whether

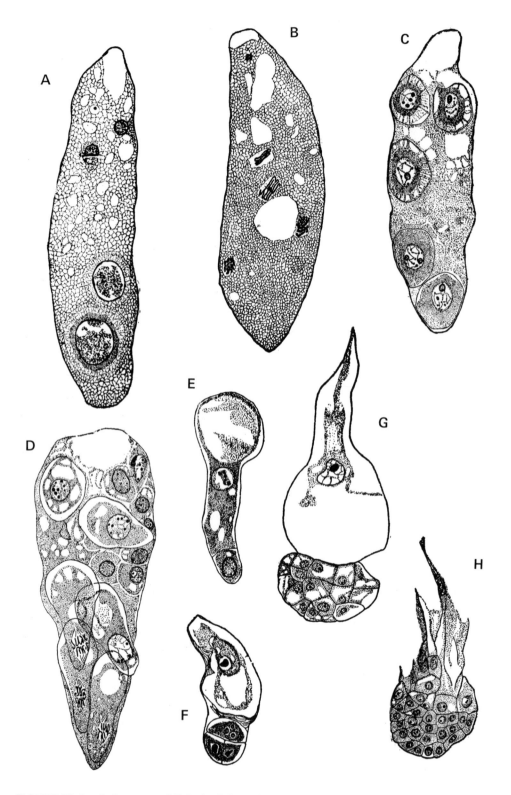

FIGURE 26–6. Embryogeny of *Ephedra foliata*, after Khan (1943). *A* to *D*. Stages leading to the establishment of free proembryos within the archegonium. *E* to *H*. Further development of one proembryo.

within cotyledons or hypocotyl, is found in the Gnetopsida and in angiosperms.

Ephedra is an old genus, and R. A. Scott (1960), who described Upper Triassic pollen, thinks it is one of the oldest of extant genera. The pollen of *Ephedra* has a characteristic bilateral shape and longitudinal ridges (see Steeves and Barghoorn, 1959). K. A. Wilson (1959) described pollen grains under the names *Ephedripites* and *Vittatina* from Permian rocks that combine features of *Ephedra* and *Welwitschia* and that he thought to be early ancestral forms of both.

Gnetum

Gnetum includes some 30 to 35 woody, dioecious, tropical species primarily occurring in rainforests. Most are vines, as are all of the Western Hemisphere species, but a few are trees, as is the cultivated and most familiar species, *G. gnemon*. The opposite leaves are broad (Fig. 26–7, *A*) and the plants present a very dicotlike appearance. In many there is a shoot dimorphism with indeterminate long shoots bearing reduced, cuplike pairs of scale leaves, and there are determinate short shoots bearing a pair of broad leaves above one long internode (Fig. 26–7, *A*). The nodes are often conspicuously swollen and have an internal cavity lined with periderm and much sclerenchyma, suggesting a response to insect attack.

The leaves of *Gnetum* are each supplied by from three to seven traces, varying both intra- and interspecifically. In the central portion of an internode there is a ring of collateral bundles (Fig. 26–7, *B*) usually totaling four times the number of traces to each leaf at the node above. In *G. gnemon* (a tree) the internodal number is usually 24 or 28, in *G. leyboldii* (a vine) it is usually 28; others are reported to have from 8 to 20 (Pearson, 1929). Every other bundle in the ring departs as a leaf trace. Half the departing number goes to each of the two opposite leaves. The traces that stay within the ring remain undivided or divide into two or three. The divisions may occur before the leaf traces depart, so it may appear that the traces arise here and there as every third or fourth bundle rather than alternate ones. The total bundle number of the next-higher internode may be established just above leaf-trace departure or there may be a delay of up to 0.5 cm. In *G. gnemon* there is an excess of bundles established at the base of an internode (up to 46), and some interbundle fusion then occurs uniformly around the ring to re-establish the number 28. The highest frequency of division among bundles that remain within the ring occurs between the more medianly situated traces to a given leaf. In *G. leyboldii* those between leaf traces 3 and 4 (the median one of a leaf) and 4 and 5 usually divide into three, those between 2 and 3 and 6 and 7 usually two. Those between 1 (a far lateral) and 2 and 6 and 7 (the other far lateral) often remain undivided and extend as units from internode to internode.

Branch traces arise from leaf traces. Each leaf trace gives off from one to four small bundles, these arising on no particular side. The branch traces come to be situated in a long arc of nearly 180 degrees between the arc of leaf traces and the cauline ring. Those of the branch system located farthest from the median bundle of the leaf curve inward, so that a ring is established at the base of a branch. As this happens, the bundles fuse together here and there to reduce the total bundle number. A completely hidden accessory bud is present at the base of the axillary one.

The petiolar bundles, at first arranged more or less in a U, arrange themselves in a single line within the midvein region (Fig. 26–7, *E*) and then involve themselves within the reticulate vein system of the lamina.

The primary xylem elements are similar in structure to those of *Ephedra*, with the characteristic circular bordered pits occurring in early-matured helical elements. The foraminate perforation plates (Fig. 27–10, *B*, *C*) bear fewer pores than those of *Ephedra* (rarely more than six); those in the later metaxylem bear still fewer, which are usually in contact with each other. Simple plates, many of which are transversely oriented, are common in the secondary xylem (Fig. 27–12, *A* to *F*). There is evidence that simple plates in *Gnetum* (*D* to *F*) represent compound structures resulting from disruption of secondary wall material between adjacent pores as well as simple structures resulting from loss of all other pores of the plate.

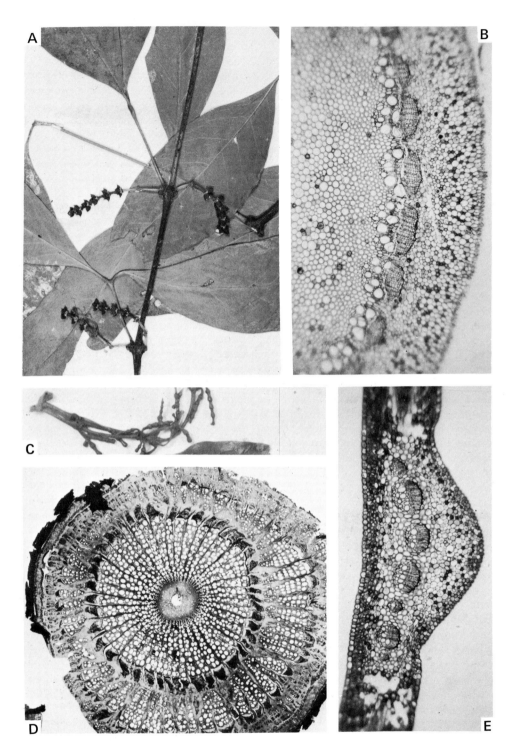

FIGURE 26–7. *A.* Part of a shoot of *Gnetum gnemon* with megasporangiate strobili. *B.* Portion of a cross section of a stem of *G. leyboldii.* *C.* Microsporangiate strobili of *G. leyboldii.* *D.* Cross section of a stem of *Gnetum* sp. showing several concentric zones of secondary vascular tissues referable to different cambia, from a slide prepared by R. Rodin. *E.* Cross section through the central part of a leaf of *G. gnemon.*

Anomalous secondary thickening occurs in the viny species as accessory cambia arise either from secondary phloem or cortical parenchyma (Fig. 26–7, *D*). Typical periderm occurs on older stems (upper left in Fig. 26–7, *D*). Much branched astrosclerids occur in the pith, cortex, petiole, and lamina of many species. These peculiar cells are found among vascular plants in many dicot and monocot families, in *Gnetum*, *Welwitschia*, and in certain conifers (e.g., *Pseudotsuga* and *Sciadopitys*) but in no cycadophytes or in any non-seed-bearing vascular plants. The stem apex of *Gnetum* has a well-defined tunica in which only anticlinal divisions occur.

The fructifications of *Gnetum* are lax to compact strobili (Fig. 26–7, *A*, *C*; Fig. 26–8, *A*, *D*, *E*) and arise from the accessory buds below the axillary ones (Fig. 26–7, *A*).

Microsporangiate strobili have short internodes (Fig. 26–8, *A*) and a pair of reduced and modified bracts that form a complete cup around each node. The bract traces give off other traces just as leaf traces produce branch traces, but instead of regrouping to form a branch stele, they remain separate, parallel, and nearly vertically oriented. Each such trace supplies a linear series of reproductive structures above the bract cup, and still higher, in some species, it curves back and reconnects to a strand in the axial ring. In the microsporangiate strobilus each vertical series consists of a nonfunctional ovule above (Fig. 26–8, *A*; NFO in *B*, which is part *A* enlarged; cross section with edge of strobilar axis at left in Fig. 26–9, *D*) and a series of functional microsporangiate structures below. Each of the latter is equivalent to a microsporangiate simple strobilus of *Ephedra* with a two-parted enclosing sheath below and an extending sporangiophore (Fig. 26–8, *C*). The units of each linear vertical series arise in basipetal progression (Fig. 26–9, *A* to *C*) from a meristem close to the axil of the bract, in a manner similar to (and probably homologous to) the way in which accessory buds originate in both *Ephedra* and *Gnetum*. A dense mass of dark hairs accompanies the reproductive organs (Fig. 26–8, *B*).

At the tip of each microsporangiophore are two separate sporangia (Fig. 26–8, *B*, *C*; right center in Fig. 26–9, *D*). There is a single outer sporangial wall layer that is separated from the fertile tissue at an earlier stage in ontogeny by two tapetal layers.

The ovules are arranged in a single verticil above each bract cup on the megasporangiate strobilus (Fig. 26–8, *D*, *E*). Each one is supplied by a trace similar in disposition to one that supplies an entire linear, vertical series in the microsporangiate strobilus. The ovule constitutes the entire simple strobilus, but its parts are comparable to more than just the ovule in *Ephedra*. There are three pairs of bracts, each of which has advanced to the state of a complete integumentary envelope (Fig. 26–10, *A*, *C*), whereas in *Ephedra* only two are so advanced. The inner integument in *Gnetum* extends upward (I_3 in Fig. 26–10, *C*) and projects as a thin micropylar tube (Fig. 26–8, *D*). The nonfunctional ovule of the microsporangiate strobilus has only two integuments (Fig. 26–9, *D*) with the inner one only slightly developed. The outer integument of the functional ovule (I_1) eventually forms the thick fleshy layer of the seed and contains many idioblastic sclereids.

The mega-archesporium in *Gnetum* is a tissue composed of 8 to 15 megaspore mother cells (Fig. 26–11, *H*; and a later stage in *I*). These undergo meiosis without wall formation (Fig. 26–11, *J*, *K*; Fig. 26–10, *B* is comparable to Fig. 26–11, *K*). The tetrasporic gametophytes continue to develop by free-nuclear divisions (Fig. 26–11, *L*; Fig. 26–10, *D*), but as things progress most of them abort. Frequently ovules ripen as seeds without ever having a single female gametophyte, except in a very early stage. These seeds may well act as vegetative propagules.

The male gametophyte (Fig. 26–11, *A* to *D*) has a single prothallial cell, a tube nucleus, and a generative nucleus, and when the grains are released all internal walls have broken down (Fig. 26–11, *D*). The pollen is pulled into the ovule by the drying of a pollination drop and it germinates on an irregular lysiginous concavity at the apex of the nucellus (Fig. 26–10, *C*; Fig. 26–11, *E*). As the tube grows toward the female gametophyte, the generative cell divides to produce two sperm (Fig. 26–11, *F*, *G*). As this is going on, the female gametophyte has become cellular at its base adjacent to the conspicuous pad tissue of the nucellus. Walls

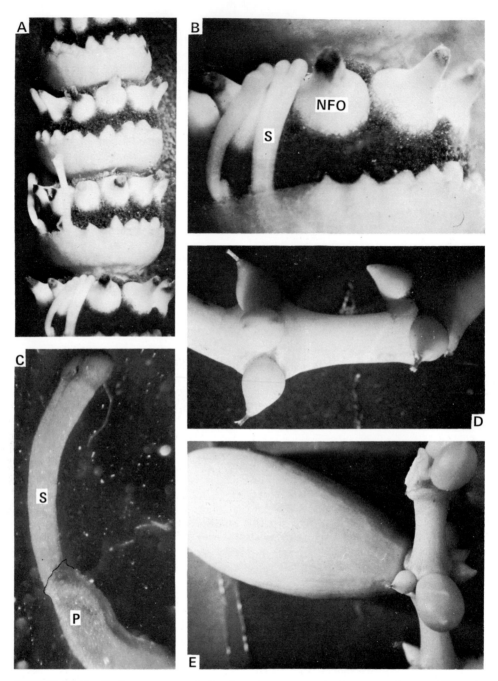

FIGURE 26–8. *Gnetum gnemon.* *A.* Portion of a compound microsporangiate strobilus. *B.* Portion of *A* enlarged. *C.* A simple microsporangiate strobilus. *D, E.* Portions of a megasporangiate strobilus. NFO = nonfunctional ovule; S = sporangiophore; P = "perianth."

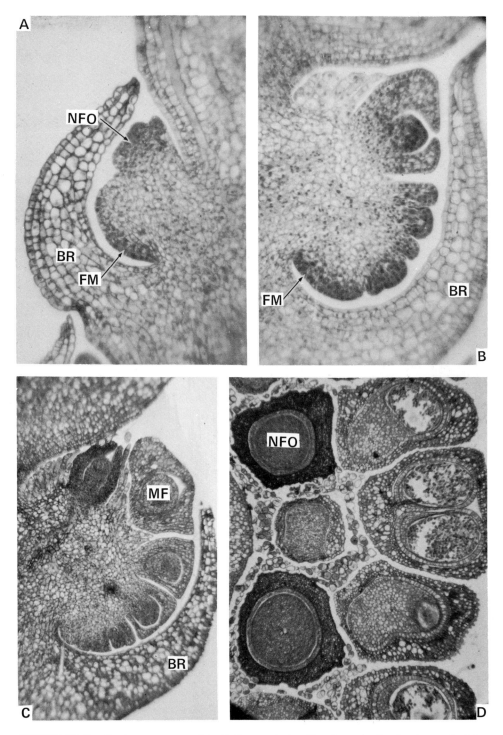

FIGURE 26–9. *Gnetum gnemon. A* to *C.* Successively older stages in the development of the axillary complex in the microsporangiate strobilus. *D.* Cross section through the axillary complex in the microsporangiate strobilus. NFO = nonfunctional ovule; BR = bract; FM = basal meristem of axillary complex; MF = microsporangiate simple strobilus.

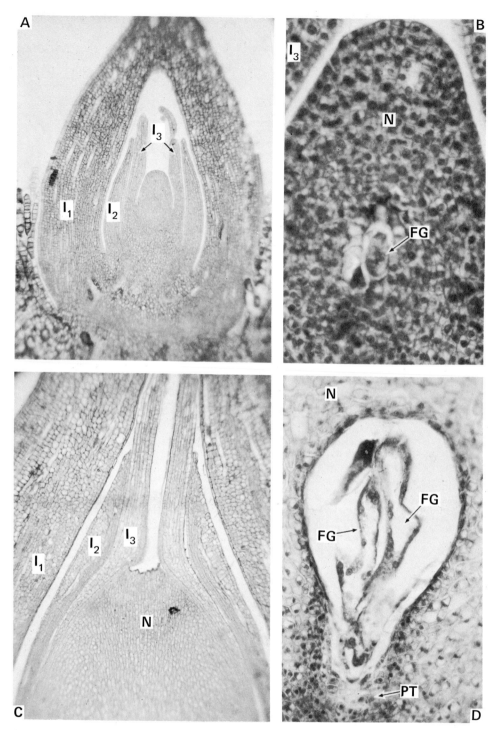

FIGURE 26–10. *Gnetum gnemon.* *A.* Longitudinal section through the megasporangiate simple strobilus. *B.* Portion of *A* enlarged. *C.* As *A*, but a later stage in development. *D.* Central part of the nucellus of the same structure in *C.* I_1 = outer (oldest) integument; I_2, I_3 = inner (younger) integuments; N = nucellus; FG = female gametophyte.

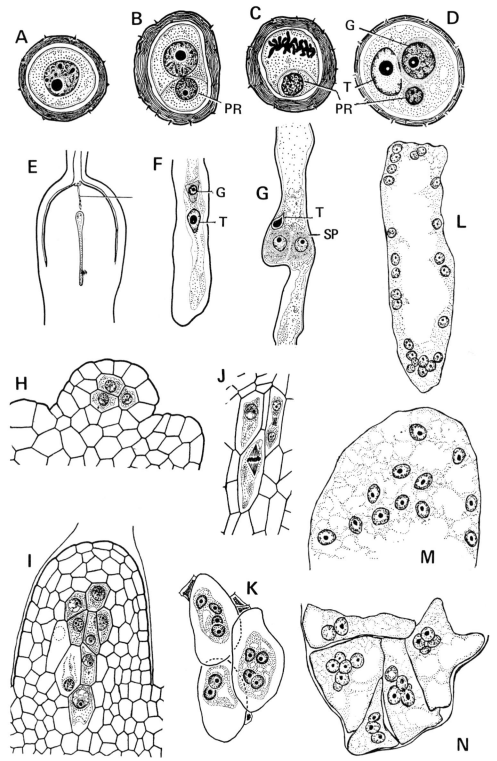

FIGURE 26–11. *A* to *D*. Stages in the development of the male gametophyte up to the pollen grain stage. *A* to *C. Gnetum ula. D. G. gnemon. E.* Part of an ovule of *G. gnemon,* showing the pollen tube within the nucellus nearing the female gametophyte. *F, G.* Pollen tube of *G. ula* before and after the final nuclear division. *H.* Nucellus of a young ovule of *G. gnemon,* showing three cells of the sporogenous tissue. *I.* Slightly older nucellus, showing a number of spore mother cells of *G. ula. J.* Meiosis in several spore mother cells within the nucellus of *G. gnemon. K.* Three of the tetrasporic embryo sacs after completion of meiosis in *G. ula. L* to *N*. Later stages in female gametophyte development in *G. africanum. A* to *K* after Negi and Lata (1957); *L* to *N* after Pearson (1914). PR = prothallial cell; T = tube nucleus; G = generative nucleus; SP = sperm.

479

form that enclose up to 12 nuclei at the extreme end (Fig. 26–11, *N*) and fewer nuclei toward the free-nuclear end (Fig. 26–11, *M*). Nuclei within the cells eventually fuse, resulting in a gradate ploidy from 12*N* to 1*N* within the gametophyte. The pollen tube penetrates the free-nucleate portion, where the free nuclei act as eggs. The total number of zygotes may be high, depending on the number of male gametophytes penetrating a single female gametophyte.

The zygote elongates, producing a tube, as in *Ephedra*. The nucleus divides and the distal one then produces four more, which arrange themselves at the tip of the tube and organize a cellular proembryo. Much of the later embryogeny occurs after the seeds fall to the ground. Eventually a dicotyledonous embryo is formed. An outgrowth of the embryonic axis, called a feeder, extends into the nutritive tissue (female gametophyte) of the seed.

Welwitschia

Welwitschia bainesii (Hook.) Carr. (= *W. mirabilis* (Hooker), the sole species of the genus, is restricted to certain extremely arid areas of west Africa.

The plant body is peculiar, to say the least. It has been referred to as a persistent seedling. The very tough plant axis is shaped like an inverted cone with a deep apical concavity (upper part cut lengthwise in Fig. 26–12, *C*). The lower part tapers down to the main root, which penetrates the soil to a very great depth. Along the upper rim of the axis two leaves are attached, the only two that the plant produces other than the cotyledons (Fig. 26–12, *A*). The body grows in thickness as accessory cambia appear and produce zones of complete bundles. At the base of each leaf and well within a slit, there is a meristematic zone that adds to the leaf base as well as adding tissue along the inside of the slit, which expands and matures up and over each edge. The leaves die at the distal ends and their length is usually only 2 to 4 ft. The basal meristem of the leaf frequently becomes injured and discontinuous (Fig. 26–12, *B*) and the individual segments then continue to grow independently. The oldest plants are somewhat over 2 ft in diameter

and more than 1,000 years old. The specimen in Fig. 26–12, *C* was approximately 14 inches across and estimated to be about 600 years old by extrapolation of data on similar plants dated by radiocarbon by Elso Barghoorn.

Axes bearing compound strobili (Fig. 26–12, *A*, *D*, *E*) are produced mostly on the inner, but a few on the outer, side of the plant crown. The surface shown in Fig. 26–12, *B* shows several old axial scars (arrows).

The main axis below the crown has a ring of collateral bundles, which are shown for a 15-year-old plant in Fig. 26–14, *C*. Outside these in older plants are a number of incomplete rings of secondary bundles from accessory cambia. Within the flanges of the crown are two parallel series of bundles (drawn in part on the right in Fig. 26–12, *C*; and in cross section in Fig. 26–14, *A*) with the xylem portion on the inside (one bundle shown in isolation in Fig. 26–14, *B* with the xylem pole indicated). Traces from these bundles extend toward the surface, presumably to old reproductive axes. Some originate from a bundle and extend outward on that side while others curve around and proceed through the vertical bundle complex to the other side of the plant (arrow in Fig. 26–14, *A*). Throughout the plant axis are large, mostly unbranched sclereids (dark areas left and right of the bundle in Fig. 26–14, *B*) with numerous crystals embedded in their cell walls. An additional peculiarity is the occurrence of isolated, unconnected vessels of up to about 12 cells, which are coiled up into tight wormlike masses (Fig. 26–14, *G*).

Early-formed tracheary elements show circular bordered pits between gyres of the secondary wall helix as in other gnetophytes and coniferophytes. Vessels are present with usually singly-occurring circular pores, which are either transversely or obliquely oriented, and apical, subapical, or quite lateral in position. A few vessel members show pores in pairs, and a rare one exhibits a foraminate plate with three pores (Fig. 27–10, *D*). In the very thick-walled later-formed elements complex ramiform bordered pit systems occur.

The mature embryo of *Welwitschia* has two cotyledons and a feeder or foot, as in *Gnetum* (Fig. 26–14, *F*). The two permanent leaves (inner, smaller ones in Fig. 26–14, *E*; also

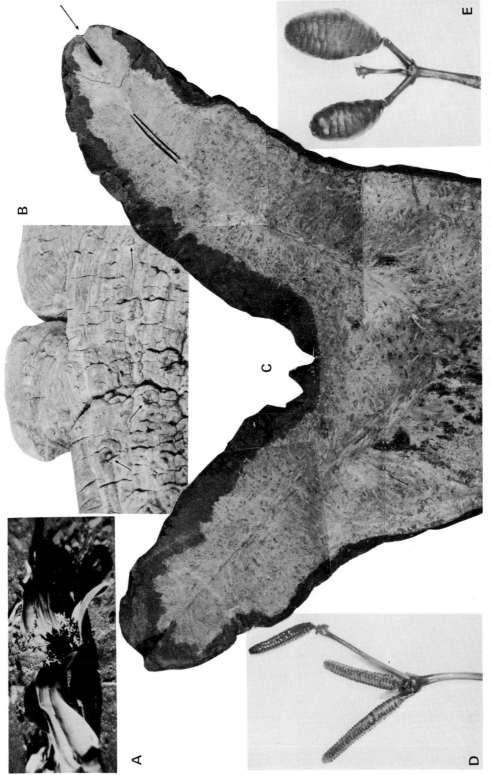

FIGURE 26–12. *Welwitschia bainesii.* *A.* Plant in its native dessert, from a slide taken by R. Rodin. *B.* Part of the upper edge of the crown of the specimen in *C* as seen from the inside. *C.* Longitudinal section through the upper part of an old plant. The arrow indicates leaf insertion. *D.* Three microsporangiate strobili on a branch of the reproductive axis. *E.* Two megasporangiate strobili.

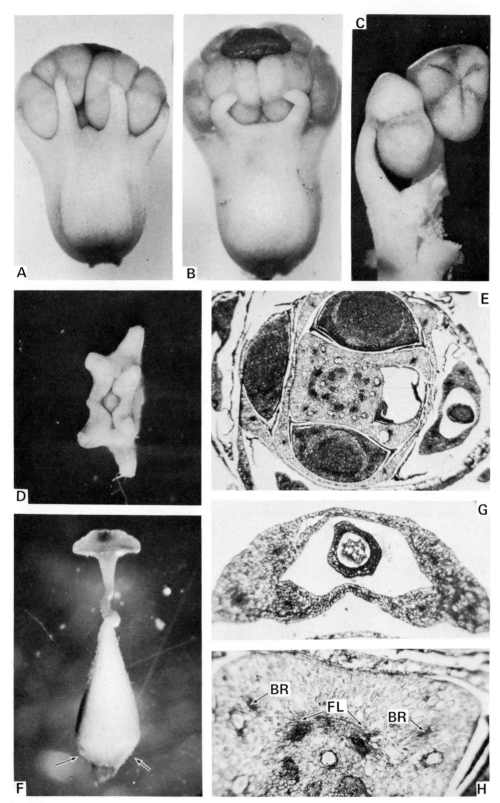

FIGURE 26–13. *Welwitschia bainesii,* the microsporangiate fructification. *A, B.* Adaxial and abaxial view of a simple strobilus. *C.* Structure in *A* partly dissected. *D.* Top view of the structure in *A* with sporangia removed. *E.* Cross section of the compound microsporangiate strobilus. *F.* Nonfunctional ovule from the structure in *A.* The arrows indicate the positions of the reduced bracts. *G.* Cross section of the simple microsporangiate strobilus below the level of the free sporangiophore stalks. *H.* Portion of the compound strobilar axis in *E* enlarged. BR = traces to bract subtending simple strobilus; FL = traces to simple strobilus.

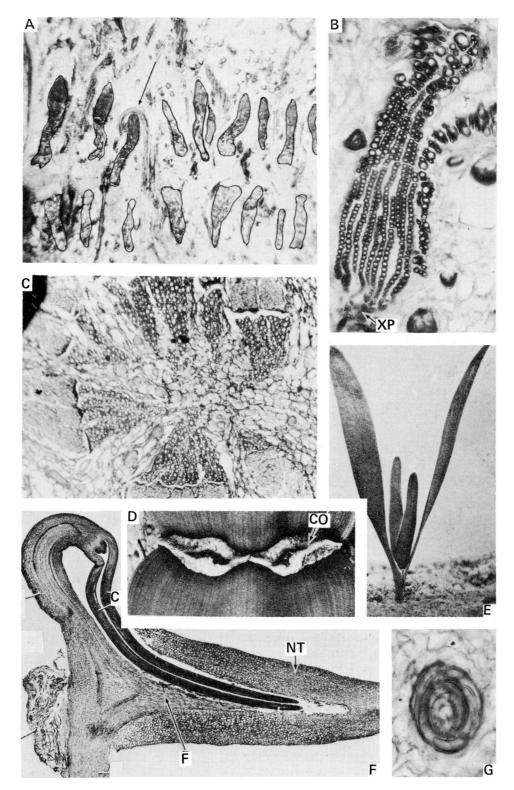

FIGURE 26–14. *Welwitschia bainesii.* *A.* Cross section through the vascular system of the crown below the level of the leaf meristem. The two transverse series of bundles are shown in longitudinal section as two lines drawn in on the right in Fig. 26–12, *C.* *B.* One bundle from *A* enlarged. *C.* Cross section through the terete part of the axis below the crown in a 15-year-old seedling. *D.* Crown of a seedling as seen from the top. *E.* Seedling with its two cotyledons (longer leaves) and its two permanent leaves. *F.* Longitudinal section of a germinating seed. *G.* Isolated coiled vessel from an old plant. *D* to *F* after Martens and Waterkeyn (1964). XP = xylem pole; CO = tissue outgrowth at site of former cotyledon; C = cotyledon; NT = nutritive tissue of seed; F = feeder.

483

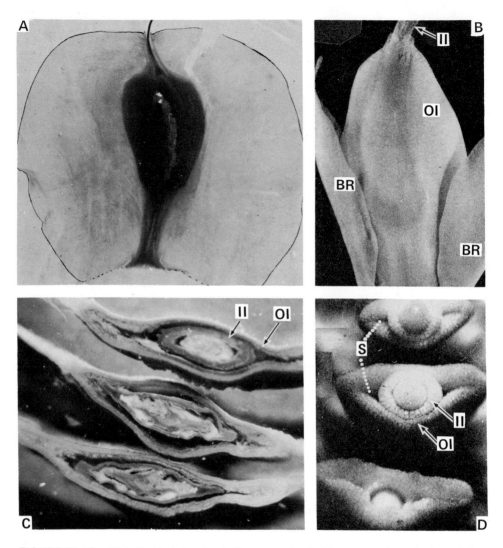

FIGURE 26–15. *Welwitschia bainesii.* *A.* Mature seed. *B.* Megasporangiate simple strobilus. *C.* Cross sections of three seeds. *D.* Three young megasporangiate simple strobili. II = inner integument; OI = outer integument; BR = bract; S = furrow. *B, D.* After Martens (1959).

barely visible on stem apex in *F*) appear soon after germination. The cotyledons grow for about 6 months and eventually die. As the bases of the permanent leaves extend themselves laterally, the positions of the cotyledons come to be represented by two corky ridges (Fig. 26–14, *D*). In the young seedling each permanent leaf is supplied by two traces, and farther out the parallel veins are interconnected by obliquely oriented anastomizing bundles. The stem apex during its short existence show several medianly situated superficial initials which divide both periclinally and anticlinally.

The microsporangiate compound strobilus is strongly four-angled and bears four ranks of broad decussate bracts (Fig. 26–12, *D*) each with a simple, flowerlike, unstrobiloid strobilus (Fig. 26–13, *A*, *B*; Fig. 26–16, *B*) in its axil. Each simple strobilus (shown diagrammatically by Martens' reconstruction in Fig. 26–16, *B*) consists from the outside inward of two pairs of asymmetrically disposed bracts, then six microsporangiophores basally fused into a

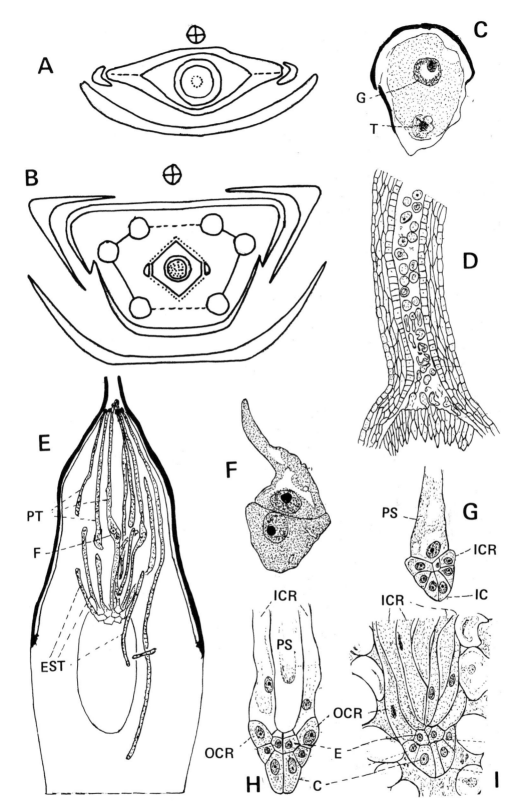

FIGURE 26–16. *Welwitschia bainesii. A, B.* "Floral" diagrams of the megasporangiate and micro- **485** sporangiate simple strobili and associated bract and cone axis. *C.* Immature male gametophyte. *D.* Micropyle with germinating pollen grains. *E.* Ovule at fertilization time. *F* to *I.* Stages in embryogeny. *A, B* after Martens (1959); *D* to *I* after Pearson (1929). G = generative nucleus; T = tube nucleus; PT = pollen tube; EST = embryo sac tube; F = fertilization; PS = primary suspensor; ICR = inner cortical tier; OCR = outer cortical tier; IC = terminal initial cells; C = cap; E = embryonic plate.

sheath (Fig. 26–13, *A*, *B* with bracts removed; *D* from the top with sporangia removed), then a pair of minute bracts that appear as slight nipples at the base and on either side of the centrally located nonfunctional ovule (Fig. 26–13, *F* with sporangiophores removed). The nonfunctional ovule has a single integument that is extended upward and flanged out at the apex (Fig. 26–13, *B*, *F*). The cross section in Fig. 26–13, *G* shows the nucellus in the very center surrounded by the integument and this in turn by the sporangiophore sheath with six vascular bundles. Each microsporangiophore bears three fused sporangia with their lines of dehiscence radiating from near the point where the septa converge (Fig. 26–13, *C*). Each sporangium has an outer layer of cells, two tapetal layers, then the fertile tissue.

Both the bract upon the compound strobilar axis (BR in Fig. 26–13, *H*, which is an enlargement of the left side of the central axis in *E*) and the subtended simple strobilus (FL) receive two vascular bundles.

The ovulate strobilus is somewhat thicker and also bears broad decussate bracts (Fig. 26–12, *E*). In the axil of each bract is a pair of bracts, then the bitegumented ovule (Fig. 26–16, *A*; Fig. 26–15, *B*). The outer integument is clearly a pair of bracts (Fig. 26–15, *D*) that fuse at an early stage in ontogeny and later come to form the conspicuous fibrous wings of the seed (Fig. 26–15, *A*, *C*). The inner integument arises as a complete ring of tissue (Fig. 26–15, *D*) as in *Gnetum* and thus shows no indication of bipartedness as it does in *Ephedra*. It later extends apically as a thin micropylar tube as in *Gnetum* and *Ephedra*.

The microgametophyte of *Welwitschia* has no prothallial cells. It is shed in a binucleate state, containing a tube nucleus and a generative nucleus (Fig. 26–16, *C* after a tube has begun to form). The grains germinate within the micropylar canal and upon the nucellus (Fig. 26–16, *D*).

The female gametophyte is tetrasporic, as it is in *Gnetum* (Martens, 1962). The four free megaspore nuclei continue to divide without wall formation, but eventually walls appear. Some adventitious female gametophytes begin to form, but do not mature, within the tissues of the compound ovulate cone axis. A number of cells of the functional megagametophyte

produce tubes up into the nucellus (EST in Fig. 26–16, *E*) which encounter and fuse apically with the pollen tubes (PT). The female nucleus migrates upward through the embryo sac tube (EST) and into the pollen tube, where the two sperm of generative nucleus origin are encountered. Following fertilization the zygote moves down into the female gametophyte.

The early stages in the development of the embryo are much like those in *Ephedra* and *Gnetum*. There is a short primary suspensor tube formed and a transverse division occurs (Fig. 26–16, *F*). From this stage onward the embryogeny of *Welwitschia* shows some peculiarities but also suggests conifers. The terminal cell divides to produce an apical mass (Fig. 26–16, *G*). The outer cells adjacent to the primary suspensor (inner cortical ring, ICR, Fig. 26–16, *G*) elongate along with the latter and come to surround it (*H*). The same thing happens in the formation of the outer cortical ring (OCR). The terminal initial cells (IC in *G*), in addition to producing the cortical cells of the secondary suspensor, produce an apical calyptra (C in *H* and *I*) as well as the cells that will eventually form the embryo proper (E).

General Considerations

It should be apparent that *Ephedra*, *Gnetum*, and *Welwitschia* are each highly specialized, both vegetatively and reproductively. Most authors have recognized *Ephedra* as retaining a few more primitive features, such as its archegonium, its more cellular male gametophyte, its cauline stele (which is readily describable in generalized coniferophytic terms), and the gross morphology of its fructifications (which relate well to those of the cordaites).

The differences among *Ephedra*, *Gnetum*, and *Welwitschia* are so striking that the many similarities are easily clouded. At the histological level, especially in terms of protoxylem, protoxylem–metaxylem transition, perforation plate structure, and the sieve cells, the three genera share a great many features, and they share a few of these features with coniferophytes. Each has an ovule with an attenuated inner integument that forms a thin micropylar tube and one or two additional integuments derived ontogenetically each from a pair of bracts. The entire ovulate simple strobilus is comparable in position and may be compared part for part among the three genera. The male gametophyte shows a gradate reduction series from *Ephedra* to *Gnetum* to *Welwitschia*. Microsporangial wall structure is consistent as well. Early formation of a unicellular primary suspensor occurs in all three, followed by a transverse division. Other similarities of apparent importance are those in the pollen between *Ephedra* and *Welwitschia* and in the tetrasporic female gametophyte between *Gnetum* and *Welwitschia*.

The position of the microsporangiate organs in *Gnetum* and that of the stalk which bears several compound strobili in *Welwitschia* seem anomolous. In each case it might well be considered adventitious, but possibly the kind of meristematic activity preceding the formation of each is homologous. That is, the growth of a near-linear meristem adjacent to a leaf base in *Welwitschia* forming upward folds of tissue on which the reproductive stalks originate may well have its counterpart in the strobilus of *Gnetum*, where a meristem of similar form above the bract produces tissue upward on which the microsporangiate simple strobili form. These both may be ultimately related to the less bizarre mode of formation of accessory buds in the comparable position in the vegetative shoots of *Gnetum* and *Ephedra*.

Eames (1952) presented the most convincing case for the derivation of *Ephedra* from near the Cordaitales, reference to which has already been made, but he also concluded that *Gnetum* and *Welwitschia* are not even distantly related to *Ephedra*. Coulter and Chamberlain (1910) state the view held by most subsequent botanists that "... whatever may be the connection of *Ephedra* with other gymnosperms it cannot be separated from *Welwitschia* and *Gnetum*." This conclusion has come to be more and more supported by facts uncovered since 1910.

27

Angiosperms: Vegetative Structure

The angiosperms, or flowering plants, are represented in the extant flora by 300 to 400 families and from 200,000 to 300,000 species. Their morphological diversity is tremendous, but common features of their life cycles seem to hold them together as a natural taxon that is recognized at the class, subdivision, or division level depending on the system of classification followed.

The angiosperms seem naturally divisible into two subtaxa, the monocots and dicots, recognized as subclasses here. Despite the names, the mere number of cotyledons is not a prime feature in separating the subclasses, but the structure and embryonic origin of what are referred to as cotyledons in each taxon certainly are. In addition, there are a number of other significant differences expressed at the tissue and organ level of both vegetative and reproductive parts of the somata. The monocots include about one fourth to one fifth of the total angiosperm species and in two commonly followed systems are divided into 11 orders and 45 families (Engler and Diels, 1936) or 26 orders and 69 families (Hutchinson, 1959). The dicots are divided by these same authors into 44 orders and 358 families and 76 orders and 342 families respectively.

It is obvious that in a volume such as this one the angiosperms cannot receive a treatment parallel to that of other taxa. Angiosperm morphology is treated by many botanists as a speciality in itself. The intent here is to present some concept of the range in variation that the angiosperms exhibit, to describe them in terminology parallel to that used in the preceding chapters, to attempt to point out what may be their generalized features, and thus to place them into the same comparative context as the nonflowering plants.

489

The sporophytic body of angiosperms, as Eames (1961) points out, seems to be fundamentally an axis that at one end is root and at the other stem bearing appendages (leaves). This may be in evidence only in the embryo or, in some species, later in ontogeny if a tap-root system is maintained. In these regards the flowering plants are comparable to other seed plants (cycadophytes, coniferophytes, and gnetophytes) and differ sharply from the embryologically known non-seed-bearing vascular plants (with the possible exception of some species of *Equisetum*), in which there is no continuous root-stem axis.

The angiosperm root is anatomically clearly differentiated from other parts of the plant body except in the axial transition. It is regularly present except in an occasional reduced floating aquatic. It bears a calyptrate apex in which the initial zone is either a common one or differentiated into definite histogen layers. A solid core of procambium occurs in the center, distal to the apex proper, in which appear exarch poles of primary xylem alternating with primary phloem poles. The number of poles varies from two as the lower limit in many families to well over a hundred in large roots of some palms. When the number is extremely high, the central core of the stele is often not a solid mass of metaxylem or metaxylem surrounding a core of stelar parenchyma, but in the form of separate islands intermixed with stelar parenchyma. The endodermis and pericycle are distinct and generally of a common ontogenetic origin with the inner cortical cells. A vascular cambium occurs in most dicot roots and rarely in monocots, originating between primary xylem and primary phloem and eventually coming to be a complete cylinder. Anomalous types of secondary thickening occur in a limited number of families. Periderm originates in the outer cortex or in the pericycle with nearly equal frequency among angiosperms. Its presence is usually correlated with the presence of secondary vascular tissues. Old woody roots frequently exhibit a complex rhytidome.

Nonseptate root hairs are generally present, arising as extensions of small epidermal cells (trichoblasts) that are frequently produced by unequal, oblique, anticlinal divisions of protodermal cells. Branch roots arise from the endodermis, pericycle, or endodermal–pericyclic region before differentiation and most commonly in positions opposite primary xylem poles.

The angiosperm root, in summary, is recognizable and definable by the same criteria used in other taxa, the prime features being the presence of a calyptra, alternating xylem and phloem poles, and exarch primary xylem maturation. All other features that may tend to distinguish the root from a stem are less diagnostic and less consistent. Histological attributes of the xylem, phloem, and cortex, with the possible exceptions of the presence of vessels in roots of certain monocots that do not possess them in their stems, and a much greater degree of endopolyploidy in developing vessels of roots, commonly cited as differences between roots and stems, are in reality differences between underground organs and aerial organs, irrespective of their morphology.

The angiosperm shoot consists of an axial entity, the stem, which bears appendages, the leaves, in a fixed order according to species. The order, or phyllotaxy, is spiral (alternate), with variations from taxon to taxon in the angle between two successive leaves in the genetic spiral, or opposite or whorled. When opposite or whorled, some imprecision is often apparent in the groupings, and even when precisely arranged, the leaves of a node may not originate synchronously. The alternate (spiral) condition is usually considered the generalized type of leaf arrangement, although according to one interpretation, stipules represent modified leaves of a whorl.

The leaf itself in dicots is often recognized as being composed of leaf base or buttress, petiole, stipules, and lamina. The base is an ill-defined entity but assumes some significance when it produces a major proportion of the entire leaf, as it may in the case of certain bud scales and possibly in most monocots (see Troll, 1967). The base in ordinary types of leaves may be conspicuous (Fig. 27–2, *B*). In the case of *Coleus*, a rather ordinary labiate, the base originates from a relatively massive slab of stem apex tissue which is recognizable before the distal part of the leaf primordium has erupted. In Fig. 27–4, *A, C* the pair of leaf promordia lateral to the main stem apex is situated at right angles to another, still younger,

FIGURE 27–1. External vegetative features of dicots. *A.* Proximal portion of a leaf of *Rosa rugosa.* *B.* Portion of shoot of *Begonia* sp.; *C.* of *Hibiscus rosa-sinensis*; *D.* of *Viola* sp.; *E.* of *Coffea arabica*; *F.* of *Magnolia soulangeana*; *G.* of *Galium* sp. S = stipule; P = petiole; A = axillary bud or shoot; SS = stipule scar; L = leaf blade.

FIGURE 27–2. External vegetative features of dicots. *A.* Portion of shoot of *Casuarina equisetifolia*; *B.* of *Euphorbia* sp. *C.* One node of *Parthenocissus tricuspidata*; *D.* of *Berberis thunbergii*. *E.* Part of an internode of *Onopordum acanthium*. *F.* One node of *Crataegus* sp.; *G.* of *Asclepias curisavica*. T = thorn; L = leaf; PD = peduncle.

pair, which is represented merely by two squared-off edges (leaf bases) of a flattened apex (in cross section in the center of Fig. 27–4, *A*). Immediately above the oldest leaf pair in *B*, which is the sixth youngest pair of the specimen, are the lateral edges of the bases of leaf pair five.

Stipules are considered parts of the leaf with which they are associated or to which they are attached, although certain interpretations imply otherwise. The occurrence of stipules in dicots is widespread and they are often consistently present or absent in given families. They are often vestigial or absent by reduction, but their presence as a primitive feature has never been well supported. In position they are epipetiolar (Fig. 27–1, *A*), epicauline (Fig. 27–1, *B* to *D*, *G*), or both, in part (Fig. 27–1, *E*, *F*). Fusion between stipules of adjacent leaves is common (Fig. 27–1, *E*) as well as fusion of those of a single leaf (Fig. 27–1, *F*, in which the stipules, S, are in the form of a bud scale enclosing younger primordia and SS represents a circular scar left by abscissed stipule). The vascular supplies to stipules branch off from that of the leaf itself, which is a major point in considering them part of that organ.

Stipules in monocots are rare, occurring in the Hydrocharitaceae, Butomaceae, Najadaceae, and some Dioscoriaceae (Fig. 27–3, *C*). Their occurrence in the first two families is significant in any argument put forth to support derivation of monocots from primitive dicots or dicotlike plants, since these families also show floral features suggestive of such relationships.

Dicot leaves and stems occur in a wide variety of sizes, shapes, and patterns of histological organization. It is important that every student of botany examine a large number of species and learns to recognize the individual organs as well as the common plan, regardless of its obscurity, of shoot organization. A few examples are illustrated in Fig. 27–2, *A* to *G*. In *A* a shoot of *Causuarina* is shown with photosynthetic stems and highly reduced, whorled scale leaves. In *B* a fleshy stem of *Euphorbia* appears with small leaves and massive leaf cushions in conspicious orthostichies. In *C* a portion of a shoot of *Parthenocissus* is shown with a leaf situated opposite a modified holdfast shoot system. The latter is neither subtended by a leaf nor bears a bud in its axil. One might expect that the holdfast system was actually terminal at a point of overtopping in the main shoot, but Millington (1966) showed that it arises in the axil of the leaf at the next lower internode, which at maturity is some distance below. In *D* a part of a shoot of *Berberis* appears and it shows a sharp-pointed bladeless leaf subtending a more typical axillary shoot. In *E* a piece of stem of the scotch thistle (*Onopordum*) is shown on which massive wings have been produced by adventitious marginal meristematic activity. In *F* a node of *Crataegus* is shown with a leaf, L, subtending an axillary shoot in the form of a thorn, T. A very anomalous morphological shoot type appears in *G*, which shows in *Asclepias* a peduncle, PD, on the stem in an interpetiolar position. In origin (Nolan, 1967) the peduncle is not an axillary structure but seems to arise as a result of a dichotomy of the stem apex.

Among all the deviations from the stereotyped dicot plant body which botanists have described, that which occurs in the Nymphaeaceae (Cutter, 1957) may be the most fundamental. In some of these water lilies, a branch (pedicel in this case) replaces a leaf in the phyllotactic spiral. When this was first described, it was quite unacceptable to many plant morphologists. It was immediately assumed that Miss Cutter had overlooked a vestigial leaf subtending the flower bud, but attempts to find the bract by the present author and others proved fruitless. The replacement of one organ by another in a uniform sequence has been used to indicate homology between the two in other taxa (e.g., Psilotaceae and Hyeniaceae), but the application of this reasoning to the leaf and the entire flower is indeed difficult.

The monocot soma shows many significant departures from that of a dicot. The leaves are mostly simple, and many families exhibit sheathing leaf bases and predominantly parallel major veins (Fig. 27–3, *A*, *B*). The leaf itself is derived in many cases by expansion of the leaf base and is often considered the homolog of only that part of the dicot leaf (the "phyllode theory"). The leaves of certain genera (e.g., *Pontederia*, *Eichhornia*, and *Smilax*) have been interpreted as having

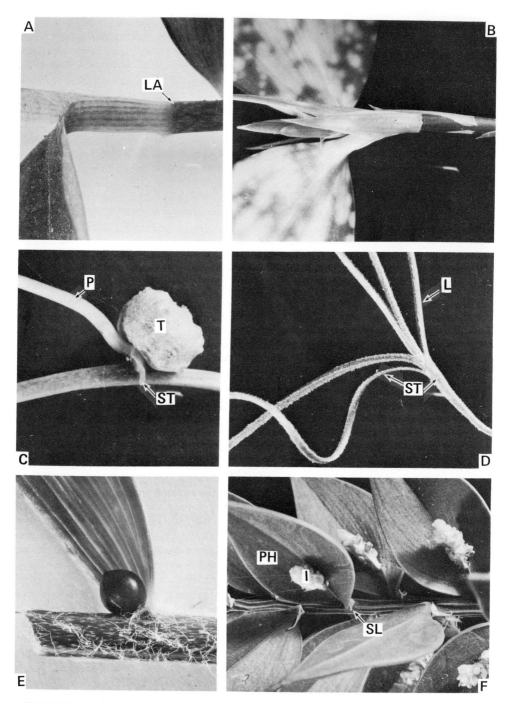

FIGURE 27–3. External vegetative features of monocots. *A.* Node of *Zebrina*. *B.* Terminal part of a shoot of *Dracaena* sp. *C.* Node of *Dioscorea* sp. *D.* Node of *Tillandsia*; *E.* of *Lilium tigrinum*. *F.* Shoot of *Ruscus aculeatus*. LA = leaf attachment; P = petiole; T = tuber; S = stipule; L = leaf; ST = stem; PH = leaflike shoot; SL = scale leaf; I = inflorescence.

produced a secondary blade by elaboration of the base. Axillary buds are frequently slightly out of position in monocots, often toward one side of the center of insertion of a clasping leaf base. In still other monocots, axillary buds may be associated only with certain leaves (e.g., Hydrocharitaceae). Cutter (1964) described the buds in *Hydrocharis* as originating above the subtending leaf within the shoot apex itself.

Intercalary growth both in stems and in leaves is a conspicuous feature of many monocot families and is closely correlated with the sheathing leaf base. To appreciate the mechanical interrelationship of parts, it is only necessary to carefully peel off all leaves from an elongating shoot of a large grass or member of the Commelinaceae and observe the inability of the stem to support itself at the meristem. The longitudinal section of the shoot tip of *Bambusa* in Fig. 27–4, *D* is approximately 4 cm long and shows about 40 nodes, above each of which is an intercalary meristem. The darker bands across the body are the nodal diaphragms, and below the lowermost the beginning of the internodal pith cavity is shown.

In palms and certain other large-stemmed monocots the plant axis attains nearly full diameter a very short distance below the stem apex. A longitudinally sectioned apical plug about 1 cm in diameter of the palm *Howea* appears in Fig. 27–4, *B*, in which the stem apex is somewhat sunken. The apex itself has the generalized angiosperm organization with a tunica and a corpus. Across the base of each leaf is an intercalary meristem. Just below the level of the stem surface, extending laterally from the edge of the stem apex, is a meristematic zone some 50 to 80 cells thick at the margins of the section, the primary thickening meristem as described by Ball (1941), in which cell divisions are periclinal and anticlinal, resulting in the production of the bulk of the stem tissue. In smaller-stemmed monocots (e.g., *Eichhornia*) a similar meristematic zone appears, but it curves downward into the axis and is continuous below as the outer portion of the inner cylinder of the stem (see below).

Several superficial types of modification of the monocot body are shown in Fig. 27–3, *C* to *F*. In *C* a reproductive tuber, T, of *Dioscorea* developed from an axillary bud, is shown. In *E* a bulblet of *Lilium* is shown in a similar position. In *D* a portion of the reduced body of Spanish moss, *Tilandsia*, is shown. The continuity of the stem, S, is difficult to recognize, owing to a very thin portion immediately above a node. The leaf, L, subtends an axillary shoot bearing three other leaves, each quite small but retaining the characteristic sheathing leaf base of the larger bromeliads. In *F* leaflike lateral shoots, PH, are shown on a stem of *Ruscus*, each subtended by a scale leaf, SL, and bearing an inflorescence, I, on its face.

Although venation of most monocots is predominantly parallel, with minor cross connections and with major veins converging at the leaf tip, netted systems occur in some families (e.g., Lilaceae rarely and Araceae commonly). A more consistent, but not absolute, difference between dicot and monocot venation is the presence in the latter and the absence in the former of blindly ending veinlets within the vein system.

Dichotomies or suggestions of them have been described as occurring in a number of angiosperms. Van der Hammer (1948) cites the underground axes of saprophytic Orchidaceae, Burmanniaceae, rhizomes of *Nuphar*, *Alstroemeria*, and upright stems of some palms. In the latter three, he suggests, there is an angle leaf. He also cites about 18 families in which he has recognized, either clearly or obscurely, dichotomous venation in leaves and more numerous cases in perianth parts. In submerged aquatics dichotomous venation is generally more apparent, and, in van der Hammer's view, in these species the weaker veins (which obscure dichotomies) are reduced in number, exposing a primitive vein system. *Kingdonia* and *Circaeaster*, both herbaceous dicots and neither particularly reduced, each shows predominantly open dichotomous venation (Foster, 1959, 1968). Foster (1968) states: "Whether the venation patterns in these two remarkable dicotyledons represent (1) the retention of a condition which appeared during early evolution of angiosperms or (2) are the result of reversion from a more complex vasculature, are questions which cannot be convincingly answered until future paleobotanical discoveries have clarified the origin and major trends of phylogeny of the angiosperms as a

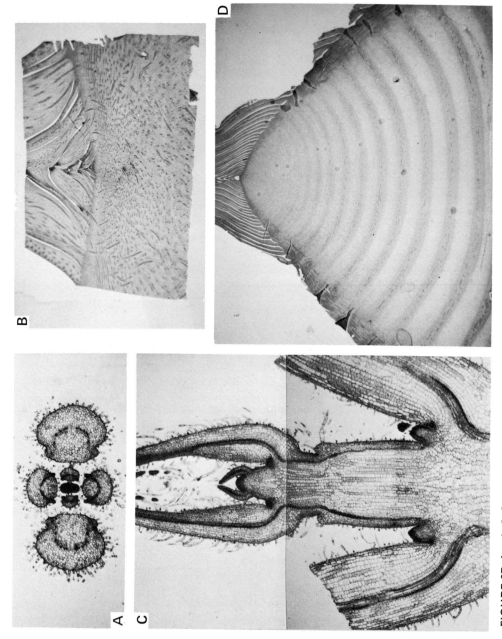

FIGURE 27–4. *A, C.* Cross and longitudinal section of shoot tip of *Coleus.* *B.* Longitudinal section of shoot tip of *Howea;* *D.* of *Bambusa.*

whole." This seems to be the only view possible at present. To dogmatically assume that any indication of a dichotomy in an angiosperm is a primitive feature and to describe telomes in this taxon, which is so far removed from the taxa of telomic reference (i.e., rhyniophytes or their presumed algal predecessors), is to carry plant morphology back to the age of topology (i.e., the geometry of form in a nonphylogenetic context).

Slade's (1959) theory of vein breakage suggests that blind endings in a leaf-vein system result from the pulling apart of established connections during ontogeny. This then might imply that the completely closed vein system (as in most monocots) is more primitive within angiosperms than the partly open system (as in most dicots). Lersten's (1965) observations on the ontogeny of the vein system of *Trifolium* contradict this. He suggests that the state of maturation of one vein in the system determines whether or not a developing procambial strand can attain a connection. This latter concept particularly emphasizes the phylogenetic importance of the effect of synchrony and non-synchrony in the development of vein systems.

Florin (1931) described stomatal apparatuses as syndetocheilic, in which the guard cells and adjacent subsidiary cells develop from the same mother cell, and haplocheilic, in which they do not. He claimed that these two types could be distinguished in their mature states, as in the former the subsidiary cells are adjacent to the guard cells and in the latter the subsidiary cells surround the guard cells. The feature has frequently been emphasized in comparative treatments, especially by paleobotanists, since they are always short of available characters and this one is frequently preserved. More recently Pant and Verma (1963) showed that the haplocheilic mature form is referable to a syndetocheilic pattern of development in *Notonia* (Compositae), and Maheshwari and Vasil (1961) showed the reverse in *Gnetum*. Paliwal and Bhandari (1962) found syndetocheilic stomatal apparatuses on leaves and haplocheilic ones on flower parts of species of the Magnoliaceae. These features can no longer be considered conservative or of great comparative value, but from a systematic point of view they are particularly significant at the ordinal and at subordinal levels within certain taxonomic assemblages.

Dicot stems are artificially distinguished as woody or herbaceous. They completely intergrade, however, in size, toughness, and relative degree of secondary tissue development. Some woody stems produce much less secondary xylem than do many soft and herbaceous ones.

A "typical" woody dicot stem might be represented by *Ligustrum* (Fig. 27–5, *A* to *F*). There is a distinct pith surrounded by a cylinder of vascular tissue and outside of this a cortex and an epidermis Fig. 27–5, *A*). The primary vascular tissue forms a nearly complete cylinder, but at a young level the vascular tissues are precociously matured below leaf insertion (Fig. 27–5, *C*, which is part of *A* enlarged; this specimen had whorled leaves, whereas the species generally has opposite ones). At a higher level each of the three well-developed vascular areas seen in *A* separates from the cylinder, supplies a leaf, and leaves a single gap. The cortex becomes differentiated into an outer collenchymatous zone and an inner parenchymatous one (*C*, *E*). Primary xylem is uniformly endarch in maturation, as it is in all angiosperm stems. Cambial activity appears very early in the development of the *Ligustrum* stem, as it does in many woody dicot stems. It would appear in the young stem in *C* that secondary xylem has already matured. This section is well within the region of elongation and all xylem elements seen are extensible types. Most definitions of primary and secondary xylem, although vague in their distinction of the two, are fundamentally mutually exclusive. According to some concepts, protoxylem and metaxylem are necessarily part of the primary xylem, although the distinguishing features of these are not related to those which distinguish primary and secondary. In a previous chapter the expression "cambial protoxylem" was used, and it is considered a particularly convenient concept when telescoping of ontogeny has resulted in the production of secondary xylem in the region of elongation.

In the *Ligustrum* stem parenchyma of the protophloem region later differentiates and matures as a zone of fibers (Fig. 27–5, *E*, *D*), a common phenomenon among dicots. Without

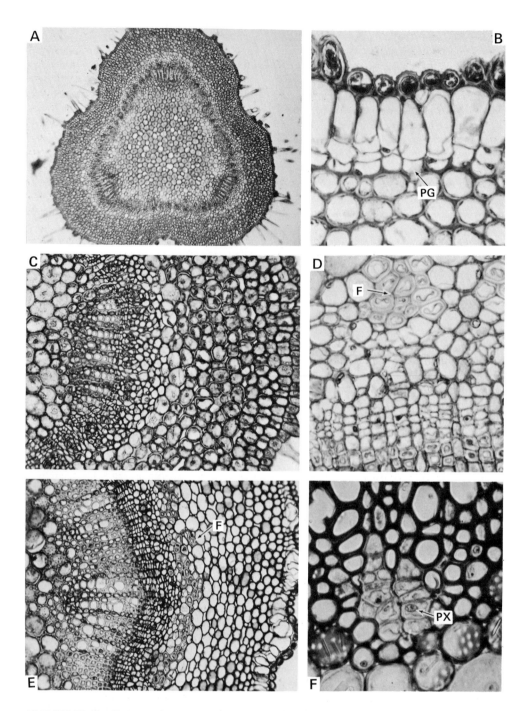

FIGURE 27–5. Cross sections of the stem of *Ligustrum vulgarum*. *A*. From near the lower end of the region of elongation. *C*. Portion of *A* enlarged. *E*. Older portion near the end of the first growing season. *B*. Outer portion of *E* enlarged. *D*. Portion of *E* enlarged, showing the phloem, cambium, and outer part of the xylem. *F*. Protoxylem region from *E* enlarged. PG = phellogen; F = fibers; PX = protoxylem.

developmental information, fibers in the comparable position are best referred to as perivascular, as in some stems they are referable to the cortex developmentally. The pith cells, as in many woody dicots, become secondarily sclerified (Fig. 27–5, *F*) such that the islands of protoxylem parenchyma and distorted, early-matured tracheary elements stand out conspicuously. Periderm originates in the outermost layer of the cortex (Fig. 27–5, *B, E*) as it does in an estimated 60 per cent of dicots that produce the tissue. In approximately 30 to 40 per cent the first phellogen forms in the area of the inner cortex, and a small percentage of species form epidermal phellogen.

Herbaceous stems frequently show in cross section a complete vascular cylinder (Fig. 27–6, *A*) but more commonly a series of discrete vascular bundles (*B*) with little or no cambial activity or with appreciable cambial activity restricted to the below-ground part.

Less-common patterns of tissue organization ("anomalous types") occur in many families (see Metcalfe and Chalk, 1950). The anomalies occur in the form of differential cambial activity (Fig. 27–6, *C*), accessory cambia that are particularly common among woody vines, additional bundles outside the vascular ring or complete additional rings (Fig. 27–6, *D*), or anomalous patterns of tissue differentiation within the secondary xylem (e.g., islands of phloem within the xylem). More common than the abovementioned anomalies is the presence of internal phloem either as a complete ring or as isolated patches on the pith side of vascular bundles. Metcalfe and Chalk (1950) list a number of families showing internal phloem, most important among which are the Cucurbitaceae, Solanaceae, Apocynaceae, and Asclepiadaceae.

The most common type of nodal vascular structure among the dicots, occurring in many primitive as well as advanced families such as the Rosaceae, Fagaceae, Casuarinaceae, Ranunculaceae, Compositae, and Winteraceae, is the three trace–trilacunar type, which is illustrated for *Ribes* (Fig. 27–6, *E*). An extensive leaf base appears around the right side of the section. Three traces are seen at about the level at which they depart from the cauline cylinder and leave each a single gap. The single trace–unilacunar node is relatively common,

occurring in such families as the Oleaceae, Asclepiadaceae, and Apocynaceae (described for *Ligustrum* above). Multilacunar nodes (with five or more gaps) are relatively uncommon, occurring in five families, including the Umbelliferae and Polygonaceae, where one trace departs from each gap. In *Degeneria*, considered by many to be one of the most primitive dicots, there are five gaps. From the median gap a cluster of usually three traces arises (Fig. 27–6, *F*), while a single trace arises from the two gaps on either side. Other known dicot nodal types are the multitrace–unilacunar and two trace–unilacunar. The latter has been interpreted as "the" primitive type (Canright, 1955) and occurs in the Austrobaileyaceae and Monimiaceae. Evidence cited in support includes (1) the correlated primitiveness of the flower of *Austrobaileya*, (2) the most common cotyledonary supply is a double one, (3) the common occurrence of this type of node in nonangiospermous plants, and (4) a series within the Monimiaceae commencing with a two trace–unilacunar node followed by types with three, five, or seven traces. There is room for argument with respect to each of these points and the issue is far from settled.

Axillary branch vascular supplies are always double in dicots. The number of leaf gaps is always odd, and the branch supply arises from the sides of the median gap.

A few submerged aquatic angiosperms, both monocots and dicots, show extremely reduced vascular systems with protosteles and simple leaf traces and with almost no xylem.

The generalized monocot stem may be one with two or more concentric rings of vascular bundles. The rings are occasionally recognizable (e.g., in *Convallaria*), but more often the rings are disrupted and the arrangement appears irregular—hence the term "atactostele" to describe monocot steles in general. The term infers a lack of order, but with some diligence, as Zimmermann and Tomlinson (1965) demonstrated, even in massive palm stems with thousands of bundles in a cross section a definite pattern is discernible. Monocot stems that show a single ring of bundles in internodes, as in *Triticum*, are undoubtedly derived from more complex types.

A common structural pattern exhibited by monocot stems is one with a central cylinder

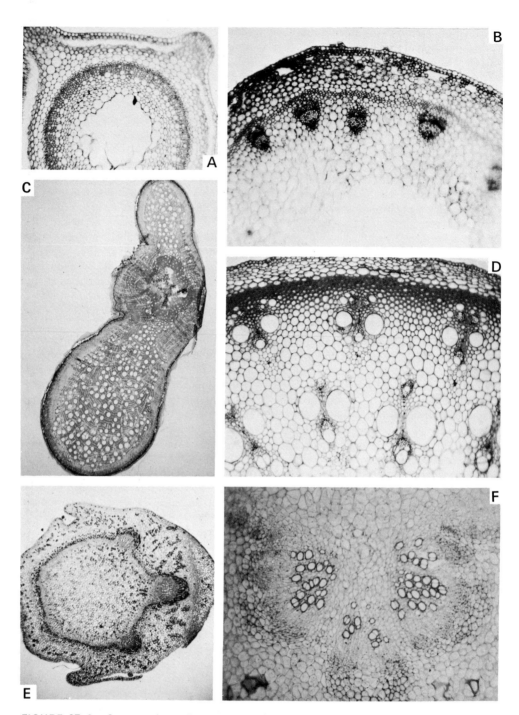

FIGURE 27–6. Cross sections of stems, or portions, of various dicots. *A. Galium. B. Osmorhiza. C. Bauhinia. D. Convolvulus. E. Ribes*, at the node. *F. Degeneria*, at the node and showing only the median leaf gap.

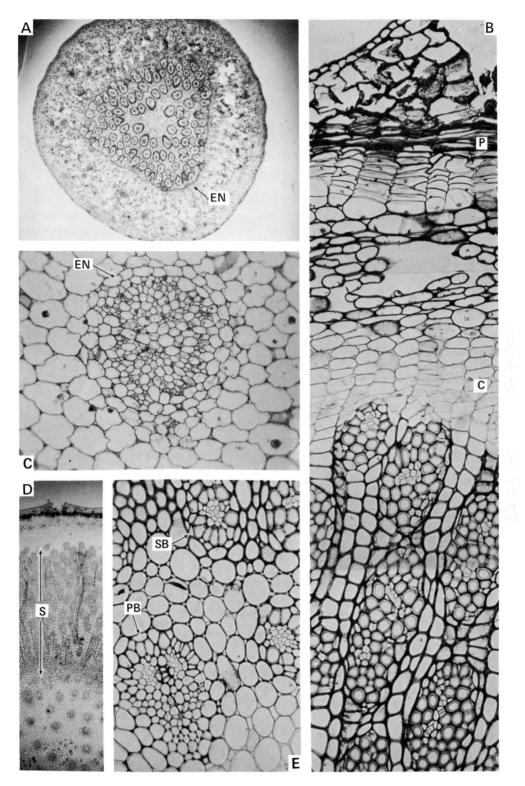

FIGURE 27–7. Cross sections of monocot stems. *A. Smilax. C. Corallorhiza*, central part only. *D.* Sector from *Cordyline. B.* Outer portion of *D* enlarged. *E.* Deeper portion of *D* enlarged. EN = endodermis; S = secondary tissue; P = periderm; C = cambial zone; PB = primary bundle; SB = secondary bundle.

surrounded by an endodermis, as is found in essentially all cylindrical underground stems, creeping aerial stems, and upright stems of some genera (Fig. 27–7, *A*). In the central cylinder are large bundles more closely aggregated and often not vertically oriented just inside the endodermis. In the outer cylinder are numerous smaller bundles that supply the next higher leaf. What is leaf tissue and what is stem tissue is an arbitrary designation. The upright aerial stems of most monocots lack the outer cylinder and the endodermis, although it may persist for several inches above the ground level, and just below leaf insertion the outer cylinder is recognizable as the leaf base.

The individual vascular bundles vary in their structure within individual stems and among taxa. Large bundles frequently have sclerenchymatous sheaths, the interpretation of which is clouded by the frequent presence of bordered pits in the component fiber walls. The xylem is endarch, but many bundles are oriented with their xylem–phloem axis not precisely along a radius. Xylem surrounding phloem is a very common feature, but still protoxylem is on the inside of the bundle only. Many monocots show evidence of a very limited amount of cambial activity, interpreted as vestigial, between xylem and phloem of larger stem bundles (Bucur, 1935).

Stems of saprophytic and mycorrhizic orchids such as *Corallorrhiza* (Fig. 27–7, *C*) are so highly modified that they closely simulate roots. The outer cylinder shows no vascular bundles except for an occasional poorly developed leaf trace that barely leaves the endodermal sheath (lowermost one in Fig. 27–7, *C*). In the figure the islands of small phloem cells are clear, but the few xylem cells are essentially unthickened.

The stems of the Agavaceae (if split away from the Amaryllidaceae) exhibit secondary thickening of an anomalous type. In Fig. 27–7, *D* a central cylinder appears in the lower part of the photograph, in which the bundles are scattered uniformly and in which each bundle possesses protoxylem. Outside of this is a zone of denser tissue in which the bundles are more closely spaced and in which the interfascicular parenchyma is radially aligned (the inner edge of the zone appears at the upper edge of *E*, the

outer edge of the zone in *B*). An active cambial zone, appearing just outside the mature vascular tissue in *B*, produces some secondary cortex and the tissues toward the inside. In the latter are entire vascular bundles, each with an island of phloem surrounded by tracheids, and secondary interfascicular tissue. In addition, there is a periderm (Fig. 27–7, *B*) that may appear similar to dicot periderms but is not referable to a single-layered phellogen.

A reasonable understanding of the overall form of monocot steles, especially larger ones, is difficult to obtain by ordinary anatomical procedures. Zimmermann and Tomlinson (1965) presented a detailed analysis of the stem of the palm *Rhapis* obtained by a combination of classical techniques and serial cinematographic ones. They photographed a large number of sections in serial order and by continuous running of the film strips they achieved a reasonable understanding of this stem, which was relatively small for a palm, with only about 1,000 vascular bundles in a cross section.

Zimmermann and Tomlinson showed that all vascular bundles in the stem behave essentially alike. In the stem, major and minor bundles, with transitions, differ in relative positions and in the vertical distance between their successive ramifications. A large number of smaller and a lesser number of major bundles supply each leaf. Within the stem all bundles run continuously lengthwise. Each vertical bundle gives off a leaf trace at intervals (their diagrams indicate every five to seven gyres of the genetic spiral). The minor bundles produce leaf traces more frequently than major ones. The vertical course of the bundles is not straight, but each one is tilted inward toward the center of the stem. At intervals the bundle curves sharply outward and, after giving off a leaf trace, recurves sharply inward. In addition, the bundles follow a shallow helix around the stem, rotating about one fourth of the circumference in a vertical distance of about 15 cm. There are also additional minor satellite bundles that branch off and rejoin larger ones as they move outward and minor vascular bridges between individual vertical bundles. The axillary buds, which in *Rhapis* seem to be vestigial inflorescences, receive vascular supplies from the same outwardly "moving" major bundles that supply the subtending leaf.

Many monocots possess a plexus of vascular tissue at each node (e.g., grasses, Commelinaceae, etc.) which are less well known and not yet comparable. Zimmermann and Tomlinson point out similarities between *Rhapis* and a few other "nonnodal" monocots, and it is conceivable that there is but one fundamental vascular pattern within the monocots, as has been inferred elsewhere.

The structure of tracheary elements of angiosperms, as well as the ontogenetic sequence in which they fall, are generalized and comparatively compatible with what is found in cycadophytes, all ferns except the Ophioglossaceae, all articulates except *Equisetum*, aneurophytes, and the Cordaitales. The sequence is basically an annular, helical, reticulate, pitted one with numerous separate specialization series expressed in many genera and families, especially herbaceous ones and those of unusual habit or mode of nutrition. Later-matured tracheary elements of angiosperms show a helical first-order secondary wall framework between the gyres of which is deposited second-order secondary wall in the form of sheets or strands. Figure 27–9, *Q* to *S*, from the fern *Pteridium*, could just as well represent any one of a great many angiosperms. The single, apically growing element of *Sassafras* in Fig. 27–9, *O* shows much the same ontogeny of a pitted wall within a single cell. In only advanced genera is the entire secondary wall pattern (first order plus second order) deposited synchronously.

Heterogeneity within individual cells of second-order secondary wall occurs in various families, conspicuously in the Gesnericaeae (Fig. 27–9, *N*). Another example of peculiar specialization occurs in many genera of the Commelinaceae (Fig. 27–11, *H*), where vertically oriented second-order strands frequently subdivide the thin-walled areas between either rings or gyres into rectangular pitlike openings. Open pits (i.e., those which occur between gyres of a helix and are extended laterally as long slits) seem to be primarily an angiosperm feature and occur in woody members of a great many families (Fig. 27–9, *P*).

Alternate pitting (i.e., pits in irregular arrangements or in distinct or indistinct oblique rows) tend to appear in advanced angiosperm genera. They are referable to either a true opposite arrangement in which the individual pit axes do not fall within the line of the pits or to gross distortions of the entire framework before the final wall deposition to form the pit border (see Bierhorst and Zamora, 1965, for more details).

Vessels occur in most angiosperms. They may be primitively absent in taxa such as the Winteraceae, Tetracentraceae, Trochodendraceae, some Chloranthaceae, and some Monimiaceae, as in these the feature is closely correlated with a number of other presumed primitive characteristics. On the other hand, the vessel-less condition of some submerged aquatics, parasites, and some Cactaceae has more often been interpreted as the result of loss. In a number of monocots, vessels are absent or rare in all but roots or all but creeping rhizomes. Cheadle (1944) interpreted this to mean that within the monocots vessels arose within the root, but loss of vessels in certain parts of the body remains a possibility.

Vessels are frequently discontinuous. When so, they are represented by two or more cells within a more extensive longitudinal system of tracheids. This is a particularly common feature of monocots and of the protoxylem of dicots. It is guessed that many large trees in which most tracheary elements are perforate have in reality no vessels that run the entire length of the plant. This has particular potential significance in the evaluation of the selective value and physiology of vessels as opposed to a lineage of imperforate tracheary elements.

Scalariform perforation plates (Fig. 27–10, *F*, *G*, *L*), which occur in the secondary xylem of all or part of about 110 families of dicots, in the primary xylem of many more, and in nearly all monocot families, are generally considered to be the primitive types among angiosperms. In dicots the basic type is probably a plate with approximately 15 to 25 pores, but in monocots the number is more likely in the range 50 to 100. In a number of individual families of both dicots and monocots transitions from the basic type to the simple type (Fig. 27–10, *I*, *J*, *O*, *P*) have been seen. In some the transition involves plates with various degrees of disruption of the transverse bars of the plate (Fig. 27–10, *M*, *N*). In others the series involves the elaboration of a single pore and the reduction and loss of all

FIGURE 27–8. Portions of tracheary elements. *A* to *E. Lycopodium*. *F* to *K. Equisetum*. In *I* the face of a carinal metaxylem element in contact with the lacuna is shown. *J, K* are single rings from *G.* *L, N* to *P. Botrychium*. *M. Ophioglossum*. *Q. Helminthostachys*. *R. Marattia*. *S, T. Psilotum*. *U* to *X, Z. Blechnum*. *Y. Pteridium*, annular elements distorted by tyloses.

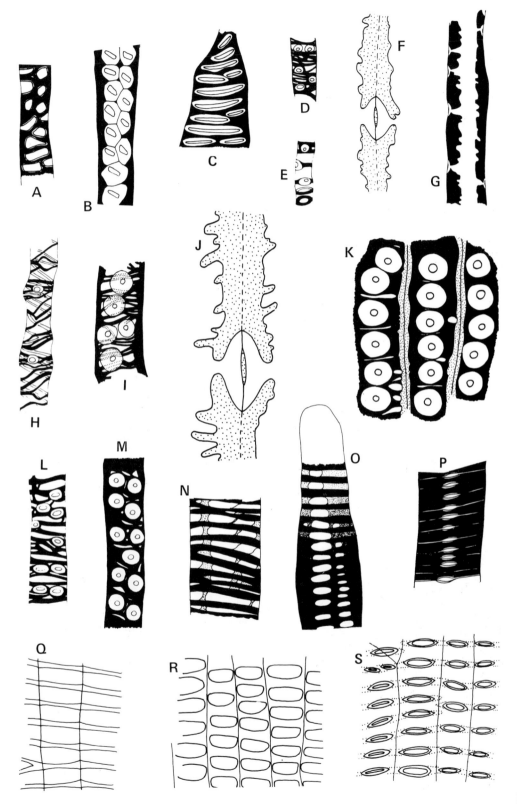

FIGURE 27–9. Portions of tracheary elements. *A* to *C. Cycas*, in sequence of their appearance from early to late metaxylem. *D. Taxus. E. Ephedra. F, I* to *K. Pinus. J* is a sectional view of *I* and the wall of the adjacent cell. *G. Welwitschia. H, L, M. Ginkgo. N. Saintpaulia. O. Sassafras*, an apically growing element. *P. Prunella. Q* to *S*. Three stages in the development of the pitted wall.

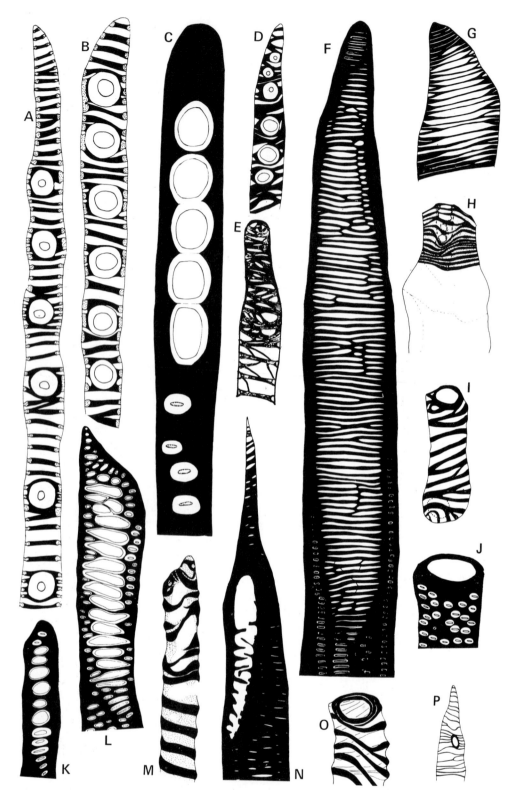

FIGURE 27–10. Perforation plates of vessel members. *A. Ephedra. B, C. Gnetum. D. Welwitschia. E. Equisetum. F. Smilax. G. Penthorum. H. Nepenthes. I. Peperomia. J. Amyema. K, L. Geissois. M. Prunella. N. Agrimonia. O. Mertensia. P. Drosera.*

FIGURE 27–11. *A, B, D, E.* Secondary xylem of *Trochodendron. A,* cross section; *B,* tangential section; *D, E,* radial section. *C.* Tracheids of *Pinus strobus* in radial section. *F, G.* Secondary xylem of *Juniperus virginiana* in cross and tangential sections. *H.* Portion of a tracheary element of *Aneilema.*

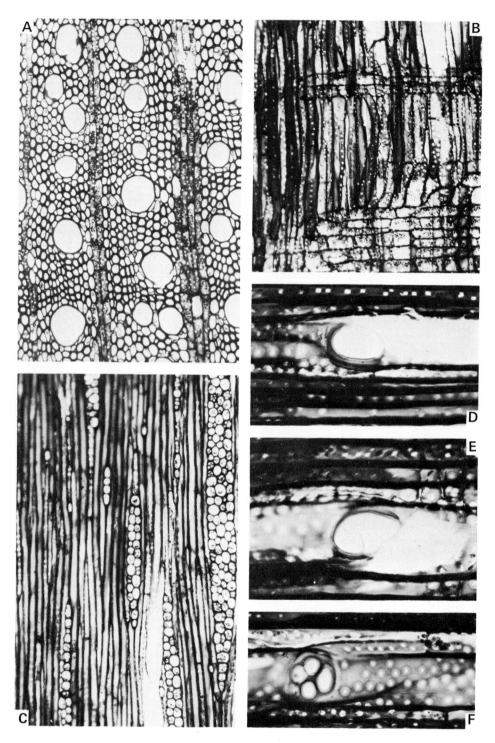

FIGURE 27–12. Secondary xylem of *Gnetum gnemon.* *A.* Cross section. *B.* Radial section. *C.* Tangential section. *D* to *F.* Perforation plates as seen in radial section.

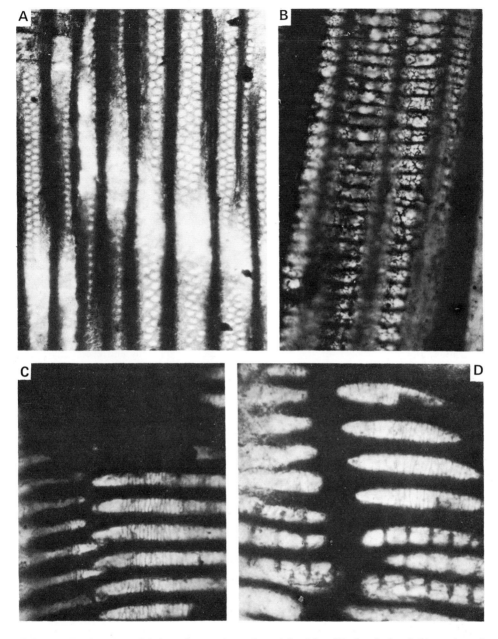

FIGURE 27–13. *A*. Radial view of secondary xylem of *Cordaites* (*Dadoxylon*). *B*. Metaxylem of *Asteroxylon* in longitudinal section. *C*. Scalariform pits of *Lepidodendron vasculare* traversed by Williamson's striations. *D*. Same in *Stigmaria ficoides*.

others. Both types of transitions occur in some families, such as the Cyperaceae. In genera that retain a primitive type of plate as a rare or infrequent feature, it tends to be expressed in the early-matured primary xylem.

A variety of other types of multiperforate plates also occurs in angiosperms, generally in specialized families such as the Convolvulaceae, Flagellariaceae, and Begoniaceae. Among these the foraminate plate, illustrated from the

Angiosperms: Vegetative Structure **509**

cunoniaceous genus *Geissois* in Fig. 27–10, *K*, is particularly mentioned because of its close conformance to those of gnetophytes (compare this with Fig. 27–10, *A* to *D*). In some angiosperms, at least, circular pits and circular pores are not referable in origin, phylogenetically or ontogenetically, to a segmentation of elongate ones but merely a necessary consequence of cell face narrowing, as in most other vascular plant taxa.

The secondary xylem of angiosperms as a tissue has received much attention, and an extensive list of presumed primitive and presumed specialized features has been constructed (the student is advised to read the introductory chapter in Metcalfe and Chalk, 1950, for further details and references to the works of Bailey, Tupper, Frost, Tippo, et al). The wood of *Trochodendron* (Fig. 27–11, *A*, *B*, *D*, *E*) is selected to illustrate the following primitive features: (1) absence of vessels, (2) scalariform pitting, (3) scanty vertical parenchyma, (4) some uniseriate rays, (5) heterogeneous rays (i.e., some ray cells longer in the vertical direction and some in the radial direction), (6) absence of libriform fibers, and (7) recognizable first- and second-order secondary wall in mature elements of late-formed wood (right side of Fig. 27–11, *E*; the transverse bars between

pits and elsewhere where no pits are present are not to be confused with the "tertiary" spirals, which appear as a presumed specialization in many families). *Trochodendron* also shows a considerable amount of uniseriate, circular bordered pitting (Fig. 27–11, *D*), which is difficult to interpret phylogenetically but strongly suggests coniferophyte pitting (Fig. 27–11, *C*).

The phloem of angiosperms is in general a more complex tissue than in other taxa. Consistently present are specialized sieve areas on longitudinal overlap areas (in primitive forms) or on common transverse walls (in advanced forms) occurring singly as simple sieve plates or in multiples as compound sieve plates. The most extensive compound plates are found in woody monocots such as palms, cyclanths, Flagellariaceae, or *Smilax*. Reduction series from compound to simple plates have been shown to occur in both dicots (Zahur, 1959) and in monocots (Cheadle, 1948). Also in both groups, as sieve-tube-member specialization progresses, the lateral sieve areas become less and less conspicuous and eventually are frequently lost. Companion cells appear in all described angiosperm taxa, but in most that have been studied extensively certain sieve-tube members in minority frequency are not associated with them.

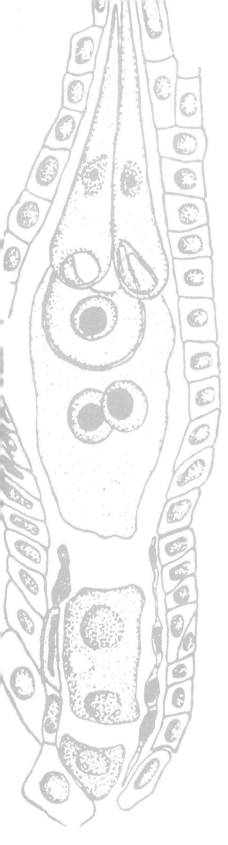

28

Angiosperms: Reproductive Morphology

The angiosperm fructification is the flower, a structure that because of its various degrees of completeness cannot adequately be defined in words. As a substitute for a definition, it is necessary for a student to develop a working concept based on a knowledge of a number of variants and to be able to recognize homologous parts from one to the next. The classical interpretation of the flower, which has been assailed by several contradictory theories during the past 50 years, but still stands firm, holds it to be an axis, or receptacle, bearing, in its complete form, four zones of appendages that are considered the homologs of leaves.

The receptacle ranges in form from axial (Magnoliaceae, Fig. 28–1, *E*) to cone- or dome-shaped (many Ranunculaceae, Fig. 28–1, *H*, *G*; Nymphaeaceae, Fig. 28–2, *A*), to discoid or short-domed (probably the majority of angiosperms), to cup-shaped, to almost nonexistent, as in the microsporangiate flowers of most species, and the diminutive flowers of many species such as the minute ones on the face of the highly modified inflorescence in Fig. 28–2, *E*. Anatomically the receptacle possesses a telescoped dictyostele (Fig. 28–1, *G*, *H*) from which the traces to floral appendages arise.

The zones of floral appendages include, from the proximal end, the calyx, composed of sepals; the carolla, composed of petals; the androecium, composed of the microsporangiate organs, the stamens; and the gynoecium, composed of the megasporangiate or ovulate organs, the carpels. The calyx and carolla collectively make up the perianth, but this term is often reserved

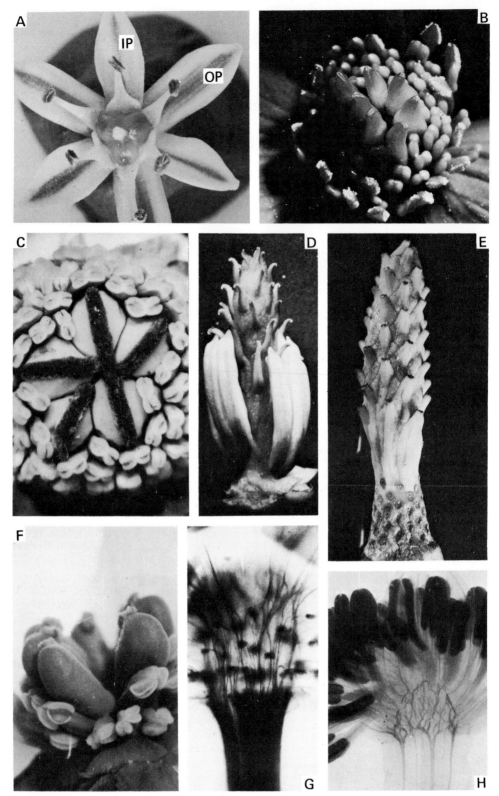

FIGURE 28–1. *A.* Flower of *Ornithogalum. B.* Androecium and gynoecium of the flower of *Caltha. C.* As *B,* but of *Expospermum stipitatum. D, E.* Flower of *Magnolia soulangiana.* Perianth and some stamens removed in *D. E* is postpollination and perianth, stamens, and stigmas have abscissed. *F.* Flower of *Drimys winteri. G.* Cleared receptacle of *D. winteri. H.* Cleared flower of *Caltha.* OP = outer perianth segment; IP = inner perianth segment.

512

for those taxa, especially monocotyledonous ones, in which the sepals and petals are morphologically poorly differentiated from each other. In Fig. 28–1, *A*, *Ornithogallum* (Liliaceae), which might be considered to represent the fundamental floral organization of a great many monocots, the four floral zones are shown and consist of the outer and inner perianth of three segments each (OP and IP), then the androecium of six stamens, then the gynoecium of a tricarpelate compound structure or syncarpel.

The primitive flower is considered a bisexual or bisporangiate one with an undifferentiated perianth, many stamens and many carpels, all in spiral order and showing neither conation nor adnation. Flowers in which spiral arrangement is expressed throughout are rare, occurring in the winteraceous genera *Drimys* and *Wintera*. The perianth among genera of the presumed primitive liliaceous subfamily Melanthioideae shows transitions from spiral to cyclic arrangement. The androecium alone or this along with the gynoecium more commonly exhibits spiral arrangement, especially in families such as the Ranunculaceae (Fig. 28–1, *B*), Dilleniaceae, Rosaceae, Winteraceae (Fig. 28–1, *C*, *F*, *G*), Nymphaeaceae, and Magnoliaceae (Fig. 28–1, *D*, *E*).

Sepals are in general more leaflike than other floral appendages, both in vasculature and in mature form. As a generality, the sepals are supplied by three vascular traces arising from the receptacular stele, or, if otherwise, there tends to be conformance between the number of sepal traces and the number of leaf traces of the species. Sepals are occasionally indistinguishable from reduced leaves occurring on the flower stalk below, as is common in *Heleborus*.

Petals throughout monocots and in some dicots (e.g., woody Ranales) seem to have arisen by differentiation of sepals or as dimorphism appeared within an undifferentiated perianth. In other dicots, probably the majority (e.g., Ranunculaceae and Rosaceae), the petals presumably arose by stamen modification. In the latter there are frequent transitional forms between petals and stamens, and most commonly both petals and stamens are supplied by a single trace, whereas sepals are supplied by three traces. The most complete transitional series between corolla and androecium parts

occurs in the Nymphaeaceae, in which all floral appendages as a basic condition are supplied by three traces.

In the context of the classical floral theory, the more primitive a floral appendage is, the more leaflike it is. Leaflike or laminar stamens are known from several dicot families, including the Nymphaeaceae (Fig. 28–4, *H*; Fig. 28–6, *D*), Austrobaileyaceae (Fig. 28–6, *A*), Himantandraceae (Fig. 28–6, *B*), and Degeneriaceae (Fig. 28–6, *C*). Stamens whose vascular supplies are more suggestive of those of presumed primitive leaves are similarly interpreted as primitive. The single trace condition, as occurs in the majority of angiosperms, is thus considered derived, as opposed to the three-trace condition common in the Magnoliaceae, Winteraceae, and Nymphaeaceae, among the dicots, and the Musaceae, Zingerberaceae, and Marantaceae, among the monocots, or as opposed to the two-trace condition, which is expressed in *Austrobaileya* (below the level shown in Fig. 28–6, *A*) a few Nymphaeaceae, Casuarinaceae, and Gesneriaceae.

A (polyphyletic) reduction–modification series is readily read from the laminar stamen with two pairs of elongate more or less sunken sporangia, a triple vascular supply, and an appreciable amount of sterile tissue distal to, between, and lateral to the sporangial pairs to the ordinary staminal type. The changes involved are (1) loss of sterile lamina lateral to the sporangial pairs (Fig. 28–4, *I*), (2) reduction of the sterile tissue between them, (3) simplification of the vascular supply, and (4) reduction or loss of the distal sterile tip of the stamen (this has become peculiarly modified or extended in certain advanced genera). A stamen is thus produced which has a well-defined anther attached distally to a well-defined filament. In still more specialized stamens, the line of dehiscence has become highly restricted or changed in orientation or the attachment of the sporangial pairs has become greatly shortened. In a number of both dicot and monocot families, early breakdown of intersporangial wall results in anthers with two instead of the usual four sporogenous locules. Anthers with only two sporangia (not to be confused with locules) have been described from nine families, and one family is reported to produce eight sporangia (Table 28–1).

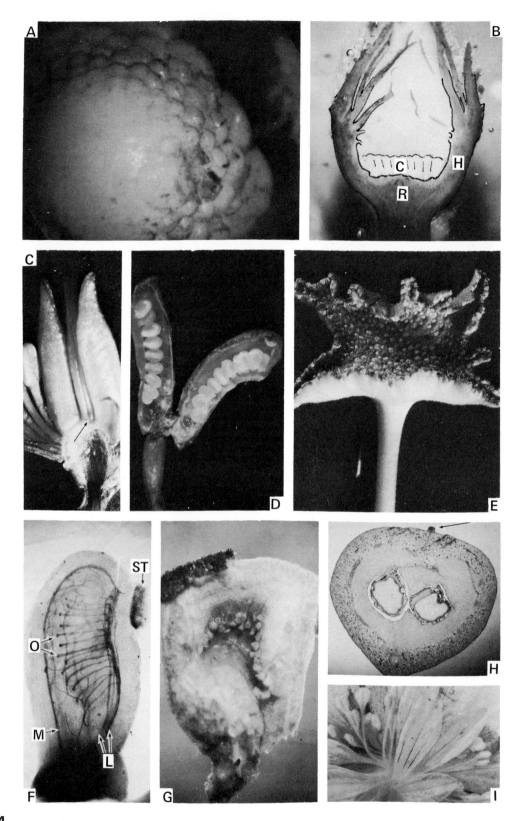

Stamens, like other floral organs, originate from the floral meristem (same as the apical meristem of the reproductive shoot) much the same as do leaves (Fig. 28–2, *A*). The ordinary (nonlaminar) stamen type is soon distinctly two-lobed (Fig. 28–4, *C*, *D*; Fig. 28–6, *E*), or three-lobed if a distal extension is to be formed. The two lateral bulges, it should be noted, are formed very early, before the earliest stages in sporangial initiation. The individual sporangia originate one or two cells beneath the surface (Fig. 28–6, *F*). The sporogenous tissue, tapetum, and inner wall layers are traceable to the subsurface initials (Fig. 28–6, *G*).

In certain angiosperms, such as certain palms, Onagraceae, and so on (Fig. 28–5, *H*), stamens occur in fascicles, the number of which corresponds to the number of parts in the other floral cycles. In such species two concepts of homology are applied, one to individual stamens and the other to the cites of initiation.

In several dicot families, especially those of the Euphorbiales and Bombacales, stamens of unusual form occur that exhibit bifurcations, irregular branching, and variability in locule number. Some have even been described in terms of telomes (Wilson, 1942). The cannon-ball tree, *Couroupita*, bears two kinds of stamens. Its primary stamens are of ordinary form, are present in great numbers (PS in Fig. 28–5, *G*), and are derived from the floral apex. Its secondary stamens (one only shown in Fig. 28–5, *F*) are fleshy stalked, irregularly branched, and do not bear a constant number of anther locules. They are borne on a very specialized stamenophore that originates as a flap of tissue at the base of the primary staminal zone (SSP in Fig. 28–5, *E*), which grows up and over the entire gynoecium and primary androecium (shown half-grown in Fig. 28–5, *G*).

Secondary stamens of a different type occur in the Malvaceae, as illustrated for *Thespesia* (Fig. 28–5, *A* to *D*). The cycle of five primary stamens are shown in primordial stage in *A*, where each one (one outlined) is of quite ordinary form with a distal lobe and two lateral ones. Entirely over the abaxial surface of each primary stamen a number of secondary ones originate as shown in *D*. Even at this stage the overall form of each primary stamen is still comparable to ordinary stamens, although they are fused lengthwise except at their tips (D in *B*, which is a view of the same specimen as is in *D* cut open and viewed from the inside). Only the secondary stamens produce sporogenous tissue, which comes to be continuous across the top of the structure as seen in *C*.

The gynoecium in its primitive state is composed of free, spirally arranged, and leaflike carpels that show no differentiation into ovary, style, and stigma. Most carpels, even of highly specialized gynoecia, are leaflike in primordial stages (Fig. 28–4, *C*, *D*), but they soon fold upward (adaxially or ventrally) or fuse laterally to adjacent carpels producing a closed structure. The later in ontogeny closure of free carpels occurs, the more primitive they are interpreted to be. Those of some Winteraceae (Fig. 28–1, *C*, *F*), Degeneriaceae, some Helobiales, and a few other genera of scattered taxonomic placement are still open at pollination time, but most of these accomplish complete closure later on as the fruit develops. In *Caltha* (Fig. 28–2, *C*) the carpel in the center as viewed at pollination time from its adaxial (ventral) side is still open at its base (arrow).

The stigmatic area of primitive carpels is located along the margins (the dark zone of hairs on each carpel in Fig. 28–1, *C*), and it becomes more restricted as carpel specialization proceeds (Fig. 28–1, *B*, *F*; Fig. 28–2, *F*). In still more specialized forms the stigma becomes elevated on a sterile extension of the

FIGURE 28–2. *A.* Floral apex of *Nuphar* during the initiation of stamen primordia. *B.* Longitudinally cut young flower of *Rosa rugosa* partly inked over. *C, D. Caltha.* The flower in *C* has been cut open longitudinally and the central carpel of the three shown exposes its ventral suture, which is still unfused at arrow. In *D* one carpel is shown split open lengthwise. *E.* Peltate inflorescence of *Dorstenia*, bearing many flowers on its face. *F.* Cleared carpel of *Drimys winteri*. *G.* Split-open carpel of *Exospermum stipitatum*. *H.* Cross section of a carpel in the young fruit stage of *Degeneria*. The arrow indicates the conduplicate margin. *I.* Flower of a mutant form of *Hepatica* with leafy carpels. H = hypanthium; C = carpels; R = receptacle; ST = stigmatic area; O = ovule attachments; M = median or dorsal vein; L = lateral or ventral veins.

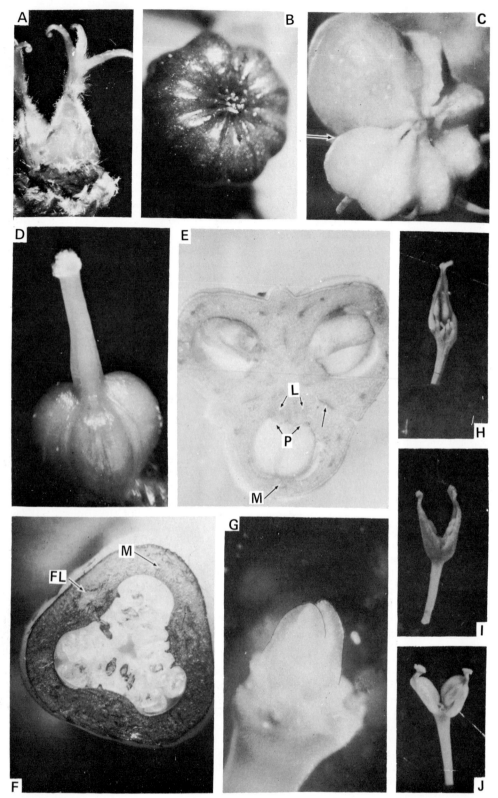

FIGURE 28–3. *A.* Gynoecium of *Fagus*. *B, C. Phytolacca octandra.* In *B* the gynoecium is shown at pollination time. In *C* the gynoecium is somewhat older and at one point, at the arrow, adjacent carpels remained unfused. *D, E. Ornithogalum* gynoecium entire and in cross section. *F.* Cross section of the ovary of *Passiflora*. *G.* Carpel primordia of *Ornithogalum* free at their tips and fused basally. *H* to *J.* Carpeloid stamens of *Salix*. L = lateral veins of carpel; P = placentae; M = median vein of carpel; FL = fused lateral veins of carpel.

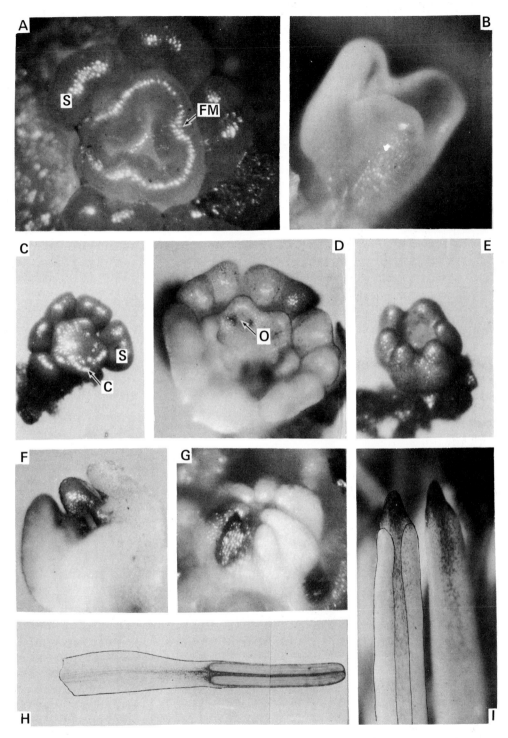

FIGURE 28-4. *A*. Very young flower of *Lilium tigrinum*. *B*. Carpel primordia of *Passiflora* free distally and fused basally. *C* to *G*. Gynoecial development in *Phytolacca octandra*. *H*. Stamen of *Nymphaea*. *I*. Stamens of *Magnolia soulangiana*. S = stamen; FM = fused margins of two adjacent carpels; C = carpel; O = ovule.

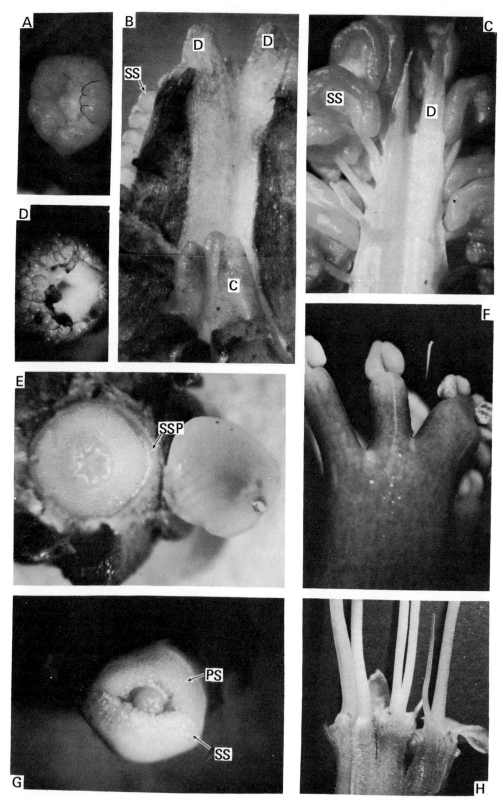

FIGURE 28–5. *A* to *D*. Primary and secondary stamen development in *Thespesia*. *E* to *G*. *Couroupita*. Two stages in the development of the secondary stamenophore shown in *E, G. F* shows one secondary stamen from a mature stamenophore. *H*. Bases of stamen fascicles in *Fuchsia*. SS = secondary stamen; D = distal portion of primary stamen; C = carpel; SSP = secondary stamenophore; PS = primary stamens.

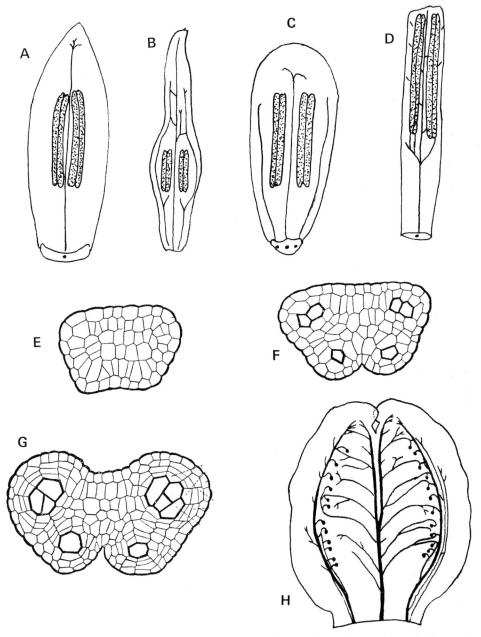

FIGURE 28–6. *A* to *D*. Laminar stamens. *A. Austrobaileya. B. Himantandra. C. Degeneria. D. Nuphar. E* to *G*. Three stages in stamen development in *Chrysanthemum. H*. Carpel of *Drimys* artificially opened and planated. *A* to *C* redrawn from Canright (1952); *D* redrawn from Moseley (1958); *E* to *G* from Wettstein (1911) after Warming; *H* redrawn from Bailey and Nast (1943).

carpel, the style (Fig. 28–1, *D*, shown abscissed in *E*; Fig. 28–3, *B*, in the compound state in *A*, *D*).

The primitive carpel is supplied by three major veins, one median (dorsal) and two lateral (ventral) (shown cleared in Fig. 28–2, *F*; opened out in Fig. 28–6, *H*). The ovules are in two marginal or submarginal lines shown in

TABLE 28–1. Frequency of occurrence of certain features of the angiosperm life cycle. The familes are those of Hutchinson (1959), who recognizes 342 families among the dicots and 69 families among the monocots. Data from Davis (1966).

Feature		Total No. Families	No. Dicot Families	Notes
Microsporangia per				
stamen	4	190	159	Irrespective of number
	2	9	7	of locules
	8		1	Bixaceae
Pollen shed in tetrads				
consistently		4	4	
inconsistently		8	6	
Pollen in masses (pollinia)		2	1	Orchidaceae, Asclepiadaceae
Pollen shed in				
2–celled condition		137	115	
3–celled condition		55	14	
variable		51		
Ovules				
anatropous		204	172	Other types rare; many
orthotropous		20	14	families variable; no ovules
hemianatropous		13		in Balanophoraceae & Loranthaceae
Ovules				
with 2 integuments		208	155	No integuments in some
with 1 integument		90	90	Olaceae
feature variable		15	13	
Micropyle formed by				Micropyle prevented by nucellar
inner integument		88		beak in Trapaceae, some Com-
outer		4		melinaceae, some Euphorbiaceae
both integuments		74		
variable		23		
Megaspore tetrad of four		221		In nearly all the tetrad is linear;
distinct cells				rare instances of tetrahedral
				tetrads reported
Micropylar megaspore		2		Variable in a few other families
functional				and genera
Female-gametophyte type				
Polygonum		239	207	
Allium		4	3	
Adoxa		1		Adoxaceae
Drusa		1		Limnanthaceae
Penaea		1		Penaeaceae
Oenothera		1		Onagraceae
Non consistent		48		Euphorbiaceae, Compositae, and Liliaceae produce six different types each

the split-open carpel of *Caltha* in Fig. 28–2, *D*. Vascular supplies to ovules are all or nearly all derived from the two lateral veins of the carpel. In the families Winteraceae and De-generiaceae the lines of ovules are quite far removed from the margins. The sterile zone between the ovular line and the margin of the carpel (Fig. 28–6, *H*; the ridge at arrow in the young fruit of *Degeneria* in Fig. 28–2, *H*; the broad zone between the ovules and the stigmatic mustache in Fig. 28–2, *G* of each side comes to be situated face to face with that of the other, and the two thus project as a ridge and are not in contact with the locule. Such a carpel has been termed "conduplicate" and interpreted as "the" primitive angiosperm carpel or as "one of the" primitive carpel types (see Eames, 1961).

Laminar placentation (i.e., that condition in which the ovules are inserted over the inner face of the carpel rather than in two marginal or submarginal series) has frequently been interpreted (but not in this text) as being more primitive than other arrangements. It occurs in the helobialean family Butomaceae, where the placenta is actually in the form of a reticulum. In *Exospermum* in the Winteraceae, instead of two lines of ovular attachments, there are two more or less linear, irregular submarginal zones (one shown in Fig. 28–2, *G*) with an occasional ovule located well out on the inner face of each half of the carpel.

Anomalous open carpels are common in certain genera that produce flowers of various degrees of "doubleness" (i.e., flowers in which stamens and carpels are completely or partly petaloid). It is not uncommon to find in *Paeonia* petaloid carpels with projecting marginal ovules. A mutant individual of *Hepatica* is shown in Fig. 28–2, *I*, in which the stamens were not affected but the carpels are leaflike. The three veins of one are partly drawn in.

Angiosperms, which ordinarily produce unisexual flowers, occasionally produce bisexual ones. Usually when this happens it is merely the result of the appearance of the missing or undeveloped component. In a more unusual case, intermediates between stamens and carpels are formed, as in *Salix* (Fig. 28–3, *H* to *J*). In each carpelloid stamen there is a short style and stigma. The one in *J* was from the proximal end of the catkin and shows well-developed anther tissue and suggestions of outgrowths below. Those in *H* and *J* are more carpelloid and, although still open, are cupped and partly enclose anther tissue below the style and several small ovules below this.

Intercarpellary fusion in compound gynoecia is accomplished in various ways, begins at

various stages in ontogeny, and is expressed to various degrees in the mature syncarpel. In the Violaceae, Passifloraceae, and some other families the individual carpels remain completely open and unfolded with the edge of one fused to that of the next. In *Passiflora* (Fig. 28–3, *F*) the median veins of each carpel (M) and the nearly completely fused pairs of laterals (FL) are recognizable in the ovary wall, and, as a consequence of the mode of fusion, the placentae are parietal. An earlier stage in ovary development in *Passiflora* appears in Fig. 28–4, *B*, in which the distal part of each carpel is free but the basal parts have become fused and the syncarpel at this level is growing as a unit (i.e., by zonal growth). The carpels of a liliaceous gynoecium also fuse laterally while each is completely open (Fig. 28–4, *A*). Zonal growth then results in the syncarpel covering the floral apex. The free tips of each carpel (Fig. 28–3, *G*) grow upward to form the style and stigma (Fig. 28–3, *D*). The fused margins of adjacent carpels become folded inward and their position shifts during ontogeny from parietal (Fig. 28–4, *A*) to central (Fig. 28–3, *E*). This shift may be visualized by placing the tips of ones fingers together and then allowing their back sides to come together from the tips proximally. At maturity in the Liliaceae the two lateral veins (L in Fig. 28–3, *E*) range from completely individual to completely fused, and the walls of adjacent carpels in contact frequently show zones where they have not fused (the arrow in Fig. 28–3, *E*).

A still different kind of carpel fusion occurs in *Thespesia* (Malvaceae). The carpels are distinct and completely folded adaxially (C in Fig. 28–5, *B*) before they fuse to each other outer face to outer face.

A gynoecium, primitive in some respects and specialized in others, occurs in *Phytolacca* (Fig. 28–3, *B*), in which there is a cycle of carpels fused laterally around and over a persistent floral apex. Each carpel bears a single basal ovule and each bears its own style and stigma. Between certain carpels (the arrow in Fig. 28–3, *C*) occasionally there is no fusion. The leaflike carpel primordia grow outward (Fig. 28–4, *C*), then upward (Fig. 28–4, *D* to *G*). The single ovule arises in a median position on the face of each carpel in the position indicated by O in Fig. 28–4, *D*. Each carpel then folds inward to enclose its ovule (in Fig. 28–4, *F* one carpel appears almost closed).

Zonal growth is not restricted to the gynoecium. It is expressed during the development of any individual floral cycle or two or more of them together. The degree of fusion in a mature sympetalous carolla, as an example, is reflective of the size of the individual primordia when a common meristematic zone connects them basally, the relative growth rates of the zone and the free distal tips, and also the duration of ontogeny. In some Rosaceae, as well as probably most other flowering plants in which perigyny is expressed, growth of a single zone formed by basal extension of all floral appendage primordia, except those of carpels, results in a cup-shaped mass of tissue called the hypanthium (H in Fig. 28–2, *B*). The flattened receptacle, R, is below and on it are the carpels, C. The free tips of the other floral appendages are inserted along the rim of the hypanthium. On the basis of vascular anatomy alone the hypanthium appears to be a fusion product of all the floral appendages involved, since their vascular supplies are distinct from the receptacle below. This interpretation is highly simplified, however, since the kind of meristematic growth that produced the hypanthium does not exist in flowers with free parts.

The angiosperm ovule originates as an outgrowth of the placental tissue. A prominent cell differentiates one or at least a very few cells inward from the terete apex, which generally divides periclinally to produce a parietal cell and usually a single megaspore mother cell. Further divisions, usually of the parietal cell, result in the fertile cell becoming more deep-seated. The pattern of divisions that establishes the "megasporangium" is therefore particularly comparable to that which establishes the "microsporangium" in the anther. The sporangium in each case is interpreted, as it was by Eames (1961), as being composed of the sporogenous tissue and the parietal cell or cells and its derivatives. A very different interpretation is necessary if one elects to designate the nucellus as megasporangial wall.

After or at about the same time as the megasporangial initial is differentiated, the ovular envelopes or integuments begin as complete collars below the apex of the nucellus. The bitegmic condition is generally considered primitive, occurring in 209 families (Table 28–1) as opposed to 90 that are consistently unitegmic and 15 in which the feature is inconsistent. Neither the form of the integuments nor the vascularization of ovules in angiosperms gives evidence of multipartedness of individual integuments. Each one is a complete unit from inception. The vascularization varies from very simple to complex, depending on the tissue complexity. As Eames points out: "The vascular system of an ovule resembles in amount and branching the supply to accessory tissues in enlarged, fleshy parts of fruits."

The ovule of the majority of angiosperms (204 families) is anatropous. When so, it is more or less straight but is oriented with its apex toward the base of the funiculus and fused lengthwise to it. Three variations of anatropous ovules appear in Fig. 28–7, *A* to *D*. In *A* and *B* (*Strelitzia*) only the outer integument, forming the outer part of the micropyle, is visible. The flat micropylar face fits flush against the ovarian tissue when *in situ*. In *C* (*Hippeastrum*) both integuments are visible, the inner protruding and forming the micropyle, which is directed into the ovarian cavity. In *D* (*Passiflora*) only the outer integument is visible. The flattened micropylar end is turned and flush against the free part of the funiculus.

The mature megagametophyte or embryo sac of angiosperms most commonly has eight nuclei but varies from four-nucleate to multinucleate and is derived from one, two, or four megaspores. There are more than 10 types of sacs recognized but of these, one, the *Polygonum* or ordinary type, is a constant feature of 239 families, and all other types are relatively uncommon. The *Polygonum* type is monosporic in origin. It begins its development as the functional megaspore enlarges (Fig. 28–8, *A*). Three mitotic divisions of the megaspore nucleus result in eight nuclei (Fig. 28–8, *A* to *D*). These rearrange themselves such that there are three at the chalazal end (the antipodals), three at the micropylar end (the egg apparatus composed of the egg and two synergids), and two in the center or near the micropylar end (the polar nuclei). The polar nuclei frequently fuse with each other before the pollen tube enters the sac (Fig. 28–8, *E*). The nuclei of the egg apparatus become organized cells and enlarge. Antipodals in the

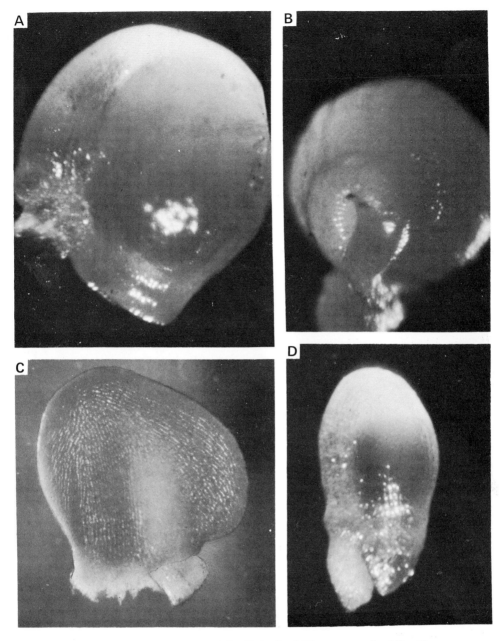

FIGURE 28–7. *A, B*. Ovule of *Strelitzia*; *C*. of *Hippeastrum*; *D*. of *Passiflora*.

mature embryo sac are also generally distinct cells, but in seven families (monocots and dicots) they are not. Multiplication of anti-podals, either cells or free nuclei, occurs in a number of genera in various families. Haus-torial outgrowths occasionally develop from synergids or antipodals or both (Fig. 28–8, *M*).

Synergid extensions frequently seem to serve to plug up the micropyle (Fig. 28–8, *N*).

The *Oenothera* type of embryo sac is very similar to the *Polygonum* type, but in it only two mitoses occur, and of the four nuclei three differentiate as the egg apparatus and one is a polar nucleus. In the disporic *Allium* type two

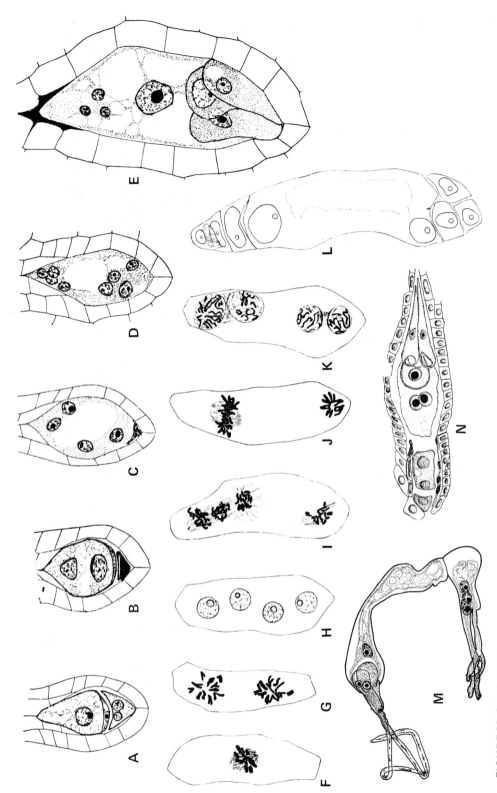

FIGURE 28–8. A to E. Embryo sac development in *Thismia*; F to L in *Lilium*. M. Embryo sac of *Quichamalium* showing synergid (upper left) and antipodal (lower right) haustoria. N. Ovule of *Cotula* in which synergid extensions have grown into the micropyle. A to E after Pfeiffer (1918); F to L after Cooper (1935); M after Johri and Agarwal (1965); N after Davis (1962).

megaspore nuclei in a common wall go through two divisions to form an eight-nucleate sac similar in structure to the Polygonum type.

The *Fritillaria* type, which is one of the tetrasporic types, develops as follows (Fig. 28–8, *F* to *L*). Meiosis takes place without wall formation (*F*, *G*). Each of the four megaspore nuclei in the first four-nucleate stage (*H*) then begins division (*I*). During this division (or later according to species) the nuclear material and spindles of the three at the chalazal end fuse (*J*). The divisions are completed and the second four-nucleate stage with two triploid and two haploid nuclei is formed (*K*). Another division results in the eight-nucleate sac and the nuclei then act as do those in the *Polygonum* type of sac. There are thus three triploid antipodals, three haploid cells in the egg apparatus, and a pair of polar nuclei, one haploid and one triploid (*L*).

The microgametophytes of angiosperms are shed as pollen grains in the two-celled condition in 137 families or in the three-celled condition in 55 others. In 51 families the feature is not constant. When there are two cells, one is a tube cell and the other the generative cell. The three-celled condition results from the precocious division of generative cell to form two sperm, which more generally occurs after the pollen tube begins to grow on the stigma. Pollen transfer is accomplished by vectors such as insects, birds, wind, or water. Insect pollination may be the more fundamental mode, but this interpretation has often been rejected. It is certain that within angiosperms insect pollination has on occasion been derived from wind pollination, and vice versa. Beetle pollination has often been considered the most primitive mode, but the very great destructiveness of flower-visiting beetles makes it hard to accept the interpretation that flowering plants ever were at a state of adaptation in which they depended on them.

The pollen tube extends itself and grows ultimately into the ovarian cavity. As it does it frequently deposits plugs proximal to its three cells, isolating them from the other parts of the tube. The tube generally grows along and against the ovary wall adjacent to the cavity and into the micropyle. Uncommonly the tube enters the ovule by way of the chalaza as in *Casuarina*. All three nuclei, two sperm, and the tube nucleus enter the embryo sac, where double fertilization takes place. When there are a number of tubes in the vicinity several may enter the same ovule. One sperm fertilizes the egg and the other fuses with the two polar nuclei or their fusion product to form the endosperm nucleus. The endosperm nucleus is triploid in species with the *Polygonum* type of embryo sac, triploid in those with the *Allium* type of embryo sac, diploid in those with the *Oenothera* type, pentaploid in those with the *Fritillaria* type, and of even higher ploidy in those with certain other types.

The endosperm generally develops ahead of the embryo. The early stages are either free-nucleate or cellular. According to genus, the endosperm may or may not be present in the mature seed, but it is generally present at an early stage.

The zygote generally divides transversely. The cell nearer the micropyle (lower one in Fig. 28–9, *B*, *H*) may form the entire suspensor or the other cell may form part of it. In any case the structure comes to be a globular to elongate proembryo inserted on the distal end of a short or elongate, uniseriate or multiseriate suspensor with or without a distinctly enlarged basal cell (Fig. 28–9, *E*, *M*). In dicots the globular proembryo by differential growth soon becomes heart-shaped (Fig. 28–9, *G*), the two lobes representing the cotyledons. The stem apex (epicotyl) develops later in the median apical position. Monocots in general form a single terminal cotyledon with the stem apex developing laterally (Fig. 28–9, *M*, *N*). There is an occasional dicot in which one cotyledon develops and the stem apex forms in an apparent subapical position on the side of the aborted cotyledon. Dicotyledonous embryos develop rarely in monocots (Commelinaceae). There is, therefore, some basis for considering the cotyledons of most monocots as in reality pseudoterminal and their entire embryos as derivatives of dicot types.

The embryo of *Paeonia* (Paeoniaceae in Dilliniales) is at first a large coenocytic cell that gives rise to the functional embryo by budding. This has been considered a unique embryogeny for angiosperms, but not all descriptions are in agreement (see Davis, 1966).

Angiosperms were abundant and diverse by early Upper Cretaceous times and many floras

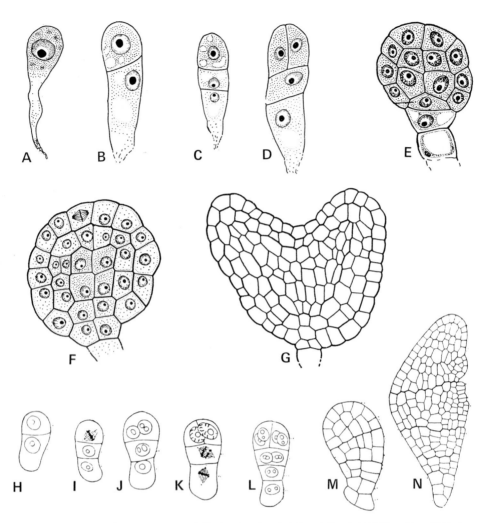

FIGURE 28-9. *A to G.* Embryogeny of *Eluthraria*, after Johri and Singh (1959). *H* to *N.* Embryogeny of *Poa*, after von Guttenberg et al. (1954), by permission of Gustav Fischer Verlag, Jena.

were dominated by them. There are perhaps 30 or more families of angiosperms described as leaf impressions and petrified wood from Early Cretaceous rocks, such as Magnoliaceae, Salicaceae, Araliaceae, Cabambaceae, Platanaceae, Trochodendraceae, Ranunculaceae, Rosaceae, Cucurbitaceae, Fagaceae, and Moraceae. In contrast to those from the Upper Cretaceous, these occurred in floras in which ferns and gymnosperms were dominant.

Pre-cretaceous angiosperms are few in number and the accuracy of the identification of many of them as angiosperms has been questioned, primarily because they are pre-Creta-

ceous. One of the oldest is *Sanmiguelia*, described by Brown (1956). It was a particularly palmlike pleated leaf that was simple, elliptic, 25 cm wide by 40 cm long, and borne on a very tapering stem. The Lower Jurassic *Propalmophyllum*, described as early as 1904, may also be a palm. The mid-Jurassic *Phyllites* is a leaf conforming in many aspects to that of the extant dicot *Cercidiphyllum*. Pollen that may be nymphaeaceous has been described from Jurassic rocks.

The morphology of most dicots may be readily rationalized in terms of modifications of a woody plant body that combines features

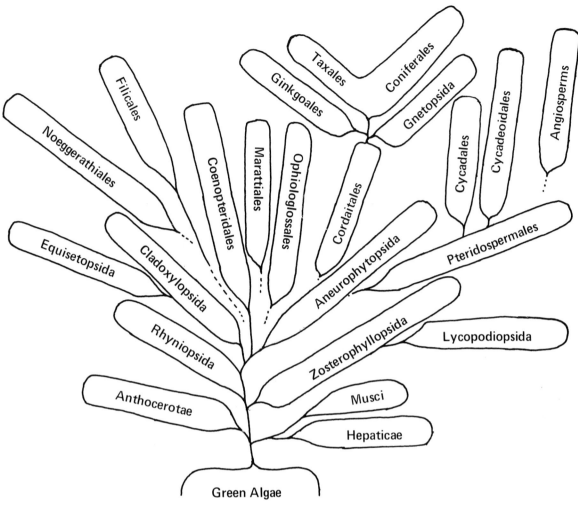

FIGURE 28–10. Interrelationships of land plants. Summary of the interpretations presented in the text.

of the ranalean families Winteraceae, Degeneriaceae, Austrobaileyaceae, Magnoliaceae, Chloranthaceae, Trochodendraceae, Himantandraceae, and in part a few others. Each of the primitive families of the Ranales, as Eames (1961) and others have recognized, is a relict and isolated group, supporting the interpretation that angiosperms arose and differentiated into several lines long before Cretaceous times.

Consistent or recurring features of the gametophyte, the early embryo, the stem apex, the root apex, the phloem, and the xylem indicate strongly and quite definitively to many mor-

phologists that the angiosperms as a whole are of monophyletic origin. Some of the recurring features, such as kinds of vessel perforation plates and of sieve plates and various histological features of the secondary xylem, are certainly of polyphyletic origin, but undoubtedly their recurrence is a manifestation of a common degree of genomic flexibility.

It has not yet been possible to satisfactorily link the woody monocots (palms and some other families), some of which seem to be primitively woody, to the aquatic ones (Butomaceae and related families) or those of aquatic ancestry, nor the apparently primitive

Angiosperms: Reproductive Morphology **527**

Nymphaeaceae and certain families of the amentiferous complex with primitive woody dicots, nor any line of monocots with dicots, even though in each case features may be cited to indicate ultimate affinity. Some of these seemingly separate lines probably converge, possibly as far back as Permian or Triassic times. When the common ancestor (if there is just one) is found it may or·may not be designated an angiosperm, but it will likely possess many of the features of one. The common ancestor has been suggested to be similar to *Gnetum* on the basis of its similarity to angiosperms in embryo sac development and embryo (as compared to *Paeonia*). The ancestor may have been a pteridosperm or pterodosperm derivative of the *Caytonia* or peltasperm or other type, as their ovulate fructifications strongly suggest angiosperm carpels, and outgrowths at the base of certain angiosperm ovules may indicate vestigial cupules (see Meeuse, 1966). The ancestor may be a homosporous fern as Eames (1961) suggests, primarily on the basis of vegetative anatomy and his interpretation that the ovule of angiosperms is an outgrowth of the leaf surface and that its integuments have no organ counterparts. For still additional interpretations see Melville (1960, 1962, 1963), Lam (1950), Takhtajan (1954), and Corner (1949).

Literature Cited

Andrews, H. N., Jr. 1948. Some evolutionary trends in the pteridosperms. *Bot. Gaz.* **110**:13–31. By permission.

———. **1959.** Evolutionary trends in early vascular plants. *Cold Spring Harbor Symp. Quant. Biol.* **24**:217–234. By permission of the author.

———. **1961.** *Studies in Paleobotany.* John Wiley & Sons, New York.

———, and S. N. Agashe. **1965.** Some exceptionally large calamite stems. *Phytomorphology* **15**:103–108.

———, and S. H. Mamay. **1955.** Some recent advances in morphological paleobotany. *Phytomorphology* **5**:272–393.

———, and T. L. Phillips. **1968.** *Rhacophyton* from the Upper Devonian of West Virginia. *J. Linn. Soc. Bot.* **61**:37–64. By permission.

———, T. L. Phillips, and N. W. Radforth. **1965.** Paleobotanical studies in Arctic Canada. I. *Archaeopteris* from Ellesmere Island. *Canad. J. Bot.* **43**:545–554. By permission.

Arnold, C. A. 1947. *An Introduction to Paleobotany.* McGraw-Hill, New York.

Bailey, I. W. 1925. Some salient lines of specialization in tracheary pitting. I. Gymnospermae. *Ann. Bot.* **39**:587–598.

———, and C. G. Nast. **1943.** The comparative morphology of the Winteraceae. II. Carpels. *J. Arnold Arb.* **24**:472–481. By permission.

Balbach, M. K. 1962. Observations on the ontogeny of *Lepidocarpon. Am. J. Bot.* **49**:984–989.

Baldwin, W. K. 1933. The organization of the young sporophyte of *Isoetes Engelmani,* A. Br. *Phil. Trans. Roy. Soc. London* **27**:1–19. Figs. 5–7 J–K reproduced by permission of the Royal Society of Canada from W. K. W. Baldwin's article, "The Organization of the Young Soporophyte of Isoëtes Engelmanni, A. Br." in *Proceedings and Transactions of the Royal Society of Canada,* 3d ser., XXVII (1933), Section II, 13.

Ball, E. 1941. The development of the shoot apex and of the primary thickening meristem in *Phoenix canariensis* Chaub., with comparisons to *Washingtonia filifera* Wats. and *Trachycarpus excelsa* Wendl. *Am. J. Bot.* **28**:820–832.

Banks, H. P. 1960. Notes on Devonian lycopods. *Senckenbergiana Biol.* **41**:59–88. By permission of the author.

———. **1964.** Putative Devonian ferns. *Mem. Torrey Bot. Club* **21**:10–25.

———. **1968a.** The early history of land plants. *Symposium on Evolution and Environment,* E. T. Drake, ed. Yale University Press, New Haven, (pp. 73–107). By permission of the author.

———. **1968b.** The stratigraphic occurrence of early land plants and its bearing on their origin. In *Proceedings of the International Symposium on the Devonian System,* D. Oswald, ed. Calgary, Alberta, Canada.

————, and M. R. Davis. 1969. *Crenaticaulis*, a new genus of Devonian plant allied to *Zosterophyllum*, and its bearing on the classification of early land plants. *Am. J. Bot.* **56**:436–449.

Bannan, M. W. 1958. An occurrence of perforated tracheids in *Thuja occidentalis* L. *New Phytol.* **57**:132–134.

Barnard, P. D. 1959. On *Eosperma oxroadense* gen. et sp. nov.: A new Lower Carboniferous seed from East Lothian. *Ann. Bot.* **23**:285–296. By permission.

Baxter, R. W. 1950. *Peltastrobus Reedae*: A new sphenopsid cone from the Pennsylvanian of Indiana. *Bot. Gaz.* **112**:174–182.

————. 1951. *Ankyropteris glabra*, a new species of the Zygopteridaceae. *Am. J. Bot.* **38**:440–452. By permission of author and publisher.

————. 1963. *Calamocarpon insignis*, a new genus of heterosporous, petrified calamitean cones from the American Carboniferous. *Am. J. Bot.* **50**:469–477.

Beck, C. B. 1958. *Levicaulis arranensis*, gen. et. sp. nov., a lycopsid axis from the Lower Carboniferous of Scotland. *Trans. Roc. Soc. Edinburgh* **58**:445–457.

————. 1960. The identity of *Archaeopteris* and *Callixylon*. *Brittonia* **12**:351–368.

————. 1962. Reconstruction of *Archaeopteris*, and further considerations of its phylogenetic position. *Am. J. Bot.* **49**:372–382. By permission of author and publisher.

————. 1967. *Eddya sullivanensis*, gen. et sp. nov., a plant of gymnospermic morphology from the Upper Devonian of New York. *Palaeontographica* **121**:1–22. By permission of the author.

Belajeff, W. 1885. Antheridien der heterosporen Lycopodiaceen. *Bot. Zeit.* **43**:793–802, 809–819.

————. 1898. Prothallien der Wasserfarne (Hydropterides) *Bot. Zeit.* **56**:141–194.

Bell, P. R. 1960. The morphology and cytology of sporogenesis of *Trichomanes proliferum* Bl. *New Phytol.* **59**:53–59.

Bertrand, P. 1911. Structure des stipes d'*Asteroclaena laxa* Stenzel. *Mem. Soc. Geol. Nord.* **7**:1–72. By permission.

Bierhorst, D. W. 1953. Structure and development of the gametophyte of *Psilotum nudum*. *Am. J. Bot.* **40**:649–658.

————. 1954a. The gametangia and embryo of *Psilotum nudum*. *Am. J. Bot.* **41**:274–281.

————. 1954b. The origin of branching in the aerial shoot of *Psilotum nudum*. *Virginia J. Sci.* **5**:72–78.

————. 1954c. The subterranean sporophytic axes of *Psilotum nudum*. *Am. J. Bot.* **41**:732–739.

————. 1955. A note on spore germination in *Psilotum nudum*. *Virginia J. Sci.* **6**:96.

————. 1956. Observations on the aerial appendages in the Psilotaceae. *Phytomorphology* **6**:176–184.

————. 1958a. Observations on the gametophytes of *Botrychium virginianum* and *B. dissectum*. *Am. J. Bot.* **45**:1–9.

————. 1958b. Systematic changes in the shoot apex of *Psilotum*. *Bull. Torrey Bot. Club* **85**:231–241.

————. 1958c. The tracheary elements of *Equisetum* with observations on the ontogeny of the internodal xylem. *Bull. Torrey Bot. Club* **85**:416–433.

————. 1958d. Vessels in *Equisetum*. *Am. J. Bot.* **45**:534–537.

————. 1959. Symmetry in *Equisetum*. *Am. J. Bot.* **46**:170–179.

————. 1960. Observations on tracheary elements. *Phytomorphology* **10**:249–305.

————. 1965. Older gametophytes and young sporophytes of *Schizaea melanesica*. *Bull. Torrey Bot. Club* **92**:475–488.

————. 1966. The fleshy, cylindrical, subterranean gametophyte of *Schizaea melanesica*. *Am. J. Bot.* **53**:123–133.

————. 1967. The gametophyte of *Schizaea dichotoma*. *Am. J. Bot.* **54**:538–549.

————. 1968a. Observations on *Schizaea* and *Actinostachys* spp., including *A. oligostachys*, sp. nov. *Am. J. Bot.* **55**:87–108.

———. **1968b.** On the Stromatopteridaceae (fam. nov.) and the Psilotaceae. *Phytomorphology* **18**:232–268.

———. **1969a.** On *Stromatopteris* and its ill-defined organs. *Am. J. Bot.* **56**:160–174.

———. **1969b.** Leaf development in *Schizaea* and *Actinostachys*. *Am. J. Bot.* **56**:860–870.

———, and P. M. Zamora. **1965.** Primary xylem elements and element associations of angiosperms. *Am. J. Bot.* **52**:657–710.

Binford, R. **1907.** The development of the sporangium of *Lygodium*, *Bot. Gaz.* **44**:214–224.

Bonamo, P. M. **1966.** *Tetraxylopteris Schmidtii*: The fertile branching system. Thesis, Cornell Univ., Ithaca, N.Y. By permission of the author.

———, and H. P. Banks. **1966.** *Calamophyton* in the Middle Devonian of New York State. *Am. J. Bot.* **53**:778–791.

Boodle, L. A. **1900.** Comparative anatomy of the Hymenophyllaceae, Schizaeaceae, and Gleicheniaceae. I. On the anatomy of the Hymenophyllaceae. *Ann. Bot.* **14**:455–496.

Boullard, B. **1963.** Le gamétophyte des Ophioglossacées. Considérations biologiques. *Bull. Soc. Linn. Normandie* **4**:81–97.

Boureau, E. **1964.** *Traité de paléobotanique*, Vol. III, Sphenophyta, Noeggerathiphyta. Masson et Cie, Paris.

———. **1967.** *Traité de Paléobotanique.* Tome II, Bryophyta, Psilophyta, Lycophyta. Masson et Cie, Paris.

Bower, F. O. **1889.** The comparative examination of the meristems of ferns as a phylogenetic study. *Ann. Bot.* **3**:305.

———. **1894.** Studies in the morphology of spore-producing members. Equisetineae and Lycopodineae. *Phil. Trans. Roy. Soc. London* **185**:473–572.

———. **1896.** *Studies in the Morphology of Spore-Producing Members*, II, Ophioglossaceae. Dulau & Co., London.

———. **1912.** Studies in the phylogeny of the Filicales. II. *Lophosoria*, and its relation to the Cyatheoideae and other ferns. *Ann. Bot.* **26**:269–323. By permission of the Clarendon Press.

———. **1917.** Studies in the phylogeny of the Filicales. VI. The "acrostichoid" condition, with special reference to dipterid derivatives. *Ann. Bot.* **31**:1–39. By permission of the Clarendon Press.

———. **1913.** Studies in the phylogeny of the Filicales. III. On *Metaxya* and certain other relatively primitive ferns. *Ann. Bot.* **27**:443–477.

———. **1918.** Studies in the phylogeny of the Filicales. VII. The Pteroideae. *Ann. Bot.* **32**:1–68. By permission of the Clarendon Press.

———. **1923, 1926, 1928.** *The Ferns*, Vols. I, II, and III. Cambridge University Press, New York. By permission of the publisher.

Brown, R. W. **1956.** Palmlike plants from the Dolores formation (Triassic) of southwestern Colorado. *U. S. Geol. Survey Prof. Paper* **274–H**:205–209.

Browne, I. **1933.** The *Noeggerathiae* and *Tingiae*. *New Phytol.* **32**:344–358. By permission.

Bruchmann, H. **1898.** *Über die Prothallien und Keimpflanzen mehrer europaischer Lycopodien.* Gotha.

———. **1904.** Ueber das Prothallium und die Keimpflanze von *Ophioglossum vulgatum* L. *Bot. Zeit.* **62**:227–247.

———. **1909.** Vom Prothallium der grossen Sporen und von der Keimes-Entwicklung einiger *Selaginella*-anten. *Flora* **99**:12–51. By permission.

———. **1910.** Die Keimung der Sporen und die Entwicklung der Prothallien von *Lycopodium clavatum*, *L. annotinum* und *L. selago*. *Flora* **101**:220–267. By permission.

———. **1912.** Zur Embryologie der Selaginellaceen. *Flora* **104**:180–224. By permission.

Buchholz, J. T. **1931.** The suspensor of *Sciadopitys*. *Bot. Gaz.* **92**:243–262. By permission.

———. **1940.** The Embryogeny of *Torreya* with a note on *Austrotaxus*. *Bull. Torrey Bot. Club* **67**:731–754.

————, and J. W. Selett. 1941. The hybridization of water ferns—*Marsilea* and *Pilularia*. *Am. J. Bot.* **75**:90–93.

Bucur, E. 1935. *Cambium si tesuturi vasculare secunadre la monocotiledonate*. Thesis, Univ. din Bucuresti.

Burges. N. A. 1935. Additions to our knowledge of the flora of the Narrabeen stage of the Hawkesbury Series in New South Wales. *Proc. Linn. Soc. New South Wales* **60**:257–264.

Caldwell, O. W. 1907. *Microcycas calocoma*. *Bot. Gaz.* **44**:118–141.

Campbell, D. H. 1904. Affinities of the Ophioglossaceae and Marsileaceae. *Am. Nat.* **38**:761–775.

————. 1905. *The Structure and Development of Mosses and Ferns*, 2nd ed. Macmillan, New York.

————. 1907. Studies on the Ophioglossaceae. *Ann. Jard. Bot. Buitenzorg* **6**:138–194.

————. 1911. The Eusporangiatae. *Carnegie Inst. Publ. No. 140*.

————. 1928. *The Structure and Development of Mosses and Ferns*, 3rd ed. Macmillan, New York.

Campbell, E. O. 1936. The embryo and stelar development of *Histiopteris incisa*. *Trans. Roy. Soc. New Zealand* **66**:1–11. By permission.

Canright, J. E. 1952. The comparative morphology and relationships of the Magnoliaceae. I. Trends of specialization in the stamen. *Am. J Bot.* **39**:484–497. By permission of the author.

————. 1955. The comparative morphology and relationships of the Magnoliaceae. IV. Wood and nodal anatomy. *J. Arnold Arb.* **36**:119–140.

Cardiff, I. D. 1905. Development of sporangium in *Botrychium*. *Bot. Gaz.* **39**:340–347.

Chaloner, W. G. 1967. Spores and land-plant evolution. *Rev. Palaeobot. Palynol.* **1**:83–93. By permission of the author.

————. 1968. The cone of *Cycostigma kiltorkense* Haughton, from the Upper Devonian of Ireland. *J. Linn. Soc. Bot.* **61**:25–36.

————, and M. A. Pettitt. 1964. A seed megaspore from the Devonian of Canada. *Paleontology* **7**:29–36.

Chamberlain, C. J. 1909. Spermatogenesis in *Dioon edule*. *Bot. Gaz.* **47**:215–236. By permission of The University of Chicago Press, publisher.

————. 1910. Fertilization and embryogeny in *Dioon edule*. *Bot. Gaz.* **50**:415–429. By permission of The University of Chicago Press, publisher.

————. 1916. *Stangeria paradoza*. *Bot. Gaz.* **61**:353–372. By permission of The University of Chicago Press, publisher.

————. 1935. *Gymnosperms. Structure and Evolution*. The University of Chicago Press, Chicago.

Cheadle, V. I. 1944. Specialization of vessels within the xylem of each organ in the Monocotyledoneae. *Am. J. Bot.* **31**:81–92.

————. 1948. Observations on the phloem in Monocotyledoneae. II. Additional data on the occurrence and phylogenetic specialization in structure of the sieve tubes in metaphloem. *Am. J. Bot.* **35**:129–131.

Chiarugi, A. 1960. Tavole chromosomiche delle Pteridophyta. *Caryologia* **13**:27–150.

Chrysler, M. A. 1910. The fertile spike in Ophioglossaceae. *Ann. Bot.* **24**:1–18.

————. 1943. The vascular structure of the leaf of *Gleichenia*. I. The anatomy of the branching region. *Am. J. Bot.* **30**:735–743. By permission.

————. 1944. The vascular structure of the leaf of *Gleichenia*. II. The petiolar bundle. *Am. J. Bot.* **31**:483–491. By permission.

Conrad, H. S. 1908. The structure and life-history of the hay-scented fern. *Carnegie Inst. Publ. 94*. By permission,

Cookson, I. C. 1949. Yeringian (Lower Devonian) plant remains from Lilydale, Victoria, with notes on a collection from a new locality in the Siluro-Devonian sequence. *Mem. Nat. Mus. Melbourne* **16**:117–131. By permission.

Cooper, D. C. 1935. Macrosporogenesis and development of the embryo-sac of *Lilium henryi*. *Bot. Gaz.* **97**:346–355. By permission of The University of Chicago Press, publisher.

Copeland, E. B. 1947. *Genera Filicum*. Ronald Press, New York.

Corner, E. J. H. 1949. The Durian theory or the origin of the modern tree. *Ann. Bot.* **13**:367–414.

Coulter, J. M., and C. J. Chamberlain. 1910. *Morphology of Gymnosperms*. The University of Chicago Press, Chicago.

Croft, W. N., and W. H. Lang. 1942. The Lower Devonian flora of the Senni beds of Monmouthshire and Dreconshire. *Phil. Trans. Roy. Soc. London* **231B**:131–163.

Cross, G. L. 1931. Embryology of *Osmunda cinnamomea*. *Bot. Gaz.* **92**:210–217. By permission of The University of Chicago Press, publisher.

Cutter, E. G. 1957. Studies of morphogenesis in the Nymphaeaceae. I. Introduction: Some aspects of the morphology of *Nuphar lutea* (L.) Sm. and *Nymphaea alba* L. *Phytomorphology* **7**:45–56.

————. 1964. Observations on leaf and bud formation in *Hydrocharis morsus-ranae*. *Am. J. Bot.* **51**:318–324.

Daber, R. 1960. *Eogaspesiea gracilis* n. g. n. sp. *Geologie* **4**:418–425.

Darnell-Smith, G. P. 1917. The gametophyte of *Psilotum*. *Trans. Roy. Soc. Edinb.* **52**:79–91. By permission.

Daugherty, L. H. 1960. *Itopsidema*, a new genus of the Osmundaceae from the Triassic of Arizona. *Am. J. Bot.* **47**:771–777.

Davis, G. L. 1962. Embryological studies in the Compositae. I. Sporogenesis, gametogenesis, and embryogeny in *Cotula australis* (Less.) Hook. F. *Austral. J. Bot.* **10**:1–12. By permission.

————. 1966. *Systematic Embryology of the Angiosperms*. Wiley, New York.

Dawson, J. W. 1859. On fossil plants from the Devonian rocks of Canada. *Quart J. Geol. Soc. London* **15**:477–488.

————. 1871. The fossil plants of the Devonian and Upper Silurian formations of Canada. *Geol. Survey Canada* 1–92.

Delevoryas, T. 1953. A new male cordaitean fructification from the Kansas Carboniferous. *Am. J. Bot.* **40**:144–150.

————. 1955. A *Palaeostachya* from the Pennsylvanian of Kansas. *Am. J. Bot.* **42**:481–488. By permission of the author.

————. 1962. *Morphology and Evolution of Fossil Plants*. Holt, Rinehart and Winston, New York. By permission of the author.

————. 1963. Investigations of North American cycadeoids: Cones of *Cycadeoidea*. *Am. J. Bot.* **50**:45–52. By permission.

————, and J. Morgan. 1954. Observations on petiolar branching and foliage of an American *Botryopteris*. *Am. Midl. Nat.* **52**:374–387. By permission.

Demalsy, P. 1953. Études sur les Hydroptéridales. III. Le sporophyte d'*Azolla nilotica*. *Cellule* **56**:7–60.

Demalsy-Fellar, M. 1957. Études sur les Hydroptéridales. V. Gamétophytes et gamétogènese dans le genre *Marsilea*. *Cellule* **58**:171–207. By permission.

De Sloover, J. L. 1963. Études sur les Cycadales. II. La paroi megasporale chez *Encephalartos poggei* Asch. *Cellule* **63**:331–358.

Dickason, F. G. 1946. A phylogenetic study of the ferns of Burma. *Ohio J. Sci.* **46**:73–107.

Diels, L. 1902. In A. Engler and K. Prantl, *Die Natürlichen Pflanzen Famalien*. Bd. I. Wilhelm Engelmann Verlag, Leipzig.

Doak, C. C. 1932. Multiple male cells in *Cupressus arizonica*. *Bot. Gaz.* **94**:168–182. By permission of The University of Chicago Press, publisher.

Dorf, E. 1934. Lo Devonian flora from Bearthooth Butte, Wyoming, *Bull. Geol. Soc. Am.* **45**:425–440.

Doyle, J. A. 1969. Cretaceous angiosperm pollen of the Atlantic coastal plain and its evolutionary significance. *J. Arnold Arb.* **50**:1–35.

Dwyer, D. M. 1967. *The Apical Meristem of Lycopodium phlegmarioides*. Thesis, Cornell University.

Eames, A. J. 1936. *Morphology of Vascular Plants, Lower Groups*. McGraw-Hill, New York.

————. 1952. Relationships of the Ephedrales. *Phytomorphology* 2:79–100.

————. 1961. *Morphology of the Angiosperms*. McGraw-Hill, New York.

Eggert, D. A. 1961. The ontogeny of Carboniferous arborescent Lycopsida. *Palaeontographica* 108:43–92.

————. 1962. The ontogeny of Carboniferous arborescent Sphenopsida. *Palaeontographica* 110:99–127.

————. 1963. Studies of Paleozoic ferns: The frond of *Ankyropteris glabra*. *Am. J. Bot.* 50: 379–387. By permission of the author.

————. 1964. The question of the phylogenetic position of the Coenopteridales. *Mem. Torrey Bot. Club* 5:38–57. By permission of the author.

———— and T. Delevoryas. 1967. Studies of Paleozoic ferns: *Sermaya*, gen. nov., and its bearing on filicalean evolution in the Paleozoic. *Paleontographica* 120:169–180.

————, and T. N. Taylor. 1966. Studies of Paleozoic ferns: On the genus *Tedelea*, gen. nov. *Palaeontographica* 118:53–73. By permission.

Eicher, D. L. 1968. *Geologic Time*. Prentice-Hall, Englewood Cliffs, N.J.

Emberger, L. 1944. *Les plantes fossiles dan leur rapports avec les végétaux vivants*. Masson et Cie, Paris. By permission.

————. 1954. Sur les Ginkgoales et quelques rapprochements avec d'autres groupes systématiques. *Sv. Bot. Tidskr.* 48:361–367.

Engler, A., and L. Diels. 1936. *Syllabus der Pflanzenfamilien*, Aufl. 11. Gebrüder Borntraeger, Berlin.

Fagerlind, F. 1961. The initiation and early development of the sporangium in vascular plants. *Sv. Bot. Tidskr.* 55:299–312.

Farmer, J. B., and T. G. Hill. 1902. On the arrangement and structure of the vascular strands in *Angiopteris evecta* and some other Marattiaceae. *Ann. Bot.* 16:371–402.

Faull, J. H. 1909. The stele of *Osmunda cinnamomea*. *Trans. Canad. Inst.* 8:515–534.

Florin, R. 1931. Untersuchungen zur Stammesgeschichte der Coniferales und Cordaitales. *K. Sv. Vet–akad. Handl.* 10:1–588.

————. 1951. Evolution in Cordaites and Conifers. *Acta Horti Berg.* 15:285–388. By permission.

Foster, A. S. 1938. Structure and growth of the shoot apex in *Ginkgo biloba*. *Bull. Torrey Bot. Club* 65:531–556.

————. 1959. The morphological and taxonomic significance of dichotomous venation in *Kingdonia uniflora* Balfour f. et W. W. Smith. *Notes Bot. Gard. Edinb.* 23:1–12.

————. 1968. Further morphological studies on anastomoses in the dichotomous venation of *Circaeaster*. *J. Arnold Arb.* 49:52–67.

————, and E. M. Gifford, Jr. 1959. *Comparative Morphology of Vascular Plants*. Freeman, San Francisco.

Foster, D. B. 1964. The gametophytes and embryogeny of five species of *Botrychium*, Thesis, Cornell University, Ithaca, N.Y.

Freeberg, J. A., and R. H. Wetmore. 1957. Gametophytes of *Lycopodium* as grown *in vitro*. *Phytomorphology* 7:204–216.

Frenguelli, J. 1944. Las especies del genero *Zuberia* en la Argentina. *Ann. Mus. Plata* (n.s. Paleontol, sec. B) *No. 1*:1–30.

Fry, W. L. 1954. A study of the Carboniferous lycopod, *Paurodendron*, gen. nov. *Am. J. Bot.* 41:415–428. By permission.

Gaudet, J. L. 1964. Morphology of *Marsilea vestida*. II. Morphology of the adult land and submerged leaves. *Am. J. Bot.* 51:591–597. By permission.

Gensel, P., A. Kasper, and H. N. Andrews. 1969. *Kaulangiophyton*, a new genus of plants from the Devonian of Maine. *Bull. Torrey Bot. Club* 96:265–276.

Gewirtz, M., and A. Fahn. 1960. The anatomy of the sporophyte and gametophyte of *Ophioglossum lusitanicum* L. *Phytomorphology* **10**:342–351. By permission.

Gifford, E. M. 1943. The structure and development of the shoot apex of *Ephedra altissima* Desf. *Bull. Torrey Bot. Club* **70**:15–25.

Goebel, K. 1918. *Organographie der Pflanzen*, 2nd ed. Gustav Fischer, Jena. By permission.

———. 1930. *Organographie der Pflanzen*, 3rd ed. Gustav Fischer, Jena. By permission.

Gordon, W. T. 1910. A note on the prothallus of *Lepidodendron veltheimianum*. *Ann. Bot.* **24**:821–822. By permission of the Clarendon Press.

Grand'Eury, C. 1887. Mémoire sur la flore carbonifère der département de la Loire et du centre de la France. *Mém. l'Acad. Sci. Inst. France* **24**.

Greguss, P. 1955. *Identification of Living Gymnosperms on the Basis of Xylotomy*. Akadémiai Kiadq, Budapest.

Grierson, J. D., and H. P. Banks. 1963. Lycopods of the Devonian of New York State. *Palaeontogr. Am.* **4**:219–280.

Gunckel, J. E., and R. H. Wetmore. 1946, Studies of development in long shoots and short shoots of *Ginkgo biloba* L. *Am. J. Bot.* **33**:285–295.

Gwynne-Vaughan, D. T. 1901. Observations on the anatomy of solenostelic ferns. I. *Loxsoma*. *Ann. Bot.* **15**:71–91.

———. 1902. On an unexplained point in the anatomy of *Helminthostachys zeylanica*. *Ann. Bot.* **16**:170–173.

Hagemann, W. 1965. Vergleichende Untersuchungen zur Entwicklungsgeschichte des Farnsprosses. II. Die Blattentwicklung in der Gattung *Adiantum* L. *Beitr. Biol. Pflanz.* **41**: 405–468.

———. 1967. Bemerkungen zur Entwicklung und Differenzierung des Farnblattes und das Fiederwachstum von *Regnellidium diphyllum* Lindm. *Zeit. Pflanzenphysiol.* **57**:26–45.

Hall, J. 1952. The phloem of *Heterangium*. *Am. Midl. Nat.* **47**:763–768.

Halle, T. G. 1933. The structure of certain fossil spore-bearing organs. *Sv. Vet-akad. Handl.* **12**:5. By permission.

Hara, N. 1962. Histogenesis of the venation in the pinnule of *Matteuccia Struthiopteris* Todaro. *Sci. Pap. Coll. Gen. Educ. Univ. Tokyo* **12**:57–63.

———. 1964. Ontogeny of the reticulate venation in the pinna of *Onoclea sensibilis*. *Bot. Mag. Tokyo* **77**:381–387.

Harms, V. L., and G. A. Leisman. 1961. The anatomy of certain *Cordaites* leaves. *J. Paleontol.* **35**:1041–1064.

Harris, T. M. 1935. The fossil flora of Scoresby Sound, East Greenland. Part 4. Ginkgoales, Coniferales, Lycopodiales and isolated fructifications. *Meddeleser om Grönland* **112**:1–176.

———. 1951. The relationships of the Caytoniales. *Phytomorphology* **1**:29–39. By permission.

Hauke, R. L. 1957. The stomatal apparatus of *Equisetum*. *Bull. Torrey Bot. Club* **84**:178–181.

———. 1968. Gametangia of *Equisetum bogotense*. *Bull. Torrey Bot. Club* **95**:341–345.

Hawkins, L. A. 1907. The development of the sporangium of *Equisetum hyemale*. *Ohio Nat.* **7**:122–128.

Helby, R., and A. R. H. Martin. 1965. *Cylostrobus* gen. nov., cones of lycopsidean plants from the Narrabeen group (Triassic) of New South Wales. *Austral. J. Bot.* **13**:389–404.

Hewitson, W. 1962. Comparative morphology of the Osmundaceae. *Ann. Missouri Bot. Gard.* **49**:57–93. By permission of the author.

Hickling, G. 1907. The anatomy of *Palaeostachya vera*. *Ann. Bot.* **21**:369–386. By permission of the Clarendon Press.

Hill, J. B. 1914. The anatomy of six epiphytic species of *Lycopodium*. *Bot. Gaz.* **58**:61–85.

Hills, L. V. 1967. *Azolla primaeva* and its phylogenetic significance. *Canad. J. Bot.* **45**:1179–1191.

Hirmer, M. 1927. *Handbuch der Paläobotanik*. R. Oldenbourg-Verlag, Munich. By permission.

Høeg, O. A. 1942. The Downtonian and Devonian flora of Spitzbergen. *Norg. Svalbard-Og Ishavs-Undersokel-ser.* **83**:1–228.

Hofmeister, W. 1862. *The Higher Cryptogamia.* Ray Soc., London.

Holloway, J. E. 1918. The prothallus and young plant of *Tmesipteris*. *Trans. New Zealand Inst.* **50**:1–44. By permission of Royal Society of New Zealand.

———. 1935. The gametophyte of *Phylloglossum Drummondii*. *Ann. Bot.* **49**:513–519.

———. 1939. The gametophyte, embryo, and young rhizome of *Psilotum triquetrum* Sw. *Ann. Bot.* (n.s.) **3**:313–336.

———. 1944. The gametophyte, embryo and developing sporophyte of *Cardiomanes reniforme* (Forst.) Presl. *Trans. Roy. Soc. New Zealand* **74**:196–206.

Holttum, R. E. 1954. *A Revised Flora of Malaya*, Vol. II, Ferns of Malaya. Government Printing Office, Singapore. By permission.

———, and U. Sen. 1961. Morphology and classification of the tree ferns. *Phytomorphology* **11**:406–420.

Hopping, C. A. 1956. On a specimen of "*Psilophyton robustius*" Dawson, from the Lower Devonian of Canada. *Proc. Roy. Soc. Edinb.* **66B**:10–28. By permission.

Horner, H. T., Jr., and H. J. Arnott. 1963. Sporangial arrangement in North American species of *Selaginella*. *Bot. Gaz.* **124**:371–383.

Hueber, F. M. 1964. The psilophytes and their relationships to the origin of ferns. *Mem. Torrey Bot. Club* **21**:5–9. By permission of the author.

———, and H. P. Banks, 1967. *Psilophyton princeps*: The search for organic connection. *Taxon* **16**:81–85.

Hutchinson, A. H. 1914. The male gametophyte of *Abies*. *Bot. Gaz.* **57**:148–153. By permission of The University of Chicago Press, publisher.

Hutchinson, J. 1959. *The Families of Flowering Plants*, Vol. I, Dicotyledons; Vol. II, Monocotyledons. Oxford University Press, New York.

Janssen, R. E. 1939. Leaves and stems from fossil forests. *Ill. State Mus. Popular Sci. Sec.* **1**:1–190. By permission of Illinois State Museum.

Jeffrey, E. C. 1896. The gametophyte of *Botrychium virginianum*. *Trans. Canad. Inst.* **5**:265–294.

———, and M. A. Chrysler. 1907. The microgametophyte of the Podocarpineae. *Am. Naturalist* **41**:355–364. By permission of The University of Chicago Press, publisher.

Johnson, D. S. 1898. On the leaf and sporocarp of *Pilularia*. *Bot. Gaz.* **26**:1–24.

Johri, B. M. 1936. Contribution to the life-history of *Cedrus deodara* Loud I. The development of the Pollen Grains. *Proc. Indian Acad. B.* **3**:246–257. By permission.

———, and S. Agarwal. 1965. Morphological and embryological studies in the family Santalaceae. VIII. *Quinchamalium chilense* Lam. *Phytomorphology* **15**:360–372. By permission.

———, and H. Singh. 1959. The morphology, embryology and systematic position of *Elytraria acaulis* (Linn. f.) Lindau. *Bot. Not.* **112**:227–251. By permission.

Jongmans, W. 1954. Contribution to the knowledge of the flora of the seam Girondelle (lower part of Westphalian A) Part I. *Mededel. Geol. Sticht. Ser. C No.* **4**:1–16.

Jongmans, W. J., and P. Kukuk. 1913. Die Calamariaceen des Rheinish-Westfalischen Kohlenbeckens. *Meded. v. Rÿks Herb.* **20**:1–89. By permission.

Kershaw, E. M. 1912. Structure and development of the ovule of *Bowenia spectabilis*. *Ann. Bot.* **26**:625–646.

Khan, R. 1940. A note on "double fertilization" in *Ephedra foliata*. *Curr. Sci. Bangalore* **9**:323–324.

———. 1943. Contributions to the morphology of *Ephedra foliata* Boiss. II Fertilization and Embryogeny. *Proc. Natl. Acad. Sci. India* **13**:357–375. By permission.

Kidston, R. 1925. Fossil plants of the Carboniferous rocks of Great Britain. *Geol. Surv. Great Britain, Mem. Paleontol.* 2.

———, and D. T. Gwynne-Vaughan. 1907. On the fossil Osmundaceae. I. *Trans. Roy. Soc. Edinb.* **45**:759–780. By permission.

————, and W. J. Jongmans. 1917. A monograph of *Calamites* of Western Europe. I. *Mededel Ryks, s'Gravenhage.* **7**:1–207.

————, and W. H. Lang. 1917. Old Red Sandstone plants showing structure from the Rhynie chert bed. Aberdeenshire. I. *Rhynia Gwynne-Vaughani* Kidston and Lang. *Trans. Roy. Soc. Edinb.* **51**:761–784. By permission.

————, and W. H. Lang. 1921. Old Red Sandstone plants showing structure. IV. Restorations of the vascular cryptogams, and discussions of their bearing on the general morphology of the Pteridophyta and the origin of the organization of the land plants. *Trans. Roy. Soc. Edinb.* **52**:831–854. By permission.

Klein, L. 1884. Vergleichende Untersuchungen über Organbildung und Wachsthum am Vegetationspunkte dorsiventraler Farne. *Bot. Zeit.* **577**.

Konar, R. N., and S. Ramchandani. 1958. The morphology and embryology of *Pinus Wallichiana* Jack. *Phytomorphology* **8**:328–346. By permission.

Kon'no, E. 1929. On genera *Tingia* and *Tingiostachys* from the Lower Permian and Permo-Triassic beds of Northern Korea. *Jap. J. Geol. Georg.* **6**: nos. 3–4.

Kräusel, R., and H. Weyland. 1923. Beiträge zur Kenntnis der Devonflora. *Senckenbergiana Biol.* **5**:154–184.

————, and H. Weyland. 1926. Beiträge zur Kenntnis der Devonflora. II *Abhandl. Senckenberg. Naturforsch. Ges.* **40**:115–155. By permission.

————, and H. Weyland. 1930. Die Flora des deutschen Unterdevons. *Abhandl. Preuss. Geol. Landesanst.* (n.f.) **131**:1–92.

————, and H. Weyland. 1932a. Pflanzenreste aus dem Devon. III. Über Hyenia Nath. *Senckenbergiana Biol.* **14**:274–280. By permission.

————, and H. Weyland. 1932b. Pflanzenreste aus dem Devonian. IV. *Senckenbergiana Biol.* **14**:391–403. By permission.

Kubitzki, K., and R. Borchert. 1964. Morphologische Studien an *Isoetes triquetra* A. Braun und Bemerkungen über das Verhältnis der Gattung *Stylites* E. Amstutz zur Gattung *Isoetes* L. Ber. *Deutsch. Bot. Ges.* **77**:227–233.

Kuehnert, C. C. 1967. Developmental potentialities of leaf primordia of *Osmunda cinnamomea*. The influence of determined leaf primordia on undetermined leaf primordia. *Canad. J. Bot.* **45**:2109–2113.

Kulp, J. L. 1961. Geologic time scale. *Science* **133**:1105–1114.

Kupper, W. 1906. Über Knospenbildung an Farnblätter. *Flora* **96**:337–408. By permission.

Labouriau, L. G. 1952. "*Regnellidium diphyllum*" Lindm., a lactescent fern. *Rev. Brasil Biol.* **12**:181–183.

Lachmann, P. 1906. *Origine et développent des racines et des radicelles du Ceratopteris thalictroides*. Paris.

Lagerberg, T. 1906. Zur Entwicklungsgeschichte des *Pteridium aquilinum* (L) Kuhn. *Arkiv. Bot.* **6**:1–28. By permission of Svenska Vetenskapsakademien.

Lam, H. J. 1950. Stachyospory and phyllospory as factors in the natural system of the Cormophyta. *Sv. Bot. Tidskr.* **44**:517–534.

La Motte, C. 1933. Morphology of the megagametophyte and the embryo sporophyte of *Isoetes lithophila*. *Am. J. Bot.* **20**:217–233. By permission.

————. 1937. Morphology and orientation of the embryo of *Isoetes*. *Ann. Bot.* (n.s.) **1**:695–716. By permission.

Lamoureux, C. H. 1961. *Comparative Studies on Phloem of Vascular Cryptogams*. Thesis, University of California at Davis.

Land, W. J. G. 1904. Spermatogenesis and oogenesis in *Ephedra trifurcata*. *Bot. Gaz.* **38**:1–18.

————. 1907. Fertilization and embryogeny in *Ephedra trifurcata*. *Bot. Gaz.* **44**:273–292.

Lang, A. G. 1936. Spermatogenesis in *Marsilea*. *J. Elisha Mitchell Soc.* **52**:307–336.

Lang, W. H. 1902. On the prothalli of *Ophioglossum pendulum* and *Helminthostachys zeylanica*. *Ann. Bot.* **16**:23–56.

————. 1912. On the interpretation of the vascular anatomy of the Ophioglossaceae. *Mem. Proc. Manchester Lit. Phil. Soc.* **56**:1–15.

————. 1914. Studies in the morphology and anatomy of the Ophioglossaceae. II. On the embryo of *Helminthostachys*. *Ann. Bot.* **28**:19–37.

————. 1915. Studies in the morphology and anatomy of the Ophioglossaceae. III. On the anatomy and branching of the rhizome of *Helminthostachys zeylanica*. *Ann. Bot.* **29**:1–54.

Leclercq, S. 1935. Sur un épi fructifère de Sphenophyllales. Première partie. *Ann. Soc. Geol. Belg.* **58**:182–194. By permission of the author.

————. 1957. Étude d'une fructification de Sphenopside à structure conservée du Devonian Superier. *Mem. Acad. Roy. Belg.* **14**:1–39. By permission of the author.

————. 1961. Strobilar Complexity in Devonian Sphenopsids. *Recent advances in Botany. Univ. of Toronto Press* **II**:968–971.

————, and H. N. Andrews, Jr. 1960. *Calamophyton bicephalum*, a new species from the Middle Devonian of Belgium. *Ann. Missouri Bot. Gard.* **47**:1–25. By permission of the author.

————, and H. P. Banks. 1962. *Pseudosporochnus nodosus* sp. nov., a Middle Devonian plant with cladoxylalean affinities. *Palaeontographica* **110B**:1–34.

————, and H. J. Schweitzer. 1965. *Calamophyton* is not a sphenopsid. *Bull. Acad. Roy. Belg.* **11**:1394–1402.

Lehmann-Baerts, M. 1967. Ovule, gametophyte femelle et embryogenese chez *Ephedra distachya* L. *La Cellule* **67**:51–87.

Leisman, G. A. 1964a. *Mesidiophyton paulus* gen. et sp. nov., a new herbaceous sphenophyll. *Palaeontographica* **114**:135–146.

————. 1964b. *Physostoma calcaratum* sp. nov., a tentacled seed from the Middle Pennsylvanian of Kansas. *Am. J. Bot.* **51**:1069–1075.

————, and C. Graves. 1964. The structure of the fossil sphenopsid cone, *Peltastrobus reedae*. *Am. Midl. Nat.* **72**:426–437.

————, and B. M. Stidd. 1967. Further occurrences of *Spencerites* from the Middle Pennsylvanian of Kansas and Illinois. *Am. J. Bot.* **54**:316–323.

Lemoigne, Y. 1966. Les tissues vasculaires et leur histogenèse chez les Lépidophytales arborescentes du Paléozoique. *Ann. Sci. Nat. Botan. Biol. Vegetale* **7**:445–474.

————. 1967. Caractères anatomique d'un fragment de bois appartenant a l'espèce *Walchia* (*Lebachia*) *piniformis* du Permien d'allemagne. *Compt. Rend. Acad. Paris* **265**:595–597.

————. 1968. Observations d'archégones portés par des axes du type *Rhynia gwynne-vaughanii*, Kidston et Lang. Existence de gamétophyte vascularisés au Dévonien. *Compt. Rend. Acad. Paris* **266**:1655–1657. By permission of the author.

————, and F. Schaarschmidt. 1968. Caractères anatomique der bois d'*Ulmannia bronni* Goeppert, d'après des échantillons d'axes feuilles Provenant der Permien d'Allemagne. *Compt. Rend. Acad. Paris.* **266**:875–877.

Lersten, N. 1965. Histogenesis of leaf venation in *Trifolium wormskioldii* (Leguminosae). *Am. J. Bot.* **52**:767–774.

Levittan, E. D., and E. S. Barghoorn. 1948. *Sphenostrobus thompsonii*, a new genus of the Sphenophyllales. *Am. J. Bot.* **35**:350–358.

Lilpop, J. 1937. New plants from the Permo-Carboniferous rocks of Poland. I. *Bull. Intern. Polon. Sci. Lettres* **B(1)**:1–10.

Long, A. G. 1944. On the prothallus of *Lagenostoma ovoides* Will. *Ann. Bot.* (n.s.) **8**:105–117.

————. 1960. On the structure of *Calymmatotheca kidstoni* Calder (emended) and *Genomosperma latens* gen. et sp. nov. from the Calciferous Sandstone Series of Berwickshire. *Trans. Roy. Soc. Edinb.* **64**:29–44.

Loze, J. C. 1965. Étude de l'ontogénese de l'appareil reproducteur femelle de l'If *Taxus baccata* L. *Rev. Cotol. Biol. Vegetale* **28**:211–256.

Lyon, A. G. 1964. The probable fertile region of *Asteroxylon Mackiei* K. and L. *Nature* **203**:1082–1083.

Lyon, H. L. 1905. A new genus of Ophioglossaceae. *Bot. Gaz.* **40**: 455–458.

Mägdefrau, K. 1931. Zur Morphologie und phytogenetischen Bedeutung der fossilen Pflanzengattung *Pleuromeia. Beih. Bot. Cbl.* **48**:119–140.

————. 1932. Über *Nathorstiana*, eine Isotacee aus dem Neokom von Quedlinburg a. Harz. *Beih. Bot. Cbl.* **49**:706–718. By permission of the author.

————. 1966. *Die Geschichte der Pflanzen.* Boehringer u. Soehne, Mannheim.

————. 1967. Die Geschichte der Pflanzen. In G. Heberer, *Die Evolution der Organismen*, S. Aufl., Band 1. Gustav Fisher, Stuttgart. By permission.

Maheshwari, P., and V. Vasil. 1961. The stomata of *Gnetum. Ann. Bot.* (n.s.) **25**:313–319.

Majumdar, G. P. 1942. The origin of siphonostele in three species of *Selaginella* Spr. *Proc. Indian Acad. B.* **15**:172–175.

Mamay, S. H. 1950. Some American Carboniferous fern fructifications. *Ann. Missouri Bot. Gard.* **37**:409–476.

————. 1954. A new sphenopsid cone from Iowa. *Ann. Bot.* **18**:230–239.

————. 1957. *Biscalitheca*, a new genus of Pennsylvanian coenopterids, based on its fructification. *Am. J. Bot.* **44**:229–239. By permission of author and publisher.

————. 1969. Cycads: Fossil evidence of late Paleozoic origin. *Science* **164**:295–296.

————, and H. N. Andrews, Jr. 1950. A contribution to our knowledge of the anatomy of *Botryopteris. Bull. Torrey Bot. Club* **77**:462–494. By permission.

Marchant, C. J. 1968. Chromosome patterns and nuclear phenomena in the cycad families Stangeriaceae and Zamiaceae. *Chromosoma* **24**:100–134.

Marsden, M. P. F., and T. A. Steeves. 1955. On the primary vascular system and the nodal anatomy of *Ephedra. J. Arnold Arb.* **36**:241–258.

Martens, P. 1959. Études sur les Gnétales—III. Structure et ontogenèse du cone et de la Fleur femelles de *Welwitschia mirabilis. La Cellule* **60**:171–286. By permission.

————. 1962. Recherches sur *Welwitschia mirabilis*. III. L'ovule et le sac embryonnaire. Les sacs embryonnes extra-floraux. *Cellule* **63**:309–329.

————, and L. Waterkeyn. 1964. Recherches sur *Welwitschia mirabilis*—IV. Germination et plantules. *La Cellule* **65**:7–68. By permission.

Matten, L. C., and H. P. Banks. 1966. *Triloboxylon ashlandicum* gen. and sp. n. from the Upper Devonian of New York. *Am. J. Bot.* **53**:1020–1027.

Maxon, W. R. 1911. The tree ferns of North America. *Smithsonian Inst. Rep. 2120*:463–491. By permission.

McLean, R. V. 1912. Two fossil prothalli from the Lower Coal Measures. *New Phytol.* **11**:305–318. By permission.

McVeigh, I. 1937. Vegetative reproduction of the fern sporophyte. *Bot. Rev.* **3**:457–497.

Meeuse, A. D. J. 1966. *Fundamentals of Phytomorphology.* Ronand Press, New York.

Melchior, R. C., and J. W. Hall. 1961. A calamitean shoot apex from the Pennsylvanian of Iowa. *Am. J. Bot.* **48**:811–815.

Melville, R. 1960. A new theory of the angiosperm flower. *Nature* **188**:14–18.

————. 1962. A new theory of the angiosperm flower. I. The gynoecium. *Kew Bull.* **16**:1–50.

————. 1963. A new theory of the angiosperm flower. II. The androecium. *Kew Bull.* **17**:1–63.

Metcalfe, C. R., and L. Chalk. 1950. *Anatomy of the Dicotyledons.* Oxford University Press, New York.

Mettenius, G. 1857. *Ueber einige Farngattungen*, Vols. 2 and 3. Abhandlungen der Senckenbergischen Naturforschenden Gesellschaft, Frankfurt.

Meunier, A. 1887. Étude anatomico-genetique du sporocarpe chez la *Pilularia globulifera. Cellule* **4**:1–84.

Miller, C. N., Jr. 1967. Evolution of the fern genus *Osmunda. Contr. Mus. Paleontol. Univ. Mich.* **21**:139–203.

Millington, W. F. 1966. The tendril of *Parthenocissus inserta*: Determination and development. *Am. J. Bot.* **53**:74–81.

Morgan, J. 1959. The morphology and anatomy of American species of the genus *Psaronius*. *Ill. Biol. Monogr.* 27. By permission of The University of Illinois Press.

Mortimer, M. G., and W. G. Chaloner. 1967. Devonian megaspores from the Wyboston borehole, Bedfordshire, England. *Palaeontol.* 10:189–213.

Moseley, M. F., Jr. 1958. Morphological studies in the Nympheaceae. I. The nature of the stamens. *Phytomorphology* 8:1–29. By permission.

Mulay, B. N. 1941. A study of the pistillate plants of *Ephedra foliata* Boiss found at Drigh Road near Karachi in Sind. *Proc. Indian Sci. Congr.* 28, Part III, p. 158.

Nakai, T. 1933. An observation on the gametophyte of *Cheiropleuria bicuspis* var. *integrifolia*. *Bot. Mag. Tokyo* 47:1–5. By permission.

Namboodiri, K. K., and C. B. Beck. 1968. A comparative study of the primary vascular system of conifers. *Am. J. Bot.* 55:447–472.

Nathorst, A. G. 1902. Zur Oberdevonischen Flora der Bäreninsel. *Sv. Vet-akad. Handl.* 36:1–60.

Negi, V., and M. Lata. 1957. Male gametophyte and Megasporogenesis in *Gnetum*. *Phytomorphology* 7:230–236.

Nessel, H. 1939. *Die Bärlappgewächse (Lycopodiaceae)*. Gustav Fischer, Jena.

Ninan, C. A. 1956. Cytology of *Psilotum nudum* (L.) Beauv. (*P. triquetrum* Sw.). *Cellule* 57:307–318.

Nishida, M. 1956. Studies on the systematic position and constitution of Pteriodophyta. 7. Vascular behaviour in the phyllomophore of *Helminthostachys zeylanica* Hooker. *Bot. Mag. Tokyo* 69:76–83. By permission of the author.

———. 1957. Studies on the systematic position and constitution of Pteriodophyta. 10. A further investigation on the vascular dichotomy in the phyllomophore of Ophioglossales, with special reference to phylogeny. *J. Coll. Arts Sci. Chiba. Univ.* 2:179–211.

———. 1962. Systematic position of *Ceratopteris thalictroides*. *J. Japan. Bot.* 37:193–200. By permission of the author.

Nolan, J. R. 1967. *Development Morphology of the Asclepiadaceous Inflorescence*. Thesis, Cornell University.

Norstog, K. 1966. In research report. *Bull. Fairchild Trop. Garden, Miami.*

Ogura, Y. 1938. Anatomie der Vegetationsorgane der Pteridophyten. In K. Linnsbauer, *Handbuch der Pflanzenanatomie*. Gebrüder Borntraeger, Berlin. By permission.

Oliver, F. W. 1909. On *Physostoma elegans* Williamson, an archaic type of seed from Paleozoic rocks. *Ann. Bot.* 23:73–116. By permission of The Clarendon Press.

———, and D. H. Scott. 1904. On the structure of the Palaeozoic seed *Lagenostoma lomaxi*. *Phil. Trans. Roy. Soc. London.* 197B:193–247.

Oltmanns, F. 1922. *Morphologie und Biologie der Algen*. Gustav Fischer, Jena. By permission.

Paliwal, G. S., and N. N. Bhandari. 1962. Stomatal development in some Magnoliaceae. *Phytomorphology* 12:409–412.

Palser, B. F., and V. F. Barrick. 1941. Anatomy and sorus development of *Cystopteris bulbifera*. *Bot. Gaz.* 103:168–176. By permission of The University of Chicago Press, publisher.

Pant, D. D. 1958. The structure of some leaves and fructifications of the *Glossopteris* flora of Tanganyika. *Bull. Brit. Mus. Nat. Hist.* (*Geology*) 3:127–175.

———. 1962. Some recent contributions towards our knowledge of the *Glossopteris* flora. In *Proceedings of the Summer School of Botany*. Darjeerling, pp. 302–319. By permission.

———, and J. Walton. 1961. *Lycostachys protostelicus* gen. et sp. nov. and some associated megaspores from the Lower Carboniferous of Scotland. *Palaeontographica* 108:1–10.

———, and B. K. Verma. 1963. Development of stomata in leaves of *Notonia grandiflora* DC. *J. Indian Bot. Soc.* 42:384–391.

Paolillo, D. J., Jr. 1963. The developmental anatomy of *isoetes*. *Ill. Biol. Monogr.* 31.

Pearson, H. H. W. 1914. Notes on the morphology of certain structures concerned in reproduction in the genus *Gnetum. Trans. Linn. Soc. London. Ser. 2.* **8**:311–330. Published by permission of The Linnean Society of London.

———. 1929. *Gnetales.* Cambridge University Press, New York. By permission.

Petry, L. C. 1915. Branching in the Ophioglossaceae. *Bot. Gaz.* **59**:345–364.

Pettitt, J. M. 1966. A new interpretation of the structure of the megaspore membrane in some gymnospermous ovules. *J. Linn. Soc. Bot.* **59**:253–263.

———, and C. B. Beck. 1967. Seed from the Upper Devonian. *Science* **156**:1727–1728.

———, and C. B. Beck. 1968. *Archaeosperma arnoldii*—A cupulate seed from the Upper Devonian of North America. *Contr. Mus. Paleontol. Univ. Mich.* **22**:139–154.

Pfeiffer, N. E. 1918. The sporangia of *Thismia americana. Bot. Gaz.* **66**:354–363. By permission of The University of Chicago Press, publisher.

Phillips, T. L., and H. N. Andrews, Jr. 1965. A fructification of *Anachoropteris* from the Middle Pennsylvanian of Illinois. *Ann. Missouri Bot. Gard.* **52**:251–261. By permission.

———, and H. N. Andrews, Jr. 1966. *Catenopteris simplex* gen. et sp. nov., a primitive pteridophyte from the Upper Pennsylvanian of Illinois. *Bull. Torrey Bot. Club* **93**:117–128.

———, and G. A. Leisman. 1966. *Paurodendron*, a rhizomorphic lycopod. *Am. J. Bot.* **53**: 1086–1100.

Pichi-Sermolli, R. E. G. 1958. The higher taxa of the Pteridophyta and their classification, in *Systematics of Today*, O. Hedberg, ed. Uppsala Univ., Ursskrift, pp. 70–90. By permission of the author.

———. 1959. Pteridophyta, in *Vistas in Botany*, W. B. Turrill, ed. Pergamon Press, London, pp. 421–493.

———. 1962. Adumbratio Florae Aethiopicae. 8. Gleicheniaceae. *Webbia.* **17**:33–43.

———. 1963. Adumbratio Florae Aethiopicae. 10. Actinopteridaceae. *Webbia* **17**:317–328. By permission of the author.

Pilger, R. 1926. Gymnospermae. In A. Engler and K. Prantl, *Die Natürlichen Pflanzenfamilien. 13. Band.* Wilhelm Engelmann Verlag, Leipzig.

Pixley, E. Y. 1964. *A Study of the Ontogeny of the Primary Xylem in the Roots of Several Lycopodium Species.* Thesis, Cornell University.

Plumstead, E. P. 1952. Description of two new genera and six species of fructifications borne on *Glossopteris* leaves. *Trans. Geol. Soc. S. Africa* **55**:281–328. By permission.

Potonié, H. 1902. In A. Engler and K. Prantl, *Die Natürlichen Pflanzenfamilien. Bd. I.* Wilhelm Engelmann Verlag, Leipzig.

———. 1904. *Pleuromeia Sternbergi* Corda und *Pl. oculina. Abhandl. Besch. Fos. Pflanz. Lief.* **2**.

———, and C. Bernard. 1904. *Flore Dévonienne de l'étage H. de Barrande.* Leipzig.

Potonié, R. 1890. Über einige Carbonfarne ii. *Jahrb. Preuss. Geol. Landes. Berlin.*

Pringsheim, N. 1863. Zur morphologie der *Salvinia natans. Jahrb. Wiss. Bot.* **3**:484–541.

Radczenko, G. P. 1957. Morphological and anatomical characteristics of certain types of plants of the Carboniferous of Kuznetsk province. *Sb. Pamjati A. N. Kryshtofovich, Inst. Bot. Kamarov. Akad. Nauk. S.S.S.R.* 33–54.

Radforth, N. W. 1937. An analysis and comparison of the structural features of *Dactylotheca plumosa* Artis sp. and *Seftenbergia ophiodermatica* Goppert sp. *Trans. Roy. Soc. Edinb.* **59**:385–396. By permission.

Rasskazova, E. S. 1961. Upper Palaeozoic articulates of the Tunguska basin. *Nauchn.-Issled. Inst. Geol. Artiki, Sb. Stat. Paleont. Biostratigr.* **23**:35–76.

Rauh, W., and H. Falk, 1959. *Stylites* E. Amstutz, eine neue Isoetacee aus den Hochanden Perus. *Sitzber. Heidelberg. Akad. Wiss. v.* 1–160. (Figs. 5–1A, from Rauh, W. and H. Falk: Stylites E. Amstutz eine neue Isoëtacee aus den Hochanden Perus. In: Sitzungsberichte der Heidelberger Akademie. Jg. 1959, 1. Abhandlung. Berlin-Göttingen-Heidelberg: Springer 1959. Fig. 5–4 is from Jg. 1959, 2.)

Reed, F. D. 1941. Coal flora studies: Lepidodendrales. *Bot. Gaz.* **102**:663–683.

Remy, R., and W. Remy. 1959. *Pflanzenfossilien.* Akademie-Verlag, Berlin.

———, and W. Remy. 1961. Beitrage zur Flora des Autuniens. II. *Mber. dtsch. Akad. Wiss. Berlin.* 3:213–225.

Renault, B. 1876. Sur les fructifications de quelques végétaux silicifies provenant des gisements d'autun et de Saint-Étienne, *Ann. Sci. Nat. Bot.* (VI) 3:5–29.

———. 1879. Structure comparée de quelques tiges de la flore carbonifère. *Mus. Hist. Nat. Paris. Nouv. Archives Ser. 2.* 2-213–326.

———. 1881. *Cours de botanique fossile*, Vols. 1–4. Paris.

Ren-Chang, C. 1934, 1935. *Icones Filicum Sinicarium*, Fasc. 2 and 3. Fan Memorial Institute of Biology, Peiping.

Renier, A. 1910. *Paleontologie der terrain houiller.* Liege.

Reymanowne, M. 1962. *Pleuromeia rossica* Newburg, nowy gatunek Z Dolnego Triasu Rosju Europejskeij. *Wiadomosci Bot.* 6:327–331.

Rogers, L. M. 1927. Development of the archegone and studies in fertilization in *Lygodium plamatum. Cellule* 37:327–350.

Roth, I. 1963a. Histogenese der Luftsprosse und Bildung der "dichotomen" Verzweigungen von *Psilotum nudum. Advan. Frontiers Plant Sci.* 7:157–180.

———. 1963b. Histogenese und morphologische Deutung der Blätter von *Psilotum nudum. Flora* 153:90–111.

Rouffa, A. S. 1967. Induced *Psilotum* fertile-appendage aberrations. Morphogenetic and evolutionary implications. *Canad. J. Bot.* 45:855–861. By permission of the author.

———. 1968. An appendageless form of *Psilotum. Am. J. Bot.* 55:714 Abstract.

Sadebeck, R. 1902. In A. Engler and K. Prantl, *Die Natürlichen Pflanzen Famalien, Bd. I.* Wilhelm Engelmann Verlag, Leipzig.

Sahni, B. 1932. A petrified *Williamsonia* (*W. Sewardiana*, sp. nov.) from the Rajmahal Hills, India, *Paleont. Indica.* (n.s.) 20:1–19.

Schenk, A. 1867. *Fossil Flora der Grenzschichten des Keupers und Lias Frankens.* Wiesbaden.

Schlanker, C. M., and G. A. Leisman. 1969. The herbaceous carboniferous lycopod *Selaginella fraiponti* Comb. Nov. *Bot. Gaz.* 130:35–41.

Schmalhausen, J. 1879. Jura-Flora Russland. *Mem. Acad. Sci. St. Petersbourg. Ser.* 7:28.

Schopf, J. M. 1965. Anatomy of the axis in *Vertebraria americana. Geophysical Union, Washington, D.C., Antarctic Res. Sec.* 6:217–228.

Schuster, R. M. 1966. *The Hepaticae and Anthocerotae of North America East of the Hundredth Meridian.* Vol. I. Columbia Univ. Press, New York.

Scott, D. H. 1898. On the structure and affinities of fossil plants from the Palaeozoic rocks: On *Cheirostrobus*, a new type of fossil cone, from the Lower Carboniferous strata (Calciferous Sandstone Series). *Phil Trans. Roy. Soc. London* 189B:1–34.

———. 1901. Seed-like fructifications of *Lepidocarpon. Phil. Trans. Roy. Soc. London.* 194B:291–333.

———. 1906. The occurrence of germinating pores in *Stauropteris oldhamia. New Phytol.* 5:170–172. By permission.

———. 1920–1923. *Studies in Fossil Botany.* A. & C. Black, London. By permission of A. & C. Black, Ltd., publishers.

Scott, R. A. 1960. Pollen of *Ephedra* from the Chinle formation (Upper Triassic) and the genus *Equisetosporites. Micropaleontol.* 6:271–276.

Seelinger, I. 1954. Studien am Sprossvegetationskegel von *Ephedra fragilis* var. *campylopoda* (C. A. Mey.) Stapf. *Flora* 141:114–162.

Seward, A. C. 1898. *Fossil Plants.* Cambridge University Press, New York.

Shapiro, S. 1951. Stomata on the ovules of *Zamia floridana. Am. J. Bot.* 38:47–53.

Sharma, U. 1960. Studies on Indian Hymenophyllaceae. I. Contributions to our knowledge of *Crepidomanes latealatum* (V. D. B.) Copeland comb. nov. *Proc. Natl. Inst. Sci. India B.* 26:339–351.

Sharp, L. W. 1912. Spermatogenesis in *Equisetum*. *Bot. Gaz.* **54**:89–119. By permission of The University of Chicago Press, publisher.

———. 1914. Spermatogenesis in *Marsilea*. *Bot. Gaz.* **58**:419–430. By permission of The University of Chicago Press, publisher.

Singh, H. 1961. The life history and systematic position of *Cephalotaxus drupacea* Sieb. et Zucc. *Phytomorphology* **11**:153–197. By permission.

Sinnott, E. W. 1909. On mesarch structure in *Lycopodium*. *Bot. Gaz.* **48**:138–145.

Slade, B. F. 1959. The mode of origin of vein endings in the leaf of *Liriodendron tulipifera* L. *New Phytol.* **58**:299–305.

Slagg, R. A. 1932. The gametophyte of *Selaginella Kraussiana*. *Am. J. Bot.* **19**:106–127. By permission of the American Journal of Botany.

Smith, D. L. 1959. *Geminitheca scotica* gen. et sp. nov.: A pteridosperm from the Lower Carboniferous of Dunbartonshire. *Ann. Bot.* **23**:477–491. By permission.

———. 1964. Secondary cortex in the arborescent lycopods. *New Phytol.* **63**:418–421.

Steeves, M. W., and E. S. Barghoorn. 1959. The pollen of *Ephedra*. *J. Arnold Arb.* **40**:221–255.

Steeves, T. A., and W. R. Briggs. 1958. Morphogenetic studies on *Osmunda cinnamomea* L.— The origin and early development of vegetative fronds. *Phytomorphology* **8**:60–72.

Steil, W. N. 1935. Incomplete nuclear and cell division in the tapetum of *Botrychium virginianum* and *Ophioglossum vulgatum*. *Am. J. Bot.* **22**:409–425.

———. 1939. Apogamy, apospory, and parthenogenesis in the pteridophytes. *Bot. Rev.* **5**: 433–453.

Sterzel, J. T. 1887. Über den Grossen *Psaronius* in der Naturwissenschaftlich Sammlung der Stadt Chemnitz. X. *Ber. d. Naturwissensch. Gesel. zu Chemnitz.*

Stewart, W. N., and T. Delevoryas. 1956. The medullosan pteridosperms. *Bot. Rev.* **22**:45–80. Reproduced by permission of The New York Botanical Garden.

Stockmans, F. 1948. Végétaux du Dévonian supérior de la Belgique. *Mus. Roy. Hist. Nat. Belg. Mem.* **110**:1–85.

Stokey, A. G. 1930. Prothallia of the Cyatheaceae. *Bot. Gaz.* **90**:1–45. By permission of The University of Chicago Press, publisher.

———. 1945. The gametophyte of *Dipteris conjugata*. *Bot. Gaz.* **106**:402–411. By permission of The University of Chicago Press, publisher.

———. 1948. Reproductive structures of the gametophytes of *Hymenophyllum* and *Trichomanes*. *Bot. Gaz.* **109**:363–380. By permission of The University of Chicago Press, publisher.

———. 1950. The gametophyte of the Gleicheniaceae. *Bull. Torrey Bot. Club* **77**:323–339. By permission.

———. 1951. The contribution by the gametophyte to classification of the homosporous ferns. *Phytomorphology* **1**:39–58.

———, and L. R. Atkinson. 1952. The gametophyte and young sporophyte of *Matonia pectinata* R. Br. *Phytomorphology* **2**:138–150. By permission.

———, and L. R. Atkinson. 1956a. The gametophyte of *Loxsoma cunninghami* R. Br. and *Loxsomopsis costaricensis Phytomorphology* **6**:249–261. By permission.

——— and L. R. Atkinson. 1956b. The gametophytes of *Plagiogyria glauca* (BL.) Mett. and *P. semicordata* (PR.) Christ. *Phytomorphology* **6**:239–249. By permission.

———, and L. R. Atkinson. 1956c. The gametophyte of the Osmundaceae. *Phytomorphology* **6**:19–40. By permission.

Stone, I. G. 1958. The gametophyte and embryo of *Polyphlebium venosum* (R. BR.) Copeland (Hymenophyllaceae). *Austral. J. Bot.* **6**:183–203. By permission.

———. 1960. Observations on the gametophytes of *Grammitis billardieri* Willd. and *Ctenopteris heterophylla* (Labill.) Tindale (Grammitidaceae). *Austral. J. Bot.* **8**:11–37. By permission.

Stur, D. 1885. Die Karbonflora der Schatzlarer Schichten. *Abhandl. Geol. Anstalt Wien* **II**:abt.I.

———. 1887. Beiträge zur Kenntnis der Flora der Vorwelt. 2. Die Karbon-Flora der Schatzlarer Schichten. *Abhandl. K. K. Gerl. Reichsanst.* **11**:228–235.

Svenson, H. K. 1944. The new world species of *Azolla*. *Am. Fern J.* **34**:69–100. By permission.

Takhtajan, A. L. 1954. *Origins of Angiospermous Plants*. Soviet Science Press (Am. Inst. Biol. Sci. transl., 1958).

Tansley, A. G. 1907. Lectures on the evolution of the filicinean vascular system. *New Phytol.* **6**:25–35. By permission.

———, and R. B. J. Lulham. 1905. A study of the vascular system of *Matonia pectinata*. *Ann. Bot.* **19**:475.

Taylor, T. N. 1969. Cycads: Evidence from the Upper Pennsylvanian. *Science* **164**:294–295.

Thomas, A. P. W. 1901. Preliminary account of the prothallium of *Phylloglossum*. *Proc. Roy. Soc. London* **69**:285–290.

Thomas, D. E. 1935. A new species of *Calamopitys* from the American Devonian. *Bot. Gaz.* **97**:334–345. By permission of The University of Chicago Press, publisher.

Thomas, H. H. 1911. On the leaves of *Calamites* (*Calamocladus* section). *Phil. Trans. Roy. Soc. London* **202B**:51–92. By permission.

———. 1913. The fossil flora of the Cleveland district. *Quart. J. Geol. Soc. London* **69**:223–251. By permission.

———. 1925. The Caytoniales, a new group of angiospermous plants from the Jurassic rocks of Yorkshire. *Phil. Trans. Roy. Soc. London* **213B**:299–363.

———. 1955. Mesozoic pteridosperms. *Phytomorphology* **5**:177–185. By permission.

———. 1958. *Lidgettonia*, a new type of fertile *Glossopteris*. *Bull. Brit. Mus. (Nat. Hist.) Geol. London* **3**:177–189. By permission.

Thompson, R. P. 1934. Modification of the form of the haustorium in *Marsilea* on development in culture fluid. *Trans. Roy. Canad. Inst.* **20**:69–72. By permission.

Tournay, R. 1951. Études sur les Hydropteridales I. Le sporophyte de *Marsilea*. *Cellule* **54**:165–218. By permission.

Treub, M. 1884. Études sur les Lycopodiacées. *Ann. Jard. Bot. Buitenzorg* **4**:107–138.

Troll, W. 1937. *Vergleichende Morphologie der höheren Pflanzen*. Gebrüder Borntraeger, Berlin.

———. 1967. *Vergleichende Morphologie der höheren Pflanzen*. Gebrüder Borntraeger, Berlin.

Troop, J. E., and J. T. Mickel. 1968. Petiolar shoots in the dennstaedtioid and related ferns. *Am. Fern J.* **58**:64–70.

Tryon, A. 1964. *Platyzoma*—a Queensland fern with incipient heterospory. *Am. J. Bot.* **51**:939–942. By permission.

Tryon, R. 1964. Evolution in the leaf of living ferns. *Mem. Torrey Bot. Club* **21**:73–85.

———. 1965. Paraphyses in the ferns. *Taxon* **14**:213–218.

van der Hammer, L. 1948. Traces of ancient dichotomies in Angiosperms (a contribution to our knowledge of phyllospory and stachyospory). *Blumae* **6**:282–301.

Velenovsky, J. 1905. *Vergleichende Morphologie der Pflanzen*. Fr. Rivnac, Prag.

von Guttenberg, H., H. Heydel, and H. Pankow, 1954. Embryologische Studien an Monolotyledonen. I. Die Entstehung der Primärwurzel bei *Poa annua* L. *Flora* **141**:298–311. By permission.

Voth, P. D. 1934. A study of the vegetative phases of *Ephedra*. *Bot. Gaz.* **96**:298–313.

Wagner, W. H., Jr. 1952. Types of foliar dichotomy in living ferns. *Am. J. Bot.* **39**:578–592.

———. 1963. A remarkably reduced vascular plant in the United States. *Science* **142**:1483–1484.

———. 1964a. The evolutionary patterns of living ferns. *Mem. Torrey. Bot. Club* **21**:86–95.

———. 1964b. Paraphyses: Filicineae. *Taxon* **13**:56–64.

Walker, E. R. 1937. The gametophyte of *Equisetum scirpoides*. *Am. J. Bot.* **24**:40–43. By permission.

Walton, J. 1940. *An Introduction to the Study of Fossil Plants*. A. & C. Black, London. By permission of A. & C. Black, Ltd., publishers.

———. 1957. On *Protopitys* (Göppert): With a description of a fertile specimen "*Protopitys scotica*" sp. nov. from the calciferous sandstone series of Dunbartonshire. *Trans. Roy. Soc. Edinburgh* **63**:333–339.

———, and J. R. Wilson. 1932. On the structure of *Vertebraria*. *Proc. Roy. Soc. Edinb.* **52**: 200–207. By permission.

Wardlaw, C. W. 1924. Size in relation to internal morphology. I. Distribution of the xylem in the vascular system of *Psilotum*, *Tmesipteris*, and *Lycopodium*. *Trans. Roy. Soc. Edinburgh* **53**:503–532.

———. 1944. Experimental and analytical studies of Pteridophytes. IV. Stelar morphology: The initial differentiation of vascular tissues. *Ann. Bot. N.S.* **8**:173–188.

Webster, T. R., and T. A. Steeves. 1964. Developmental morphology of the root of *Selaginella kraussiana* A. Br. and *Selaginella wallacei* Hieron. *Canad. J. Bot.* **42**:1665–1676.

Weiss, C. E. 1876. Beiträge zur fossilen Flora Steinkohlen-Calamarien, mit besonderer Berücksichtigung ihrer Fruktifikationen. *Abhandl. Geol. Spez. Press. Thüring. Staat.* **2**:1–149.

Weiss, F. E. 1902. The vascular branches of stigmarian rootlets. *Ann. Bot.* **16**:559.

Wettstein, R. 1911. *Handbuch der Systematischen Botanik*. Franz Deuticke, Leipzig.

White, R. A. 1961. Vessels in roots of *Marsilea*. *Science* **133**:1073.

———. 1963. Tracheary elements of the ferns. II. Morphology of tracheary elements; conclusions. *Am. J. Bot.* **50**:514–522.

Wieland, G. R. 1906. American fossil cycads. *Carnegie Inst. Publ. No. 34*. By permission.

Wilce, J. H. 1965. Section *Complanata* of the genus *Lycopodium*. *Nova Hedwigia* **19**:1–233.

Wilde, M. H. 1944. A new interpretation of coniferous cones. *Ann. Bot.* (n.s.) **8**:1–41.

Williams, S. 1927. A critical examination of the Vittarieae with a view to their systematic comparison. *Trans. Roy. Soc. Edinburgh* **55**:173–217. By permission.

Williamson, W. C. 1887. *A Monograph on the Morphology and Histology of Stigmaria*. Palaeontology Society, London.

Wilson, C. W. 1942. The telome theory and the origin of the stamen. *Am. J. Bot.* **29**:759–764.

Wilson, K. A. 1958a. Ontogeny of the sporangia in *Xiphopteris serrulata* and *Pyrrosia nuda*. *J. Arnold Arb.* **39**:478–493.

———. 1958b. Ontogeny of the sporangium of *Phlebodium* (*Polypodium*) *aureum*. *Am. J. Bot.* **45**:483–491.

———. 1959. Sporangia of the fern genera allied with *Polypodium* and *Vittaria*. *Contr. Gray Herb. Harvard Univ. No. 185*.

———. 1960. The leptosporangium of the New Zealand fern *Anarthropteris dictyopteris*. *Contr. Gray Herb. Harvard Univ. No. 187*.

Yasui, K. 1911. On the life-history of *Salvinia natans*. *Ann. Bot.* **25**:469–483. By permission of the Clarendon Press.

Zahur, M. Z. 1959. Comparative study of secondary phloem of 423 species of woody dicotyledons belonging to 85 familes. *Cornell Univ. Agr. Exp. Sta. Mem. No. 358*:1–160.

Zamora, P. 1958. *Comparative Anatomy of the Protoxylem Elements of Several Selaginella Species*. Thesis, Cornell University.

Zeiller, R. 1900. *Eléments de paléobotanique*.

———. 1911. Étude sur le *Lepidostrobus Brauni* (Ung.) Schimp. *Mem. Acad. Sci. Paris* **152**:1–67. By permission.

Zimmermann, M. H., and P. B. Tomlinson. 1965. Anatomy of the palm *Rhapis excelsa*. I. Mature vegetative axis. *J. Arnold Arb.* **46**:160–178.

Zimmermann, W. 1930. *Die Phylogenie der Pflanzen*. Gustav Fisher, Jena. By permission.

Index

550 Index